Introduction to Passive, Linear, and Digital Electronics

Introduction to Passive, Linear, and Digital Electronics

Clyde O. Kale
PROFESSOR OF INDUSTRIAL STUDIES
MOORHEAD STATE UNIVERSITY

RESTON PUBLISHING COMPANY, INC.
A PRENTICE-HALL COMPANY
RESTON, VIRGINIA

Library of Congress Cataloging in Publication Data

Kale, Clyde O.
    Introduction to passive, linear, and digital
    electronics.

    1. Electric circuits.   2. Digital electronics.
    3. Semiconductors.   I. Title.
TK454.K35 1984   621.3815'3   84-3473
ISBN 0-8359-3263-X

© 1985 by Reston Publishing Company, Inc.
A Prentice-Hall Company
Reston, Virginia 22090

1   3   5   7   9   10   8   6   4   2

PRINTED IN THE UNITED STATES OF AMERICA

Contents

5   Batteries and Magnetism   101

6   Alternating Current and Voltage   121

10   *RLC* Circuits   219

PART TWO: Linear Circuits   247

11   The *PN* Junction Diode   249

21   Digital Gating Circuits   491

22   Digital Integrated Circuits   507

23   Flip-Flop Circuits   527

24   Combinational Logic Circuits   547

25   Register and Counter Circuits   567

Preface

The major objective in writing this book is to provide, under one cover, coverage of the more important topics included in a study of passive, solid state linear, and digital circuits. The book is primarily aimed at those programs in industrial technology, industrial arts, computer science, and other baccalaureate level programs where an exposure to a wide range of electronics at the non-calculus level is important to the student's education. The book can also be used in post-secondary vocational-technical programs where electronics is important, but is not the curriculum major. It might also be used in more rigorous high school industrial arts and vocational education programs. A basic knowledge of algebra is required. Although trigonometry is used, it can be learned at the time it is introduced in the book. Calculus is not used.

Topic coverage is divided into three parts–passive circuits, linear circuits, and digital circuits. Material selected for each part is such that most of the more important devices and circuits encountered in electronics are included. In parts two and three, devices are first introduced. These are followed by circuits which employ those devices.

The text is designed to be used in a three quarter or two semester sequence. Each part can be used in a quarter sequence. In a semester system, one-half of the book can be used for the first semester and the other half for the second semester.

The chapters are structured in the familiar four-step teaching format. These include the preparation, presentation, application, and evaluation steps. The preparation step is included in the introduction section of the chapters. The chapter text material forms the presentation step. Performance objectives identify that material which should be mastered.

Practice exercises provide the application step. Solutions and answers provide reinforcement. Questions appearing at the end of each chapter serve as the evaluation step. Answers to the questions provide further reinforcement.

A special thank you goes to Dr. Joseph F. Thomas, University of Wisconsin at Platteville and Mr. Jack L. Waintraub, Middlesex County College who reviewed the manuscript as it was being written. Mr. Wallece Peck, graphic arts professor at Moorhead State University, performed the photography work. I wish to thank my wife Sharon for proofreading the manuscript and daughters Brenda, Mindy, and Kathy for providing the motivation to complete the project.

Introduction to Passive, Linear, and Digital Electronics

PART ONE

Passive Circuits

1
Electrical Principles

OBJECTIVES

Upon completion of this chapter you should be able to do the following:

1. Identify the major parts of an atom.
2. Describe one way in which atoms differ from one another.
3. Define the terms *charge, current, voltage,* and *resistance.*
4. Identify the unit of measurement associated with charge, current, voltage, and resistance.
5. Differentiate between electron flow current and conventional current.
6. Identify the two ratings associated with resistors and use the EIA color code to determine the nominal resistance of carbon composition resistors.
7. Place numbers in scientific notation format and add, subtract, multiply, and divide numbers in this format.
8. Attach the proper prefixes to very small or very large electrical quantities.

1-1 INTRODUCTION

There have been a great number of technological developments in the last 100 years. All have contributed to make the quality of life what it is today. One of the more important of these has been electricity. At first a laboratory curiosity, applications began appearing by the end of the last century for lighting, powering machinery, and telephone communications.

During the first decade of the twentieth century, electron tubes were developed. This led to radio communications. By the late 1920s millions of people across the country were listening to radio. A decade later television had been developed and was showing promise for commercial broadcast applications. At the same time radar had evolved and was being used for national security and for increasing the safety of air travel. World War II interrupted the further development of television for a few years. The war brought about developments in other areas of electronics, many of which had nonmilitary applications after the war. By 1948 both television broadcasting and microwave communications were a reality. The invention of the transistor occurred also that year. About this same time the digital computer made its debut. The decade of the 1950s saw refinement of the many devices and applications developed during the prior decade. By the 1960s most people in the United States had access to television viewing. Scientific and data processing applications for computers were common. Transistors had replaced electron tubes in most electronic equipment. The integrated circuit was developed.

Many new devices, circuits, and applications evolved during the 1970s. One of the most important of these was the microprocessor. This device is revolutionizing technology. The 1980s is seeing this device used in almost everything from toys and kitchen appliances to automobiles and industrial controls. In fact, most microprocessors are found in applications traditionally unaffected by electronics.

Until the microprocessor came along, the only individuals who had to have any appreciable knowledge of electronics were the scientists, engineers, technicians, and servicemen who designed, built, and repaired electronic equipment. This is not true today. More and more individuals who work in areas other than electronics are finding that a knowledge of electronics is essential to their work.

I-2 THE STRUCTURE OF MATTER

Electricity is related to electrons. Electrons, of course, are part of the atom. The atom is the smallest building block of matter. Matter is anything which occupies space and has mass. Matter composed of materials made from the same kinds of atoms are called elements. Some examples of elements include iron, copper, and gold. There are more than 100 different kinds of elements. Some materials are made up of two or more different elements. These are called compounds. There are hundreds of different kinds of compounds. Some examples include water (H_2O); salt, or sodium chloride (NaCl); and sulfuric acid (H_2SO_4).

1-3 ATOMS

The atom itself is composed of smaller particles. As shown in Figure 1–1, the atom consists of a central mass, called the nucleus, around which negatively charged particles, called electrons, revolve. The nucleus is made up of neutrons and protons. Protons exhibit a positive charge, whereas the neutrons have no charge. The electrical charges associated with the electron and proton are equal in amplitude but opposite in polarity. The protons are not free to move around and are much heavier than the electron. The protons, along with the neutrons, give the atom weight. In the normal or balanced state an atom will have the same number of electrons orbiting the nucleus as it has protons within the nucleus. An atom in this state is said to be neutral. It exhibits no charge. Atoms may become unbalanced, in which case they are called ions. An atom which has gained electrons exhibits a negative charge and is called a negative ion. A negative ion is an atom which has more electrons than it has protons. An atom which has lost electrons and has more protons than electrons exhibits a positive charge and is called a positive ion.

One of the ways in which atoms differ from one another is the number of electrons and protons they have. The simplest atom is the hydrogen atom. It has only 1 electron and proton. The element helium has 2 electrons and protons; carbon has 6; silicon has 14; and germanium has 32. Each of the different kinds of atoms, or elements, has a different number of electrons and protons. A method used to identify an atom is its atomic number. The atomic number refers to the number of electrons the atom has. The atomic number of an atom may be obtained by looking in the Periodic Chart of the Elements found in most chemistry and physics books.

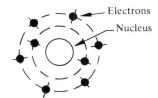

Figure I–I   Model of an atom.

1-4 ELECTRON PATHS

The electrons which orbit the nucleus do so in a systematic fashion. Although they have no specific orbital paths, as the planets have which orbit the sun, they do maintain a specific radius as they travel around the nucleus. The model of a copper atom appears in Figure 1–2. This atom has an atomic number of 29. The 29 electrons are distributed about the nucleus in bands or shells. The first band is called the K band. This band can hold a maximum of 2 electrons. The L band is the next higher band. It takes 8 electrons to fill it. The third band is called the M band and can contain 18 electrons. The fourth band can hold 32 electrons when filled and is called the N band. For the copper atom the K, L, and M bands have taken 28 of the atom's 29 electrons. This leaves only 1 electron for the N band. Generally speaking, all the lower-level bands have to be filled before electrons can exist in the next higher band.

The outermost band of any atom is called the valence band. Electrons in this band are called valence electrons. Electrons revolving about the nucleus contain energy. For this reason, the bands about the nucleus are sometimes called energy bands or energy shells.

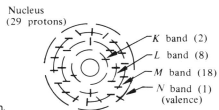

Nucleus
(29 protons)

K band (2)
L band (8)
M band (18)
N band (1)
(valence)

Figure I–2 Atom with electron bands shown.

1-5 CHARGE

Charge is a force which is associated with electrons and protons. As previously mentioned, atoms in their normal state are electrically neutral. This means that they have the same number of electrons revolving about the nucleus as they have protons within the nucleus. Atoms can gain or lose valence electrons, in which case they become unbalanced or charged. A charged atom is called an ion.

When atoms comprising materials have electrons added to, or taken from, their valence band, the material, or object, becomes charged. An example of this occurs when an individual walks across a carpeted floor and the humidity is low. The action of the feet moving across the carpet causes electrons to be taken from the carpet fibers and transferred to the body. The evidence of the charge is experienced when the individual reaches out to grasp a door knob.

All charged objects are surrounded by invisible lines of force. As il-

lustrated in Figure 1–3, if the object is positively charged, the lines of
force emit from the charged material. The lines of force point toward the
material if it is negatively charged. These lines of force are called electrostatic lines of force.

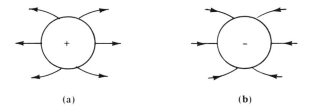

(a)   (b)

Figure I–3   Charged bodies and electrostatic lines of force: (a) positively charged object;
(b) negatively charged object.

One of the most fundamental laws of electricity is the law of
charges. This law states that like charges repel one another and unlike
charges attract one another.
    The letter Q is used as the symbol to represent electric charge. The
unit of measurement associated with charge is the coulomb, abbreviated
C. As indicated by Equation (1–1), 1 C of charge is equal to the individual
charges of 6.24 billion billion electrons.

$$1 \text{ C} = 6.24 \times 10^{18} \text{ electrons}$$ (1–1)

I-6 CURRENT

Current is the rate of flow of charged particles through a conductive medium. The concept of current flow has been known for centuries. Until
well into the twentieth century current was regarded as the flow of positive charges. The development of the modern model of the atom and
more sophisticated test instruments have refuted that concept. Scientists
now know that current is the flow of negative charges (electrons) through
a conductive medium. This is easy to understand when a model of an
atom is considered. The diagram of an atom having the atomic number
of 3 appears in Figure 1–4. As such, the atom contains three protons and
three neutrons within its nucleus. Revolving about the nucleus are three
electrons. The electrons are free to move and revolve about the nucleus
at a fixed distance or radius. The positively charged protons are locked

into the nucleus and are not free to move about as the negatively charged electrons are.

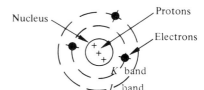

Figure 1–4   Atom having an atomic number of 3.

As long as the electrons are revolving about the nucleus, they are attached to the atom. To become current carriers, they must first be freed from the influence of the nucleus. This is accomplished by imparting energy to the atom. Energy can be supplied in the form of light, heat, or electromotive force (voltage). In most electrical applications it is supplied from a source of electromotive force. With the application of sufficient electromotive force, the valence band electron(s) is moved from the valence band into an outer band called the conduction band. Electrons in the conduction band are called free electrons and when under the influence of an electromotive force become current carriers. For the atom shown in Figure 1–4, the electron in the L shell is the one which becomes the free electron when it is raised into the conduction band.

The electrons revolving about the nucleus are attached to the nucleus by the electrostatic force which exists between the negatively charged electrons and positively charged nucleus. The centrifugal force of the electrons moving around the nucleus prevents them from being pulled into the nucleus. An electromotive force is required to overcome the attractive electrostatic force created by the unlike charged electrons and nucleus. A discrete amount of energy is required to raise the valence electron(s) from the valence band to the conduction band. An energy diagram, similar to that shown in Figure 1–5, is often used to show the relationship between the valence band and conduction band. Notice that there is a forbidden region between the valence band and conduction band. Sufficient energy must be imparted to the atom to cause the valence band electron(s) to move from that band into the conduction band. Electrons cannot remain in the forbidden region.

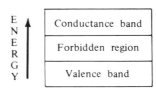

Figure 1–5   Energy diagram of a material.

Materials which have few valence band electrons are good electrical conductors. It takes less energy to cause these electrons to go into the conduction band than it does if the valence band is almost filled. When a conductive material, such as copper, is connected to an electromotive force supply, the conduction band electrons move in a uniform direction as indicated in Figure 1–6. In this illustration a copper conductor is connected across the positive and negative terminals of a battery which serves as a source of electromotive force. A section of the conductor is magnified to better see the movement of the electrons. Although the copper conductor is formed from millions of copper atoms, only four are shown for the sake of simplicity.

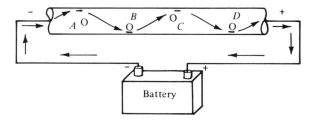

Figure 1–6   Electrons flowing through a conductor.

Since current is the flow of valence electrons raised into the conduction band, only the single valence electron associated with each atom is depicted. When the conductor is connected to the battery terminals, the valence electrons are immediately elevated up into the conduction band. At the same time, the law of charges causes the electrons to move from the negative terminal to the positive terminal of the battery. In the magnified portion of the conductor this is caused by the conduction electron associated with atom D being attracted to the positively charged atom to its right. This causes atom D to become a positive ion. The electron revolving about atom C is attracted to atom D. This, in turn, causes atom C to become positively charged. The electron moving around atom B is now attracted to atom C causing atom B to become positively charged, which, in turn, attracts the electron revolving about atom A. In this fashion electrons move through the conductor, traveling from the negative terminal to the positive terminal of the battery. The net movement is at about the speed of light.

In actual practice, current flow consists of millions of electrons moving in the fashion just described. The intensity, or magnitude, of movement is measured by the quantity of charges moving during a specified period of time. The unit of measurement for current flow is the ampere (abbreviated A); 1 A of current flow is defined as being the flow of 1 C of charge past a point in 1 s of time, as indicated by Equation (1–2). The letter I is used to symbolize current.

$$1\ A = \frac{1\ C}{1\ s}$$

$$I = \frac{Q}{t}$$

(1–2)

As previously mentioned, for a long time scientists thought that current flow was the movement of positive charges. Although it is now known that current is the flow of negatively charged particles (electrons), most scientific and technical literature continue to use the positive concept of current. This is because of tradition. This current theory is called conventional current. The only difference between electron flow theory (the flow of electrons) and conventional current theory is the direction of current flow. As indicated in Figure 1–7, for electron flow current, current flows from the negative terminal of the battery (source) to the positive terminal. Current flow, using the conventional theory, moves from the positive terminal of the source to the negative terminal. It makes no difference which theory is used. Although some technical books and literature utilize electron flow current, most use conventional current. Conventional current will be used throughout this book unless otherwise indicated.

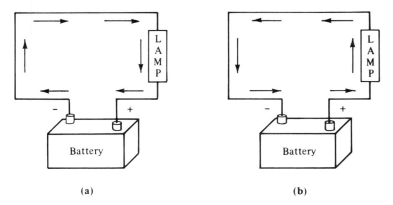

(a)   (b)

Figure 1–7   Direction of current flow for both electron flow and conventional current theories: (a) electron flow theory; (b) conventional flow theory.

I-7 VOLTAGE

Voltage is the external electrical potential force which must be applied to a circuit to cause current to flow. Voltage is a form of potential energy or pressure. Just as it takes pressure to cause water to flow through a pipe, pressure is also required to cause current to flow through a conductor. Water pressure can be created by a pump or by storing the water in a reservoir high above the pipe. The higher the reservoir, the greater the water pressure. The water stored in the reservoir is a form of potential energy. The reservoir stores energy by virtue of its position.

The terms *difference in potential, IR drop, potential difference,* and *electromotive force (EMF)* are all used to denote voltage. Electromotive force, or voltage, is the energy force required to raise electrons into the conduction band to cause them to become current carriers. Voltage is created when a difference in charges exists across two points. This is illustrated in Figure 1–8.

Two charged balls appear in Figure 1–8(a). Ball *A* is negatively charged and ball *B* positively charged. A difference of potential energy exists between the two balls as shown by the energy diagram. Ball *B* is at a higher potential than ball *A*. In similar fashion, an electromotive force, or potential difference, exists between the two balls appearing in Figure 1–8(b). Although both balls are negatively charged, they are not charged the same amount. Ball *A* is more negatively charged than ball *B*. Therefore, ball *B* is at a higher energy level than ball *A*, or ball *B* is "positive" with respect to ball *A*. In like fashion, ball *B* is more positive than ball *A* in Figure 1–8(c) even though both balls are positively charged. Ball *A* is actually "negative" with respect to ball *B*.

It must be emphasized that the concept of voltage operates on the principle of two bodies, or points, having different charges. The body which has the most negative (or less positive) charge is usually the reference body or reference level.

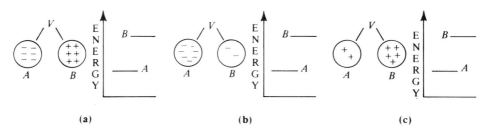

Figure I–8 Potential difference between balls having different charges.

The unit of measurement for electromotive force is the volt (abbreviated V). Voltage is related to work. Because the two unlike charged bodies want to pull together due to the attracting force between them, work must be performed to hold them apart. Voltage is also related to charge. The symbol for work is W while its unit of measurement is the joule (abbreviated J); 1 V is equal to 1 J/C as indicated by Equation (1–3). The symbols used to denote voltage are E and V.

$$1 \text{ V} = \frac{1 \text{ J}}{1 \text{ C}}$$

$$V = \frac{W}{Q} \tag{1–3}$$

I-8 RESISTANCE

Resistance is the third of the three major electrical variables—the other two being current and voltage. Resistance refers to the opposition to the flow of current a conductive medium offers to an electromotive force. Resistance makes itself known in the form of heat. Any time current flows through a conductive material, heat is produced. Resistance is analogous to friction in mechanical systems. Any time two surfaces rub together, heat is produced because of the friction. Surfaces are made as smooth as possible and lubrication is used to minimize friction.

Resistance comes from two sources. One represents the energy required to raise the valence electrons into the conduction band of the conductive medium. The other represents the kinetic energy given up by those electrons which strike the nucleus of the individual atoms comprising the material. Although most electrons merely become momentarily attached to the conduction band of the atoms as they travel through a conductor, some actually strike the nucleus because of the speed at which they are traveling.

Like friction, resistance is usually not desirable. Conductive materials which have few valence electrons and which have large cross-sectional areas are used to minimize resistance losses. Although the effect of resistance can be minimized, it can never be completely eliminated.

The unit of resistance is the ohm (abbreviated as the Greek letter Ω). As indicated by Equation (1–4), 1 Ω is equal to 1 V/A.

$$1\ \Omega = \frac{1\ V}{1\ A}$$

$$R = \frac{V}{I} \qquad\qquad\qquad\qquad\qquad (1-4)$$

This means that if 1 A of current flow is measured in a conductive medium which has an electromotive force of 1 V connected across it, the material has a resistance of 1 Ω.

1-9 RESISTORS

All materials have resistance. It is essential that conductors have very little resistance. Often, it is necessary to introduce additional resistance into a circuit to reduce the intensity, or amplitude, of the current flowing in the circuit. When this is the case, physical devices called resistors are placed in the circuit. This is analogous to the automobile. Friction resistance is introduced via the braking system to slow or stop the movement of the car.

Resistors are manufactured in various sizes and shapes. There are two ratings associated with resistors. These include the resistance rating in ohms and the power rating in watts (abbreviated W). Although resistors can be manufactured from many different substances, the two major types of resistors are made from a carbon composition material and from resistance wire. These are called carbon composition and wire-wound resistors, respectively. Most are of the carbon composition type. Wire-wound resistors are used mainly in high-current circuits where they must be capable of dissipating large amounts of power in the form of heat. Wire-wound resistors are also used as precision resistors.

Carbon composition resistors are easy to recognize. They are cylindrical in shape and have three or four colored bands around one end as shown in Figure 1–9. The bands are used to indicate the resistance of the device. The power rating is indicated by its physical size. Resistors are manufactured in specific resistance values which have been standardized by the Electronics Industry Association (EIA).

It is fairly easy to learn how to use the colored bands appearing on the resistor to determine its manufactured (nominal) value. Ten colors are associated with the first two bands, eight colors are associated with the

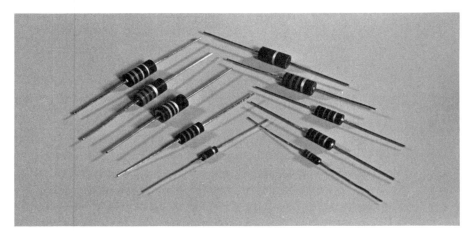

Figure 1–9   Examples of carbon composition resistors.

third band, and two colors are associated with the fourth band as indicated in Table 1–1. Called the EIA color code, each color has a number assigned to it.

Carbon composition resistors have either three or four bands as indicated in Figure 1–10. The first two bands are called the first and second significant bands; the third band is called the multiplier band; and the

TABLE 1–1   EIA Color Code

First Two Band Colors	Third Band Colors	Number	Fourth Band Colors
Black	Black	0	Gold, Tolerance
Brown	Brown	1	±5%
Red	Red	2	
Orange	Orange	3	Silver, Tolerance
Yellow	Yellow	4	±10%
Green	Green	5	
Blue		6	No Band, Tolerance
Violet		7	±20%
Gray		8	
White		9	
	Gold	0.1	
	Silver	0.01	

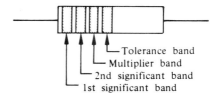

Figure I–10 Carbon composition resistor
band identification.

fourth band is called the tolerance band. The following examples serve to illustrate the procedure used to determine the nominal value of carbon composition resistors using the EIA color code. Consider the diagram of the resistor appearing in Figure 1–11. Note the numbers associated with the first two bands. Since red corresponds to the number 2 and violet corresponds to the number 7, these two numbers represent 27. The third band represents the multiplier band. Record the number of zeros the number associated with this color represents. Since yellow is associated with the number 4, four zeros are placed behind the number 27. The nominal value of the resistor is 270,000 Ω. The fourth band is called the tolerance band. Since it is gold, the resistor has a tolerance of ±5 percent. If a carbon composition resistor has only three bands (the tolerance band is missing) a tolerance of ±20 percent is assumed.

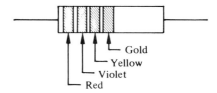

Figure I–II Carbon composition resistor.

A three-band resistor is depicted in Figure 1–12. This resistor has a nominal value of 1000 Ω and a tolerance of ±20 percent. Because resistors are mass produced, it is expensive and somewhat difficult to obtain precise resistor values. For the resistor shown in Figure 1–11, the actual value can vary as much as 5 percent above or below 270,000 Ω and still be considered to be a good resistor. This means that the resistance can range from a low of 256,500 Ω to a high of 283,500 Ω and still be within tolerance. For the resistor appearing in Figure 1–12, the actual resistance can range from a low of 800 Ω to a high of 1200 Ω. Although some circuits require very precise resistors, most circuits operate very satisfactorily with resistors having tolerances of 10 or 20 percent.

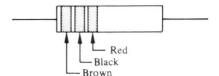

Figure 1–12   Carbon composition resistor.

Occasionally very small carbon composition resistors are encountered. For resistors whose nominal values are less than 10 Ω, a multiplier band of silver or gold is used. As indicated in Table 1–1, gold represents a multiplier of 0.1 and silver 0.01. The resistor appearing in Figure 1–13(a) has a nominal value of 4.7 Ω ±10 percent. The resistor illustrated in Figure 1–13(b) has a nominal value of 0.15 Ω and a tolerance of 5 percent.

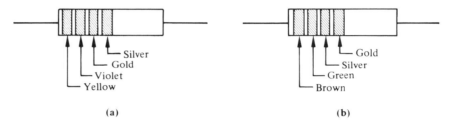

Figure 1–13   Small-value carbon composition resistors.

As current flows through a resistor, heat is produced. Resistors must be large enough physically to handle the heat without burning out. For this reason, resistors have power ratings in addition to resistance ratings. Carbon composition resistors can be purchased in ⅛-, ¼-, ½-, 1-, 2-, and 3-W sizes. The relative sizes of these devices are shown in Figure 1–14.

Wire-wound resistors are used where power requirements exceed 3 W. These resistors do not utilize the EIA color code. Instead, the resistor value is usually printed on the side of the device. Examples of these resistors appear in Figure 1–15.

Sometimes it is necessary to vary the current flowing through a circuit or the voltage across a device. This is accomplished by placing a variable resistor in the circuit. There are three general kinds of variable resistors. These include the adjustable, the potentiometer, and the rheostat. Representative pictures of these devices are shown in Figure 1–16.

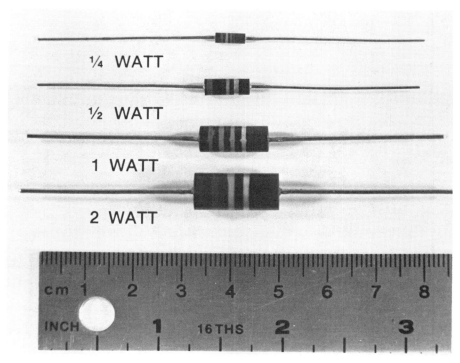

Figure 1–14   Wattage ratings of carbon composition resistors.

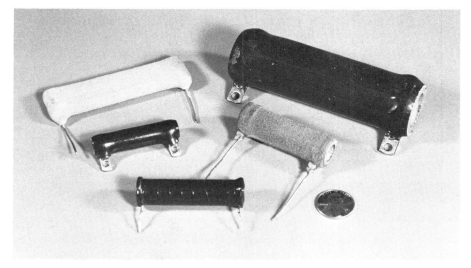

Figure 1–15   Wire-wound power resistors.

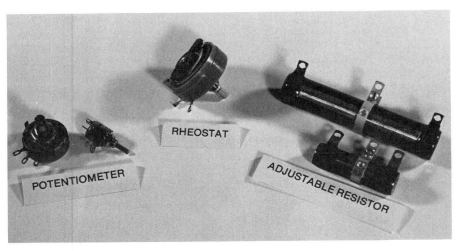

Figure 1–16   Variable resistors.

1-10 SCIENTIFIC NOTATION

Scientific notation is a short-hand method of displaying very large or very small numbers. A brief review of the decimal numbering system follows. This will aid in learning how numbers are placed in scientific notation format. For the number shown in Example 1–1(a), each digit has a certain significance, or weight, by virtue of its position. The number represents the sum of the numbers appearing in Example 1–1(b). If a larger number was used, additional digits would appear to the left of the decimal point. If the fraction was larger, additional digits would appear to the right of the decimal point.

Example I–I   Decimal digit position and weight

$$
\underbrace{2\,5\,4\,1\,.\,3\,8}_{(a)} = \underbrace{2\times10^{3}+5\times10^{2}+4\times10^{1}+1\times10^{0}\,.\,3\times10^{-1}+8\times10^{-2}}_{(b)}
$$

Scientific notation refers to the practice of indicating a number in such a way that the decimal point appears to the immediate right of the most significant digit as shown in Example 1–2. The number appearing above, and to the right, of the 10 is called the exponent. The exponent represents the number of digit positions the decimal point was moved to place it in scientific notation format. For the example shown, the decimal point was moved three digit positions. This causes the exponent to have a value of 3. Whenever the decimal point is moved to the left, each suc-ceeding digit increases the exponent by a factor of $+1$. For decimal frac-tions, as shown in Example 1–3, the decimal point is moved to the right to place it in scientific notation. The exponent in this case has a negative value. Each succeeding digit increases the exponent by a factor of -1, whenever the decimal point is moved to the right.

Example I–2   Decimal number placed in scientific notation format

$$2\,5\,4\,1\,.\,3\,8 = 2.54138 \times 10^3$$

Example I–3   Decimal fraction placed in scientific notation

$$0.00525 = 5.25 \times 10^{-3}$$

Numbers placed in scientific notation can be added, subtracted, multiplied, and divided with other numbers which are placed in scientific notation form. Numbers that are to be added and subtracted must have the same exponent power as indicated in Example 1–4. Notice that the coefficients are added together to obtain the sum. The resulting exponent is the same as that of the two numbers being added together.

Example I–4   Addition and subtraction of numbers in scientific notation format

$$
\begin{array}{cc}
7.5 \times 10^4 & 6.3 \times 10^{-2} \\
+\,2.3 \times 10^4 & -\,4.1 \times 10^{-2} \\
\hline
9.8 \times 10^4 & 2.2 \times 10^{-2}
\end{array}
$$

(a) addition   (b) subtraction

The exponents are added together for numbers to be multipled to-gether as illustrated in Example 1–5(a). Whenever one number is to be divided by another, the exponents are subtracted as shown in Example 1–5(b).

Example I–5   Multiplication and division of numbers in scientific format

$$
\begin{array}{cc}
(4.3 \times 10^5)(5.1 \times 10^2) & \dfrac{3.6 \times 10^4}{9.0 \times 10^3} = 0.4 \times 10^1 \\
= 21.93 \times 10^7 & = 4 \times 10^0 \\
= 2.193 \times 10^8 & = 4
\end{array}
$$

(a) multiplication   (b) division

The exponent is divided by 2 when the square root of a number placed in scientific notation is to be taken, as indicated in Example 1–6.

Electronic calculators have simplified and eliminated much of the tedious work when performing calculations associated with electronics analysis and design. Due to the limited number of digits on a calculator and the very large and very small numbers often associated with electrical variables, numbers are often placed in scientific notation format before being entered into the calculator.

Example I–6   Taking the square root of a number appearing in scientific notation

$$\sqrt{25 \times 10^4}$$
$$= 5 \times 10^2$$

I-II SI UNITS

A number of different electrical quantities are encountered in electronics. Each has a unit of measurement associated with it. A worldwide standard, called the International System of Units (SI), has been adapted. Each quantity has a symbol associated with it. In addition, each unit of measurement has an associated symbol. The more commonly encountered electrical quantities, their symbols, SI unit name, and unit symbol appear in Table 1–2. Notice that a few symbols are from the Greek alphabet. One

TABLE 1–2   Electrical quantities, SI units, and symbols

Quantity	Symbol	SI Unit	Symbol
Voltage	V or E	Volt	V
Current	I	Ampere	A
Charge	Q	Coulomb	C
Capacitance	C	Farad	F
Frequency	f	Hertz	Hz
Energy/Work	W	Joule	J
Impedance	Z	Ohm	Ω
Conductance	G	Siemen	S
Inductance	L	Henry	H
Power	P	Watt	W
Time	t	Second	s
Reactance	X	Ohm	Ω
Resistance	R	Ohm	Ω
Wavelength	λ	Meter	m

of these has already been encountered—Ω, the symbol for the unit of measurement for resistance.

1-12 SUBMULTIPLE AND MULTIPLE UNITS

Submultiple units are units whose values are less than 1. Units greater than 1 are called multiple units. Electrical units range from the very small to the very large. This causes the numbers associated with electrical variables to become cumbersome. To overcome this, prefixes are often used with the variables. Prefixes used with very small numbers appear in Table 1–3 along with the prefix abbreviation, numerical fraction, decimal fraction, and scientific notation.

Prefixes used with very large numbers are shown in Table 1–4. Notice the advantage of scientific notation for both small and large numbers.

TABLE 1–3   Submultiple Prefixes

milli (m)	$\dfrac{1}{1,000}$	0.001	1×10^{-3}
micro (μ)	$\dfrac{1}{1,000,000}$	0.000001	1×10^{-6}
nano (n)	$\dfrac{1}{1,000,000,000}$	0.000000001	1×10^{-9}
pico (p)	$\dfrac{1}{1,000,000,000,000}$	0.000000000001	1×10^{-12}

TABLE 1–4   Multiple Prefixes

kilo (k)	1,000	1×10^{3}
mega (M)	1,000,000	1×10^{6}
giga (G)	1,000,000,000	1×10^{9}

Some examples of how the prefixes are used appear in Example 1–7.

Example 1–7   Prefix applications

0.000007 A = 7 microamperes or 7 μA.
15,000,000 W = 15 megawatts or 15 MW.
0.025 V = 25 millivolts or 25 mV.
115,000 Ω = 115 kilohms or 115 kΩ.
0.00000000020 F = 200 picofarads or 200 pF.
85,000,000,000 Hz = 85 gigahertz or 85 GHz.

SUMMARY

1. The major parts of the atom include the nucleus, protons, neutrons, and electrons.
2. Matter is made up of atoms.
3. Matter formed from the same kinds of atoms are called elements.
4. Matter formed from two or more different kinds of atoms are called compounds.
5. Electrons and protons have charges associated with them. Electrons have a negative charge and protons have a positive charge.
6. The unit of measurement for charge is the coulomb; 1 C of charge equals 6.24×10^{18} electrons.
7. Current represents charge in motion. The unit of measurement for current flow is the ampere; 1 A represents the flow of 1 C of charge past a point in 1 s of time.
8. Although current is actually the flow of electrons (electron flow theory), the older concept of positive charge flow (conventional current flow theory) is commonly used when describing the direction of current flow through a device or circuit.
9. Resistors are devices used to limit the intensity, or amplitude, of current flowing in a circuit. There are two general types of resistors—fixed and variable.
10. The two most common types of fixed resistors are the carbon composition and wire wound.
11. Resistors have two ratings—a resistance rating and a power rating.
12. The manufactured (nominal) resistance of a carbon composition resistor can be determined from the colored bands located on the resistor.
13. The power rating of a carbon composition resistor is determined by its physical size. Carbon composition resistors can be purchased with wattage ratings ranging from a low of ⅛ W to a high of 3 W.
14. Power resistors are resistors that must dissipate power in excess of 3 W.
15. Power resistors are usually of the wire-wound type.
16. Low-tolerance precision resistors are often wire-wound resistors.
17. Scientific notation is a short-hand method of displaying large and small numbers.
18. Prefixes are often used with very large or very small electrical units.

PRACTICE EXERCISES

1. Define the following terms: **a.** charge **b.** current flow **c.** voltage
2. Describe one way in which atoms differ from one another.
3. Discuss the difference between the theory of electron flow current and the theory of conventional current.
4. Identify the major components of the atom.
5. Identify the unit of measurement associated with the following electrical quantities:
   a. voltage **b.** charge **c.** current **d.** resistance
6. Place the following numbers in scientific notation format:
   a. 8349   **b.** 0.0736   **c.** 56.85   **d.** 0.00000107

7. Place the following two numbers in scientific notation format and add them together: 386 and 521.
8. Repeat exercise 7 for the following numbers: 36 and 473.
9. Multiply the following two numbers together after placing them in scientific notation format: 235 and 879.
10. 0.0075 A = _____ mA.
11. 560,960 Hz = _____ kHz.
12. 15 mA = _____ μA.
13. 0.001 μF = _____ pF.
14. 230 μA = _____ mA.
15. 150 kW = _____ W.
16. 2500 MHz = _____ GHz.
17. Identify the nominal value and tolerance for each of the carbon composition resistors appearing in Figure 1–17.
18. Place the following two numbers in scientific notation format: 543 and 6631. Divide the second by the first number.
19. Subtract the first number from the second number after placing them in scientific notation form: 0.0065 and 0.08.
20. Add the following two numbers after placing them in scientific notation format: 5367.89 and 0.0056.

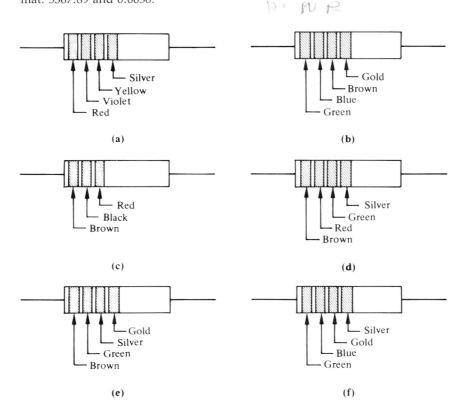

Figure 1–17

ANSWERS TO PRACTICE EXERCISES

1. **(a)** Charge is the force associated with the electron and proton. Materials which have lost or gained electrons are considered to be either positively or negatively charged, respectively.
   (b) Current flow in a device or circuit is the flow of charged particles.
   (c) Voltage is the difference of electrical potential which exists between two materials or bodies which have unequal charges.
2. Atoms differ from each other in the number of protons and electrons they have. Each different atom has its own atomic number.
3. Electron flow theory considers current flow to be the flow of negatively charged particles (electrons) through a component or circuit. The flow of positively charged particles is the concept used for conventional current.
4. The major components forming the atom include electrons, protons, neutrons, and the nucleus.
5. **a.** The unit of measurement for voltage is the volt.
   b. The coulomb is the unit of measurement associated with charge.
   c. Ampere is the unit of measurement for current flow.
   d. The ohm is the unit of measurement for resistance.
6. **a.** 8.349×10^3 **b.** 7.36×10^{-2} **c.** 5.685×10^1 **d.** 1.07×10^{-6}
7. $386 + 521 = 3.86 \times 10^2 + 5.21 \times 10^2 = 9.07 \times 10^2$.
8. $36 + 473 = .36 \times 10^2 + 4.73 \times 10^2 = 5.09 \times 10^2$.
9. $(235)\ (879) = (2.35 \times 10^2)\ (8.79 \times 10^2) = 20.6565 \times 10^4 = 2.06565 \times 10^5$. (Always adjust the decimal point for position.)
10. $0.0075\ A = 7.5\ mA$.
11. $560,960\ Hz = 560.96\ kHz$.
12. $15\ mA = 15,000\ \mu A$. (When converting from a larger unit to a smaller, multiply by the appropriate number.)
13. $0.001\ \mu F = 1000\ pF$.
14. $230\ \mu A = 0.230\ mA$. (When converting from a smaller unit of measurement to a larger, divide by the appropriate number, that is, $1000\ \mu A = 1\ mA$.)
15. $150\ kW = 150,000\ W$.
16. $2500\ MHz = 2.5\ GHz$.
17. **a.** $270,000\ \Omega \pm 10$ percent (270k)   **b.** $560\ \Omega \pm 5$ percent
    c. $1000\ \Omega \pm 20$ percent (lk)   **d.** $1.2\ M\Omega \pm 10$ percent
    e. $0.15\ \Omega \pm 5$ percent   **f.** $5.6\ \Omega \pm 10$ percent
18. $\dfrac{6.631 \times 10^3}{5.43 \ \times 10^2} = 1.221 \times 10^1$.
19. $8.0 \times 10^{-2} - 0.65 \times 10^{-2} = 7.35 \times 10^{-2}$.
20. $5.36789 \times 10^3 + 0.0000056 \times 10^3 = 5.3678956 \times 10^3$.

CHAPTER EXAMINATION

1. Matter made up of the same kind of atoms best describes
   a. elements   **c.** molecules
   b. compounds   **d.** monomatter

  2. Water is an example of a (an)
    a. element   **c.** compound
    b. mixture   **d.** molecule
  3. The flow of charged particles through a conductor, circuit, or device is known as
    a. a coulomb   **c.** an electrostatic force
    b. current flow   **d.** an electromotive force
  4. Potential difference and electromotive force are two other terms used to denote
    a. voltage   **c.** conductance
    b. current   **d.** an electrostatic force
  5. The unit of measurement used to indicate charge is the
    a. volt   **c.** ampere
    b. joule   **d.** coulomb

Choose true or false for questions 6 to 24.

  6. T F Protons have a negative charge and travel around the nucleus of the atom.
  7. T F According to the law of charges, like charges repel one another and unlike charges attract each other.
  8. T F An electrostatic field exists around charged materials.
  9. T F A negative ion is an atom which has lost some of its electrons.
  10. T F The coulomb is the unit of measurement for electric charge.
  11. T F Current is the difference of potential between two charged bodies.
  12. T F The unit of measurement for current flow is the ampere.
  13. T F A balanced, or neutral, atom is one which has its valence band completely filled.
  14. T F Current carriers are valence electrons which have been raised to the conduction band.
  15. T F A material composed of atoms which has few valence electrons is a good conductor of electricity.
  16. T F 150 μA = 0.150 mA.
  17. T F 196 kHz = 196,000 MHz.
  18. T F 25 A = 250 mA.
  19. T F 1057 GHz = 1.057 MHz.
  20. T F 165 kW = 0.165 MW.
  21. T F The sum of 2350 and 305 equals 2.655×10^2.
  22. T F The product of 0.057 and 0.13 equals 7.41×10^{-3}.
  23. T F A resistor whose bands are red, violet, red, and silver in color has a resistance value of 2600 $\Omega \pm 5$ percent.
  24. T F A resistor whose bands are brown, green, orange, and gold has a resistance value of 15 k$\Omega \pm 5$ percent.
  25. 0.00076 V = 760 mV.

2

Series Resistive Circuits

OBJECTIVES

Upon completion of this chapter you should be able to do the following:

1. Identify, or draw, the schematic symbols for the fixed-value resistor, potentiometer, rheostat, adjustable resistor, light bulb, switch, fuse, generator, motor, meter, battery, connected conductors, and crossing conductors which are not connected.
2. List the three requirements for a functional electric circuit.
3. Discuss the standard used in the manufacture of conducting wire by identifying the name of the standard and describing the relationship between the numbering system used to gauge the wire and the diameter of the wire.
4. Describe the purpose of switches and fuses, or circuit breakers, as used in circuits.
5. Identify at least three safety precautions which must be observed when working with electricity.
6. Write the formulas for the three forms of Ohm's law and describe the relationship between voltage, current, and resistance.
7. Use Ohm's law to calculate voltage, current, or resistance.
8. Define the terms *energy* and *power*.
9. Calculate the cost of operating an electrical device for a specified period of time.
10. Write the three forms of Watt's law.
11. Use Watt's law to compute power, resistance, voltage, or current.
12. Define a series circuit.
13. Calculate the total resistance, total current, individual voltage drops, and total power consumption in a series circuit.
14. State Kirchhoff's voltage law.
15. Discuss the effects on circuit current and resistance when additional resistive devices are connected in series.

2-1 INTRODUCTION

In the last chapter it was determined that current flow is the movement of negatively charged particles, called electrons, through a conductor. A source of electromotive force is required to cause current to flow. A number of new concepts, principles, and laws will be introduced in this chapter. It is important that they be mastered, as they form the basis for more advanced work.

2-2 SCHEMATIC SYMBOLS

Instead of using pictorial representations of electrical devices in diagrams of electrical circuits, a symbolic diagram, called a schematic diagram, is usually used. Each electrical device has a symbol associated with it. This simplifies drawing circuit diagrams. The schematic symbols for some of the more commonly used components are shown in Figure 2–1. The ap-

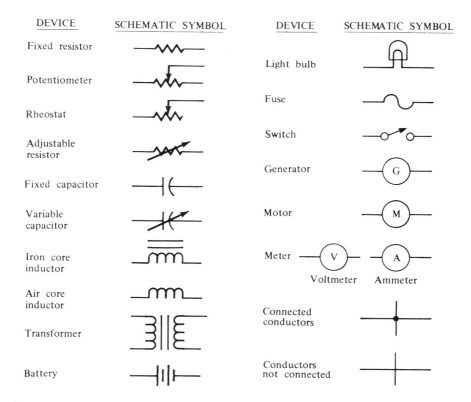

DEVICE	SCHEMATIC SYMBOL	DEVICE	SCHEMATIC SYMBOL
Fixed resistor		Light bulb	
Potentiometer		Fuse	
Rheostat		Switch	
Adjustable resistor		Generator	
Fixed capacitor		Motor	
Variable capacitor		Meter	Voltmeter Ammeter
Iron core inductor			
Air core inductor		Connected conductors	
Transformer		Conductors not connected	
Battery			

Figure 2–1   Schematic symbols of selected electrical devices.

plications for these devices will be discussed as they are introduced in later sections.

2-3 THE ELECTRIC CIRCUIT

2-3.1 The Functional Circuit. In order to make electricity functional, it must perform work. This might involve lighting a light bulb, turning a motor, or heating a room. Electric current flowing through a bulb, motor, or heating element produces work. The device on which the work is performed is called a load. The light bulb, motor, and heating element, just identified, constitute electrical loads.

A working circuit must contain at least three items. These include a voltage source (such as a battery or generator), a load, and conductors to connect the voltage source to the load. A pictorial representation of a circuit appears in Figure 2–2. A battery, serving as a source of electromotive force, is connected to a motor which serves as the load. Two conductors are required to connect the battery to the motor. One wire connects the positive terminal of the battery to the motor and the other wire connects the negative battery terminal to the motor to complete the circuit. As indicated in the diagram, current leaves the positive terminal of the battery, travels through the conductor, into the motor, out of the motor, and back to the negative terminal of the battery.

All electric circuits must have a complete path for current to flow through them. The circuit appearing in Figure 2–2 is a complete circuit because all of the current which leaves the positive terminal of the battery eventually flows back into the battery at the negative terminal. The conductors serve to complete the circuit. If one of the conductors is removed, as shown in Figure 2–3, there is no longer a complete circuit. Current cannot flow through the circuit and the motor cannot turn.

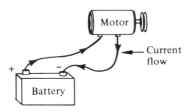

Figure 2–2   Electric circuit consisting of a battery and a motor.

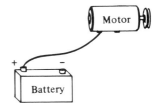

Figure 2–3   Example of an incomplete circuit.

2-3.2 Conductors. Conductors must be large enough in cross-sectional area, or diameter, to carry the current which flows through them. Wire that is used as electrical conductors is manufactured in various diameter sizes that have been standardized by the American Wire Gauge (AWG) Standard. Wire gauge sizes begin with gauge 0000 and go to size 44. Some representative wire sizes appear in Table 2–1. The resistance per 1000 ft, current capacity, and diameter, is indicated for each of the wire gauge sizes shown. Gauge 1 is the largest wire size shown in the table. It has a diameter of 0.289 in., a resistance of 0.1263 Ω/1000 ft and can carry 119.6 A of current.

Gauge 40, appearing at the bottom of the table, is the smallest wire size shown. Notice that it is only 0.0031 in. in diameter, has a resistance of 1069 Ω/1000 ft, and can handle only 0.014 A of current. From the table one can observe that as the wire gauge number increases, the diameter

TABLE 2–1   Resistance, Current Capacity, and Diameter of Selected AWG Sizes

AWG Wire Gauge Size	Ω/1000 ft	Current Capacity (A)	Diameter (in.)
1	0.1263	119.6	0.289
2	0.1592	94.8	0.258
3	0.2008	75.2	0.229
4	0.2532	59.6	0.204
5	0.3194	47.3	0.182
6	0.4027	37.4	0.162
7	0.5080	29.7	0.144
8	0.6404	23.7	0.129
9	0.8076	18.7	0.114
10	1.017	14.8	0.102
11	1.284	11.8	0.091
12	1.620	9.3	0.081
13	2.042	7.4	0.072
14	2.574	5.8	0.064
25	33.000	0.457	0.018
26	41.620	0.362	0.016
27	52.470	0.288	0.0142
38	672.6	0.022	0.0039
39	848.2	0.017	0.0035
40	1069.0	0.014	0.0031

of the wire decreases. Gauge 1 wire has a much larger diameter than gauge 40. It is also important to note that the resistance of the wire varies inversely with the diameter. The larger the diameter, the less the resistance of the wire. Gauge 40 has slightly less than 10,000 times more resistance than gauge 1 for the same length. Although gauge 1 is the largest wire size shown in the table, larger sizes do exist and include sizes 0000, 000, 00, and 0. Some representative wire diameters appear in Figure 2–4.

00   0   2   4   8   10 12

Figure 2–4   Some representative AWG sizes.

2-3.3 Switches.   It is desirable to be able to turn the load on and off in an electrical circuit. This is accomplished by placing a switch in series or in tandem with the load and voltage source, as illustrated in Figure 2–5. The switch allows the light bulb (load) to be turned on and off by making or breaking the circuit. In the closed position internal contacts are connected, allowing current to pass through the switch. In the open position the internal contacts are not connected and current cannot pass through the switch.

2-3.4 Fuses and Circuit Breakers.   An electrical circuit must have a load. In addition to serving as the device on which electrical work is being done, the load has resistance and limits the amount of current flowing in the circuit. If for some reason the conductors should touch together, as shown in Figure 2–6, current does not flow through the load.

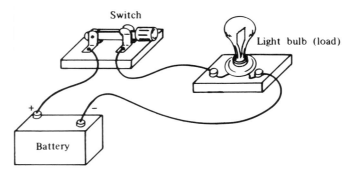

Figure 2–5   Electrical circuit with switch.

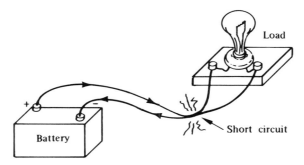

Figure 2–6   Example of a short circuit.

Instead, current flows through one wire to the point where the wires are touching and then flows back to the source through the other wire. This condition is called a short circuit. Because the load has been bypassed, there is nothing in the circuit to limit the amplitude or intensity of the current. The current flowing through the conductors will exceed their current-carrying capacity and become very hot. This may ignite flammable material that may be close by. In addition to the very definite fire hazard, the voltage source may be damaged. Conductors are usually covered with an insulating material of plastic, rubber, cloth fiber, or enamel to prevent short-circuited conditions if they should touch together. However, the insulation sometimes becomes cracked, worn, or cut. For this reason fuses and circuit breakers are placed in series with the load and voltage source as shown in Figure 2–7. A fuse is a device which contains a thin metallic strip. When the current flowing through it exceeds the current rating of the fuse, the excessive heat caused by the higher current causes the metallic strip to melt, opening the circuit.

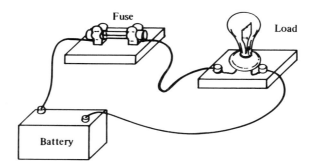

Figure 2–7   Circuit with fuse to protect the load and source.

Circuit breakers are used for the same purpose. A circuit breaker can be reset after the short-circuited condition has been removed. A fuse has to be replaced, of course. A fuse should always be replaced with one having the same current capacity. Replacing a fuse with one having a higher current capacity is a sure invitation for trouble and possible tragedy.

2-3.5 Safety.   One needs to develop safe habits when working with electricity. Approximately 0.075 A of current passing through the heart is usually fatal. The resistance of the body is usually great enough to require a voltage well in excess of 100 V to cause this amount of current to flow. The resistance of the body is much less when standing in water, however. The following precautions should be observed when working with electrical circuits:

(a) Always stand on a rubber mat, tile floor, or carpeted floor. Never work with electricity when standing directly on a metal floor, a floor which is damp or wet, or in bare feet.

(b) When making tests and troubleshooting live circuits, it is a good idea to work with one hand behind the back. Always turn off, or deenergize, an electrical circuit when making any repairs.

(c) If one encounters a shock victim, immediately turn off the power or pull the individual away from the electrical source with a rope, belt, article of clothing, or other nonconductive material. Never touch the individual directly while the circuit is live. If the person is unconscious and not breathing, call an ambulance and begin artificial respiration at once. Approximately three-fourths of the victims who have been rendered unconscious by electrical shock can be revived if artificial respiration is begun within 3 minutes. This percentage decreases rapidly for each minute respiration is delayed.

It is important that one develops the habit and discipline of consistently working safely around electricity. It is easy to develop careless habits when working with the low voltages and currents present in solid-state circuits.

2-4 OHM'S LAW

Three of the more important electrical quantities, or variables, encountered in the study of electricity are current, voltage, and resistance. During the 1820s a German scientist named Georg Simon Ohm formulated the relationship between these variables. Ohm found that the intensity of the current flowing in a circuit is directly proportional to the amplitude of the voltage applied to the circuit and inversely proportional to the resistance of the circuit. This relationship, known as Ohm's law, is one of the most important principles which exists in the discipline of electricity. This relationship is expressed in mathematical form by Equation (2–1).

$$\text{Current} = \frac{\text{Voltage}}{\text{Resistance}}$$

$$I = \frac{V}{R} \quad \text{in amperes} \tag{2–1}$$

An application of Ohm's law appears in Example 2–1. In this circuit a 5-V source is connected to a 50-Ω resistor. Notice the use of symbols used to form the schematic diagram.

Example 2–1   Application of Ohm's law

Problem
Calculate the current flowing in the circuit of Figure 2–8.

Solution

$$I = \frac{V}{R} = \frac{5 \text{ V}}{50 \text{ }\Omega} = 0.1 \text{ A}$$

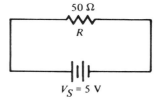

Figure 2–8

The effect of voltage on the amount of current flow is shown in Example 2–2. This circuit has the same resistance as the preceding circuit. The voltage source has been increased from 5 to 10 V. The resulting current is 0.2 A. Notice that doubling the source voltage has caused the current to double. If the voltage is tripled, the intensity of the current will triple. If the voltage is decreased by one-half, the current will decrease by a factor of one-half, also. By now it should be apparent that voltage directly affects the amount of current flowing in a circuit.

Example 2–2 Application of Ohm's law

Problem
Determine the current flowing in the circuit of Figure 2–9.

Solution
$$I = \frac{V}{R} = \frac{10\ V}{50\ \Omega} = 0.2\ A$$

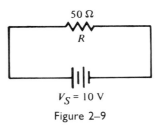

50 Ω
R

V_S = 10 V

Figure 2–9

The effect of resistance on current flow is illustrated in Example 2–3. For this circuit the voltage is the same as it was for the circuit appearing in Example 2–1 but the resistance has been doubled. Note that the resulting current is one-half the value it was when the resistance was 50 Ω. Increasing the resistance in a circuit causes the current to decrease. Decreasing the resistance in a circuit results in an increase in current flow. Thus, resistance inversely affects the amount of current flowing in a circuit.

Example 2–3 Application of Ohm's law

Problem
Compute the circuit current for the circuit in Figure 2–10.

Solution
$$I = \frac{V}{R} = \frac{5\ V}{100\ \Omega} = 0.05\ A$$

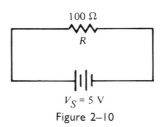

100 Ω
R

V_S = 5 V

Figure 2–10

Ohm's law can be rearranged and written as shown by Equation (2–2).

Voltage = (Current)(Resistance)
$$V = (I)(R) \quad \text{in volts}$$

(2–2)

This form of Ohm's law is used when the circuit current and resistance values are known and it is required to find the voltage. A 25-Ω load allows 1.5 A of current to flow in the circuit diagram appearing in Example 2–4. As indicated, the voltage required to cause a current of this intensity is 37.5 V.

Example 2–4   Application of Ohm's law

Problem
Calculate the source voltage for the circuit in Figure 2–11.

Solution

$V_S = (I)(R) = (1.5 \text{ A})(25 \text{ Ω}) = 37.5 \text{ V}$

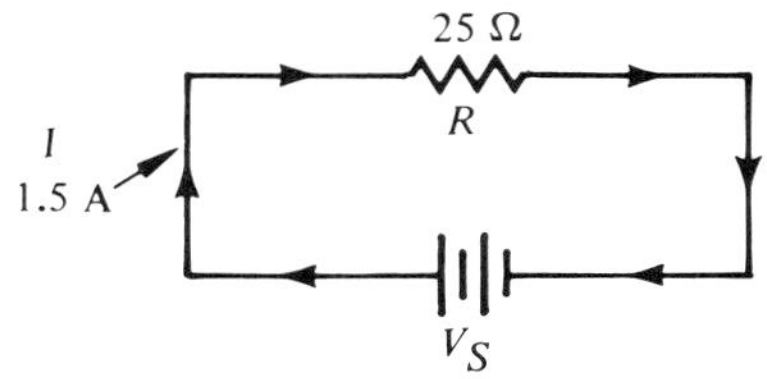

Figure 2–11

Ohm's law can also be written as shown by Equation (2–3).

$$\text{Resistance} = \frac{\text{Voltage}}{\text{Current}}$$

$$R = \frac{V}{I} \quad \text{in ohms} \tag{2–3}$$

This form of Ohm's law is used when the voltage and current values are known and resistance must be calculated. For the circuit shown in Example 2–5, a 50-V source causes 0.02 A of current to flow through a load whose resistance is unknown. By applying Ohm's law, a resistance of 2500 Ω is obtained.

Because current, voltage, and resistance vary from circuit to circuit, these quantities (and other electrical quantities) are often called variables. The three forms of Ohm's law are shown in Table 2–2. Which one of the three equations is used depends upon what two variables are known and the variable to be calculated.

For example, it may be necessary to determine the resistance of a motor while it is running. This is impossible to measure with an ohmmeter because resistance measurements must be made with the circuit turned off, or deenergized. However, both voltage and current can be

Example 2–5   Application of Ohm's law

Problem
Calculate the resistance of the load for the circuit in Figure 2–12.

Solution

$$R = \frac{V}{I} = \frac{50\ V}{0.02\ A} = 2500\ \Omega$$

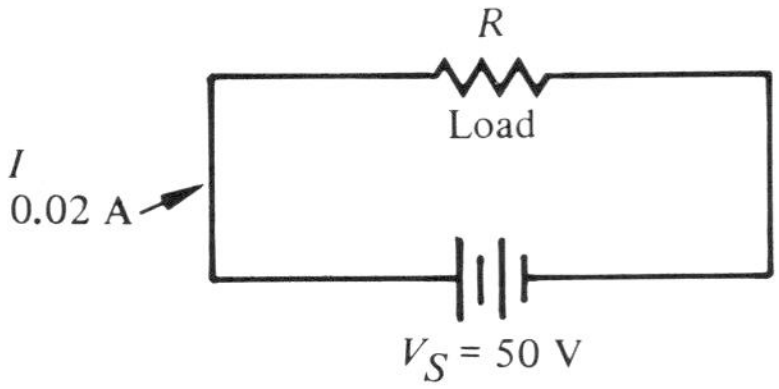

I
0.02 A

R
Load

$V_S = 50\ V$

Figure 2–12

TABLE 2–2   The Three Forms of Ohm's Law

$I = \dfrac{V}{R}$	$V = (I)(R)$	$R = \dfrac{V}{I}$

measured with the motor running. The motor's resistance can be obtained by dividing the measured voltage by the measured current.

An aid that is useful in using Ohm's law appears in Figure 2–13. The three equations can be obtained by covering the variable one wishes to calculate. The remaining two variables indicate the mathematical operation that must be performed to obtain the desired variable.

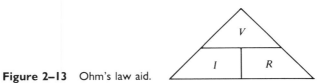

Figure 2–13   Ohm's law aid.

2-5 METER MEASUREMENTS

Although current, voltage, and resistance cannot be seen with the eye, they can be measured by the use of meters. The meter becomes an extension of one's senses. Voltage is measured with a voltmeter, current is measured with an ammeter, and resistance is measured using an ohmmeter. These are three separate kinds of meters. Often they are incorporated into one test instrument called a multimeter or volt-ohm-milliammeter

(VOM). Voltage, current, and resistance are all measured differently. It is important to understand how to make these measurements properly. An improper method of measurement can easily damage or ruin an expensive test instrument or, at the least, result in an erroneous measurement for the variable being measured.

The circuit shown in Figure 2–14 illustrates how a voltmeter is connected to measure voltage. If the voltage across the resistor is to be measured, the voltmeter is placed parallel with, or across, the device as shown. Meter lead polarity must be observed when measuring DC voltage. The positive lead (usually red) of the meter is placed on the positive side of the device whose voltage is being measured, and the negative (usually black) meter lead is placed on the negative side. To measure the source voltage, the meter is placed across the supply as indicated in Figure 2–15.

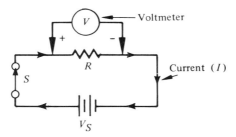

Figure 2–14   Voltage measurement.

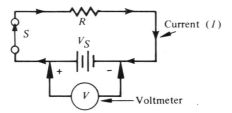

Figure 2–15   Voltage measurement.

An ammeter is used to measure current. The ammeter leads are placed in the circuit by physically breaking the circuit and inserting the meter between the two disconnected conductors as shown in Figure 2–16. This is a series type of connection. The ammeter can be placed anywhere in the circuit where it is convenient to break the circuit. Like voltage measurements, polarity must be observed when making DC current measurements.

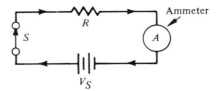

Figure 2–16   Current measurement.

Resistance measurement is illustrated in Figure 2–17. To measure the resistance of a resistor or a load, the circuit must first be turned off. The ohmmeter is then connected across the device whose resistance is to be measured. The ohmmeter can be damaged or ruined if measurements are attempted in an energized circuit. Polarity does not have to be observed when making resistance measurements. Like voltage measurements, resistance measurements are parallel measurements.

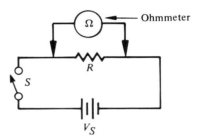

Figure 2–17   Resistance measurement.

2-6 ENERGY AND POWER

2-6.1 Energy.   Three major electrical variables have been encountered thus far. These include current, voltage, and resistance. Another variable is energy. Energy is defined as the ability to do work. This is often a more difficult concept to understand due to the many ways in which the word is used. All energy ultimately comes from the sun. Some of this energy heats and lights the earth. The rest is stored in various mediums, such as plant life, and is eventually converted to other forms of energy by devices called transducers. Common forms of energy include thermal, electrical, mechanical, light, hydro, and chemical. Some familiar types of transducers include batteries, engines, motors, and generators. The internal combustion engine, for example, converts chemical energy (gasoline) into mechanical energy. A generator converts mechanical energy into electrical energy. Work is performed whenever one form of energy is converted into another. The unit of measurement for electrical energy (and work) is the joule. As indicated in Equation (2–4), electrical energy is the product of charge and voltage.

$$\text{Work} = \text{Energy} = (\text{Voltage})(\text{Charge})$$
$$W = (V)(Q) \text{ in joules} \tag{2–4}$$

2-6.2 Power.   Closely associated with energy is the electrical variable called power. As shown by Equation (2–5), power is the rate at which energy is used and is measured in watts.

$$\text{Power} = \frac{\text{Energy}}{\text{Time}}$$
$$P = \frac{W}{t} \quad \text{in watts} \tag{2–5}$$

This formula can be rewritten in terms of energy, as shown by Equation (2–6).

$$\text{Energy} = (\text{Power})(\text{time})$$
$$W = (P)(t) \quad \text{in watt-seconds or joules} \tag{2–6}$$

This is a more practical equation for computing energy requirements. As indicated by the formula, energy is the amount of power used for a specified period of time. Either the joule or watt-second can be used as a unit of measurement.

   Whenever current flows through a resistance, power is consumed in the form of heat. Electrical power can be expressed as the product of voltage and current, as shown by Equation (2–7). Notice that voltage and current are both expressed in terms of charge as used in their respective definitions in Chapter 1.

$$\text{Power} = \left(\frac{\text{Charge}}{\text{Time}}\right)\left(\frac{\text{Energy}}{\text{Charge}}\right)$$
$$P = (I)(V) \quad \text{in watts} \tag{2–7}$$

2-6.3 Calculating Energy Costs. One purchases energy, not power, from the utility company. Although the unit of measurement for energy is the watt-second (Ws), a larger unit, called the kilowatt-hour (kWh), is used when determining the amount of energy the utility company supplies to the customer. The kilowatt-hour meter is used to measure this energy. It is rather simple to determine the cost of operating an electrical device or appliance for a given period of time if one knows the kilowatt-hour price charged by the utility company (see Example 2–6).

Example 2–6 Computing energy cost

Problem
If a utility company charges \$0.07/kWh for its energy, how much does it cost to operate a color television set for 10 h if the set is connected to a 110-V source and draws 0.8 A of current?

Solution
1. Calculate the power: $P = (V)(I) = (110 \text{ V})(0.8 \text{ A}) = 88 \text{ W}$

2. Calculate the energy: $W = (P)(t) = (88 \text{ W})(10 \text{ h}) = 880 \text{ Wh}$

3. Convert watt-hours to kilowatt-hours: $\text{kWh} = \dfrac{880 \text{ Wh}}{1000} = 0.88 \text{ kWh}$

4. Determine cost: $\dfrac{(\$0.07)}{\text{kWh}} \dfrac{(0.88 \text{ kWh})}{1} = \$0.0616$ or 6.16 cents

2-6.4 Watt's Law. As previously mentioned, anytime current flows through a resistor, heat is produced. This is an indication that work is being done and power is being dissipated, or consumed. In mechanics power is measured in horsepower. In electricity the unit of measurement for power is the watt, of course. In fact, 1 HP is equal to 746 W. As identified earlier, electrical power is the product of voltage and current, as expressed by Equation (2–7). This equation is often called Watt's law. This law can be expressed mathematically in three different ways, as shown below. Which one of the equations is used depends upon the known variables in a circuit. Notice that Equations (2–8) and (2–9) are derived by substituting the Ohm's law equivalent for the voltage and current variables, respectively.

1. $P = (I)(V)$ [Equation (2–7)]
2. $P = (I)(V)$ since $V = (I)(R)$, then $P = (I)(IR)$, or $P = (I^2)(R)$ **(2–8)**
3. $P = (I)(V)$ since $I = V/R$, then $P = (V/R)(V)$, or $P = V^2/R$ **(2–9)**

As an example of how Watt's law is applied, consider the circuit appearing in Example 2–7. Since the voltage, current, and resistances are all given, any one of the three formulas can be used. The results will be identical.

Example 2–7 Application of Watt's law

Problem
Calculate the power consumed by the resistor in Figure 2–18.

Solution
$$P = (I)(V) = (0.5 \text{ A})(10 \text{ V}) = 5 \text{ W}$$
or
$$P = (I^2)(R) = (0.5)^2(20 \text{ }\Omega) = (0.25)(20) = 5 \text{ W}$$
or
$$P = \frac{(V^2)}{R} = \frac{(10)^2}{20 \text{ }\Omega} = \frac{100}{20 \text{ }\Omega} = 5 \text{ W}$$

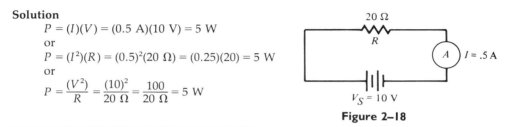

Figure 2–18

2-7 THE CONCEPT OF A LOAD

As discussed earlier, a functional circuit must contain a load. The load is what the electrical source performs work on. A load might be a light bulb, a motor, a heating element in a toaster, or any one of a number of similar electric devices or appliances. These types of loads all contain resistance. As far as the voltage source is concerned, the resistance of the load is the important factor. This is what determines the amount of current that will flow in the circuit. For example, if a light bulb has a resistance of 25 Ω and is connected to a 10-V source, the current flow is 0.4 A. The bulb could be replaced with a 25-Ω resistor, as shown in Figure 2–19, and the source will still have to supply 0.4 A of current. In other words, the light bulb has an equivalent resistance of 25 Ω.

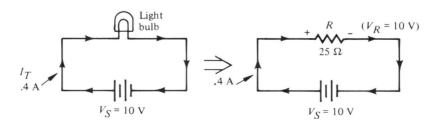

Figure 2–19 Load and equivalent resistance.

It is important to realize that anytime current flows through a load, or a resistor, that a voltage is developed across the device. This can be verified by Ohm's law as illustrated in Example 2–8. This means that a difference of potential (or charge) exists across the device. This is often called a voltage drop. For conventional current flow, the end of the device that current flows into is positive with respect to the end that current exits. The inverse of this is true for electron flow current. The amplitude of the voltage developed across a load or resistor can be determined by Ohm's law. Notice that the voltage dropped across the load is the same as the source voltage. This is always true for a circuit containing a single load or resistor.

Example 2–8   The source voltage is dropped across the load

Problem
Determine the voltage developed across the resistor for the circuit shown in Figure 2–19.

   Solution
   $V_R = (I_T)(R)$

   $V_R = (0.4 \text{ A})(25 \ \Omega)$

   $V_R = 10 \text{ V}$

2-8 THE USE OF SUBSCRIPTS

There are usually several of the same type of electrical variables associated with a circuit. To identify variables, suffixes are used. For the circuit appearing in Figure 2–19, V_S represents the source voltage and V_R represents the voltage dropped across the resistor. The suffixes S and R identify the source and resistor voltages, respectively. The suffix T associated with current represents total current.

2-9 SERIES-CONNECTED DEVICES

2-9.1 Introduction.   Electrical devices can be connected together in one of three general configurations to form circuits. These include series, parallel, and series-parallel. Whenever two or more components are connected together end-to-end, as shown in Figure 2–20, and the same current flows through all the devices, the components are said to be connected in series and the circuit configuration is called a series circuit. Two

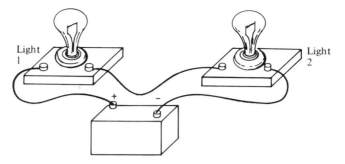

Figure 2–20   Two light bulbs connected in series.

light bulbs are shown connected together in Figure 2–20. As indicated, current leaves the positive side of the battery, travels through the conductor to light 1, flows through the filament, and out to the conductor connecting the bulbs together. The current continues through the filament of light 2, exits this light, and flows through the conductor connecting light 2 to the negative side of the battery. The circuit could be opened anywhere, an ammeter connected, and the same current intensity measured. Each light bulb will have equal brilliance if the filament resistance is the same for both. They will not glow with the same brightness, however, if the filaments have unequal resistances. Because each bulb has resistance, a voltage will be developed, or dropped, across each as current flows through it.

The light bulbs have been replaced with their equivalent resistances as shown in the schematic diagram appearing in Figure 2–21. The ability to analyze such a circuit and determine the electrical variables is important. These include the total resistance, current flow, voltages developed across the individual resistances, and power consumption. The following examples and calculations pertain to the circuit appearing in Figure 2–21.

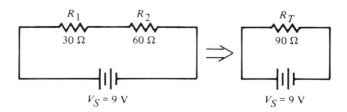

Figure 2–21   Two resistances connected in series.

2-9.2 Total Resistance. The total resistance of resistive devices connected in series is the sum of the individual resistance values. For the circuit whose diagram appears in Figure 2–21, the total resistance is 90 Ω. Equation (2–10) is used to calculate the total resistance of resistors, or resistive loads connected in series.

$$R_T = R_1 + R_2 + R_3 + \ldots R_N \qquad \text{where } N = \text{number of resistors} \qquad \textbf{(2–10)}$$

This represents the total opposition to the flow of current that the circuit offers to the voltage source. As far as the source is concerned, a single resistance, representing the sum of the individual resistances, represents its load.

2-9.3 Total Current. The current flowing through a series circuit has the same intensity in all parts of the circuit. This is referred to as the total current (I_T) and can be calculated using Ohm's law as illustrated in Example 2–9.

Example 2–9 Method of calculating total current

Problem
Calculate the current flowing through the circuit appearing in Figure 2–21.

Solution

$$I_T = \frac{V_S}{R_T}$$

$$I_T = \frac{9 \text{ V}}{90 \text{ Ω}} = 0.1 \text{ A}$$

2-9.4 Individual Voltage Drops. Ohm's law is used to compute the voltage drops across individual resistances as shown in Example 2–10. Notice that the sum of individual drops equals the applied, or source, voltage. This is known as Kirchhoff's voltage law (KVL) and is true for all series circuits, no matter how many devices are connected together.

Example 2–10   Calculating individual voltage drops

Problem
Compute the voltages dropped across the resistors for the circuit shown in Figure 2–21.

Solution

$V_{R1} = (I_T)(R_1) = (0.1 \text{ A})(30 \ \Omega) = 3 \text{ V}$

$V_{R2} = (I_T)(R_2) = (0.1 \text{ A})(60 \ \Omega) = 6 \text{ V}$

$V_S = (V_{R1}) + (V_{R2}) = 3 + 6 = 9 \text{ V}$

2-9.5 Power Consumption.   The total power consumed, or dissipated, in the form of heat in a resistive series circuit is the sum of the powers consumed by the individual devices, as illustrated in Example 2–11, and is equal to the power produced by the source.

Example 2–11   Calculating total power consumption

Problem
Calculate the power supplied and consumed in the circuit depicted in Figure 2–21.

Solution

$P_T = (I_T)\ (V_S) = (0.1 \text{ A})(9 \text{ V}) = 0.9 \text{ W}$

$P_{R1} = (I_T)\ (V_{R1}) = (0.1 \text{ A})\ (3 \text{ V}) = 0.3 \text{ W}$

$P_{R2} = (I_T)\ (V_{R2}) = (0.1 \text{ A})\ (6 \text{ V}) = 0.6 \text{ W}$

$P_T = P_{R1} + P_{R2} = 0.3 + 0.6 = 0.9 \text{ W}$

2-9.6 Effect on Circuit Variables of Connecting Additional Resistances in Series.   If an additional resistance is placed in series in the circuit just analyzed, the total resistance increases, the circuit current decreases, and the voltages developed across the two original resistances decrease, as shown in Example 2–12. Notice that the sum of the individual voltage drops does not exactly equal the applied voltage. The reason for this is that the new current is a repeating decimal and was rounded off. The actual current is 0.0818181818 A (accurate to 10 decimal places). For most circuit analysis applications, electrical quantities may be rounded off to two or three decimal positions. Although this will produce a small amount of error as noted above, it is usually not significant.

Example 2–12 Results on circuit variables of placing an additional resistance in a series circuit

Problem
Calculate the variables for the circuit shown in Figure 2–22.

Solution
$$R_T = R_1 + R_2 + R_3 = 30 + 60 + 20 = 110 \ \Omega$$

$$I_T = \frac{V_S}{R_T} = \frac{9 \ V}{110 \ \Omega} = 0.0818 \ A$$

$$V_{R1} = (I_T)(R_1) = (0.0818 \ A)(30 \ \Omega) = 2.454 \ V$$

$$V_{R2} = (I_T)(R_2) = (0.0818 \ A)(60 \ \Omega) = 4.908 \ V$$

$$V_{R3} = (I_T)(R_3) = (0.0818 \ A)(20 \ \Omega) = 1.636 \ V$$

$$V_S = V_{R1} + V_{R2} + V_{R3} = 2.454 + 4.908 + 1.636 = 8.998 \ V$$

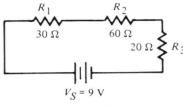

Figure 2–22

SUMMARY

1. The three requirements for an electrical circuit include a voltage source, a load, and conductors connecting the source to the load.
2. Conductor wire is manufactured in specific cross-sectional area sizes as standardized by the American Wire Gauge (AWG) Standard.
3. Switches allow a load to be turned on and off in a circuit by completing or opening the circuit.
4. Fuses and circuit breakers protect both the circuit and personnel if a short circuit occurs.
5. A short circuit occurs when current bypasses the load and excessive current flows.
6. One should exercise care when working with electricity. It takes only a relatively small amount of current passing through the heart to be fatal.
7. One of the most basic laws of electricity is Ohm's law. According to Ohm's law, the current flowing in a circuit is directly proportional to the voltage applied to the circuit and inversely proportional to the resistance of the circuit.
8. The three forms of Ohm's law are $I = \dfrac{V}{R}$, $V = IR$, $R = \dfrac{V}{I}$.
9. A voltmeter is used to measure voltage. The voltmeter must be connected in parallel, or across, the device whose voltage is being measured.
10. Current flow is measured with an ammeter. An ammeter is placed in series with the devices in the circuit whose current is to be measured.
11. Resistance is measured with an ohmmeter. The ohmmeter is connected in parallel, or across, the device whose resistance is to be measured. Resistance measurements must not be made in an energized circuit.

12. Energy is the ability to do work. The unit of measurement for electrical energy is the joule or watt-second.
13. Energy is purchased from the utility company in kilowatt-hour units.
14. Power is the rate at which energy is used. The unit of measurement for electrical power is the watt.
15. Anytime current flows through a resistance, power is consumed in the form of heat.
16. The relationship between voltage, current, resistance, and power is expressed by Watt's law.
17. Electrical devices can be connected together in one of three circuit configurations. These include the series, parallel, and series-parallel connections.
18. A series circuit is one which has only one path for current flow.
19. The total resistance of a series circuit is the sum of the individual resistance values.
20. The current flowing in a series circuit can be determined from Ohm's law.
21. Kirchhoff's voltage law states that the sum of the voltages dropped across series-connected resistances is equal to the applied voltage.
22. The power consumed in a series circuit is the sum of the powers consumed by the individual devices.
23. As more resistance is added to a series circuit, the total resistance increases and the current decreases.

PRACTICE EXERCISES

1. Draw the schematic symbols for the following devices:
   - **a.** potentiometer   **b.** variable capacitor
   - **c.** generator   **d.** resistor
   - **e.** rheostat   **f.** capacitor
   - **g.** connected
        conductors
2. Identify the three requirements for an electric circuit.
3. Discuss the relationship between AWG size and wire cross-sectional area.
4. What is the purpose of a switch as used in a circuit?
5. What function does a fuse or circuit breaker perform in a circuit?
6. List three safety precautions which should be observed when working with electricity.
7. Write the formulas for the three forms of Ohm's law.
8. Describe the relationship between voltage, current, and resistance.
9. Define the term *electrical energy* and identify its unit of measurement.
10. Define the term *electrical power* and identify its unit of measurement.
11. Write the three formulas for Watt's law.
12. What is a series circuit?
13. State Kirchhoff's voltage law (KVL).
14. Discuss the effects on circuit current and resistance when additional loads or resistors are connected in series.

15. What is the function of an electrical load?
16. A resistor in a transistor amplifier causes 22.2 mA of current to flow from a 6-V battery. What is the value of the resistance?
17. Compute the total resistance, circuit current, and voltage dropped across each device for the circuit in Figure 2–23.
18. An electric furnace has 4.889 Ω of resistance and draws 45 A of current. What is the amplitude of the voltage source connected to the furnace?
19. A soldering iron is rated at 25 W. If the iron is plugged into a 117-V source, how much current flows through its heating element?
20. An electric hot water heater is connected to 220 V and draws 9 A of current. If the heater is on an average of 3 h/day, how much does it cost to operate the heater for 30 days if energy costs $0.07/kWh?
21. Calculate the resistance of R_1 for the circuit in Figure 2–24.
22. It is desired to operate a 6.3-V DC motor from a 12.6-V source. Determine the resistance of the series resistor required to reduce the source voltage. The motor draws 1.5 A of current.
23. Determine the minimum power rating of the resistor required in exercise 22.
24. In Figure 2–25, compute the resistance of R_5 if the voltage across R_2 is 5 V.
25. For the circuit appearing in Figure 2–26 what is the voltage across points

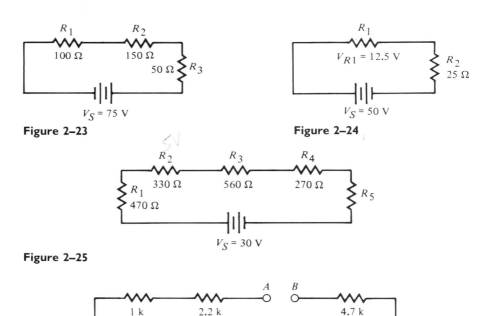

Figure 2–23

Figure 2–24

Figure 2–25

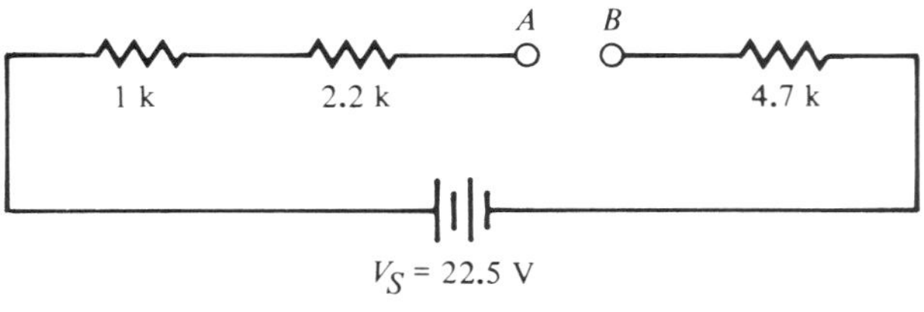

Figure 2–26

ANSWERS TO PRACTICE EXERCISES

1. a.

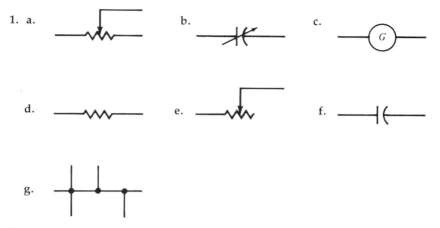

Figure 2–27

2. The three requirements for an electrical circuit include a voltage source, load, and complete path for current flow (conductors).
3. The larger the AWG number, the smaller the cross-sectional area of the wire.
4. Switches are used to energize or deenergize a load.
5. Fuses and circuit breakers are used to protect circuits, property, and personnel.
6. Safety precautions include standing on a dry nonconductive substance, working with one hand as much as possible, and ensuring that circuits are de-energized when replacing parts.
7. The three forms of Ohm's law include $I = V/R$, $R = V/I$, and $V = (I)(R)$.
8. The current flowing through a circuit is directly proportional to the voltage applied to the circuit and inversely proportional to the resistance of the circuit.
9. Electrical energy, like any form of energy, is the ability, or capacity, to perform work. It is measured either in joules or watt-seconds.
10. Electrical power is the rate at which electrical energy is used. Its unit of measurement is the watt.
11. The three forms of Watt's law include $P = (V)(I)$, $P = (I^2)(R)$, and $P = V^2/R$.
12. A series circuit is one in which the devices are connected together end-to-end and there is a single path for current flow.
13. Kirchhoff's voltage law (KVL) states that the sum of the voltages dropped in a series circuit is equal to the applied voltage.
14. When additional resistive devices are connected in series, the intensity of the current decreases and the total resistance increases.
15. The electrical load, or loads, is what the voltage source performs work on. The load also limits the magnitude of the current the source has to supply.
16. Solution

$$R = \frac{V}{I} = \frac{6 \text{ V}}{0.0222 \text{ A}} = 270.27 \ \Omega$$

17. Solution

$$R_T = R_1 + R_2 + R_3 = 100 + 150 + 50 = 300 \ \Omega$$

$$I_T = \frac{V_S}{R_T} = \frac{75 \text{ V}}{300 \ \Omega} = 0.25 \text{ A}$$

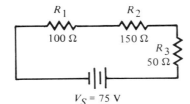

Figure 2–28 $V_S = 75$ V

$$V_{R1} = (I_T)(R_1) = (0.25 \text{ A})(100 \ \Omega) = 25 \text{ V}$$
$$V_{R2} = (I_T)(R_2) = (0.25 \text{ A})(150 \ \Omega) = 37.5 \text{ V}$$
$$V_{R3} = (I_T)(R_3) = (0.25 \text{ A})(50 \ \Omega) = 12.5 \text{ V}$$

18. Solution

$$V = (I)(R) = (45 \text{ A})(4.889 \ \Omega) = 220 \text{ V}$$

19. Solution

$$P = (I)(V); \quad I = \frac{P}{V} = \frac{25 \text{ W}}{117 \text{ V}} = 0.214 \text{ A}$$

20. Solution

$$\text{Cost} = (P)(t)(\text{cost/kWh})$$
$$\text{Cost} = \frac{(220 \text{ V})(9 \text{ A})(3 \text{ h})(30 \text{ days})}{1000/\text{kWh}} (\$0.07/\text{kWh})$$
$$\text{Cost} = \$12.48$$

21. Solution

$$V_{R2} = V_S - V_{R1} = 50 - 12.5 = 37.5 \text{ V}$$

$$I_T = I_{R2} = \frac{V_{R2}}{R_2} = \frac{37.5 \text{ V}}{25 \ \Omega} = 1.5 \text{ A}$$

$$R_1 = \frac{V_{R1}}{I_T} = \frac{12.5 \text{ V}}{1.5 \text{ A}} = 8.33 \ \Omega$$

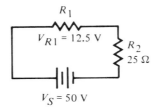

Figure 2–29 $V_S = 50$ V

22. Solution

$$R_S = \frac{V_{RS}}{I_T}$$

$$V_{RS} = V_S - V_{load} = 12.6 - 6.3 = 6.3 \text{ V}$$

$$R_S = \frac{6.3 \text{ V}}{1.5 \text{ A}} = 4.2 \text{ }\Omega$$

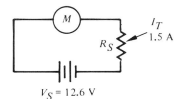

Figure 2–30 $V_S = 12.6$ V

23. Solution

$$P_R = (I_T)^2 (R_S) = (1.5 \text{ A})^2 (4.2 \text{ }\Omega) = 9.45 \text{ W}$$

24. Solution

$$R_5 = \frac{V_{R5}}{I_T}$$

$$I_T = \frac{V_{R2}}{R_2} = \frac{5 \text{ V}}{330 \text{ }\Omega} = 0.015 \text{ A}$$

Since $R_T = \dfrac{V_S}{I_T} = \dfrac{30 \text{ V}}{0.015 \text{ A}} = 2000 \text{ }\Omega$

and $R_T = R_1 + R_2 + R_3 + R_4 + R_5$

then $R_5 = R_T - R_1 - R_2 - R_3 - R_4$

$\qquad R_5 = 2000 - 470 - 330 - 560 - 270 \text{ }\Omega$

$\qquad R_5 = 370 \text{ }\Omega$

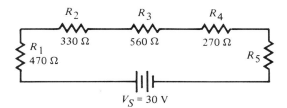

Figure 2–31 $V_S = 30$ V

25. Solution:

V_{AB} equals the applied voltage of 22.5 V. Since there is an open circuit, there will be no voltage drop

across the resistors. Thus, the applied potential is felt across the
open terminals.

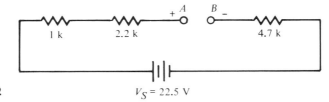

Figure 2–32 $V_S = 22.5$ V

CHAPTER EXAMINATION

1. _____ is the ability to perform work.
   (a) Power   **(c)** Voltage
   (b) Energy   **(d)** Current flow
2. The rate at which energy is used defines
   (a) power   **(c)** current
   (b) voltage   **(d)** resistance
3. The unit of measurement for power is the
   (a) watt   **(c)** joule
   (b) volt   **(d)** ampere
4. The current flowing through a circuit is proportional to the amount of voltage
   applied to the circuit and inversely proportional to the resistance of the circuit. This is a definition for _____ law.
   (a) Ohm's   **(c)** Lenz's
   (b) Watt's   **(d)** Kirchhoff's
5. Which of the following is not a form of Watt's law:

   (a) $P = I^2 R$ **(c)** $P = \dfrac{R}{I}$
   (b) $P = \dfrac{V^2}{R}$ **(d)** $P = VI$

6. The sum of the voltages dropped across series-connected devices is equal to
   the source voltage. This is a definition for
   (a) Ohm's law   **(c)** Lenz's law
   (b) Watt's law   **(d)** Kirchhoff's voltage law
7. The unit of measurement for energy is the
   (a) watt   **(c)** joule
   (b) volt   **(d)** ampere
8. The schematic symbol shown in Figure 2–33 is that for a (an)
   (a) rheostat
   (b) resistor
   (c) potentiometer
   (d) adjustable resistor

Figure 2–33

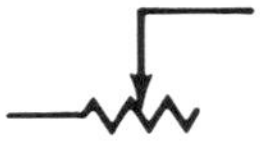

9. The symbol shown in Figure 2–34 represents a
   (a) relay
   (b) resistor
   (c) capacitor
   (d) relay contact

Figure 2–34

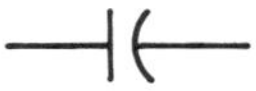

10. The symbol in Figure 2–35 represents a (an)
    (a) resistor
    (b) transformer
    (c) air core inductor
    (d) iron core inductor

Figure 2–35

Questions 11–17 pertain to the circuit appearing in Figure 2–36.
11. Calculate the total resistance of the circuit (R_T).
12. Determine the circuit current (I_T).
13. Compute the voltage dropped across R_1.
14. Find the voltage dropped across R_2.
15. Calculate the voltage appearing across R_3.
16. Compute V_{R4}.
17. What is the power required of the source?

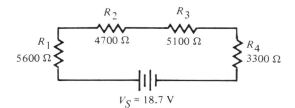

Figure 2–36

R_2 4700 Ω R_3 5100 Ω

R_1 5600 Ω

R_4 3300 Ω

$V_S = 18.7$ V

18. A 220-V source is connected to a motor which requires 25 A of current. What does it cost to operate the motor for 7 days if it is operated 14 h/day and energy costs $0.10/kWh?
19. For the circuit shown in Figure 2–37 calculate V_S.

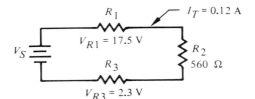

Figure 2–37

20. An AM/FM cassette tape player audio system rated at 12.6 V and 5.67 W (DC) is installed in a new automobile. What is the current supplied by the battery when the system is on?

3

Parallel and Series-Parallel Resistive Circuits

OBJECTIVES

Upon completion of this chapter you should be able to do the following:

1. Define a parallel circuit.
2. Discuss the advantages of connecting devices in parallel.
3. Describe the effect of connecting additional resistances, or loads, in parallel on the total circuit resistance.
4. Discuss the effect of connecting additional loads, or resistors, in parallel on the total circuit current.
5. Describe the relationship between the individual branch currents and total current for a parallel circuit.
6. Explain the relationship which exists between voltages across parallel-connected devices.
7. Calculate the total circuit resistance, total circuit current, and branch currents in a parallel circuit.
8. Compare the electrical variables associated with a parallel circuit with those of a series circuit.
9. Compute the total circuit resistance, total circuit current, branch currents, and individual voltage drops in a series-parallel circuit.
10. Discuss the purpose of a voltage divider network.
11. Design a voltage divider network that will provide the required voltages to operate specified loads.

3-1 INTRODUCTION

Electrical devices can be connected together in one of three different circuit arrangements—series, parallel, and series-parallel. The last chapter

55

dealt with series circuits. This chapter will be concerned with the other two types.

The series circuit is a simple method of connecting components together. It does have two rather limiting drawbacks, however. If one device becomes defective and opens, there is no longer a complete path for current flow and all the devices cease to operate. Anybody who has spent time at Christmas trying to locate a defective bulb in a string of Christmas lights can attest to this. A second disadvantage is that individual devices cannot be turned on and off. They are either all on or all off.

3-2 PARALLEL CIRCUITS

3-2.1 Definition.   The discussion which follows provides the foundation for developing the definition of a parallel circuit.

A series circuit consisting of a single lamp connected to a battery is shown in Figure 3–1(a). A second lamp is connected across, or in parallel with, the first lamp in Figure 3–1(b). Unlike the circuit appearing in Figure 3–1(a) which has one current, the circuit shown in Figure 3–1(b) has three different currents associated with it. The total circuit current, I_T, leaves the positive terminal of the battery and flows to point A. At that point the current divides. Part flows downward through lamp 1 while the remaining current flows to the right, downward through lamp 2, and to the left to point B. The current flowing through lamp 1 also flows into point B. There the two currents recombine, and the total circuit current flows to the negative terminal of the battery to complete the circuit.

A third lamp has been added to the circuit whose diagram is shown in Figure 3–2. Notice that an additional path for current flow has been created. This brings us to the definition of a parallel circuit. A parallel circuit is one in which the components are connected side-by-side so that there is more than one path for current to flow. In Figure 3–1(b) lamps 1

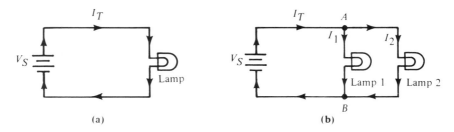

Figure 3–1   Current paths for a series and a parallel circuit: (a) single-lamp load; (b) two lamps connected in parallel.

and 2 are connected together in parallel with each other. Lamps 1, 2, and 3 are connected in parallel with each other in Figure 3–2. Each path for current flow through a lamp is called a branch circuit. The circuit appearing in Figure 3–1(b) has two branch circuits, whereas the circuit shown in Figure 3–2 has three branch circuits.

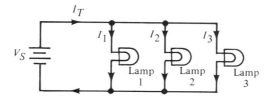

Figure 3–2   Three-branch parallel circuit.

3-2.2 Voltages Across Parallel-Connected Devices.   When components are connected in parallel with each other, each device has the same voltage across it. This is due to the fact that the conductors connecting the devices together and to the terminals of the battery have negligible resistance. This is illustrated in Figure 3–3. If the resistance of the conductor connecting the positive terminal of the battery is neglected, electrically points A, B, and C are at the same potential. No voltage drop exists across the conductor between points A and C. In similar fashion points D, E, and F are at the same potential. Therefore, the voltages across R_1 and R_2 are the same as the source, or battery, voltage. Equation (3–1) expresses this relationship.

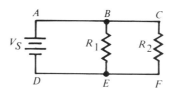

Figure 3–3   Voltages across parallel-connected devices are equal.

$$V_S = V_{R1} = V_{R2} = \cdots = V_{RN}$$
where N represents the number of parallel-connected devices

(3–1)

3-2.3 Current Relationships in a Parallel Circuit. A parallel circuit consisting of three branches is shown in Figure 3–4. As illustrated, Ohm's law can be used to calculate the current flowing through each branch. As indicated, the total circuit, or source, current is equal to the sum of the individual branch currents. This relationship is expressed by Kirchhoff's current law (KCL). According to this law, the current flowing into a junction must be equal to the current flowing out of the junction. Kirchhoff's current law is expressed below in Equation (3–2).

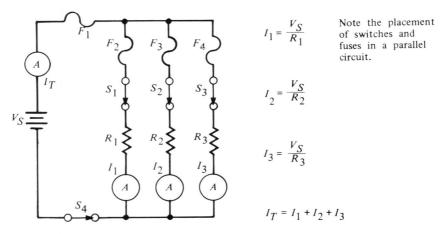

$$I_1 = \frac{V_S}{R_1}$$

Note the placement of switches and fuses in a parallel circuit.

$$I_2 = \frac{V_S}{R_2}$$

$$I_3 = \frac{V_S}{R_3}$$

$$I_T = I_1 + I_2 + I_3$$

Figure 3–4 Current relationships in a parallel circuit.

$$I_T = I_1 + I_2 + I_3 + \cdots + I_N$$
where N equals the
number of branch
circuits

(3–2)

3-2.4 Resistance in a Parallel Circuit. Two resistors are shown connected together in Figure 3–5. As indicated, Ohm's law can be applied in calculating the total resistance of the circuit. Notice that the total resistance is less than the value of the smaller resistor. This relationship is always valid, no matter what the resistance values are or the number of resistances connected in parallel.

Equation (3–3) can also be used to determine the total resistance of a circuit containing two resistors connected in parallel.

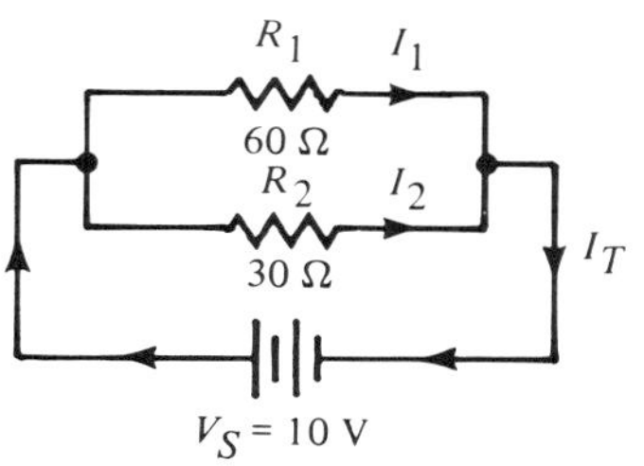

$$I_1 = \frac{V_S}{R_1} = \frac{10 \text{ V}}{60 \text{ }\Omega} = 0.167 \text{ A}$$

$$I_2 = \frac{V_S}{R_2} = \frac{10 \text{ V}}{30 \text{ }\Omega} = 0.333 \text{ A}$$

$$I_T = I_1 + I_2 = 0.167 \text{ A} + 0.333 \text{ A} = 0.5 \text{ A}$$

$$R_T = \frac{V_S}{I_T} = \frac{10 \text{ V}}{0.5 \text{ A}} = 20 \text{ }\Omega$$

Figure 3–5   Computing the total resistance of resistances connected in parallel.

$$R_T = \frac{(R_1)(R_2)}{R_1 + R_2}$$
                                                                              (3–3)

Called the product-over-the-sum equation, this equation states that the total resistance of two parallel-connected resistances is equal to the product of the two resistances divided by the sum. For the circuit appearing in Figure 3–5, the total resistance is 20 Ω as calculated in Example 3–1.

Example 3–1   Calculations using the product-over-the sum formula

Problem
Calculate the total resistance in the circuit shown in Figure 3–5.

Solution

$$R_T = \frac{(R_1)(R_2)}{R_1 + R_2} \qquad R_T = \frac{(60)(30)}{60 + 30} = \frac{(1800)}{90} = 20 \text{ }\Omega$$

The total resistance of parallel-connected resistances is often referred to as the series equivalent resistance, sometimes called R equivalent (R_{eq}). As far as the voltage source is concerned, it works into, or "sees" an equivalent resistance, which is in series with its terminals, as illustrated in Figure 3–6.

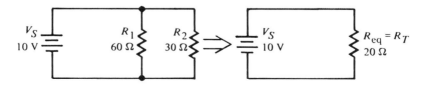

Figure 3–6   Parallel-connected resistances and their series equivalent resistance.

The circuit diagram appearing in Figure 3–7 is the same as that shown in Figure 3–5, except that a third resistor has been added. Because this circuit has an additional current path, the total current will increase. This implies that the total circuit resistance has decreased. Notice that the current has increased from 0.5 to 1.167 A with the addition of the third resistor. The total resistance has decreased from 20 to 8.57 Ω. This illustrates the principle that increasing the number of branch circuits in a parallel-connected circuit increases the total current and decreases the total, or series equivalent, resistance.

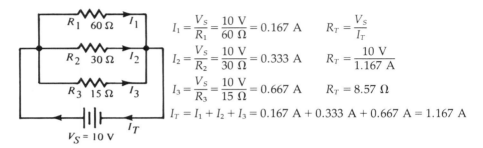

$$I_1 = \frac{V_s}{R_1} = \frac{10 \text{ V}}{60 \text{ }\Omega} = 0.167 \text{ A} \qquad R_T = \frac{V_s}{I_T}$$

$$I_2 = \frac{V_s}{R_2} = \frac{10 \text{ V}}{30 \text{ }\Omega} = 0.333 \text{ A} \qquad R_T = \frac{10 \text{ V}}{1.167 \text{ A}}$$

$$I_3 = \frac{V_s}{R_3} = \frac{10 \text{ V}}{15 \text{ }\Omega} = 0.667 \text{ A} \qquad R_T = 8.57 \text{ }\Omega$$

$$I_T = I_1 + I_2 + I_3 = 0.167 \text{ A} + 0.333 \text{ A} + 0.667 \text{ A} = 1.167 \text{ A}$$

Figure 3–7   Circuit with three parallel-connected resistances.

The total resistance of three or more parallel-connected resistors may be determined from Equation (3–4).

$$\frac{1}{R_T} = \frac{1}{R_1} + \frac{1}{R_2} + \frac{1}{R_3} + \cdots + \frac{1}{R_N} \qquad\qquad \textbf{(3–4)}$$

where N equals the number of parallel connected resistors

This equation states that the reciprocal of the total resistance is equal to the sum of the individual resistor reciprocal values. For the resistors shown connected together in Figure 3–8, the total resistance is 2 Ω. Notice that the series equivalent resistance is less than the value of the smallest resistor.

Occasionally, resistances having the same value are connected in parallel. Although the product-over-the-sum equation (for two resistors) or reciprocal equation (for three or more resistors) can be used, it is simpler to divide the value of one resistance by the number of parallel-connected resistances, as shown in Figure 3–9.

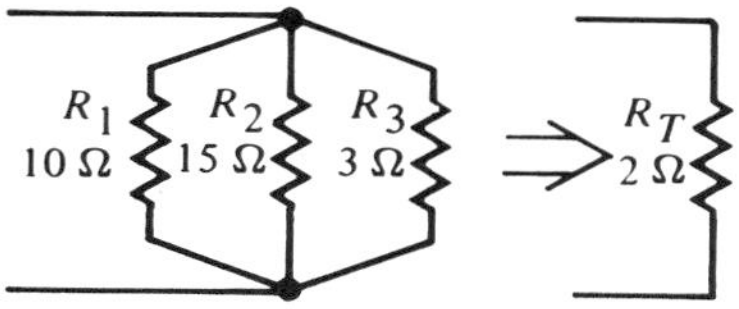

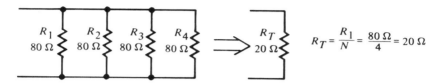

$$\frac{1}{R_T} = \frac{1}{R_1} + \frac{1}{R_2} + \frac{1}{R_3} = \frac{1}{10} + \frac{1}{15} + \frac{1}{3}$$

$$\frac{1}{R_T} = \frac{1}{10} + \frac{1}{15} + \frac{1}{3} = \frac{3}{30} + \frac{2}{30} + \frac{10}{30} = \frac{15}{30}$$

$$R_T = \frac{30}{15} = 2\ \Omega$$

Figure 3–8 Calculations using the reciprocal formula.

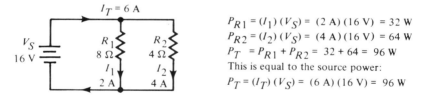

$$R_T = \frac{R_1}{N} = \frac{80\ \Omega}{4} = 20\ \Omega$$

Figure 3–9 Equivalent series resistance of equal value resistors.

3-2.5 Power Consumption in Parallel Circuits. The total power consumed, or dissipated, by resistive devices connected in parallel is the sum of the powers dissipated by the individual devices just as in series circuits. As indicated in Figure 3–10, the total power dissipated by the devices is equal to the power supplied by the source.

$$P_{R1} = (I_1)(V_S) = (2\ A)(16\ V) = 32\ W$$
$$P_{R2} = (I_2)(V_S) = (4\ A)(16\ V) = 64\ W$$
$$P_T = P_{R1} + P_{R2} = 32 + 64 = 96\ W$$
This is equal to the source power:
$$P_T = (I_T)(V_S) = (6\ A)(16\ V) = 96\ W$$

Figure 3–10 Power relationships in a parallel circuit.

3-2.6 Applications of Parallel Circuits. Parallel circuits are frequently used in electrical applications. They have the advantage that if any one device becomes defective and opens up, the devices in the other branches will continue to operate. Switches and fuses may be placed in each branch circuit to allow the load in that branch to be turned on and off without affecting the operation of the loads in other branches. The fuse in each branch protects the load in that branch. If an overload or short circuit occurs and the fuse blows, the other devices will continue to operate. House wiring circuits and the electrical system in automobiles are examples of parallel-connected circuits.

3-2.7 Contrasts between Series and Parallel Circuits. Both series and parallel methods are used to connect electrical devices together to form circuits. Each has its own unique characteristics. Although the principles for both types of circuits have been developed and discussed, it is important that one thoroughly understands the voltage, current, resistance, and power relationships that exist for each type of circuit configuration. These are summarized in Figure 3–11.

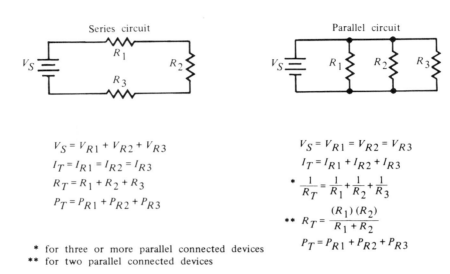

$$V_S = V_{R1} + V_{R2} + V_{R3}$$
$$I_T = I_{R1} = I_{R2} = I_{R3}$$
$$R_T = R_1 + R_2 + R_3$$
$$P_T = P_{R1} + P_{R2} + P_{R3}$$

$$V_S = V_{R1} = V_{R2} = V_{R3}$$
$$I_T = I_{R1} + I_{R2} + I_{R3}$$
$$* \quad \frac{1}{R_T} = \frac{1}{R_1} + \frac{1}{R_2} + \frac{1}{R_3}$$
$$** \quad R_T = \frac{(R_1)(R_2)}{R_1 + R_2}$$
$$P_T = P_{R1} + P_{R2} + P_{R3}$$

* for three or more parallel connected devices
** for two parallel connected devices

Figure 3–11 Comparison of series and parallel circuits.

3-3 SERIES-PARALLEL CIRCUITS

Many electrical and electronic circuits consist of components connected both in series and in parallel with each other. These are called series-parallel circuits. This is the type of circuit appearing in Example 3–2. In this circuit R_2 and R_3 are connected in parallel with each other, and this parallel combination is in series with R_1.

The current flowing through the circuit, the total resistance, and the individual voltage drops can all be found by applying formulas already presented for series and parallel circuits. To calculate the total resistance, the equivalent series resistance of the two parallel-connected resistors is computed first. The resulting equivalent resistance is in series with R_1. The total resistance is the sum of R_1 and the series equivalent resistance.

Example 3–2   A series-parallel circuit and calculations required to obtain the circuit variables

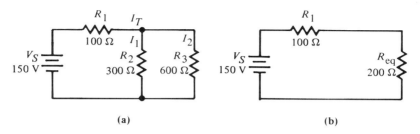

(a)   (b)

Figure 3–12   (a) Actual circuit; (b) simplified circuit.

Problem
Given the circuit shown in Figure 3–12, calculate R_T, I_T, V_{R1}, I_1, I_2, V_{R2}, and V_{R3}.

Solution
1. Calculate the equivalent resistance of the parallel-connected resistors.

$$R_{eq} = \frac{(300)(600)}{300 + 600} = 200 \ \Omega$$

2. The circuit now appears as a series circuit, as shown in Figure 3–12(b). Compute R_T.

$$R_T = R_1 + R_{eq} = 100 + 200 = 300 \ \Omega$$

3. Determine the value of I_T.

$$I_T = \frac{V_S}{R_T} = \frac{150 \ V}{300 \ \Omega} = 0.5 \ A$$

4. Compute V_{R1}.

$$V_{R1} = (I_T)(R_1) = (0.5 \ A)(100 \ \Omega) = 50 \ V$$

5. Compute V_{R2} and V_{R3}. This will be the same potential since the two resistors are connected in parallel.

$$V_{R2} = V_{R3} = (I_T)(R_{eq}) = (0.5 \ A)(200 \ \Omega) = 100 \ V$$
$$\text{or } V_{R2} = V_{R3} = V_S - V_{R1} = 150 - 50 = 100 \ V$$

6. Calculate I_1.

$$I_1 = \frac{V_{R2}}{R_2} = \frac{100 \ V}{300 \ \Omega} = 0.333 \ A$$

7. Compute I_2.

$$I_2 = \frac{V_{R3}}{R_3} = \frac{100 \ V}{600 \ \Omega} = 0.167 \ A$$

The total current is obtained by dividing the source voltage by the total resistance. The current flowing through each branch is found by applying Ohm's law to each branch. The voltage dropped across R_2 and R_3 is obtained by subtracting the voltage drop across R_1 (V_{R1}) from the source voltage.

In Example 3–3 the circuit variables of a series-parallel circuit are computed. Notice the application of Ohm's law in the various parts of the solution.

Example 3–3 A series-parallel circuit and the computations required to determine the circuit variables

Problem
For the circuit shown in Figure 3–13, compute R_T, I_T, I_1, I_2, V_{R1}, V_{R2}, V_{R3}, V_{R4}, and V_{R5}.

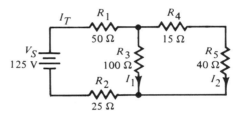

Figure 3–13

Solution
1. Calculate R_T.
   a. Compute the series resistance of R_4 and R_5.

   $$R_4 + R_5 = 15 + 40 = 55 \ \Omega$$

   b. Determine the equivalent series resistance of the series-parallel combination of R_3, R_4, and R_5.

   $$R_{eq} = \frac{(R_3)(R_4 + R_5)}{(R_3) + (R_4 + R_5)} = \frac{(100)(55)}{100 + 55} = 35.48 \ \Omega$$

   c. The circuit now appears as a simple series circuit, as shown in Figure 3–14. The total resistance (R_T) is computed by adding the individual resistance values.

   $$R_T = R_1 + R_{eq} + R_2 = 50 + 35.48 + 25 = 110.48 \ \Omega$$

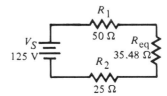

Figure 3–14 Simplified circuit.

2. The total circuit current can now be calculated.

$$I_T = \frac{V_S}{R_T} = \frac{125 \text{ V}}{110.48 \text{ } \Omega} = 1.13 \text{ A}$$

3. Compute V_{R1}.

$$V_{R1} = (I_T)(R_1) = (1.13 \text{ A})(50 \text{ } \Omega) = 56.5 \text{ V}$$

4. Determine the value of V_{R2}.

$$V_{R2} = (I_T)(R_2) = (1.13 \text{ A})(25 \text{ } \Omega) = 28.25 \text{ V}$$

5. Calculate the voltage dropped across R_3.

$$V_{R3} = (I_T)(R_{\text{eq}}) = (1.13 \text{ A})(35.48 \text{ } \Omega) = 40.09 \text{ V}$$

6. Next compute the value of I_2.

$$I_2 = \frac{V_{R4} + V_{R5}}{R_4 + R_5} = \frac{V_{R3}}{R_4 + R_5} = \frac{40.09 \text{ V}}{55 \text{ } \Omega} = 0.729 \text{ A}$$

7. Find the value of I_1.

$$I_1 = \frac{V_{R3}}{R_3} = \frac{40.09 \text{ V}}{100 \text{ } \Omega} = 0.4009 \text{ A}$$

8. Determine the voltage dropped across R_4.

$$V_{R4} = (I_2)(R_4) = (0.729 \text{ A})(15 \text{ } \Omega) = 10.94 \text{ V}$$

9. Finally, calculate the value of V_{R5}.

$$V_{R5} = (I_2)(R_5) = (0.729 \text{ A})(40 \text{ } \Omega) = 29.16 \text{ V}$$

3-4 UNLOADED VOLTAGE DIVIDERS

Unloaded voltage dividers are series circuits containing passive devices (usually resistors) used to obtain multiple fixed potentials from a single voltage source. For the circuit appearing in Figure 3–15, six different voltages can be obtained from the single voltage supply with three resistors connected together in series. A voltmeter connected one at a time across the three resistors will indicate potentials of 6.25, 31.25, and 62.5 V. A voltmeter connected across points *AC* will indicate a potential of 37.5 V. In similar fashion, a voltmeter connected across points *BD* will indicate a voltage of 93.75 V. Thus, the simple three-resistor voltage divider circuit will provide six different voltages including the source voltage. Ohm's law can be used to compute the individual voltages, as shown in Figure 3–15.

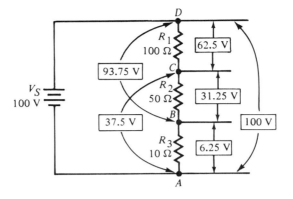

$$R_T = R_1 + R_2 + R_3 = 10 + 50 + 100 = 160 \ \Omega$$

$$I_T = \frac{V_S}{R_T} = \frac{100 \ V}{160 \ \Omega} = 0.625 \ A$$

$$V_{R3} = (I_T)(R_3) = (0.625 \ A)(10 \ \Omega) = 6.25 \ V$$

$$V_{R2} = (I_T)(R_2) = (0.625 \ A)(50 \ \Omega) = 31.25 \ V$$

$$V_{R1} = (I_T)(R_1) = (0.625 \ A)(100 \ \Omega) = 62.5 \ V$$

$$V_{AC} = (V_{R3}) + (V_{R2}) = 6.25 \ V + 31.25 \ V = 37.5 \ V$$

$$V_{BD} = (V_{R2}) + (V_{R1}) = 31.25 \ V + 62.5 \ V = 93.75 \ V$$

Figure 3–15   Unloaded voltage divider.

3-5 LOADED VOLTAGE DIVIDERS

Unloaded voltage dividers have only limited applications. When loads are connected to a voltage divider circuit, the resistance of the divider decreases because the loads are in parallel with the divider resistors, as indicated in Figure 3–16. This serves to change the voltages developed across the individual divider resistors. In order to obtain the required voltages across a voltage divider, the divider resistor values must be chosen with the required loads connected to the circuit.

Loaded voltage dividers are designed from the voltage and current requirements of the loads which are connected to the divider. For the circuit appearing in Figure 3–16, the 75-V source is supplying 10, 25, and 75 V to three separate loads, each of which has separate current requirements.

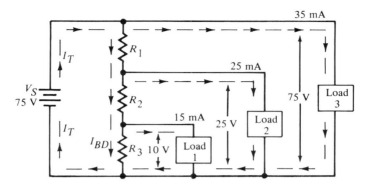

Figure 3–16   Loaded voltage divider.

The design of the voltage divider circuit consists of calculating the values of the resistors which form the divider circuit. This includes determining both the correct resistance value and proper minimum power rating for each resistor. Notice that the loaded voltage divider is in the form of a series-parallel circuit. The application of series-parallel circuit analysis is required to determine the proper resistance values. Equations (3–5) to (3–9) are used to obtain the resistance values for the resistors used in the divider circuit appearing in Figure 3–16.

As indicated, R_3 is equal to the voltage required by load 1 (because they are in parallel) divided by the bleeder current (I_{BD}). A bleeder circuit is a current which is not part of a load current that is used to develop a required voltage in a circuit. Although the value of this current is not critical, the circuit designer often uses a bleeder current which is equal to one-tenth of the total load current.

Total load current $(I_{LT}) = I_{\text{load}1} + I_{\text{load}2} + I_{\text{load}3}$ **(3–5)**

$I_{\text{Bleeder}} \ (I_{BD}) = (0.1)(I_{LT})$ **(3–6)**

$$R_3 = \frac{V_{\text{load}1}}{I_{BD}}$$ **(3–7)**

$$R_2 = \frac{V_{\text{load}2} - V_{\text{load}1}}{I_{BD} + I_{\text{load}1}}$$ **(3–8)**

$$R_1 = \frac{V_{\text{load}3} - V_{\text{load}2}}{I_{BD} + I_{\text{load}1} + I_{\text{load}2}}$$ **(3–9)**

The resistance value of R_2 is computed by dividing the voltage dropped across it by the current flowing through it. This voltage is equal to the difference between the voltages required of loads 1 and 2. The reason for this is that R_3 has already dropped part of the voltage required by load 2. Load 1, R_3 and R_2 form a series-parallel circuit. Therefore, the current flowing through R_2 is the sum of the currents flowing through R_3 (I_{BD}) and load 1.

The resistance value of R_1 is obtained by dividing the voltage dropped across it by the current flowing through it. This voltage is equal to the difference between the potential required by load 3 and the potential already dropped across resistors R_1 and R_2. The current flowing through R_1 is the sum of the current flowing through R_2 and the current required by load 2.

The calculations for the resistance values appear in Example 3–4. The closest standard EIA resistor values should be selected for each of the devices. Most electronic component catalogs contain tables of standard EIA resistor values.

The last step in designing a voltage divider network is to determine the minimum power rating of the resistors used in the network. This is accomplished by computing the actual power dissipated by each resistor

---

Example 3–4 Calculations to determine the resistance values of the voltage divider circuit appearing in Figure 3–16

Problem
Determine the resistor values required to supply the voltages identified in Figure 3–16.

Solution

$$I_{LT} = I_{\text{load}\,1} + I_{\text{load}\,2} + I_{\text{load}\,3} = 15 \text{ mA} + 25 \text{ mA} + 35 \text{ mA} = 75 \text{ mA}$$

$$I_{BD} = (I_{LT})(0.1) = (75 \text{ mA})(0.1) = 7.5 \text{ mA}$$

$$R_3 = \frac{V_{\text{load}\,1}}{I_{BD}} = \frac{10 \text{ V}}{0.0075 \text{ A}} = 1333.33 \ \Omega \quad \text{closest EIA value: } 1500 \ \Omega$$

$$R_2 = \frac{V_{\text{load}\,2} - V_{\text{load}\,1}}{I_{BD} + I_{\text{load}\,1}} = \frac{25 - 10 \text{ V}}{0.0075 + 0.015 \text{ A}} = \frac{15 \text{ V}}{0.0225 \text{ A}} = 666.67 \ \Omega$$
$$\text{closest EIA value: } 680 \ \Omega$$

$$R_1 = \frac{V_{\text{load}\,3} - V_{\text{load}\,2}}{I_{BD} + I_{\text{load}\,1} + I_{\text{load}\,2}} = \frac{75 - 25 \text{ V}}{0.0075 + 0.015 + 0.025 \text{ A}}$$

$$R_1 = \frac{50 \text{ V}}{0.0475 \text{ A}} = 1052.6 \ \Omega \quad \text{closest EIA value: } 1100 \ \Omega$$

and then overrating each by 25 percent. The power rating for resistors is rated at room temperature (25 °C). Often resistors are mounted close to heat-producing devices such as transistors. For this reason the minimum power rating should be at least 25 percent greater than the actual power being consumed by the resistor. A resistor having a larger power rating can be used, but never one smaller. The calculations shown in Example 3–5 are used to determine the minimum power ratings required of the resistors used in the circuit appearing in Figure 3–16.

Example 3–5   Determining the power rating of resistors in the voltage divider circuit

Problem
Compute the minimum power rating required of the resistors appearing in Figure 3–16.

Solution
Actual Power Dissipated
$$P_{R3} = (V_{R3})(I_{BD}) = (10 \text{ V})(0.0075 \text{ A}) = 0.075 \text{ W}$$

$$P_{R2} = (V_{R2})(I_{R2}) = (15 \text{ V})(0.0225 \text{ A}) = 0.3375 \text{ W}$$

$$P_{R1} = (V_{R1})(I_{R1}) = (50 \text{ V})(0.0475 \text{ A}) = 2.375 \text{ W}$$

Overrate by 25 percent
$$P_{R3} = (0.075 \text{ W})(1.25) = 0.094 \text{ W}$$

$$P_{R2} = (0.3375 \text{ W})(1.25) = 0.42 \text{ W}$$

$$P_{R1} = (2.375 \text{ W})(1.25) = 2.97 \text{ W}$$

Nearest Standard Power Rating
$$P_{R3} = \tfrac{1}{8} \text{ W}$$

$$P_{R2} = \tfrac{1}{2} \text{ W}$$

$$P_{R1} = 3 \text{ W}$$

3-6 THE POTENTIOMETER AS A VOLTAGE DIVIDER

The potentiometer is a device which is commonly used as a voltage divider. A picture of this component appears in Figure 1–16. A potentiometer is manufactured with a fixed resistance between terminals A and C as shown in Figure 3–17(a). The resistance between points A and B or B and C can be varied from 0 Ω to the potentiometer's maximum value. This means that if the potentiometer shown has a resistance value of 10 kΩ between terminals A and C, the resistance between points A and B can be varied from 0 to 10 kΩ depending upon the slider (point B) location. If the shaft on the potentiometer is turned so that the resistance is 8 kΩ between points B and C, the resistance between points A and B is 2 kΩ.

If a voltage source and load are connected to the potentiometer as indicated in Figure 3–17(b), the voltage applied to the load can be varied from 0 to any value up to the source potential.

Potentiometers have many applications as voltage dividers where it is necessary to have a means of controlling the voltage applied to a load. Some familiar examples include the volume control on radio and television receivers and the brightness and contrast controls on the TV set.

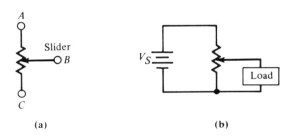

(a)   (b)

Figure 3–17   Potentiometer as voltage divider.

SUMMARY

1. A parallel circuit is one in which the devices are connected side-by-side, and each device forms a separate path for current flow.
2. The major advantage of connecting devices in parallel is that the individual components or appliances can be turned on and off without affecting the operation of the other devices.
3. Devices connected in parallel have the same difference of potential across them.
4. The source current is equal to the sum of the individual branch currents in a parallel circuit. This is an expression of Kirchhoff's current law (KCL).
5. The total, or series equivalent resistance, of two resistances connected in parallel may be computed from the product-over-the-sum formula $[R_T = R_1 R_2/(R_1 + R_2)]$.
6. The total resistance for three or more parallel-connected resistances can be found by using the reciprocal formula $\dfrac{1}{R_T} = \dfrac{1}{R_1} + \dfrac{1}{R_2} + \dfrac{1}{R_3} + \cdots + \dfrac{1}{R_N}$
7. The series equivalent resistance of equal value resistances connected in parallel may be found by dividing the resistance of one device by the number of devices connected in parallel $(R_T = R/R_N)$.

8. As additional devices are connected in parallel, the total resistance of the circuit decreases.
9. The total current flow increases as additional devices are connected in parallel.
10. The series equivalent resistance of a parallel circuit is a single resistance that represents the total resistance of the parallel-connected devices.
11. The series equivalent resistance is always less than the smallest resistance appearing in a parallel circuit.
12. A series-parallel circuit is one which contains devices connected both in series and in parallel with each other. This is the most common type of circuit configuration.
13. An unloaded voltage divider circuit consists of series-connected devices that allow several voltages to be developed from a single source.
14. A loaded voltage divider circuit consists of series-connected devices that have loads connected across them. The circuit is used to develop the required load voltages from a single voltage source. Most electronic systems, such as radio and television receivers, contain transistors and integrated circuits that require several different potentials to operate. A voltage divider network is often used to develop the required potentials from a single source.

PRACTICE EXERCISES

1. What are the three types of circuit connection arrangements?
2. What is a parallel circuit?
3. Describe the effect of adding additional resistors in parallel on
   a. total circuit resistance
   b. total circuit current
4. Discuss the relationship between the individual branch currents and total current in a parallel circuit. What law expresses this relationship?
5. Identify the formula used to compute
   a. the equivalent resistance of two parallel-connected devices
   b. the equivalent resistance of three or more parallel-connected resistances
   c. the total resistance for equal value resistances connected in parallel
6. Compare the voltage relationships between series-connected resistors and parallel-connected resistors.
7. Compare the current relationships between series-connected resistances and parallel-connected resistances.
8. What is the formula used to compute the total power consumption of resistances connected in parallel? How does this formula compare with the one used to compute power consumption for series-connected devices?
9. What is a series-parallel circuit?
10. What is an unloaded voltage divider?
11. What is a loaded voltage divider?
12. Identify an application for the loaded voltage divider.

13. A 220Ω resistor is connected in parallel with a 330Ω resistor. Calculate the series equivalent resistance of the two devices.

14. If 100, 50, and 25Ω resistors are all connected in parallel with each other, what is the total resistance of the network?

15. Three resistors are connected in parallel. They have values of 5600, 4700, and 3900 Ω. Determine the resistance of the circuit.

16. What is the effect on the resistance of placing a 2200Ω resistor in parallel with the resistors identified in the circuit appearing in exercise 15?

17. An ohmmeter is connected across a circuit containing five 100Ω resistors connected in parallel. What is the resistance indicated by the ohmmeter?

18. Calculate the following for the circuit shown in Figure 3–18.

  a. R_T e. I_3
  b. I_T f. V_{R1}
  c. I_1 g. V_{R2}
  d. I_2 h. V_{R3}
         i. P_T

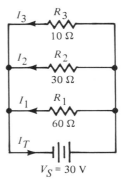

Figure 3–18

19. For the loaded voltage divider circuit appearing in Figure 3–19 determine the resistance and power requirements needed to provide the proper voltages to the loads.

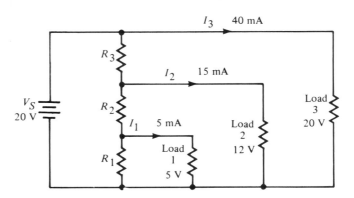

Figure 3–19

20. A microcomputer rated at 185 W is plugged into a 117-V utility outlet. Next, a disk drive memory system having a rating of 39 W is plugged into another

outlet which is connected to the same branch circuit as the first. What are the total current requirements of the system?

21. What is the resistance of the disk drive memory system identified in exercise 20?

22. A food blender rated at 120 V and 510 W, a waffle iron rated at 120 V and 630 W, and a 120-V 200-W light bulb are all connected into the same kitchen branch circuit. What is the total resistance of the three devices connected in the circuit?

23. For the series-parallel circuit appearing in Figure 3–20, calculate R_T, I_T, and V_{R4}.

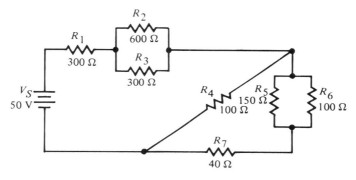

Figure 3–20

ANSWERS TO PRACTICE EXERCISES

1. The three types of circuit arrangements are the series, parallel, and series-parallel types.

2. A parallel circuit is one in which the devices are connected side-by-side and each device provides a separate path for current flow.

3. **a.** Total or equivalent resistance decreases.
   b. Total current increases.

4. The sum of the individual branch currents is equal to the total current as expressed by Kirchhoff's current law.

5. **a.** $R_T = \dfrac{(R_1)(R_2)}{R_1 + R_2}$

   b. $\dfrac{1}{R_T} = \dfrac{1}{R_1} + \dfrac{1}{R_2} + \dfrac{1}{R_3}$

   c. $R_T = \dfrac{R}{N}$

6. Series circuit: $V_S = V_{R1} + V_{R2} + V_{R3}$
   Parallel circuit: $V_S = V_{R1} = V_{R2} = V_{R3}$

7. Series circuit: $I_T = I_{R1} = I_{R2} = I_{R3}$
   Parallel Circuit: $I_T = I_{R1} + I_{R2} + I_{R3}$

8. The formula used to compute the total power consumption for resistive devices connected either in series or in parallel is $P_T = P_{R_1} + P_{R_2} + P_{R_3}$.
9. A series-parallel circuit is one in which devices are connected together both in series and in parallel.
10. An unloaded voltage divider circuit consists of devices connected together in series so that several different voltages may be obtained from one source. Anything but extremely high resistance loads connected to the divider will cause the voltages to change.
11. A loaded voltage divider is a voltage divider circuit whose resistance values have been selected with the loads connected to the divider.
12. Loaded voltage dividers are used to supply different values of voltage from a single voltage source. They are often found in radio and television receivers and other electronic systems that use transistors and integrated circuits.
13. Solution

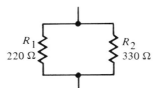

Figure 3–21

$$R_T = \frac{(R_1)(R_2)}{R_1 + R_2}$$

$$R_T = \frac{(220\ \Omega)(330\ \Omega)}{220\ \Omega + 330\ \Omega} = 132\ \Omega$$

14. Solution

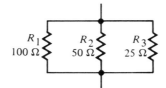

Figure 3–22

$$\frac{1}{R_T} = \frac{1}{R_1} + \frac{1}{R_2} + \frac{1}{R_3}$$

$$\frac{1}{R_T} = \frac{1}{100} + \frac{1}{50} + \frac{1}{25}$$

$$\frac{1}{R_T} = \frac{1}{100} + \frac{2}{100} + \frac{4}{100} = \frac{7}{100}$$

$$\frac{R_T}{1} = \frac{100}{7} = 14.29\ \Omega$$

15. Solution

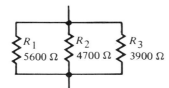

Figure 3–23

$$\frac{1}{R_T} = \frac{1}{5600} + \frac{1}{4700} + \frac{1}{3900}$$

$$\frac{1}{R_T} = 1.79 \times 10^{-4} + 2.13 \times 10^{-4} + 2.56 \times 10^{-4}$$

$$\frac{1}{R_T} = \frac{1}{6.48 \times 10^{-4}} = 0.154 \times 10^4 = 1543 \ \Omega$$

16. Solution

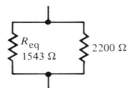

Figure 3–24

$$R_T = \frac{(R_{eq})(R_4)}{R_{eq} + R_4} = \frac{(1543)(2200)}{1543 + 2200} = 906.92 \ \Omega$$

The equivalent resistance decreases from 1543 to 906.92 Ω.

17. Solution

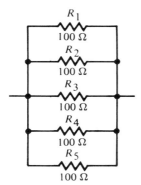

Figure 3–25

$$R_T = \frac{R_1}{N} = \frac{100 \ \Omega}{5} = 20 \ \Omega$$

18. Solution

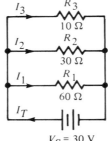

Figure 3–26

$$\frac{1}{R_T} = \frac{1}{R_1} + \frac{1}{R_2} + \frac{1}{R_3} = \frac{1}{60} + \frac{1}{30} + \frac{1}{10}$$

$$\frac{1}{R_T} = \frac{1}{60} + \frac{2}{60} + \frac{6}{60} = \frac{9}{60}$$

$$R_T = \frac{60}{9} = 6.67 \ \Omega$$

$$I_1 = \frac{V_S}{R_1} = \frac{30 \text{ V}}{60 \ \Omega} = 0.5 \text{ A}$$

$$I_2 = \frac{V_S}{R_2} = \frac{30 \text{ V}}{30 \ \Omega} = 1 \text{ A}$$

$$I_3 = \frac{V_S}{R_3} = \frac{30 \text{ V}}{10 \ \Omega} = 3 \text{ A}$$

$$I_T = I_1 + I_2 + I_3$$

$$I_T = 0.5 + 1 + 3 = 4.5 \text{ A}$$

$$V_{R1} = (I_1)(R_1) = (0.5 \text{ A})(60 \ \Omega) = 30 \text{ V}$$

$$V_{R2} = (I_2)(R_2) = (1 \text{ A})(30 \ \Omega) = 30 \text{ V}$$

$$V_{R3} = (I_3)(R_3) = (3 \text{ A})(10 \ \Omega) = 30 \text{ V}$$

$$P_{R1} = (I_1)(V_{R1}) = (0.5 \text{ A})(30 \text{ V}) = 15 \text{ W}$$

$$P_{R2} = (I_2)(V_{R2}) = (1 \text{ A})(30 \text{ V}) = 30 \text{ W}$$

$$P_{R3} = (I_3)(V_{R3}) = (3 \text{ A})(30 \text{ V}) = 90 \text{ W}$$

$$P_T = P_{R1} + P_{R2} + P_{R3} = 15 + 30 + 90 = 135 \text{ W}$$

or $P_T = (V_S)(I_T) = (30 \text{ V})(4.5 \text{ A}) = 135 \text{ W}$

Ohm's law can also be used to obtain I_T.

$$I_T = \frac{V_S}{R_T} = \frac{30 \text{ V}}{6.67 \ \Omega} = 4.5 \text{ A}$$

Notice that the total power consumed by the load equals the source power.

19. Solution

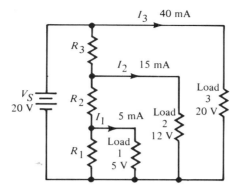

Figure 3–27

$$I_{LT} = I_1 + I_2 + I_3 = 5 + 15 + 40 = 60 \text{ mA}$$

$$I_{BD} = (0.1)(I_{LT}) = (0.1)(60 \text{ mA}) = 6 \text{ mA}$$

$$R_1 = \frac{V_{R1}}{I_{BD}} = \frac{5 \text{ V}}{0.006 \text{ A}} = 833.33 \ \Omega$$

$$R_2 = \frac{V_{\text{load 2}} - V_{R1}}{I_{BD} + I_1} = \frac{12 - 5 \text{ V}}{0.006 + 0.005 \text{ A}}$$

$$R_2 = \frac{7 \text{ V}}{0.011 \text{ A}} = 636.36 \ \Omega$$

$$R_3 = \frac{V_{\text{load 3}} - V_{\text{load 2}}}{I_{BD} + I_1 + I_2} = \frac{20 - 12 \text{ V}}{0.006 + 0.005 + 0.015 \text{ A}}$$

$$R_3 = \frac{8 \text{ V}}{0.026 \text{ A}} = 307.69 \ \Omega$$

$$P_{R1} = (V_{R1})(I_{BD})(1.25) = (5 \text{ V})(0.006 \text{ A})(1.25)$$

$$P_{R1} = 0.0375 \text{ W}$$

$$P_{R2} = (V_{R2})(I_{BD} + I_1)(1.25) = (7 \text{ V})(0.011 \text{ A})(1.25)$$

$$P_{R2} = 0.0963 \text{ W}$$

$$P_{R3} = (V_{R3})(I_{BD} + I_1 + I_2)(1.25)$$

$$P_{R3} = (8 \text{ V})(0.026 \text{ A})(1.25) = 0.26 \text{ W}$$

20. Solution

$$P_T = P_{\text{microcomputer}} + P_{\text{memory disk drive}}$$

$$P_T = 185 + 39 = 224 \text{ W}$$

$$P_T = (V)(I_T)$$

$$I_T = \frac{P_T}{V_T} = \frac{224 \text{ W}}{117 \text{ V}} = 1.915 \text{ A}$$

21. Solution

$$P_{\text{memory disk drive}} = \frac{V^2}{R}$$

$$R = \frac{V^2}{P} = \frac{(117 \text{ V})^2}{39 \text{ W}} = 351 \text{ }\Omega$$

22. Solution

$$R_{\text{blender}}: \ P = \frac{V^2}{R}; \ R = \frac{V^2}{P} = \frac{(120 \text{ V})^2}{510 \text{ W}} = 28.24 \text{ }\Omega$$

$$R_{\text{waffle iron}}: \ R = \frac{V^2}{P} = \frac{(120 \text{ V})^2}{630 \text{ W}} = 22.857 \text{ }\Omega$$

$$R_{\text{bulb}}: \ R = \frac{V^2}{P} = \frac{(120 \text{ V})^2}{200 \text{ W}} = 72 \text{ }\Omega$$

$$\frac{1}{R_T} = \frac{1}{R_{\text{blender}}} + \frac{1}{R_{\text{waffle iron}}} + \frac{1}{R_{\text{bulb}}}$$

$$\frac{1}{R_T} = \frac{1}{28.24 \text{ }\Omega} + \frac{1}{22.857 \text{ }\Omega} + \frac{1}{72 \text{ }\Omega}$$

$$\frac{1}{R_T} = 0.03541 + 0.04375 + 0.01389 = 0.09305$$

$$R_T = \frac{1}{0.09305} = 10.746 \text{ }\Omega$$

$$\text{or } R = \frac{(V)^2}{P_T} = \frac{(120 \text{ V})^2}{1340 \text{ W}} = 10.746 \text{ }\Omega$$

23. Solution

Calculation of R_T. It is easier to see the relationship of the individual circuit devices in a complex circuit if it is redrawn and all the devices are horizontally or vertically laid out. The circuit redrawn appears in Figure 3-28.

1. Compute the resistance of branch 2.

$$R_{\text{branch 2}} = \frac{(R_5)(R_6)}{R_5 + R_6} + R_7$$

$$R_{\text{branch 2}} = \frac{(150)(100)}{150 + 100} + 40$$

$$R_{\text{branch 2}} = 100 \text{ }\Omega$$

2. Determine the equivalent resistance of branches 1 and 2.

$$R_{\text{eq}_a} = \frac{(100)(100)}{100 + 100} = 50 \text{ }\Omega$$

3. Find the equivalent resistance of the parallel combination of R_2 and R_3.

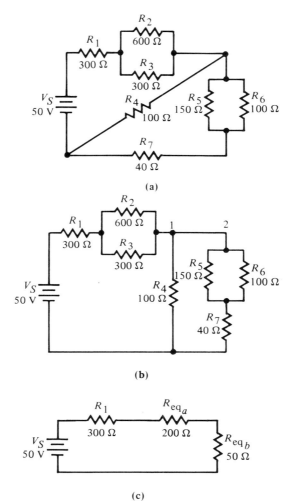

Figure 3–28

$$E_{eq_b} = \frac{(600)(300)}{600 + 300} = 200 \ \Omega$$

The circuit now appears in Figure 3–28(c).

4. Compute R_T.

$$R_T = R_1 + R_{eq_b} + R_{eq_a}$$

$$R_T = 300 + 200 + 50 = 550 \ \Omega$$

5. Calculate I_T.

$$I_T = \frac{V_S}{R_T} = \frac{50 \text{ V}}{550 \text{ }\Omega} = (0.091 \text{ A})(50\Omega)$$

6. Determine the value of V_{R4}.

$$V_{R4} = (I_T)(R_{eq_a}) = (0.091 \text{ A})(50 \text{ }\Omega)$$

$$V_{R4} = (0.091 \text{ A})(50 \text{ }\Omega) = 4.55 \text{ V}$$

CHAPTER EXAMINATION

1. For the circuit shown in Figure 3–29, calculate R_T, I_T, I_1, and I_2.

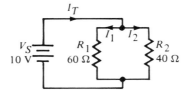

Figure 3–29

2. Calculate R_T and I_T for the circuit in Figure 3–30.

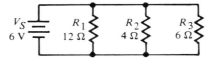

Figure 3–30

3. Determine the voltage dropped across R_1 in the circuit shown in Figure 3–31.

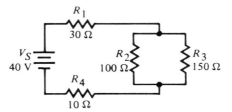

Figure 3–31

4. For the circuit shown in Figure 3–32, compute the following:
   a. R_T e. I_1
   b. I_T f. I_2
   c. V_{R1} g. V_{R4}
   d. V_{R2}

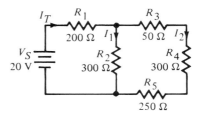

Figure 3–32

5. Calculate the resistance appearing across terminals *A* and *B* in Figure 3–33.

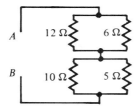

Figure 3–33

6. Four soldering irons are plugged into a 117-V line at a work station on an assembly line in an electronics manufacturing plant. The irons are rated at 25, 40, 50, and 75 W, respectively. How much current is required to heat the irons?

Choose true or false for questions 7 to 15.

7. T   F   As additional resistances are connected in parallel, the total circuit resistance increases.

8. T   F   The loaded voltage divider has only limited applications as a practical electrical circuit.

9. T   F   Kirchhoff's current law describes the relationship which exists between the source current and branch currents in a parallel circuit.

10. T   F   In a parallel circuit, if one of the devices opens up, all of the other devices become inoperative.

11. T   F   The sum of the powers dissipated by individual resistive devices connected in parallel is equal to the power produced by the voltage source.

12. T   F   As additional devices are connected in parallel, the source current increases.

13. T   F   The voltage across parallel-connected devices decreases as additional devices are connected in parallel.

14. T   F   The series-parallel circuit is probably the least often used of the three circuit configurations in electronic circuit applications.

15. T   F   The equivalent series resistance of resistors connected in parallel is always less than the value of the smallest resistor.

4

Resistive Network Analysis

OBJECTIVES

Upon completion of this chapter you should be able to do the following:

1. Describe what is meant by an ideal voltage source.
2. Calculate the terminal voltage of a voltage source when the internal resistance and load current or resistance variables are given.
3. Compute the percent regulation of a voltage source.
4. Explain what is meant by an ideal current source.
5. Use the voltage divider rule to calculate the voltages across series-connected resistors.
6. Use the current divider rule to compute the branch currents flowing through parallel-connected resistors.
7. Describe the condition which must exist for maximum-power transfer to occur from a source to a load.
8. State Thevenin's theorem.
9. Draw Thevenin's equivalent circuit, showing values for both the equivalent series resistance and voltage for a given circuit.
10. Calculate the voltage across, and the current flowing through a resistor connected to Thevenin's equivalent circuit.

4-1 INTRODUCTION

The content in the last two chapters has dealt with the three general types of circuit configurations. All electrical and electronic circuits are connected in one of these arrangements—series, parallel, or series-parallel. In the circuits discussed so far Ohm's law and the occasional use of Kirchhoff's laws were sufficient to determine the circuit variables.

Ohm's law and Kirchhoff's laws can be considered to be "tools." Just as a mechanic has tools to disassemble an engine to analyze it, technicians and engineers use these laws as "tools" to analyze the operation of a circuit. Often circuits are more complex than those encountered so far, however. They may have more than one source or the devices forming the circuit don't lend themselves to simple series or parallel circuit analysis. In these cases more specialized "tools" are required. This chapter serves the purpose of introducing some rules and theorems that can be considered as specialized "tools" to analyze more sophisticated circuits.

4-2 VOLTAGE SOURCES

The voltage source is an essential part of an electric circuit. It represents the potential force required to cause current to flow in a circuit. Although voltage sources have been discussed previously, there is further knowledge that one must be aware of when analyzing circuits.

A term often used in conjunction with voltage supplies is *ideal voltage source*. An ideal voltage source is one which has no internal resistance (R_{int}). The voltage available at the terminals of the supply (called the terminal voltage or output voltage) is equal to the potential developed by the supply (V_S). Because the ideal voltage source has no internal resistance, the terminal voltage remains constant, no matter how much current the circuit draws from the source. The graph appearing in Figure 4–1 shows the terminal voltage and load current relationship for an ideal voltage source connected to a resistive circuit.

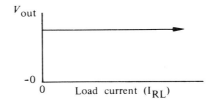

Figure 4–1   Terminal voltage and load current relationship for an ideal voltage supply.

An actual voltage source does contain some internal resistance. If the source is a battery, this resistance represents the opposition to the flow of current within the battery as the electrolyte ionizes. In electronic voltage sources, called rectifier power supplies, the internal resistance represents the combined resistance of any transformers, diodes, and filter devices which might be used in the rectifier power supply circuit. When a circuit is connected to such a source, the terminal voltage drops to a potential less than that developed by the supply. The difference between the developed electromotive force (EMF) and the terminal voltage is due to the voltage dropped across the internal resistance. It is important to understand that the internal resistance of the voltage source drops voltage only when a circuit is connected to its terminals. This provides a complete path for current to flow as illustrated in Figure 4–2. The terminal voltage is equal to the source voltage without a load connected.

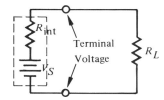

Figure 4–2 Circuit connected to a voltage source.

The effect of load current on terminal voltage is shown in Example 4–1. As the load current increases, the terminal voltage decreases.

Example 4–1 Effect of load resistance on terminal voltage

Problem
For the circuit shown in Figure 4–3, calculate the terminal voltage (load voltage) and load current for the following values of load resistance (R_L): 20, 45, 70, and 95 Ω.

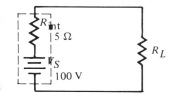

Figure 4–3

Solution

$$I_{RL} \text{ at } 20 \ \Omega = \frac{V_S}{R_{int} + R_L} = \frac{100 \text{ V}}{5 + 20 \ \Omega} = \frac{100 \text{ V}}{25 \ \Omega} = 4 \text{ A}$$

$$V_{RL} \text{ at } 20 \ \Omega = (I_{RL})(R_L) = (4 \text{ A})(20 \ \Omega) = 80 \text{ V}$$

$$I_{RL} \text{ at } 45 \ \Omega = \frac{V_S}{R_{int} + R_L} = \frac{100 \text{ V}}{5 + 45 \ \Omega} = \frac{100 \text{ V}}{50 \ \Omega} = 2 \text{ A}$$

$$V_{RL} \text{ at } 45 \ \Omega = (I_{RL})(R_L) = (2 \text{ A})(45 \ \Omega) = 90 \text{ V}$$

$$I_{RL} \text{ at } 70 \ \Omega = \frac{V_S}{R_{\text{int}} + R_L} = \frac{100 \text{ V}}{5 + 70 \ \Omega} = \frac{100 \text{ V}}{75 \ \Omega} = 1.333 \text{ A}$$

$$V_{RL} \text{ at } 70 \ \Omega = (I_{RL})(R_L) = (1.333 \text{ A})(70 \ \Omega) = 93.31 \text{ V}$$

$$I_{RL} \text{ at } 95 \ \Omega = \frac{V_S}{R_{\text{int}} + R_L} = \frac{100 \text{ V}}{5 + 95 \ \Omega} = \frac{100 \text{ V}}{100 \ \Omega} = 1 \text{ A}$$

$$V_{RL} \text{ at } 95 \ \Omega = (I_{RL})(R_L) = (1 \text{ A})(95 \ \Omega) = 95 \text{ V}$$

For the circuit appearing, notice that the terminal voltage increases as the load current decreases. This is depicted graphically in Figure 4–4. The voltage difference between the source and the load is dropped across the internal resistance of the supply.

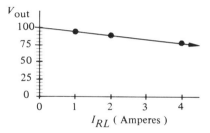

Figure 4–4 Graph of terminal voltage and load current.

The internal resistance of voltage sources should be low compared to the load resistance to which the supply is connected. One criteria used to evaluate the quality of a voltage source is its percent regulation. Equation (4–1) is used to compute the percent regulation.

$$\text{Percent Regulation} = \frac{V_{\text{no load}} - V_{\text{full load}}}{V_{\text{full load}}} \times 100 \text{ percent} \qquad \text{(4–1)}$$

The closer the percent regulation is to zero, the nearer the supply approaches an ideal source. As shown in Example 4–2, the percent regulation decreased from 25 percent with the 20-Ω load connected to 5.26 percent with the 95-Ω load connected.

Many modern voltage sources are called constant-voltage supplies. These supplies have a voltage regulator connected to the output terminals and tend to maintain a constant output voltage for changes in load current.

Example 4–2 Percent regulation for the source appearing in Figure 4–3

Problem
Calculate the percent of regulation for the two loads identified below.

Solution

$$\text{Percent Regulation} = \frac{V_{NL} - V_{FL}}{V_{FL}} \times 100\% = \frac{100 - 80 \text{ V}}{80 \text{ V}} \times 100\% = 25\%$$
(20-Ω load)

$$\text{Percent Regulation} = \frac{V_{NL} - V_{FL}}{V_{FL}} \times 100\% = \frac{100 - 95 \text{ V}}{95 \text{ V}} \times 100\% = 5.26\%$$
(95-Ω load)

4-3 CURRENT SOURCES

A current source is an energy supply that provides a nonchanging current to a load. Although not as commonly used as voltage sources, current sources are used where a constant load current is required, regardless of changes in load resistance or terminal voltage. As illustrated in Figure 4–5, the load current remains constant for changes in either load resistance or terminal voltage.

The characteristics of current sources are often compared with those of an ideal current source. This is one which has an infinite internal resistance. Although an infinite internal resistance cannot be achieved in an actual supply, a current source is designed to have a high internal resistance compared to the resistance of the circuit or load to which it is connected. Current sources are usually constructed from voltage sources. The voltage source shown in Figure 4–6 serves as a rather effective current source. As indicated, as the load resistance increases, the load current changes very little. This is due to the fact that the high internal resistance of the supply primarily determines the load current. Relatively

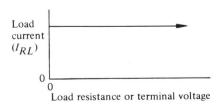

Figure 4–5 Load current characteristics for a current source.

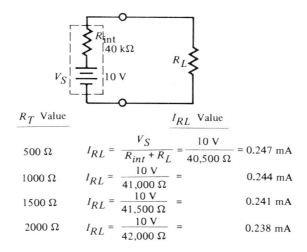

R_T Value		I_{RL} Value
500 Ω	$I_{RL} = \dfrac{V_S}{R_{int} + R_L} = \dfrac{10\text{ V}}{40{,}500\ \Omega}$	= 0.247 mA
1000 Ω	$I_{RL} = \dfrac{10\text{ V}}{41{,}000\ \Omega} =$	0.244 mA
1500 Ω	$I_{RL} = \dfrac{10\text{ V}}{41{,}500\ \Omega} =$	0.241 mA
2000 Ω	$I_{RL} = \dfrac{10\text{ V}}{42{,}000\ \Omega} =$	0.238 mA

Figure 4–6   Effect of load resistance changes on load current.

large changes in load resistance have little effect on overall circuit resistance. Therefore, the current remains fairly constant.

A current source is indicated schematically as a generator connected in parallel with an internal resistance as illustrated in Figure 4–7.

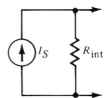

Figure 4–7   Current source.

4-4 THE VOLTAGE DIVIDER RULE

The voltage divider rule is a "tool" which can be used to compute the voltage dropped across individual resistors connected in series. It is a more direct method of calculating voltage than the Ohm's law method because current flow does not have to be computed.

Equations (4–2) to (4–4) illustrate the voltage divider rule for a series circuit containing three resistors. The equations apply for any number of series-connected resistors with the denominator indicating the sum of the series-connected devices.

$$V_{R1} = (V_S)\left(\frac{R_1}{R_1 + R_2 + R_3}\right) \qquad\qquad \text{(4–2)}$$

$$V_{R2} = (V_S)\left(\frac{R_2}{R_1 + R_2 + R_3}\right) \qquad\qquad \text{(4–3)}$$

$$V_{R3} = (V_S)\left(\frac{R_3}{R_1 + R_2 + R_3}\right) \qquad\qquad \text{(4–4)}$$

The voltage divider rule is based on the principle that the voltage across any particular resistor in a series circuit is proportional to the current flowing through the circuit and the resistance of the resistor. Since the same current flows through each resistor, the current can be factored out, resulting in the equations shown above. An application for the voltage divider rule appears in Example 4–3.

Example 4–3 An application of the voltage divider rule

Problem
Calculate the voltage across each resistor in Figure 4–8 using the voltage divider rule.

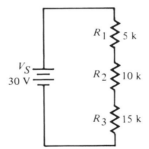

Figure 4–8

Solution

$$V_{R1} = (V_S)\left(\frac{R_1}{R_1 + R_2 + R_3}\right) = (30\ \text{V})\left(\frac{5\text{k}}{30\text{k}}\right) = 5\ \text{V}$$

$$V_{R2} = (V_S)\left(\frac{R_2}{R_1 + R_2 + R_3}\right) = (30\ \text{V})\left(\frac{10\text{k}}{30\text{k}}\right) = 10\ \text{V}$$

$$V_{R3} = (V_S)\left(\frac{R_3}{R_1 + R_2 + R_3}\right) = (30\ \text{V})\left(\frac{15\text{k}}{30\text{k}}\right) = 15\ \text{V}$$

4-5 THE CURRENT DIVIDER RULE

The current divider rule is a "tool" which can be used to calculate the branch currents flowing through resistances connected in parallel. What the voltage divider rule does for voltage in series circuits, the current divider rule does for current in parallel circuits. Equations (4–5) and (4–6) are used to compute the current in individual branch circuits.

$$I_1 = (I_T)\left(\frac{R_2}{R_1 + R_2}\right) \tag{4–5}$$

$$I_2 = (I_T)\left(\frac{R_1}{R_1 + R_2}\right) \tag{4–6}$$

The equations are based on the principle that current is inversely proportional to resistance. Notice that the resistance of the other branch circuit is used in the numerator of each equation. The current divider rule applies only to two branch parallel circuits. An application of the current divider rule is shown in Example 4–4. Although Ohm's law can be used to determine the branch currents, the current divider rule is a more direct method.

Example 4–4   An application of the current divider rule

Problem
Calculate I_1 and I_2 using the circuit in Figure 4–9.

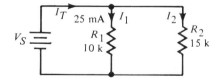

Figure 4–9

Solution

$$I_1 = (I_T)\left(\frac{R_2}{R_1 + R_2}\right) = (25 \text{ mA})\left(\frac{15k}{25k}\right) = 15 \text{ mA}$$

$$I_2 = (I_T)\left(\frac{R_1}{R_1 + R_2}\right) = (25 \text{ mA})\left(\frac{10k}{25k}\right) = 10 \text{ mA}$$

4-6 THE MAXIMUM-POWER-TRANSFER THEOREM

The maximum-power-transfer theorem states that maximum-power transfer occurs from the source to the load when the source resistance (R_{int}) is equal to the load resistance. This theorem describes the conditions which must be met if it is desired to transfer maximum power from one circuit (called the source) to another circuit (called the load).

The theorem can be verified from a circuit such as the one appearing in Figure 4–10. The power transferred from the source and dissipated by the load is computed for several different load values. The data obtained are used to plot a power curve. Notice that the power curve peaks at the point where the load resistance (R_L) and source resistance (R_{int}) are equal.

The maximum-power-transfer theorem is useful to the circuit designer who has to design a circuit where it is important to transfer maximum power from one circuit to another.

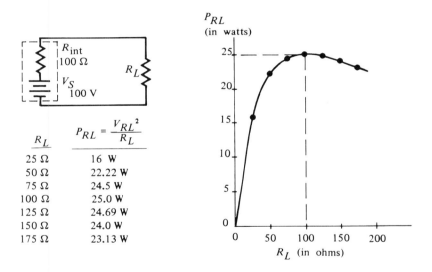

R_L	$P_{RL} = \dfrac{V_{RL}^2}{R_L}$
25 Ω	16 W
50 Ω	22.22 W
75 Ω	24.5 W
100 Ω	25.0 W
125 Ω	24.69 W
150 Ω	24.0 W
175 Ω	23.13 W

Figure 4–10   Verification of the maximum power transfer theorem.

4-7 THEVENIN'S THEOREM

Thevenin's theorem, without a doubt, is the most useful and powerful of all the network theorems. This theorem states that any resistive device or voltage source appearing in any type of resistive circuit is connected in series with an equivalent resistance (called Thevenin's resistance) and an equivalent voltage source (called Thevenin's voltage).

This theorem has many applications. For active circuits, it is useful for determining the input resistance to transistor amplifiers. It is often used to determine the equivalent voltage and resistance connected to a resistance in almost any type of circuit.

The series-connected equivalent resistance and voltage is called Thevenin's circuit. This circuit is obtained by following a four-step procedure described in Example 4–5.

Example 4–5   An application of Thevenin's theorem

Problem

A series-parallel circuit is shown in Figure 4–11.

(a) Calculate the value of Thevenin's resistance, Thevenin's voltage, and draw Thevenin's circuit.

(b) Connect the load (R_L) to Thevenin's circuit and compute the voltage across, and the current flowing through, the load.

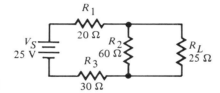

Figure 4–11

Solution

Step 1: Remove the load and label the terminals (Figure 4–12).

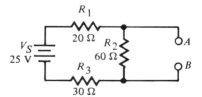

Figure 4–12   Circuit with load removed.

Step 2: Set the voltage source to zero by removing the source and short-circuiting the terminals where the circuit is connected to the source (Figure 4–13).

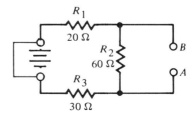

Figure 4–13   Circuit with source set to zero.

Step 3: Calculate the resistance that appears across terminals *A-B*. This is Thevenin's resistance (R_{th}) and is the resistance an ohmmeter would measure if connected across those terminals.

$$R_{th} = \frac{(R_1 + R_3)(R_2)}{(R_1 + R_3) + (R_2)} = \frac{(50)(60)}{50 + 60} = 27.27 \ \Omega$$

Step 4: Remove the short, reconnect the voltage supply, and compute Thevenin's voltage (V_{th}). For this particular circuit $V_{th} = V_{AB} = V_{R2}$. Either Ohm's law or the voltage divider rule can be used to determine V_{th}. The voltage divider rule is the most direct.

$$V_{R2} = (V_S)\left(\frac{R_2}{R_1 + R_2 + R_3}\right) = (25 \ V)\left(\frac{60 \ \Omega}{110 \ \Omega}\right) = 13.64 \ V$$

The resulting Thevenin's circuit appears in Figure 4–14. This represents the series voltage and resistance when R_L is connected to terminals *A* and *B*.

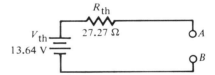

Figure 4–14   Thevenin's circuit.

    The load can now be connected (see Figure 4–15) to Thevenin's circuit and the load voltage (V_L) and load current (I_L) computed. The voltage divider rule and Ohm's law are used to determine these variables.

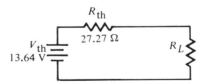

Figure 4–15   Thevenin's circuit with the load connected.

$$V_L = (V_{th})\left(\frac{R_L}{R_{th} + R_L}\right)$$

$$V_L = (13.64 \ V)\left(\frac{25 \ V}{52.27 \ \Omega}\right)$$

$$V_L = 6.52 \ V$$

$$I_L = \frac{V_L}{R_L}$$

$$I_L = \frac{6.52 \text{ V}}{25 \text{ }\Omega}$$

$$I_L = 0.261 \text{ A}$$

Although both the voltage across, and the current flowing through, the load were calculated from Thevenin's equivalent circuit, these variables could also have been computed from the original circuit using Ohm's and Kirchhoff's laws. Often, there are several ways of calculating the required variables in a circuit. At other times there may be just one method. Thevenin's theorem can also be used in a circuit which has a current source. A current source is set to zero by removing the source from the circuit and leaving the circuit terminals open circuited.

4-8 THE CONCEPT OF ZERO REFERENCE AND GROUND

Voltage is a difference of potential across two points. As such, one point is at a higher potential than the other. This is illustrated in Figure 4–16(a). In this circuit the applied voltage is dropped across the series connected resistors. It is often advantageous to have some potential identified as a reference for making voltage measurements. This reference is called ground and indicates a common connecting point for one side of the voltage or current source and one side of the circuit or load. The ground symbol appearing in Figure 4–16(b) is used to indicate the common connection and electrical reference. Voltage measurements can be made across individual devices as shown in Figure 4–16(a) or they may be made with respect to ground as in Figure 4–16(b). The voltage at point B is 4 V positive with respect to ground, point C is 7 V above ground, and point D is 9 V positive with respect to ground. Ground in most equipment represents the metal chassis or a conductor strip around the outside edge of a printed circuit board. This type of ground can be, but isn't always, connected to earth ground through the neutral wire of the AC power line.

Ground is usually considered to be electrically neutral and is at 0 V potential. When the negative terminal of the source is connected to ground, all voltages appearing in a circuit are positive with respect to ground. This is the situation in most circuits and is called negative ground.

Sometimes negative voltages are required in a circuit. These can be obtained by connecting the positive terminal of the voltage supply to ground as indicated in Figure 4–17. This is called positive ground. All voltages measured are negative with respect to ground.

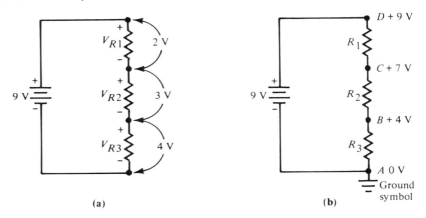

(a)   (b)

Figure 4-16 Voltage distribution across series-connected resistors and with respect to ground.

Occasionally both positive and negative voltages are required from one power supply. This can be accomplished by connecting the ground as illustrated in Figure 4–18. In this circuit, both V_C and V_D are positive with respect to ground while V_A is negative.

The use of ground sometimes reduces the number of conductors required in a circuit. For example, the chassis in the automobile is used as ground for the electrical system. As shown in Figure 4–19, the negative terminal of the battery and one end of each circuit is connected to the chassis. The return path for each circuit is through the chassis.

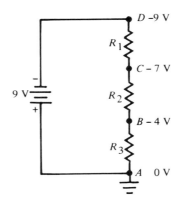

Figure 4-17 Voltage distribution in a series circuit employing positive ground.

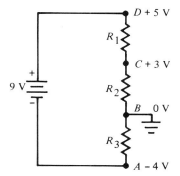

Figure 4–18 Method of obtaining both positive and negative voltages from a single source.

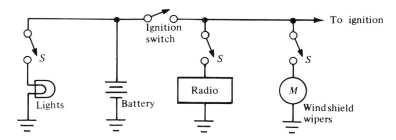

Figure 4–19 Simplified diagram of the automobile electrical system.

4-9 LOOP EQUATIONS

The ability to write loop equations is important if one is to become proficient in analyzing circuits. A circuit loop is merely a single path for current flow within a circuit. The circuit appearing in Figure 4–20 is a series circuit and contains a single loop. A loop equation is Kirchhoff's voltage law written for that loop. For the circuit shown in Figure 4–20, Kirchhoff's voltage law is satisfied. Kirchhoff's law was first introduced in Chapter 2. The law stated that the sum of the voltages dropped across series-connected resistances was equal to the applied voltage. Another way of expressing this is that the algebraic sum of the voltages encountered in any closed loop containing resistive devices and voltage sources is equal to zero. This is expressed mathematically for the circuit shown in Figure 4–20.

$$V_{R1} + V_{R2} + V_{R3} - V_S = 0$$
$$+ 100 + 30 + 20 - 150 = 0 \text{ V}$$

Notice that the loop equation contains all the voltage components, both the drops and the source. It does not matter at what point in the circuit that one begins writing the equation as long as all the devices in the loop are contained in the equation. The polarity of the voltages is determined from the end of the device that current enters. When conventional current theory is used, the polarity of the voltage developed across a resistor is positive with respect to the end that current exits. The polarity of a voltage or current source is fixed, of course.

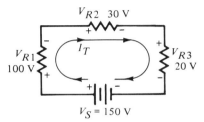

Figure 4–20 Single-loop circuit.

SUMMARY

1. An ideal voltage source is one which has no internal resistance and provides a constant output voltage for any load condition.
2. It is impossible to design voltage sources which have no internal resistance. For best results, the internal resistance of the supply should be small compared to the load or circuit to which it is connected.
3. Percent regulation is used to describe the effect a load has on a voltage source.
4. A voltage source which has a low internal resistance compared to the circuit to which it is connected has a low percent regulation. The lower the percentage of regulation, the better the source.
5. An ideal current source has an infinite internal resistance and provides a constant current to the load, regardless of the load resistance and voltage conditions. Since it is impossible to design a supply having an infinite internal resistance, the internal resistance should be high with respect to the load or circuit to which it is connected.
6. The voltage divider rule is a method of calculating voltages across series-connected resistors. This is a more direct method of computing voltages than the Ohm's law method because current does not have to be calculated.

7. The current divider rule is a method of computing individual branch currents when two loads are connected in parallel.
8. The maximum-power-transfer theorem describes the conditions which must exist for maximum power to be transferred from one circuit to another. According to the theorem, maximum-power transfer occurs when the resistance of the two circuits are equal.
9. Thevenin's theorem is a useful "tool" for analyzing some types of circuits. This theorem states that any circuit containing any number of resistances and voltage sources, connected in any fashion, can be reduced to an equivalent resistance which is in series with an equivalent voltage source.
10. Thevenin's theorem can be used to determine the equivalent series resistance and voltage to which a particular circuit device is connected.
11. Thevenin's theorem is very useful for calculating the voltage across, and the current flowing through, a load connected to a bridge circuit.
12. Chassis ground consists of a common connecting point between one side of the source and circuit devices.
13. Chassis ground is often used as a reference point for making voltage measurements. The potential at chassis ground is usually 0 V.
14. A loop is a complete path for current flow within a circuit. A series circuit has a single loop. Parallel and series-parallel circuits have two or more loops.
15. Kirchhoff's voltage law has to be satisfied when writing loop equations.

PRACTICE EXERCISES

1. What is an ideal voltage source?
2. How does an actual voltage source differ from an ideal one?
3. A voltage source has an internal resistance of 50 Ω and measures 35 V without a circuit connected to it. What is the output voltage when a circuit is connected which has 520 Ω of resistance?
4. What is the percent regulation of the voltage source identified in exercise 3?
5. How does an ideal current source differ from an actual source?
6. Four resistors are connected in series: R_1 has a value of 3.3k, R_2 equals 1.5k, R_3 is 4.7k, and R_4 equals 6.8k. If the resistors are connected to a 150-V source, calculate the voltage drop across R_2 using the voltage divider rule.
7. A 470 Ω resistor is connected in parallel with a 220 Ω resistor. Compute the current flowing through the 220 Ω resistor if the total current is 0.35 A by using the current divider rule.
8. A circuit containing 600 Ω of resistance is to be connected to a voltage source. What value should the internal resistance of the source have if maximum power transfer is desired from the source to the circuit?
9. State Thevenin's theorem.
10. List the four steps involved in using Thevenin's theorem.
11. Find the Thevenin values and draw the equivalent circuit for R_3 in the circuit appearing in Figure 4–21.
12. Calculate the voltage across, and the current flowing through, R_3 in the circuit of Figure 4–21. (Perform the calculations from Thevenin's equivalent circuit.)

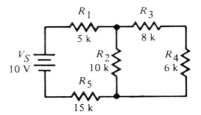

Figure 4–21

13. What is meant by the term *chassis ground?*
14. What is the usual electrical potential of chassis ground?

ANSWERS TO PRACTICE EXERCISES

1. An ideal voltage source is one which has no internal resistance and provides a constant output voltage for any load current or resistance conditions.
2. An actual voltage source does have some internal resistance. It should be small in relationship to the circuit connected to the source.
3.

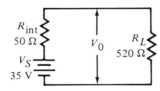

$$V_O = (V_S)\left(\frac{R_L}{R_L + R_{int}}\right)$$

$$V_O = (35 \text{ V})\left(\frac{520\ \Omega}{570\ \Omega}\right) = 31.93 \text{ V}$$

Figure 4–22

4. Percent regulation $= \dfrac{V_{NL} - V_{FL}}{V_{FL}} \times 100\% = \dfrac{35 \text{ V} - 31.93}{31.93} \times 100\% = 9.6\%$.

5. An ideal current source has an infinite internal resistance. The internal resistance of an actual current source should be extremely high compared to the resistance of the circuit connected to the source.

6. $V_{R2} = (V_S)\left(\dfrac{R_2}{R_1 + R_2 + R_3}\right) = (150 \text{ V})\left(\dfrac{1.5\text{k}}{16.3\text{k}}\right) = 13.8 \text{ V}.$

7. $I_2 = (I_T)\left(\dfrac{R_1}{R_1 + R_2}\right) = (0.35 \text{ A})\left(\dfrac{470\ \Omega}{690\ \Omega}\right) = 0.238 \text{ A}.$

8. $600\ \Omega.$

9. Any circuit containing resistive devices and voltage sources can be reduced to an equivalent resistance which is in series with an equivalent voltage source.

10. **a.** Disconnect device from the circuit and label the nodes.
    b. Set the voltage source to zero by removing the supply and shorting the resulting circuit terminals.
    c. Calculate Thevenin's resistance.
    d. Remove the short, reconnect the voltage source, and compute Thevenin's voltage.

11. Solution:

    a. Remove R_3 and label the terminals (Figure 4–23).

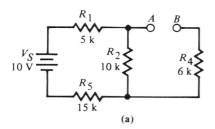 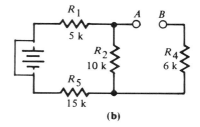

    (a)   (b)

Figure 4–23

    b. Short circuit the circuit terminals after removing voltage source and calculate R_{th}. This is the resistance an ohmmeter would measure if connected to terminals A-B.

$$R_{th} = \frac{(5k + 15k)(10k)}{(5k + 15k) + (10k)} + 6k = 12.667k \; \Omega$$

    c. Remove the short and solve for V_{th}. Since no current can flow through R_4, V_{th} equals V_{AB} which is equal to V_{R2}.

$$V_{R2} = (V_S)\left(\frac{R_2}{R_1 + R_2 + R_5}\right) = (10 \; V)\left(\frac{10k}{30k}\right) = 3.33 \; V$$

    d. Draw Thevenin's circuit (Figure 4–24).

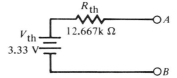

Figure 4–24   Thevenin's circuit.

12. Connect R_3 to Thevenin's circuit and solve for the voltage across, and current flowing through, R_3 (Figure 4–25).

$$V_{R3} = (V_{th})\left(\frac{R_3}{R_3 + R_{th}}\right) = (3.33 \; V)\left(\frac{8k}{20.667k}\right) = 1.29 \; V$$

$$I_{R3} = \frac{V_{R3}}{R_3} = \frac{1.29 \; V}{8k} = 0.16 \; mA$$

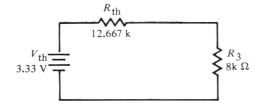

Figure 4–25

13. Chassis ground is a common connecting point for one terminal of a source and circuit devices. It is often used as a reference point for making voltage measurements.
14. The electrical potential at chassis ground is usually 0 V.

CHAPTER EXAMINATION

Choose true or false for questions 1 to 5.
1. T F   An ideal current source is one which has an internal resistance of 0 Ω.
2. T F   The voltage divider rule is useful for calculating branch currents in a parallel circuit.
3. T F   A voltage source which has a high percent regulation has characteristics similar to that of an ideal voltage source.
4. T F   Maximum power transfer occurs when the source resistance is low compared to the circuit or load resistance.
5. T F   According to Thevenin's theorem, any resistive circuit can be reduced to a single resistance which is connected in series with a current source.
6. For the circuit in Figure 4–26, compute the value of Thevenin's resistance for resistor R_1.

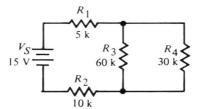

Figure 4–26

7. Determine the value of Thevenin's voltage for the circuit appearing in Figure 4–26.
8. Calculate the terminal voltage for the circuit in Figure 4–27.

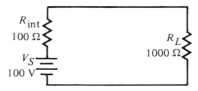

Figure 4–27

9. Four resistors are connected in series. $R_1 = 4.7k$, $R_2 = 3.3k$, $R_3 = 10k$, and $R_4 = 1.2k$. If the series network is connected to a 75-V source, calculate the voltage across R_3 using the voltage divider rule.
10. A certain voltage source has a no-load voltage (V_S) of 36 V. When connected to a 600-Ω load, the terminal voltage drops to 32 V. Determine the internal resistance of the source.
11. What is the percent regulation for the voltage supply identified in question 10?

5

Batteries and Magnetism

OBJECTIVES

Upon completion of this chapter you should be able to do the following:

1. Describe why a cell is considered to be a transducer.
2. Identify the three major parts of a cell.
3. Describe the physical factors which determine the output voltage of a cell.
4. Discuss the physical factors which determine the current capacity of a cell.
5. Describe the difference between primary and secondary cells.
6. Differentiate between wet and dry cells.
7. Identify the type of materials the electrodes are made of and the type of electrolyte used in a lead-acid cell.
8. Define the term *magnetism*.
9. Identify the two general types of magnets.
10. Describe what is meant by magnetic lines of force.
11. Identify the north and south poles of a permanent magnet from the direction of the flux lines about the magnet.
12. Discuss how a magnet is able to attract ferrous materials.
13. Define the terms *retentivity* and *permeability*.
14. Use the right-hand rule to determine the north pole of an electromagnet.
15. Identify the factors which affect the strength of an electromagnet.
16. Define the terms *flux, flux density, magnetomotive force,* and *reluctance*.
17. Identify the unit of measurement and the symbol associated with each of the terms identified in objective 16.

5-1 INTRODUCTION TO BATTERIES

In order to have current flow in a circuit, there must be a source of electromotive force connected to the circuit. This serves to elevate the conductor valence band electrons into the conduction band. These electrons are what constitute current flow in a circuit.

There are two general kinds of electromotive force. These include DC voltage sources and AC voltage sources. A DC source causes a direct current to flow in a circuit. Direct current (DC) is a type of current which always flows in the same direction in a circuit. Alternating current (AC) flows in one direction part of the time, reverses itself, and flows through the circuit in the opposite direction the other part of the time.

Both AC and DC voltage have their own unique applications. AC voltage is introduced and discussed in the next chapter. DC voltage and current is required for the operation of circuits which contain transistors, integrated circuits, electron tubes, and other DC-operated devices. There are several methods of obtaining DC potentials. These include transducers, DC generators, and rectifier power supplies. Rectifier power supplies are covered elsewhere in the book. Transducers are devices that convert one form of energy into another. Transducers which convert other forms of energy into DC energy include thermocouples, photovoltaic devices, and chemical cells. A thermocouple converts heat energy into electrical energy. Photovoltaic devices change light energy into an equivalent electrical potential, and chemical cells convert chemical energy into electrical energy. The information contained in the first part of this chapter deals with the chemical cell. This type of transducer is commonly referred to as a cell or battery.

5-2 CELL CONSTRUCTION AND CHARACTERISTICS

Cells are made up of three main parts. These include two dissimilar metals, called electrodes, and a solution, called an electrolyte. The electrodes are polarized. The positive electrode is called the anode and the negative electrode is called the cathode.

The amount of EMF developed by a cell is dependent only upon the type of materials the electrodes are made from and the type of electrolyte used. For example, a cell can be formed by pouring a small amount of sulfuric acid into a glass beaker and placing a small rod of lead peroxide and another rod of lead into the acid. A voltmeter placed across the electrodes, as shown in Figure 5–1(a), indicates a potential of 2.2 V. If a 50-

gallon drum was filled with sulfuric acid and 1-ft diameter lead peroxide and lead rods placed in the acid, as illustrated in Figure 5–1(b), a volt-meter placed across the rods would still indicate a potential of 2.2 V.

The amount of current a cell can deliver to a load over a period of time depends upon the cross-sectional area of the electrodes exposed to the electrolyte. The cell appearing in Figure 5–1(b) has a much larger cur-rent capacity than the one shown in Figure 5–1(a). Cell current capacity is measured in ampere hours (A h). This identifies the amount of current a cell can deliver to a specified load for a particular amount of time. For example, a 3-A h cell will supply 3 A of current to a given load for 1 h of time. If the load resistance is doubled, the same cell will deliver 1.5 A of current to that load for 2 h. The amount of current delivered to a load depends upon the resistance of the load, of course.

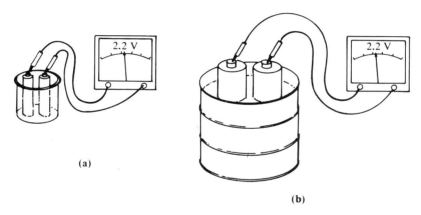

(a)

(b)

Figure 5–1   Cell EMF depends upon the type of materials used.

5-3 TYPES OF CELLS

Numerous types of cells are available for consumer and industrial use. Most obtain their names from the type of electrodes or electrolyte used in their construction. The familiar cell used in flashlights and many other consumer products is the carbon-zinc cell illustrated in Figure 5–2. Notice that the anode consists of a carbon rod and the zinc liner forms the cath-ode. Ammonium chloride and zinc chloride constitute the electrolyte. This cell produces an EMF of 1.5 V. The cell is manufactured in different sizes. All sizes have the same EMF, but the current capacities vary. Pop-ular sizes include the AAA, AA, C, and D types. Some of the more com-monly used types of cells are identified in Table 5–1 along with their no-load terminal voltages.

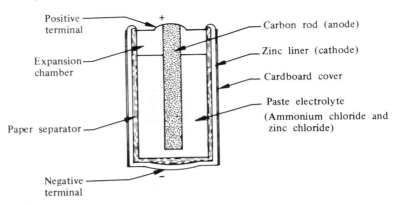

Figure 5–2   Carbon-zinc cell.

TABLE 5–1   No-Load Output Voltage for Selected Cells

Name of Cell	Terminal Voltage (V)
Edison	1.36
Silver-zinc	1.50
Carbon-zinc	1.50
Silver-oxide	1.50
Lead-acid	2.20
Nickel-cadmium	1.20
Mercury	1.30

5-4 CLASSIFICATION OF CELLS

There are many different types of cells. They can be classified as being either primary or secondary. A primary cell is one which cannot be recharged, whereas a secondary cell can be recharged many times. Another method used to classify cells is the state of the electrolyte. The electrolyte can be in one of two states—paste or liquid. Cells which have electrolyte in paste form are called dry cells. Wet cells have a liquid electrolyte. Most, but not all, dry cells are primary types. The nickel-cadmium cell, for example, is a dry cell which can be recharged very efficiently hundreds of times. This is a popular cell used in cordless electrical appliances such as grass trimmers, electric razors, and calculators.

5-5 THE BATTERY

A single cell is sometimes called a battery if it is used by itself. The carbon-zinc cell used in flashlights, for example, is often called a battery. Usually, however, a battery consists of a number of cells connected in series, in parallel, or in series-parallel with each other.

Cells are often connected in series to increase the available voltage. A carbon-zinc cell produces 1.5 V. Four of these cells can be connected in series as shown in Figure 5–3 to obtain a potential of 6 V across the outside two terminals.

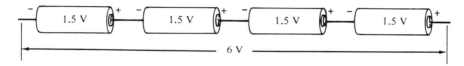

Figure 5–3 Series connected cells.

Cells are sometimes connected in parallel with each other when the load current requirement is greater than that which can be produced from a single cell. Two 1.5-V cells are shown connected in parallel in Figure 5–4. If the current capacity for each cell is 0.5 A h, the combined capacity for both cells is 1 A h. The potential across both cells remains at 1.5 V, of course.

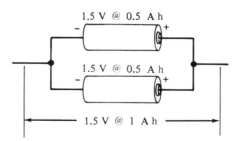

Figure 5–4 Parallel connected cells.

Cells are sometimes connected in series-parallel with each other to increase both the voltage and current capacity. Twelve lead-acid cells are shown schematically connected in a series-parallel arrangement in Figure 5–5. Each cell has a current capacity of 3 A h. The battery produced by this cell network has an output potential of 13.2 V and a current capacity of 6 A h. This is the type of cell connection used in automobile batteries.

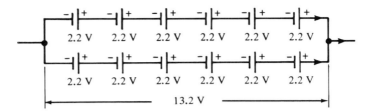

Figure 5–5 Series-parallel connected cells.

5-6 INTERNAL RESISTANCE

All batteries have some internal resistance. This is not caused by a physical resistor but is the phenomenon represented by the heat generated by the battery when a circuit is connected to it. An open-circuited load is connected to the battery shown in Figure 5–6(a). A voltmeter connected across the battery terminals indicates 13.2 V. When the load is connected by closing the switch, as indicated in Figure 5–6(b), the voltage decreases to 12.6 V. This indicates that the internal resistance of the battery is dropping 0.6 V. The internal resistance is caused by the chemical reaction which occurs between the electrodes and electrolyte while the battery is discharging. When additional loads are added, the current flowing through the battery increases. This causes the internal voltage drop to increase which, in turn, causes the output voltage to decrease further yet. You've noticed this effect if you have ever started your car with the headlights turned on. The lights dim considerably as the starter motor cranks the engine.

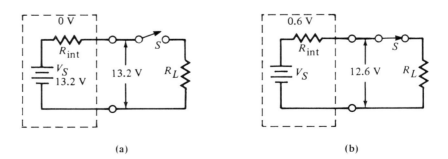

(a)   (b)

Figure 5–6 Effect of internal resistance on battery terminal voltage.

5-7 CHEMICAL ACTION WHILE DISCHARGING

When a cell or battery is discharging due to a load being connected to it, the electrolyte chemically interacts with the electrodes. The cell is completely discharged when this chemical action is completed. Secondary cells can be recharged when a DC source is connected to the cell's terminals as illustrated in Figure 5–7. Current flowing through the battery causes a reverse chemical reaction to occur. This results in the electrodes and electrolyte going back to their original state. This is not the case for primary cells such as the carbon-zinc type. During the discharging process the zinc electrode is consumed by the electrolyte. After most of the electrode has been consumed the cell is discharged and has to be discarded. Sometimes the cell can be connected to a battery charger and then reused. When this is done, the cell has not actually been recharged. The charger has depolarized the cell which reduces its internal resistance. This increases the terminal voltage of the cell and allows it to be used for an additional period of time.

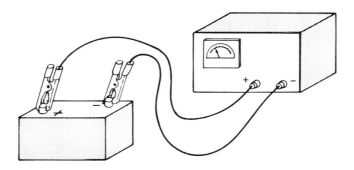

Figure 5–7   Battery charger connected to battery.

Polarization is the result of hydrogen ions migrating toward the positive electrode during the discharging process. This tends to increase the internal resistance of the cell. Many cells have chemicals added to their electrolyte to reduce the effect of polarization.

The chemical action which occurs when a cell is discharging is different for each type of cell. Because the lead-acid cell or battery is so common, the discharging action of this cell will be discussed to illustrate the process. As illustrated in Figure 5–8, the positive electrode is made of lead peroxide (PbO_2) and the negative electrode made of lead (Pb). Sul-

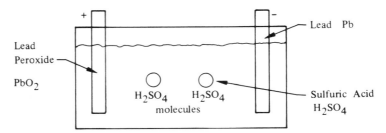

Figure 5–8 Lead-acid cell.

furic acid (H_2SO_4), which has been slightly diluted with water, is used as the electrolyte. The no-load potential of the cell is 2.2 V.

When a load is connected across the terminals as shown in Figure 5–9, the electrolyte breaks apart into individual molecules and atoms. This process is called ionization. The sulfate ions (SO_4) are attracted by the lead in both the anode and cathode electrodes. Some of the hydrogen atoms are attracted to the anode while others combine with oxygen atoms in the electrolyte to form water.

As this process continues during the discharging process, both the anode and cathode become electroplated with the sulfate molecules. This forms a metallic surface on both electrodes called lead sulfate ($PbSO_4$), as shown in Figure 5–10. The water formed by the combination of the hydrogen and oxygen atoms further dilutes the electrolyte. At the same time, hydrogen gas causes polarization to occur around the anode. When both electrodes are composed of the same material (lead sulfate) and the electrolyte weakened with water, the cell is in the discharged state.

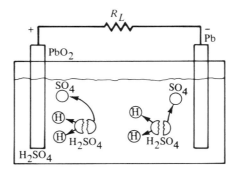

Figure 5–9 Discharging action of a lead-acid cell.

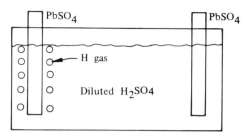

Figure 5–10   Lead-acid cell in the discharged state.

Specific gravity is important when considering the state of charge of a lead-acid cell. Specific gravity is a method of classifying liquids according to their weight with respect to an equal volume of water. Water is assigned a specific gravity of 1.000. The electrolyte in a fully charged lead-acid cell is 1.260. This means that the solution of sulfuric acid, as used in the cell, is 1.26 times as heavy as an equal volume of water. As the cell discharges, water is produced by the ionization process which dilutes the strength of the electrolyte. This lowers the acid's specific gravity. The state of charge of the cell can be determined by measuring its specific gravity. The instrument used to measure specific gravity is the hydrometer. Various cell state-of-charge specific gravity values appear in Table 5–2.

TABLE 5–2   Specific Gravity for Selected Charge States for a Lead-Acid Cell

State of Charge (%)	Specific Gravity
100	1.260
75	1.230
50	1.200
25	1.170

5-8 INTRODUCTION TO MAGNETISM

Magnetism is that property of a substance which allows it to attract ferrous materials. A ferrous material is one which contains iron.

Magnetism and electricity are related. Magnetic properties are present in all electrical circuits and some devices used in electricity operate on magnetic principles. Electric generators, for example, develop voltage from magnetic fields. To fully understand electrical phenomenon, one must have some understanding of magnetism. There are two general types of magnets—permanent magnets and electromagnets.

5-9 PERMANENT MAGNETS

Permanent magnets are created by placing a hardened ferrous material in a very strong magnetic field generated by another magnet. When the ferrous material is removed from the magnetic field, it retains most of its magnetic properties and becomes a permanent magnet.

The property of magnetism can probably best be described by discussing the magnetic field which exists about a magnet. This force is much like the gravitational force which exists between the earth and the sun or the electrostatic force which is present between two differently charged bodies. The effect of the magnetic force is readily seen by placing a glass plate over a magnet and sprinkling iron filings on the plate. The filings align themselves about the magnet, illustrating the presence of the field. The field is composed of individual magnetic lines of force.

Magnets are polarized. One end of the magnet is called the north pole and the other end the south pole. As illustrated in Figure 5–11, the magnetic lines of force leave the north pole and enter the south pole. The lines of force must be complete, just as an electrical circuit must have a complete path for current flow. The magnetic lines of force are completed by those lines which exist within the magnet.

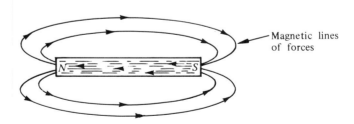

Figure 5–11   Magnetic lines of force about a magnet.

One of the more fundamental principles of magnetism is that unlike poles attract each other and like poles repel one another, as shown in Figure 5–12.

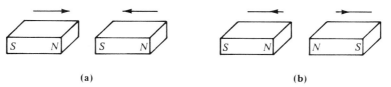

(a)   (b)

Figure 5–12   Principle of attraction and repulsion: (a) unlike poles attract; (b) like poles repel.

5-10 WHY MAGNETS ATTRACT IRON

A magnet is able to attract iron by making the iron object a temporary magnet. If a nail is placed close to a magnet, as depicted in Figure 5–13, some of the magnetic lines of force from the magnet enter the nail at one end, exit at the other end, and reenter the magnet. Because magnetic lines of force always enter a south pole and exit a north pole, the nail becomes a magnet having a north and south pole. Since unlike poles attract each other, the south pole of the magnetized nail is attracted to the north pole of the magnet.

5-11 RESIDUAL MAGNETISM

The nail shown in Figure 5–13 is a temporary magnet. When it is removed from the magnetic field of the magnet it no longer remains magnetized. Actually, a weak magnetic field does exist about the nail when it is removed from the magnet. This remaining magnetism is called residual magnetism. Residual magnetism is the magnetism that remains in a ferrous material after it has been removed from a magnetic field. The amount of magnetism that remains in a substance is a function of its re-

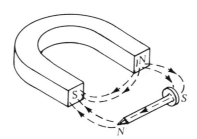

Figure 5–13   Attractive force between a magnet and nail.

tentivity. Retentivity is the ability of a material to hold its magnetism after the material has been removed from a magnetizing force. The retentivity of an object depends upon the type of material from which the item is made. Objects made from soft iron have a low degree of retentivity. For all practical purposes, as soon as the object is removed from a magnetic field it loses all of its magnetizing properties. Hard iron and steel have high degrees of retentivity. Taken from the influence of a magnetic field, they continue to remain magnetized for a period of time. You've no doubt noticed this effect with a screwdriver if you've ever had one near a magnet. It continues to remain magnetized for a period of time after it has been removed from the magnet.

For some applications, such as making a permanent magnet, materials which have high retentivity values are desirable. In other applications, such as relay coils, materials which have a low degree of retentivity are required.

5-12 MAGNETIC THEORY

The magnetic effect produced by a magnet is thought to be caused by the spin of the electrons on their axes as they revolve about the nuclei of the atoms making up the magnet. An electron spins on its own axis in the same way that the earth rotates on its axis as it revolves about the sun.

For most materials approximately half the electrons spin in the clockwise direction and the other half in the counterclockwise direction. The atom exhibits no magnetic properties because the magnetic field created by the electrons is canceled because the electrons are spinning in opposite directions. The electrons in some materials, such as iron, will align themselves and all spin in the same direction when near a magnet. The small magnetic effect of each electron is additive, which causes the material to have a rather strong magnetic field. The substance is in the magnetized state when this condition exists.

5-13 PERMEABILITY

Magnetic lines of force can exist in any medium in addition to existing in air and ferrous materials. There is no physical shield that will prevent a magnetic field from passing through a material. Some substances have a greater ability than others for magnetic lines of force to exist in them or pass through them. The ease in which magnetic lines of force can exist in a material is called permeability. The symbol used to denote permeability is the Greek symbol mu (μ). Permeability is unitless and is expressed as a number or coefficient.

The permeability of a vacuum is taken as a reference and is assigned the coefficient value of 1.00. Most materials have a permeability value which is approximately that of vacuum. These include materials and substances such as air, wood, and glass. Ferrous materials, on the other hand, have much higher values. Some of these materials may have values as high as 5000. This means that magnetic lines of force can exist in these mediums 5000 times easier than they can in a vacuum. Inductor and transformer cores are made of materials which have a high permeability coefficient.

Sometimes sensitive electronic devices must be shielded from magnetic fields. This is accomplished by enclosing the device in a material which has a high permeability. The material conducts the field around the device, effectively creating a shield for it.

5-14 ELECTROMAGNETISM

Anytime current flows through a conductor, a circular magnetic field exists around the conductor, as shown in Figure 5–14. The right-hand rule is used to determine the direction of the field. As illustrated in Figure 5–15, the conductor is grasped with the right hand, with the thumb extended at a right angle to the fingers and pointing to the direction of current flow. The fingers encircling the conductor point in the direction of the magnetic field.

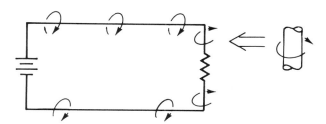

Figure 5–14   Magnetic field about a conductor.

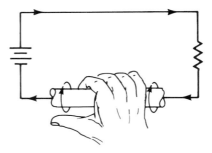

Figure 5–15   Right-hand rule to determine magnetic field polarity.

The magnetic field associated with a conductor is quite weak. The field can be concentrated by forming coils from the wire as shown in Figure 5–16. The magnetic field associated with each coil is in the same direction as the fields produced by adjacent coils. The overall field strength is made stronger because of the additive effect produced by each coil. Coiling the conductor causes a magnetic field to be present entirely about the coil in the same fashion as a field about a permanent magnet. As shown in Figure 5–16, the magnetic lines of force leave one end of the coil and enter the other end. The end of the coil that the lines exit is the north pole of the electromagnet and the end that the lines enter is the south pole.

The strength of the magnetic field can be increased considerably by coiling the conductor about an iron bar, or core, as shown in Figure 5–17. The core concentrates the magnetic lines of force which increases the strength of the electromagnet. An electromagnet formed in this fashion has the same characteristics as a permanent magnet. If a glass plate is placed over an electromagnet and iron filings sprinkled on it, the filings will align themselves in the same way they do for a permanent magnet.

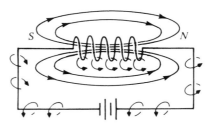

Figure 5–16   Magnetic field about a coiled wire.

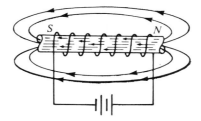

Figure 5–17   Wire wrapped around an iron core to form an electromagnet.

The north pole of an electromagnet can be found by using the right-hand rule. By extending the thumb and fingers of the right hand at a right angle to each other and wrapping the fingers around the coils in the direction of current flow, the thumb will point to the north pole. The north pole of the electromagnet appearing in Figure 5–17 is located at the right end of the core.

The strength of an electromagnet is determined by the number of turns of wire wrapped around the core, the amount of current flowing through the wire, the type of material the core is made from, and the ratio of the coil length to the core diameter.

5-15 TERMINOLOGY USED IN MAGNETISM

There are a number of different terms, symbols, and units of measurement associated with magnetism. Some of the more commonly used terms are identified below.

Magnetic flux: Magnetic flux identifies the total number of magnetic lines of force which exist about and within a magnet. The Greek letter Φ (phi) is the symbol used to denote flux. The unit of measurement is the weber (Wb). Magnetic flux, or flux lines, is a measurement of the strength of a particular magnet.

Flux Density: The number of magnetic lines of force that pass through, or exist in, a particular cross-sectional area is referred to as flux density. *Flux density* is also a term used to describe the strength of a magnet. This is a more descriptive term than flux when describing the strength of a magnet. The letter B is used to indicate flux density. Its unit of measurement is the tesla (T). The relationship between flux density, flux, and area is shown by Equation (5–1).

$$B = \frac{\Phi}{A} = \text{Wb/m}^2 \quad \text{in teslas} \tag{5-1}$$

Magnetomotive force: Magnetomotive force is the force which creates the magnetic field. It is similar to electromotive force in electric circuits. The symbol used for magnetomotive force is $\mathscr{F}$ and its unit of measurement is the ampere (A). Equation (5-2) identifies the relationship between magnetomotive force, the number of turns of wire wrapped around the core, and the amount of current flowing through the wire.

$$\mathscr{F} = NI \quad \text{in amperes} \tag{5-2}$$

Reluctance: Reluctance is to magnetic circuits what resistance is to electric circuits—that phenomenon which opposes the establishment of magnetic lines of force within a medium. In Equation (5-3) $\mathfrak{R}$ represents reluctance; the unit of measurement is amperes per weber (A/Wb).

$$\mathfrak{R} = \frac{NI}{\Phi} = \text{A/wb} \tag{5-3}$$

SUMMARY

1. A cell is a transducer which converts chemical energy into electrical energy.
2. A cell is made of two dissimilar metals (anode and cathode) and an electrolyte.
3. The voltage developed by a cell is dependent upon the type of materials the electrodes are made from and the type of electrolyte used.
4. The current capacity of a cell is dependent upon the amount of electrolyte and size of electrodes.
5. A primary cell is one which cannot be recharged.
6. A secondary cell can be recharged efficiently many times.
7. Wet cells have a liquid electrolyte.
8. Dry cells utilize an electrolyte in paste form.
9. The lead-acid cell utilizes lead peroxide as the anode, lead as the cathode, and sulfuric acid as the electrolyte.
10. Cells can be connected in series to increase the available voltage.
11. Cells can be connected in parallel to increase current capacity.

12. The two general types of magnets include the permanent magnet and the electromagnet.
13. Magnetic lines of force, sometimes called flux lines, are used to describe the force field about a magnet. The unit of measurement is the weber (Wb).
14. Magnetic flux lines leave the north pole of a magnet and enter the south pole.
15. A magnet attracts materials such as iron, cobalt, and alloys of these materials by making temporary magnets of objects made from these substances.
16. Retentivity is the degree to which materials remain magnetized after being removed from the influence of a magnetic field.
17. Permeability is the ease with which magnetic lines of force can exist in a medium.
18. The right-hand rule is used to determine the polarity of an electromagnet.
19. Electromagnetic field strength is affected by the number of turns forming the magnet, the amount of current flowing through the coils, the type of core material used, and the ratio of the coil length to the core diameter.
20. Flux density identifies the number of flux lines passing through a specific area (usually 1 m²). It is used to describe the strength of a magnet. Its unit of measurement is the tesla (T).
21. Magnetomotive force is the force which creates the magnetic field about an electromagnet and is measured in amperes (A).
22. Reluctance is the opposition to the establishment of magnetic lines of force in a substance and is measured in amperes per weber (A/Wb).

PRACTICE EXERCISES

1. Identify the two general types of electromotive force.
2. What is meant by the term *transducer?*
3. Discuss the physical construction of a cell.
4. What are the physical factors which determine the voltage developed by a cell?
5. Describe the physical factors which affect the current capacity of a cell.
6. What is the major difference between a wet cell and a dry cell?
7. Identify the types of materials used as electrodes and the type of electrolyte used in a lead-acid cell.
8. How can the state of charge be determined for a lead-acid cell?
9. What is meant by the term magnetism?
10. List the two general types of magnets.
11. For the magnet shown in Figure 5–18, which end is the north pole?

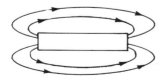

Figure 5–18

12. Define the following terms:
    a. flux   **d.** reluctance
    b. flux density   **e.** permeability
    c. magnetomotive force   **f.** residual magnetism
13. Identify the units of measurement for the following variables:
    a. flux   **c.** magnetomotive force
    b. flux density   **d.** reluctance
14. What four factors affect the strength of an electromagnet?
15. Which end of the electromagnet shown in Figure 5–19 is the north pole?

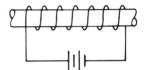

Figure 5–19

ANSWERS TO PRACTICE EXERCISES

1. The two general types of electromotive force are AC and DC.
2. A transducer is a device which converts one form of energy into another form.
3. A cell consists of two dissimilar metals, called electrodes, and a solution, called an electrolyte.
4. The output voltage of a cell is dependent upon the kinds of materials the electrodes are made from and the type of electrolyte used.
5. The current capacity of a cell depends upon the size of the electrodes and the amount of electrolyte.
6. Wet cells utilize a liquid electrolyte, whereas dry cells have an electrolyte in paste form.
7. The positive electrode (anode) is made from lead peroxide (PbO_2) and the negative electrode (cathode) is composed of lead (Pb). Sulfuric acid (H_2SO_4) which has been slightly diluted with water is utilized as the electrolyte.
8. The state of charge is checked by measuring the specific gravity of the cell with a hydrometer.
9. Magnetism is that property of certain substances which allows them to attract ferrous materials.
10. The two general kinds of magnets include permanent magnets and electromagnets.
11.

Figure 5–20 $\boxed{N \qquad\qquad S}$

12. **a.** Flux is the force about a magnet and is represented by lines.
    b. *Flux density* is a term used to indicate the strength of a magnet. It represents the number of lines passing through a specified area.
    c. Magnetomotive force is the force which creates magnetic flux.

     d. Reluctance is the opposition a medium offers to the establishment of magnetic flux.

     e. Permeability is the ease with which magnetic flux can be established in a medium.

     f. Residual magnetism is that magnetism which remains in a material after it has been removed from a magnetic field.

13. a. The unit of measurement associated with flux is the weber (Wb).

     b. Tesla (T) is the unit of measurement for flux density.

     c. The ampere (A) is the unit of measurement associated with magnetomotive force.

     d. The unit of measurement for reluctance is amperes per weber (A/Wb).

14. The strength of an electromagnet is affected by the number of turns, amount of current flow, type of core, and ratio of coil length to its diameter.

15.

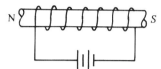

Figure 5–21

CHAPTER EXAMINATION

1. After a ferrous material has been removed from a magnetic field it retains some of its magnetizing qualities. This is called
   - **a.** retentivity
   - **b.** magnetic reluctance
   - **c.** residual magnetism
   - **d.** internal resistance
2. In the diagram shown in Figure 5–22, the north pole is located on the _____ side of the core.
   - **a.** left
   - **b.** right

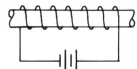

Figure 5–22

3. The strength of an electromagnetic field associated with an electromagnet is not affected by the
   - **a.** size of the core
   - **b.** number of turns forming the core
   - **c.** amount of current flowing through the coil
   - **d.** dielectric constant of the insulation covering the wire
4. Magnetism is that property of a substance which permits it to attract
   - **a.** lead   **c.** copper
   - **b.** carbon   **d.** ferrous metal

5. The term *flux* means _____.
   a. strength of the magnetomotive force
   b. the total lines of force in a magnetic field
   c. magnetic resistance of a magnetized substance
   d. conductance of the magnetized substance in a magnetic field
6. The ability of a magnetic material to hold its magnetic property is known as
   a. resistance   c. retentivity
   b. reluctance   d. reactance
7. The ability of a material to resist being magnetized is known as
   a. resistance   c. permeability
   b. reluctance   d. reactance
8. The magnetic field of an electron results from its
   a. mass   c. weight
   b. spin   d. polarity
9. The force that creates the magnetic flux field best defines
   a. magnetic force   c. electromotive force
   b. electrostatic force   d. magnetomotive force
10. _____ is defined as the ease with which magnetic flux lines can exist in a substance.
   a. Flux   c. Retentivity
   b. Reluctance   d. Permeability
11. When a material's electrons are aligned and spinning in the same direction under the influence of a magnetic field, the material is
   a. polarized   c. magnetized
   b. saturated   d. demagnetized
12. The unit of measurement for flux density is the
   a. weber   c. weber/meter^2
   b. tesla   d. ampere turn

Choose true or false for questions 13 to 20.

13. T   F   A device which converts one form of energy into another is a definition for a transponder.
14. T   F   The major parts of a cell include the cell case and the connecting posts.
15. T   F   A hydrometer can be used to measure the state of charge of a lead-acid cell.
16. T   F   Secondary cells can be either of the dry cell or wet cell types.
17. T   F   The terminal voltage of a cell depends upon the physical size of the cell.
18. T   F   The electrolyte used in a lead-acid cell is ammonium hydroxide.
19. T   F   A dry cell cannot be a secondary type cell.
20. T   F   The positive electrode in the lead-acid cell is composed of lead peroxide.

6

Alternating Current and Voltage

OBJECTIVES

Upon completion of this chapter you should be able to do the following:

1. Describe the difference between AC and DC voltage.
2. Discuss how current flow in a circuit connected to an AC source differs from that connected to a DC source.
3. Convert from peak-to-peak to peak units and vice versa.
4. Convert from peak units to rms units and vice versa.
5. Define the terms *alternation, cycle, frequency,* and *period.*
6. State Faraday's law of induction and identify those factors which affect the amplitude and polarity of the voltage induced across a conductor.
7. Define the sine, cosine, and tangent functions with respect to the sides of a right triangle.
8. Compute the value of an instantaneous voltage or current.
9. Calculate the length of a sinusoidal wave.
10. Describe how three-phase voltage and current differs from single-phase voltage and current.
11. Identify three applications of AC voltage.

6-1 INTRODUCTION

As mentioned in the last chapter, there are two kinds of electromotive force—direct (DC) and alternating (AC). It is important to understand the difference between these two types of potentials. The diagram of a circuit containing a battery, a switch, and a load is shown in Figure 6–1. When

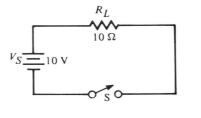
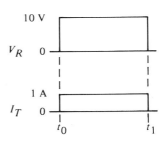

Figure 6–1   DC current flow through a circuit for a specified time.

the switch is in the open position, no current flows through the load and the load voltage is zero. When the switch is closed at time t_0, the current increases from 0 to 1 A and the load voltage goes from 0 to 10 V. As long as the switch remains closed, the circuit current and load voltage remain at these values. When the switch is opened at time t_1, the current and load voltage return to zero. During the time that the switch is closed, current flows through the circuit in one direction.

6-2 THE SINUSOIDAL WAVE

Most AC voltages are sinusoidal in nature. This means that they are in the form of a sine wave. A graph of a sine wave appears in Figure 6–2(a). The graph is formed by plotting angular displacement (the horizontal axis) versus voltage amplitude (the vertical axis). Notice that the amplitude of the voltage is continually changing. At 0° the voltage is 0 V. At 90° the voltage has increased to 10 V. Between 90° and 180° the voltage has decreased from 10 to 0 V. The voltage changes polarity and increases in the negative direction as it goes from 180° to 270°. It reaches a peak value (-10 V) at 270° and becomes less negative past 270°, returning to 0 V at 360°. It takes time to generate, or create, the sine wave. Therefore, the horizontal axis can also represent time, as shown in Figure 6–2(b).

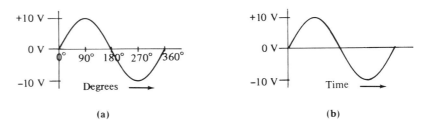

Figure 6–2   Sine wave: (a) angular displacement versus voltage; (b) time versus voltage.

A single and complete sine wave is called a cycle. One cycle of sine wave voltage is shown in Figure 6–3. A cycle consists of two alternations, a positive alternation and a negative alternation. That portion of the sine wave which occurs between 0° and 180° is called the positive alternation. The negative alternation lies between 180° and 360°. The polarity of the voltage alternates or changes for each half-cycle. For the first half-cycle, or positive alternation, the voltage values are positive. The voltage values are negative during the negative alternation, or second half-cycle.

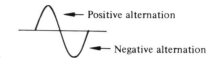

Figure 6–3   The composition of a sine wave.

6-3 CURRENT FLOW IN AC CIRCUITS

The symbol for an AC voltage source is shown in Figure 6–4. For the circuit shown, the AC source is connected to a 10-Ω load. This is the same circuit which appears in Figure 6–1, except that the battery has been replaced by an AC source.

During the positive alternation, current flows through the circuit in the direction indicated in Figure 6–4(a). The amplitude of the current is changing at a sinusoidal rate. The value of the load current can be found by using Ohm's law just as it is for DC circuits. For the circuit shown, this value is 1 A. During the positive alternation, the current intensity increases from 0 to 1 A (which occurs at 90°) and decreases back to 0 V at 180°. The intensity of the current is continually changing. The voltage developed across the load resistor follows the current and is computed by using Ohm's law.

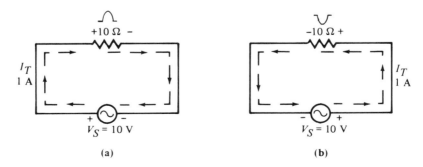

Figure 6–4   Current flow in an AC circuit.

During the negative alternation, the voltage source changes polarity, as indicated in Figure 6–4(b). Current has reversed itself and is flowing in the opposite direction. The voltage dropped across the load again follows the current. The amplitude of both the current and voltage are the same as they were for the positive alternation except they are opposite in direction and polarity. Notice how the current alternates. It flows first in one direction, stops, reverses itself, and flows in the opposite direction. This process continues as long as the switch is closed.

6-4 COMPARISON OF AC AND DC POWER

If the circuits appearing in Figures 6–1 and 6–4 are energized for the same amount of time, one can compare the power dissipated by the loads. This is illustrated in Figure 6–5. Each circuit is energized for the length of time required for the AC source to produce one cycle of voltage. Notice that the negative alternation of the AC source produces a positive power alternation. This is a result of multiplying a negative voltage by a negative current. Power represents the area under the graph or curve. It is obvious, when one compares the areas under the two curves depicted in Figure 6–6, that there is less area under the sinusoidal curves than under the DC curve. This means that for identical source voltage and load resistance values, the DC source produces more power or performs more work than an AC source. For this reason, a common unit of measurement used in AC circuits is the rms unit. This unit is introduced in the follow-

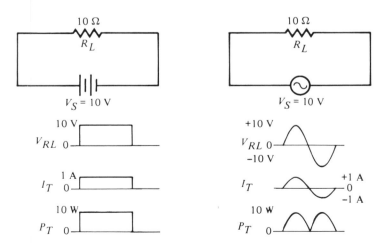

Figure 6–5   Circuit variables for both a DC and an AC circuit.

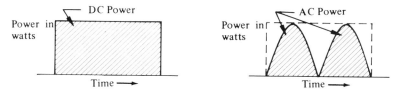

Figure 6–6   Comparison of the power produced by a DC source and an AC source.

ing section and is a method of identifying the amplitude of a voltage and current whose product produces the same amount of power as an equivalent amplitude of DC voltage and current.

6-5 NOTATIONAL METHODS USED IN AC CIRCUITS

There are several notational methods associated with AC voltage and current which are not used with DC variables. These include peak-to-peak, peak, and root mean square (rms) (often called effective) values. These are identified with the aid of the sine wave appearing in Figure 6–7. The peak-to-peak value is obtained by adding the maximum positive and negative values. For the example shown, the peak-to-peak voltage is 40 V. The peak value is merely the maximum amplitude which occurs during either the positive or negative alternation. This value is 20 V for the sine wave shown in Figure 6–7.

The rms, or effective, value is the most useful of all the AC measurements. This is a comparison of the amount of work an AC source will produce when compared to a DC source. Derived from calculus, the rms value is equal to 0.707 times the peak value. For the voltage shown in Figure 6–7, the effective value is 14.14 V. This means that 20 V peak AC is as effective, or will perform the same amount of work as 14.14 V DC. This is the most common type of AC measurement. Almost all AC voltmeters and ammeters measure rms values. Unless otherwise indicated,

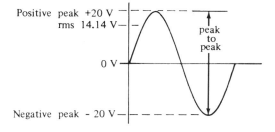

Figure 6–7   Units of measurement associated with a sine wave.

AC voltage or current measurements are assumed to be in rms units. The following equations are used to convert from one AC unit of measurement to another.

$$\text{Peak-to-peak (pk-pk)} = (\text{pk})(2) \tag{6--1}$$

$$\text{Peak (pk)} = \frac{\text{pk-pk}}{2} = \frac{\text{rms}}{0.707} = (\text{rms})(1.414) \tag{6--2}$$

$$\text{rms} = (\text{pk})(0.707) \tag{6--3}$$

Example 6–1 illustrates how these equations are used.

Example 6–1   Application of the AC conversion equations

Problem
If a sine wave has a peak amplitude of 50 V, determine its peak-to-peak and rms values.

Solution
(a) pk-pk = (pk)(2) = (50 V)(2) = 100 V pk-pk
(b) rms = (pk)(0.707) = (50 V)(0.707) = 35.35 V

Both the voltage and current will have the same notational units when calculations are performed for AC circuits. If Ohm's law is used to compute the current flowing in a circuit and the source voltage is given in peak-to-peak units, the resulting current intensity will be in peak-to-peak units. If rms voltage is used in the calculation, then the resulting current will be in rms units. Ohm's law is used in AC circuits just as it is in DC circuits as illustrated by Example 6–2.

Example 6–2   Using Ohm's law in an AC circuit

Problem
Calculate the current flowing through the circuit and the voltage across each resistor in the circuit shown in Figure 6–8.

Solution
$$I_T = \frac{V_S}{R_T} = \frac{20\text{ V}}{800\text{ }\Omega} = 0.025\text{ A}$$
$$V_{R1} = (I_T)(R_1) = (0.025\text{ A})(470\text{ }\Omega) = 11.75\text{ V}$$
$$V_{R2} = (I_T)(R_2) = (0.025\text{ A})(330\text{ }\Omega) = 8.25\text{ V}$$

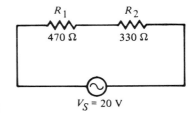

Figure 6–8 $V_S = 20$ V

6-6 PRODUCING AC VOLTAGE AND CURRENT

There are two major methods used to produce AC voltage and current. One method utilizes an AC generator and the other employs an electronic circuit called an oscillator. The generator method is used to produce the high AC power required for commercial applications. Electronic oscillators are used to generate higher-frequency lower-power AC energy and are discussed in a future chapter. The following discussion describes the method by which AC voltage is produced from a generator.

It was established in the last chapter that there is a relationship between electricity and magnetism. In that chapter it was found that an electric current produces a magnetic field. There is an inverse principle to this concept. Whenever a conductor cuts magnetic lines of force by moving through a magnetic field, a voltage is induced across the conductor. This principle is called Faraday's law of induction. According to Faraday's law, the magnitude of the induced voltage depends upon the strength of the magnetic field, the rate at which the lines are cut, and the angle at which the conductor moves through the field. The polarity of the induced voltage depends upon the polarity of the magnetic field and the direction in which the conductor is moving when the lines are cut.

A magnet having a specific flux density is shown in Figure 6–9. A conductor placed between the pole pieces and moved upward at a predetermined speed will have a voltage induced across it with the polarity shown. When the conductor is moved downward at the same speed, a voltage will be induced across the conductor which has the same magnitude but the polarity has been reversed, as illustrated in Figure 6–10.

The effect on the polarity of the induced voltage, when the magnetic field is reversed, is depicted in Figures 6–11 and 6–12. Notice that the polarity of the voltage induced across the conductor appearing in Figure 6–11 is opposite that induced across the conductor in Figure 6–9, even

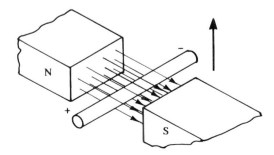

Figure 6–9   Conductor cutting magnetic lines of force.

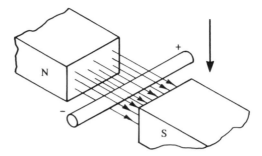

Figure 6–10   Conductor cutting magnetic lines of force.

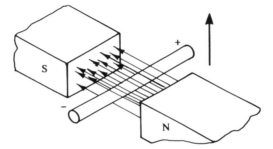

Figure 6–11   Conductor cutting magnetic lines of force.

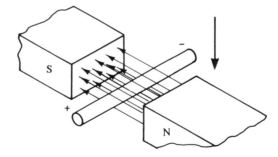

Figure 6–12   Conductor cutting magnetic lines of force.

though the conductor is moving upward in both cases. In similar fashion, the voltage induced across the conductor shown in Figure 6–12 is opposite to that appearing in Figure 6–10 even though both are moving downward. The amplitude of the induced voltage is directly proportional to the rate at which the magnetic flux lines are cut. If the conductor is moved through the field at twice its original speed, the induced voltage will be twice its former value.

Maximum voltage is induced across the conductor when it moves through the magnetic field in a direction which is perpendicular to the individual magnetic flux lines. When the conductor moves through the field at an angle which is less than 90°, a smaller amplitude voltage is developed. If the conductor is formed into a loop, as shown in Figure 6–13(a), and allowed to rotate, the voltage induced across the conductor will be determined by the angle at which the conductor cuts the magnetic lines of force. This assumes that the magnetic flux density and rotational speed remain constant.

The looped conductor can be considered to be a rotating vector as it turns in the air gap between the pole pieces. As the vector rotates it has an amplitude, or height *(H)*, perpendicular to the zero axis as shown in Figure 6–13(b). This represents the voltage induced across the conductor at that point.

If the rotating conductor is momentarily stopped every 30°, as indicated in Figure 6–13(c), and the height of the vectors at each 30° interval is projected to the right, as illustrated in Figure 6–13(d), a graph of the sine wave is obtained when the individual points are connected. An AC generator naturally produces a sine wave as a rotating conductor,

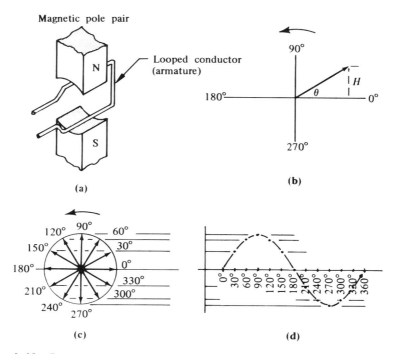

Figure 6–13   Development of the sine wave.

called an armature, rotates in the air gap between the ends of a magnet. If a load is connected to the armature, the sinusoidal voltage will cause a sinusoidal current to flow through the circuit, as shown in Figure 6–14.

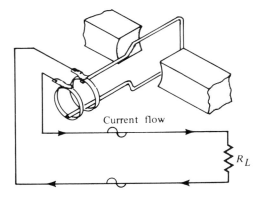

Current flow

R_L

Figure 6–14 AC current flowing through a circuit connected to the generator.

6-7 THE SINE FUNCTION

The sine function is one of six trigonometric functions associated with a right triangle. A right triangle appears in the first quadrant of the rectangular coordinate system appearing in Figure 6–15. The triangle is formed by adjacent side A, opposite side O, and the hypotenuse H. Three interior angles are associated with a triangle. The one created by the intersection of the adjacent side and the hypotenuse, located near the intersection of the X and Y axes, is the one of interest to us. We will identify this as angle theta (θ).

The six trigonometric functions are ratios of any two of the three sides of a right triangle associated with angle theta. As identified in Table 6–1, these include the sine, cosine, tangent, cotangent, secant, and cose-

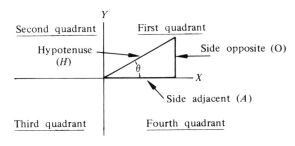

Figure 6–15 Right triangle appearing in a rectangular coordinate system.

TABLE 6–1   Definitions of the Trigonometric Functions

Function		Definition
Sine	=	$\dfrac{\text{side opposite}}{\text{hypotenuse}}$
Cosine	=	$\dfrac{\text{side adjacent}}{\text{hypotenuse}}$
Tangent	=	$\dfrac{\text{side opposite}}{\text{side adjacent}}$
Cotangent	=	$\dfrac{\text{side adjacent}}{\text{side opposite}}$
Secant	=	$\dfrac{\text{hypotenuse}}{\text{side adjacent}}$
Cosecant	=	$\dfrac{\text{hypotenuse}}{\text{side opposite}}$

cant functions. The sine, cosine, and tangent functions are those most commonly used in electrical calculations. The specific ratio values for any angle theta can be obtained from a table of trigonometric functions found in most math books or from scientific calculators. Some of the more commonly used values appear in Table 6–2.

TABLE 6–2   Trigonometric Values for Selected Angles

Angle theta	Sine (sin)	Cosine (cos)	Tangent (tan)
0°	0.000	1.000	0.000
30°	0.500	0.866	0.577
45°	0.707	0.707	1.000
60°	0.866	0.500	1.732
90°	1.000	0.000	infinity
120°	0.866	−0.500	−1.732
150°	0.500	−0.866	−0.577
180°	0.000	−1.000	0.000
210°	−0.500	−0.866	0.577
240°	−0.866	−0.500	1.732
270°	−1.000	0.000	infinity
300°	−0.866	0.500	−1.732
330°	−0.500	0.866	−0.577
360°	0.000	1.000	0.000

6-8 INSTANTANEOUS VOLTAGE AND CURRENT

Sometimes it is necessary to calculate the voltage or current which is present at some particular time or angle for a sine wave. This is accomplished by using the formulas appearing in Equation (6–4).

$$v = (V_{pk})(\sin \theta) \qquad i = (I_{pk})(\sin \theta) \tag{6–4}$$

Although the peak-to-peak, peak, and rms values of an AC voltage or current waveform are important, it is necessary occasionally to compute the instantaneous voltage or current value. This procedure is illustrated in Example 6–3.

Example 6–3 Calculating instantaneous voltage

Problem
Given the sinusoidal voltage waveform appearing in Figure 6–16, calculate the instantaneous voltage at 30° and 60°.

Solution
(a) v at 30° = $(V_{pk})(\sin 30°) = (25 \text{ V})(0.5) = 12.5$ V
(b) v at 60° = $(V_{pk})(\sin 60°) = (25 \text{ V})(0.866) = 21.65$ V

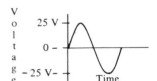

Figure 6–16

The procedure just described can be used to plot an entire sine wave. In fact, this is how the generator produces a sine wave. The voltage induced across the armature at a particular time is the product of the maximum voltage which can be induced across it (at 90°) and the angle at which the armature is cutting the magnetic flux lines. Lowercase (small) letters are used to indicate instantaneous voltage and current variables.

6-9 FREQUENCY AND PERIOD

The term *cycle* was defined earlier in the chapter. The number of cycles which occur for a particular length of time describes frequency. For the simple generator shown in Figure 6–14, the armature must rotate 360° for one complete cycle to be created. If it takes 1 s to accomplish this, the generator frequency is 1 cycle/second (cps). The unit of measurement for frequency is the hertz (Hz) which is equivalent to cycles per second. Utility power generating plants in the United States produce AC energy having a frequency of 60 Hz. AC sinusoidal signals used in communications systems range from a low of a few kilohertz to a high of several gigahertz.

Closely associated with frequency is the period. Period, whose symbol is t, is the time required to complete one cycle of voltage or current. Its unit of measurement is the second. As indicated by Equation (6–5), the period is equal to the reciprocal of frequency.

$$\text{Period} = \frac{1}{\text{frequency}} \qquad t = \frac{1}{f} \quad \text{in seconds} \qquad\qquad (6\text{--}5)$$

Example 6–4 serves to illustrate the relationship between frequency and time.

Example 6–4   Calculating the period of a cycle of current

Problem
Given a sinusoidal current waveform which has a frequency of 1000 Hz, calculate the period for one cycle.

Solution

$$t = \frac{1}{f} = \frac{1}{1000\,\text{Hz}} = 0.001 \text{ s}$$

Repeat the problem above for a frequency of 60 Hz.

Solution

$$t = \frac{1}{f} = \frac{1}{60\,\text{Hz}} = 0.0167 \text{ s}$$

6-10 WAVELENGTH

Wavelength is the length of a cycle of sinusoidal voltage or current. The symbol for wavelength is the Greek letter lambda (λ) and its unit of measurement is length, either in miles or meters or fractions of those units. The formula for computing wavelength appears in Equation (6–6).

$$\text{Wavelength} = \frac{\text{Velocity of propagation}}{\text{Frequency}}$$

$$\lambda = \frac{V_C}{f} \quad \text{in meters or miles} \tag{6-6}$$

The velocity of propagation (V_C) is that of light which is about 186,000 miles/s or 300,000,000 m/s. An example of how this equation is used appears in Example 6–5.

Example 6–5   Calculation of wavelength

Problem
Calculate the wavelength of the signal radiated from an AM broadcast band transmitter antenna if the transmitter is operating at 970 kHz.

Solution

$$\lambda = \frac{V_C}{f} = \frac{3 \times 10^8}{9.7 \times 10^5} = 309 \text{ m}$$

6-11 THREE-PHASE VOLTAGE AND CURRENT

The simple generator discussed so far produces a single cycle of AC voltage for a complete cycle of rotation. If an additional magnet is placed at right angles to the original one, as shown in Figure 6–17, two cycles of AC voltage can be produced for one revolution of the armature. This is called a two-pole pair generator and is a more efficient method of generating voltage. Each individual magnet has two poles, a north pole and a south pole. The two poles associated with the same magnet are called

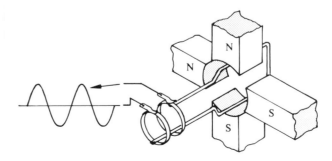

Figure 6–17   Two-pole pair generator.

pole pairs. Generators which have one armature are called single-phase generators. This means that one cycle of voltage is completely generated before the next cycle begins.

Utility power plants utilize a three-phase generating system. With this method, three armatures, located 120° apart, rotate in the magnetic field, as illustrated in Figure 6–18. One complete revolution of all three armatures results in three cycles of voltage being created if a single magnet is used. Notice that only 120° of each cycle is completed before the next cycle begins. This is a much more efficient means of generating electrical energy than the single-phase method. The efficiency can be increased further by increasing the number of magnetic pole pairs.

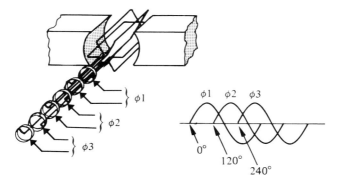

Figure 6–18   Three-phase generator.

6-12 APPLICATIONS OF AC VOLTAGE AND CURRENT

Probably the most familiar use of AC energy is that which comes into our home via the power lines coming from the utility company. It provides the energy used to light our houses, heat them (in some cases), and power the many appliances which make life convenient for us and characterizes life as we know it today. This energy is sinusoidal in nature and comes into the home in a three-wire, 220-V, single-phase, 60 Hz format.

Electronic communications is another area where AC power is utilized extensively. The electrical signals which represent voice and musical sounds that we hear on our radio and television receivers are AC in format. These frequencies range from about 50 to 15,000 Hz, which is the range in which the human ear detects sounds. The voice and musical sounds are superimposed on a high-frequency sinusoidal carrier wave and transmitted through the air from the antenna located near the broadcast studio to the receiver located in your home. Depending upon the frequency the radio is tuned to, these frequencies may range from a low of a few kilohertz to a high of several megahertz.

Not all AC voltage and current waveforms are sinusoidal in nature. Some examples of other types appear in Figure 6–19. The voltage appearing in Figure 6–19(a) is the electrical signal representing the voice or musical sounds picked up by a microphone. This signal is actually sinusoidal, but it contains a number of other signals, called harmonics, which changes its shape. The waveforms appearing in Figures 6–19(b) through (d) can be either DC or AC depending upon the position of the zero reference. The ramp voltage shown in Figure 6–19(b) is sometimes called a sawtooth, or trapezoidal, waveform. This type of voltage is used to generate horizontal lines across cathode-ray tubes such as the television picture tube. If one looks at a television receiver carefully, one sees that the picture is made up of many horizontal lines. The waveform illustrated in Figure 6–19(d) contains the information required to produce the picture seen on the television picture tube. The signal depicted in Figure 6–19(e) is called a differentiated waveform. This type of voltage is useful for synchronizing circuits where timing is important.

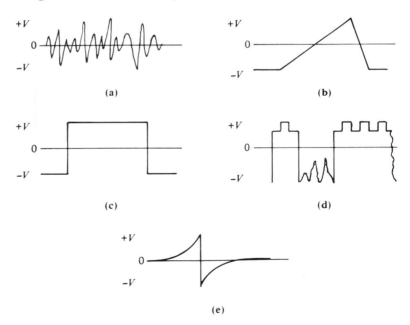

Figure 6–19 Examples of AC voltage and current: (a) audio waveform; (b) sawtooth waveform (c) pulse waveform; (d) television waveform; (e) differential waveform.

SUMMARY

1. Most, but not all, AC voltages and currents are sinusoidal in nature. They have the shape and characteristics of a sine wave.

2. A sine wave is made up of two symmetrical parts. That part above the zero axis is called the positive alternation. The part which lies below the zero axis is called the negative alternation.

3. One sine wave is called a cycle. A cycle of sine wave voltage consists of a positive half-cycle (alternation) and a negative half-cycle (alternation).

4. The amplitude of a sinusoidal voltage is continually changing. It increases from zero and reaches a maximum positive value at 90°. Between 90° and 180°, it becomes less positive and again reaches zero at 180°. It changes polarity and increases in the negative direction between 180° and 270°. At 270° it reaches its maximum negative amplitude and begins to become less negative arriving at 0 V at 360°.

5. Because the sinusoidal voltage waveform is constantly changing in amplitude and polarity, the resulting current is continually changing in intensity and direction. This is where the term *alternating current* comes from. The direction of current flow is constantly changing for every half-cycle of voltage.

6. Several different notational methods are associated with AC voltage and current measurements. These include peak-to-peak, peak, effective (rms), and instantaneous values.

7. Equal-amplitude AC and DC voltages do not perform the same amount of work. AC voltage performs less work than DC voltage. The effective, or rms, unit of measurement is used to compare the amount of work performed (or power dissipated) between AC and DC sources. The effective value is obtained by multiplying the peak, or maximum, value by 0.707. This means that 10 V of peak AC voltage will perform the same amount of work as 7.07 V of DC voltage.

8. The rms unit is the most common AC unit of voltage or current measurement. The familiar 117-V AC voltage found in one's home is an rms unit.

9. AC voltage can be produced two ways—with a generator or an electronic oscillator. The generator is the method used by the utility companies to produce the AC energy used in the home and industry.

10. A generator develops voltage because of magnetic induction. A voltage is induced across a conductor any time the conductor cuts magnetic lines of flux.

11. The amplitude of the voltage induced across a conductor depends upon the intensity of the magnetic field, the rate at which the magnetic lines are cut, and the angle at which the conductor cuts the lines.

12. The polarity of the voltage induced across a conductor depends upon the polarity of the magnetic field and the direction in which the conductor moves through the field.

13. A looped conductor rotating between the pole pieces of a magnet has a voltage induced across it which is sinusoidal in form. This means that if the voltage developed across the conductor was plotted at regularly spaced angle intervals, a sine wave curve would result.

14. The sine is one of six trigonometric functions associated with a right triangle.

15. The instantaneous voltage (voltage at a specified angle) induced across an armature can be computed by multiplying the peak value which can be induced by the sine of the angle.
16. The number of cycles of sinusoidal voltage produced within a specified length of time (usually seconds) is referred to as frequency. Frequency is measured in hertz; 1 Hz is the frequency of 1 cycle/second (cps).
17. The period is the time required to produce one cycle of voltage or current.
18. Wavelength is the length of one cycle of AC voltage or current.
19. Three-phase power is the type of AC power produced by most generators. Utility power generators and the automobile generator produce three-phase voltage.
20. There are other types of AC voltage and current in addition to the sinusoidal type. Some of these include the sawtooth, pulse, and differentiated waveforms.

PRACTICE EXERCISES

1. What is the major difference between DC voltage and AC voltage?
2. Define the following terms:
   a. alternation   **b.** cycle   **c.** frequency
3. Given a sine wave which has a peak-to-peak amplitude of 75 V, calculate **(a)** the rms value and **(b)** the peak value.
4. A 117-V rms voltage has a peak value of _____ V.
5. State Faraday's law of induction.
6. What factors determine the amplitude of the voltage induced across a conductor?
7. Identify the factors which determine the polarity of the voltage induced across a conductor.
8. If a sine wave has a peak value of 80 V, the instantaneous voltage at 60° is _____ V.
9. An rms current flowing in a circuit measures 45 mA. Calculate the peak value of this current.
10. What is the unit of measurement for frequency?
11. Define the following trigonometric functions in terms of the sides of a right triangle
    a sine   **b.** cosine   **c.** tangent
12. Calculate the length (in meters) of a sinusoidal waveform which has a frequency of 970 kHz.
13. If the effective value of a voltage is 2.7 V, what is its peak value?
14. If a sine wave has a period of 0.0125 s, what is its frequency?
15. Identify three types of AC waveforms other than the sinusoidal.
16. A certain sine wave has a wavelength of 3100 miles. What is its frequency?
17. The current flowing through a circuit measures 16.5 mA rms. What is its value in peak-to-peak units?
18. What is the period of a sine wave which has a wavelength of 480 m?

ANSWERS TO PRACTICE EXERCISES

1. A DC voltage has a constant polarity. An AC voltage has an amplitude which changes polarity. The voltage consists of two alternations—positive and negative—which cause the polarity to change every half-cycle.

2. **a.** An alternation is one-half of the voltage or current waveform.

   b. A cycle is a complete AC waveform. It consists of both a positive and a negative alternation.

   c. Frequency represents the number of cycles produced per unit of time.

3. **a.** $[(75 \text{ V})/2](0.707) = 26.51$ V

   b. $(75 \text{ V})/2 = 37.5$ V pk

4. $(117 \text{ V})/0.707 = 165.4$ V pk or $(117 \text{ V})(1.414) = 165.4$ V pk.

5. Faraday's law of induction states that any time a conductor cuts magnetic flux lines a voltage is induced across the conductor.

6. Factors which affect the amplitude of the voltage induced across a conductor include

   a. the strength of the magnetic flux field

   b. the rate at which the conductor moves through the field

   c. the angle at which the field is cut

7. The polarity of the voltage induced across a conductor depends upon the direction in which the conductor cuts the field and the polarity of the magnetic field.

8. $(80 \text{ V})(0.866) = 69.28$ V.

9. $(45 \text{ mA})/0.707 = 63.65$ mA.

10. The unit of measurement for frequency is the hertz.

11. **a.** $\text{sine} = \dfrac{\text{side opposite}}{\text{hypotenuse}} = \dfrac{O}{H}$ **b.** $\text{cosine} = \dfrac{\text{side adjacent}}{\text{hypotenuse}} = \dfrac{A}{H}$

    c. $\text{tangent} = \dfrac{\text{side opposite}}{\text{side adjacent}} = \dfrac{O}{A}$

12. $\lambda = \dfrac{V_C}{f} = \dfrac{3 \times 10^8}{9.7 \times 10^5} = 0.30928 \times 10^3 = 309.28$ m

13. $\dfrac{2.7 \text{ V}}{0.707} = 3.82$ V pk

14. $f = \dfrac{1}{t} = \dfrac{1}{0.0125 \text{ s}} = 80$ Hz

15. Three types of AC waveforms, other than the sinusoidal type, include the sawtooth, pulse, and differentiated waveforms.

16. $\lambda = \dfrac{V_C}{f};\quad f = \dfrac{V_C}{\lambda} = \dfrac{1.86 \times 10^5}{3.1 \times 10^3} = 60$ Hz

17. $\left(\dfrac{16.5 \text{ mA}}{0.707}\right)(2) = 46.68$ mA

18. $\lambda = \dfrac{V_C}{f}; \quad f = \dfrac{V_C}{\lambda} = \dfrac{3 \times 10^8}{4.8 \times 10^2} = 625$ kHz

$t = \dfrac{1}{f} = \dfrac{1}{6.25 \times 10^5} = 1.6 \ \mu s$

CHAPTER EXAMINATION

1. If the peak value of a sinusoidal voltage waveform is 155 V, its effective value is approximately equal to _____ V.
   a. 185   c. 155
   b. 220   d. 110

2. The effective value of a sinusoidal current is 60 mA. The peak value of this current is _____ mA.
   a. 84.8   c. 94.3
   b. 42.4   d. 120

3. An AC power line voltage of 120 V has a peak value of approximately _____ V.
   a. 100   c. 240
   b. 170   d. 340

4. The value of alternating current which has the same heating effect as a corresponding DC value is known as the _____ value.
   a. rms   c. instantaneous
   b. peak   d. peak-to-peak

5. The value of a sine wave at any instant is equal to _____.
   a. V/I c. $V_{pk}/0.707$
   b. $(V)(I)$ d. $(V_{pk})(\sin \theta)$

6. Most AC voltmeters measure _____ volts.
   a. peak   c. effective
   b. instantaneous   d. peak-to-peak

7. A conductor is cutting a magnetic flux field at an angle of 30°. If the maximum voltage that can be induced is 50 V, what is the amplitude of the voltage being induced?
   a. 0 V   c. 21.65 V
   b. 12.5 V   d. none of the above

8. The polarity of the voltage induced across a conductor which is cutting a magnetic field is dependent upon
   a. the size of the conductor
   b. the strength of the magnetic field
   c. the velocity in which the conductor is cutting the field
   d. the direction in which the conductor is cutting the field

9. If an AC voltage has a peak value of 80 V, its peak-to-peak value is
   a. 20 V   c. 160 V
   b. 80 V   d. none of the above

10. Given an AC voltage having a peak amplitude of 100 V, its effective value is
    a. 25 V   c. 70.7 V
    b. 31.8 V   d. none of the above

11. Given an AC voltage having an effective value of 100 V, the peak value of this voltage is _____ V.
    a. 141.4   c. 63.2
    b. 282.8   d. 70.7
12. The trigonometric function defined by dividing the adjacent side by the hypotenuse is the
    a. sine   c. tangent
    b. cosine   d. cosecant
13. The unit of measurement for frequency is the
    a. cycle   c. farad
    b. hertz   d. faraday
14. The sinusoidal waveform has peak amplitude values which occur at _____.
    a. 0° and 180°   c. 90° and 270°
    b. 45° and 225°   d. 60° and 240°
15. A sinusoidal waveform has a frequency of 120 Hz. What is its period?
    a. 0.012 s   c. 8.33 s
    b. 12.5 s   d. 0.00833 s
16. What is the wavelength of the sine wave identified in question 15?
    a. 1200 ft   c. 8,184,000 ft
    b. 3100 miles   d. none of the above
17. A sine wave has a period of 0.125 ms. Its wavelength is
    a. 52.6 ft   c. 37,500 m
    b. 287.4 miles   d. none of the above
18. A sine wave has an effective value of 100 V. Its rms value is
    a. 31.8 V   c. 200 V
    b. 63.6 V   d. none of the above
19. A certain AC voltage has a wavelength of 1000 m. Its frequency is
    a. 240 Hz   c. 300 kHz
    b. 175 kHz   d. none of the above
20. An rms indicating ammeter shows that the current flowing in a circuit is 10.5 mA. What is the peak-to-peak value of the current?
    a. 3.18 mA   c. 7.39 mA
    b. 29.7 mA   d. none of the above

7

Inductance

OBJECTIVES

Upon completion of this chapter you should be able to do the following:

1. Define the term *inductance*.
2. Identify the symbol and unit of measurement associated with inductance.
3. Describe how an inductor is able to oppose a change in current.
4. Define the L/R time constant.
5. Calculate the time required for the current to reach its DC, or steady-state value, in a circuit containing resistance and inductance when connected to a DC source.
6. Describe the difference between self-inductance and mutual inductance.
7. Compute the total inductance for two series-connected inductors.
8. Determine the total inductance for two inductors connected in parallel.
9. Define the term *inductive reactance*.
10. Calculate the value of the inductive reactance for an inductor connected to an AC source.
11. Compute the current flowing in a circuit which contains an inductor connected to an AC source.
12. Identify the voltage and current phase relationship in a circuit containing an inductor connected to an AC source.
13. Discuss the effect of an inductor in a DC circuit and an AC circuit.
14. Describe the purpose of a transformer.
15. Compute the turns ratio of a transformer.
16. Calculate the secondary voltage of a transformer when the primary voltage and turns ratio are known.
17. Compute the turns ratio required to match a secondary load resistance to a primary circuit resistance.

7-1 INDUCTORS AND DC CIRCUITS

7-1.1 Introduction. The only device that has been used in the circuits encountered so far, except for the voltage source, current source, and switch, has been the resistor. Other devices are used in many circuits. One of these is the inductor. An inductor is an electrical component which provides a circuit with inductance. Inductance is that property of an electrical circuit which stores energy in an electromagnetic field and opposes a change in current. As indicated by its definition, inductance is present in all circuits. Its effect is made present by the conductors in the circuit. Usually, the inductance of conductors is quite small and can be neglected except for very high frequency circuits. When it is desired to add inductance to a circuit, a physical device called an inductor is used.

An inductor is an electrical component which stores energy in an electromagnetic field. Its function is to oppose changes in current. Unlike resistors which oppose current flow, inductors oppose changes in current intensity. A resistor in an electrical circuit behaves like friction does in a mechanical system. An inductor in an electrical circuit serves the same purpose that a flywheel does in a mechanical system. A flywheel connected to a rotating shaft tends to smooth out sudden changes in shaft speed, making the shaft turn smoothly. It absorbs energy as the shaft accelerates, stores the energy while the shaft speed remains constant, and releases the energy when the shaft speed begins to decrease.

7-1.2 Physical Construction of the Inductor. The inductor is formed by wrapping wire around a core. Physically, it is constructed much like the electromagnet. The core may be made from iron, in which case the device is called an iron-core inductor. The wire can also be wrapped around a hollow core made of cardboard or plastic. In this case the inductor is called an air-core inductor. Iron core inductors are used in lower frequency circuits and have larger values than the air-core devices. Pictorial representations of inductors appear in Figure 7–1.

The unit of measurement for inductance is the henry, whose symbol is H. The symbol used to denote inductance is L. The schematic symbols used to depict inductors appear in Figure 7–2.

The physical construction of an inductor is illustrated in Figure 7–3. The inductance value depends upon the number of turns, type of core material, cross-sectional area of the core, and the length of the core. The formula for computing the inductance value appears in Equation (7.1).

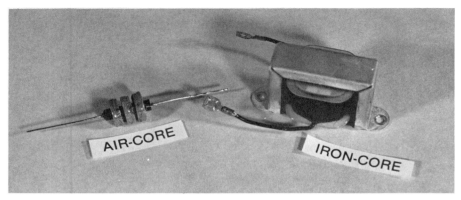

Figure 7–1 Representative size inductors: (a) iron-core inductors; (b) air-core inductors.

(a) (b)

Figure 7–2 Schematic Symbols used to represent inductors: (a) iron-core inductor; (b) air-core inductor.

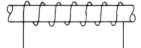

Figure 7–3 Physical construction of an inductor.

$$L = \frac{N^2 \mu A}{l} \quad in \ henries$$

L = the coil inductance in henries
N = the number of turns of wire wrapped around the core
μ = the permeability of the core
A = the cross-sectional area of the core in square meters
l = the length of the core in meters

(7–1)

7-1.3 **Principles of Operation.**   Inductors operate on the principle of magnetic induction as expressed by Faraday's law and Lenz's law. Faraday's law was introduced in the last chapter. According to this law, a voltage is induced across a conductor anytime the conductor cuts magnetic lines of force. The polarity of the induced voltage is expressed by Lenz's law. This law states that the polarity of the induced voltage is such that it opposes the voltage, or force, which created it. In Chapter 6 the magnetic field was stationary and the conductor was moved through the field. A voltage will also be induced across a conductor if a moving magnetic field cuts a stationary conductor. The results are identical as long as the flux density, rate at which the lines are cut, and angle at which the lines are cut are same in both cases.

The circuit appearing in Figure 7–4 serves to illustrate how an inductor opposes a change in current. With the switch in the open position, there is no current flowing in the circuit. When the switch is closed as shown in Figure 7–5, current begins to flow. The intensity, or amplitude, of the current is limited by the 10-Ω resistor. This will be 1 A if a 10-V source is used. As current begins to flow in the circuit, its intensity begins to increase from 0 to 1 A. This causes the magnetic field about the inductor to expand and move outward. As the flux lines move outward and away from the core, they cut the inductor coils, causing a voltage to be induced across the inductor. The polarity of the voltage induced across the inductor is opposite the polarity of the source voltage. This verifies Lenz's law. The voltage induced across the inductor is caused by self-inductance and is called a self-induced voltage. Self-induced voltage caused by an expanding magnetic flux field is called a counter electromotive force (CEMF).

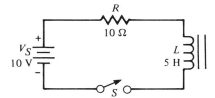

Figure 7–4   Circuit containing an inductor and a resistor.

As indicated in Figure 7–5, the voltage induced across the inductor is opposing the source voltage. This is equivalent to having two equal amplitude voltage sources connected in series-opposing as shown in Figure 7–6. The net difference of potential between points *A–B* is 0 V.

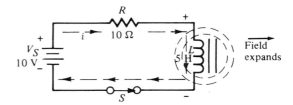

Figure 7–5 Current build-up in an inductive circuit.

Figure 7–6 Counter induced voltage opposes source voltage.

With this condition existing, the current soon begins to decrease toward zero. This weakens the magnetic field about the inductor which causes the counter-induced voltage to decrease. This, in turn, allows current flow to increase which again increases the amplitude of the counter-induced voltage. The current intensity again becomes less, which weakens the magnetic flux field about the magnet. This process continues with the current gradually increasing. After awhile it will reach its full, or steady-state, value of 1 A as shown in Figure 7–7. At that time the magnetic field about the inductor is stationary as illustrated in Figure 7–8. Since the field is not moving, no voltage is induced across the inductor. The presence of the inductor in the circuit has prevented the current flowing in the circuit to increase from 0 to 1 A instantaneously as it would have if only the resistor was in the circuit.

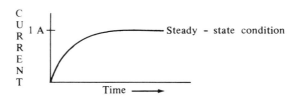

Figure 7–7 Current build-up in a circuit containing inductance.

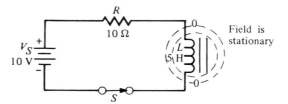

Figure 7–8 Steady-state conditions in a circuit containing inductance.

If the switch is opened after the circuit has been in operation for a period of time, the current ceases to flow. This causes the magnetic flux field about the inductor to collapse. The collapsing field causes a voltage to be induced across the inductor having a polarity which is series-aiding the source voltage, as depicted in Figure 7–9. This self-induced voltage is called a counter-counter electromotive force (CCEMF) and attempts to keep current flowing at its former intensity. Observe that the polarity of this self-induced voltage is opposite that created when the field was expanding. As mentioned in the last chapter, the polarity of the voltage induced across a conductor depends upon the direction in which the magnetic lines of force are cut. Lenz's law verifies this. In each case the polarity of the induced voltage opposed the voltage, or force, which caused the change in current. The voltage source caused the current to change from 0 to 1 A when the switch was closed and the open switch caused the current to decrease from 1 A back to 0 A.

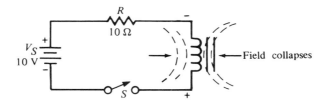

Figure 7–9 Collapsing field causes a counter-counter EMF to be developed across an inductor.

The waveforms representing the voltage dropped across the resistor, self-induced voltage developed across the inductor, and the circuit current appear in Figure 7–10. Notice that the voltage dropped across the resistor follows the current flowing through it. Initially, current tried to rise from 0 to 1 A. This change in current created a self-induced voltage across the inductor which prevented the current flowing through, and the voltage across, the resistor from increasing rapidly. As the current gradually increased, the voltage across the resistor increased. At the same time the voltage induced across the inductor decreased until it was 0 when the current reached its steady-state value of 1 A. It remained at 0 until the switch was opened, at which time a voltage having an opposite polarity was developed. The current did not immediately decrease to 0. Instead, it decreased gradually due to the inductor releasing energy stored in its magnetic field. The inductor accepted energy from the source when the circuit was first energized. The energy was stored in the mag-

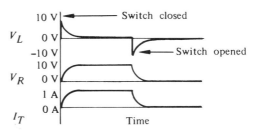

Figure 7–10 Waveforms for a circuit containing inductance and resistance and connected to a DC source.

netic field during the time that the current remained constant. When the switch was opened and the current decreased, the energy was released back to the circuit.

The inductor will have little, if any, value if it is placed in a circuit just to delay a change in current when a switch is opened or closed. Inductors are placed in DC circuits to oppose changes in current which sometimes occur when the source voltage or load resistance varies for short periods of time.

7-1.4 The L/R Time Constant. The graph of current versus time that appears in Figure 7–7 is shown again in Figure 7–11 along with the circuit that produced it. When the switch was closed at time t_0, it took the time interval from t_0 to t_1 for the current to reach its full value. This time interval is proportional to the ratio of inductance to the circuit resistance and is called the L/R time constant. The graph shown in Figure 7–12 is called a universal time constant curve and depicts the time required for the current to reach a steady-state value for a circuit containing inductance and resistance. The horizontal axis represents time, with the units given in time constants. Notice that at the end of one time constant, the

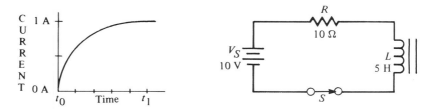

Figure 7–11 Current build-up in a circuit containing resistance and inductance.

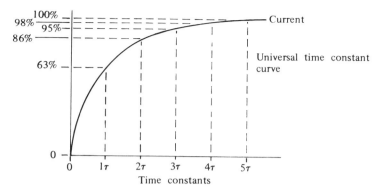

Figure 7–12   Universal time constant curve.

current has reached 63 percent of the full-scale value. At the end of the second time constant the current has increased to 63 percent of the remaining value or about 86 percent of its final value. Between the second and third time constants the current rises to 63 percent of the remaining value or is approximately 95 percent of its full-scale value. At the end of the fourth time constant the current has increased an additional 63 percent of the remaining value, which means that the current is now about 98 percent of its steady-state value. At the end of the fifth time constant the current has again increased 63 percent of the remaining value and has reached its final value. It takes five time constants for the current to approach its steady-state value in a circuit containing inductance and resistance. This applies to all resistive-inductive circuits no matter what values of resistance and inductance are used.

One time constant (TC) is the time required for the current to reach 63 percent of its steady-state value. Equation (7–2) is used to calculate this time.

$$1 \text{ TC } (\tau) = \frac{L}{R} \quad \text{in seconds} \qquad\qquad (7\text{–}2)$$

The larger the resistance value, the shorter the time required for the current to reach its full value. The Greek letter tau (τ) is used as the symbol for the time constant function. Example 7–1 serves to illustrate how the time constant formula is used to determine the time required for the current to rise in a resistive-inductive circuit.

Example 7–1 Applications of the *L/R* time constant formula

Problem

For the circuit appearing in Figure 7–13, calculate the following:
a. the time required for the current to reach 63 percent of its full value;
b. the value of the current at the end of one time constant;
c. the value of the current at the end of three time constants; and
d. the time required for the current to reach full value.

Solution

a. $1_\tau = \dfrac{L}{R} = \dfrac{7\ \text{H}}{5000\ \Omega} = 0.0014\ \text{s}$

b. $I_{\text{steady state}} = \dfrac{V_S}{R_L} = \dfrac{15\ \text{V}}{5000\ \Omega} = 0.003\ \text{A}$

 $I \text{ at } 1_\tau = (0.63)(0.003\ \text{A}) = 0.00189\ \text{A}$

c. $I \text{ at } 3_\tau = (0.95)(0.003\ \text{A}) = 0.00285\ \text{A}$

d. $5_\tau = (_\tau)(5) = (0.0014\ \text{s})(5) = 0.007\ \text{s}$

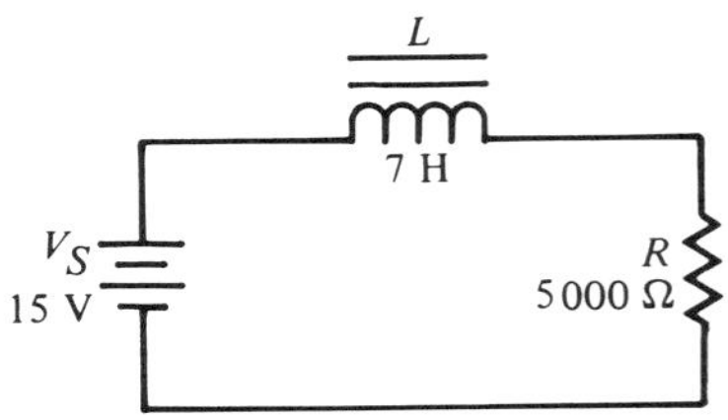

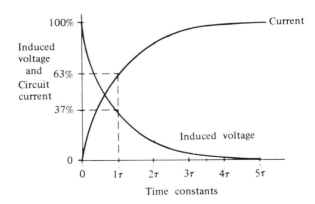

Figure 7–13

As the current rises, the voltage induced across the inductor decreases are shown in Figure 7–14. When the circuit is initially energized, the current attempts to rise from 0 to its steady-state value. This rapid change in current creates an expanding magnetic flux field about the inductor which causes a rather high counter EMF to be self-induced across the device. As time progresses and the rise in current becomes less pronounced, the voltage induced across the inductor begins to decrease. At the end of one time constant the voltage has decreased to approximately

Figure 7–14 Relationship between the current flowing through and the voltage induced across an inductor.

37 percent of its initial value. By the time that the current has reached its steady-state value, at the end of the fifth time constant, the voltage has decreased to 0.

7-1.5 The Energy Stored in an Inductor.

An inductor is an energy-storing device. It takes energy from the source during the time that the circuit is first energized and the current is rising to its steady-state value. The energy is stored in the magnetic field about the inductor after the current has reached its steady value and remains there until something causes the current to decrease, such as a switch being opened or the source voltage decreasing in amplitude. The magnetic field collapses and the energy, or work, stored by the field is released to the circuit. The amount of energy stored is a function of both the size of the inductor and the amount of current flowing through it, as indicated by Equation (7–3).

$$W_L = \frac{LI^2}{2} \quad \text{in joules} \tag{7–3}$$

For the circuit appearing in Example 7–2 the energy stored is 6 J.

Example 7–2   Application of the energy-storing formula

Problem
Calculate the energy stored by the inductor appearing in the circuit of Figure 7–15.

Solution

$$W_L = \frac{LI^2}{2} = \frac{(3 \text{ H})(2 \text{ A})^2}{2} = \frac{12}{2} = 6 \text{ J}$$

$$I = \frac{V_S}{R} = \frac{10 \text{ V}}{5 \text{ Ω}} = 2 \text{ A}$$

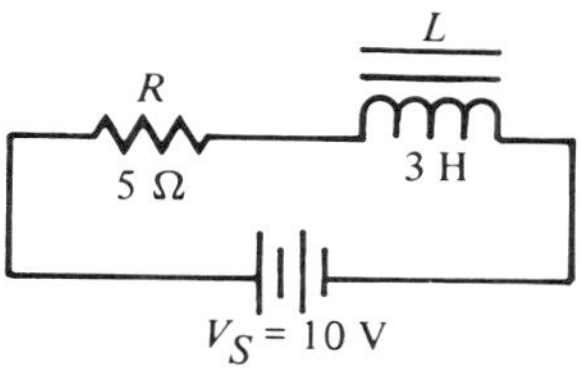

Figure 7–15

The energy stored by an inductor is often released in the form of an arc or spark. This often happens when the current suddenly drops to 0 by opening a switch. The L/R time constant is very short for such a condition causing a rather high voltage to be induced across the inductor. If you've ever pulled a power cord out of a receptacle without turning a motor-driven appliance off first, you have no doubt noticed this. The energy stored in the magnetic field about the armature and field windings is released in the form of an arc emitted from the power cord plug.

The action of an inductor opposing changes in current can be described as a choking effect. Because of this, inductors are sometimes referred to as chokes. Air-core inductors which are used in high frequency circuits are often called RFCs (radio frequency chokes).

7-1.6 Series-connected Inductors.

Inductors can be connected in series with each other just as resistors and other devices can, as illustrated in Figure 7–16. If the two inductors are located physically close to one another, the moving magnetic field about each inductor will cause a voltage to be induced across its adjacent inductor in addition to that induced across itself. The voltage induced across adjacent inductors is caused by mutual inductance. As shown in Figure 7–17, some of the magnetic flux lines created by inductor L_1 cut L_2 and vice versa. This condition is called mutual coupling. For the circuit appearing in Figure 7–17, four induced voltages are developed. These include two self-induced voltages developed across L_1 and L_2, a mutually induced voltage developed across L_1 caused by L_2, and a mutually induced voltage developed across L_2 caused by L_1.

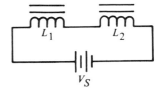

Figure 7–16   Circuit containing two series-connected inductors.

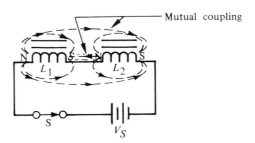

Figure 7–17   Mutual coupling between adjacent inductors.

The phenomenon of mutual coupling causing voltages to be induced across adjacent inductors is called mutual inductance (L_M). Mutual inductance is measured in henries just as inductance is. Mutual inductance is a function of the size of the inductors and the coefficient of coupling *(k)*. The coefficient of coupling refers to the extent that flux lines cut adjacent inductors. For example, if all the magnetic lines of force about L_1 cut L_2 and vice versa, the coefficient of coupling is one. If one-half of the lines about one inductor cuts the other, and vice versa, the coefficient of coupling is 0.5. Equation (7–4) is used for calculating mutual inductance.

$$L_M = k \sqrt{L_1 L_2} \quad \text{in henries} \tag{7–4}$$

For the circuit appearing in Figure 7–17, the mutual inductance is 2.9 H as illustrated Example 7–3.

Example 7–3   Calculating mutual inductance

Problem
For the circuit shown in Figure 7–17, $L_1 = 5$ H, $L_2 = 3$ H, and $k = 0.75$. Calculate the value of the mutual inductance.

Solution

$$L_M = k \sqrt{L_1 L_2}$$
$$L_M = 0.75 \sqrt{(5)(3)} = 2.9 \text{ H}$$

Inductors can be connected either in a series-aiding or a series-opposing arrangement. A circuit containing two inductors connected in a series-aiding fashion is shown in Figure 7–18. As current flows through inductors L_1 and L_2, the north poles of both inductors are located at the same end of each device.

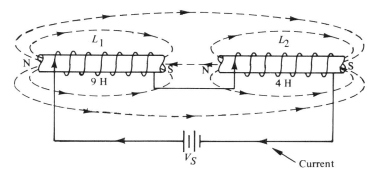

Figure 7–18   Two inductors connected series aiding.

Part of the magnetic field which leaves the north pole of each inductor enters the south pole of the other inductor. The direction of the magnetic lines of force for both inductors are in the same direction and aid one another. The total inductance for two series-aiding inductors can be determined from Equation (7–5).

$$L_T = L_1 + L_2 + 2L_M \qquad\qquad\qquad\qquad \textbf{(7–5)}$$

The total inductance for the circuit appearing in Figure 7–18 is 19 H as calculated in Example 7–4.

Example 7–4   Calculations for determining total inductance

Problem
For the circuit shown in Figure 7–18, calculate the total inductance. The coefficient of coupling is 0.5.

Solution

$L_T = L_1 + L_2 + 2L_M$
$L_M = k \sqrt{(L_1)(L_2)} = (0.5)(6) = 3 \text{ H}$
$L_T = 9 + 4 + 6 = 19 \text{ H}$

If L_2 in Figure 7–18 is turned around, the two inductors are connected series opposing as illustrated in Figure 7–19.

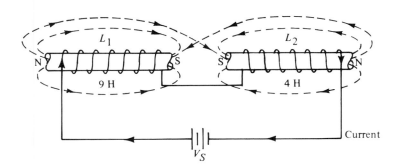

Figure 7–19   Two inductors connected series opposing.

The polarity of the magnetic flux lines oppose each other in this type of arrangement. Equation (7–6) is used for computing the total inductance of two inductors connected in this fashion.

$$L_T = L_1 + L_2 - 2L_M \qquad\qquad\qquad\qquad \textbf{(7–6)}$$

As indicated in Example 7–5, the total inductance is 7 H for the circuit shown in Figure 7–19. This is a substantial reduction in inductance for the same inductors when connected in a series-aiding arrangement. When connecting inductors together in series, care must be taken to ensure that they are connected with the proper polarity. Dot markings are often used to indicate polarity. When the dots are located on the same end of the inductor symbol as shown in Figure 7–20(a), the devices are connected series aiding. When the dots appear at opposite ends of the symbol as indicated in Figure 7–20(b), the inductors are connected in a series-opposing configuration.

Example 7–5 Calculations for determining total inductance for two series-opposing inductors

Problem
Compute the total inductance for the circuit appearing in Figure 7–19.

Solution
$L_T = L_1 + L_2 - 2L_M$

$L_T = 9 + 4 - 6 = 7$ H

(a)   (b)

Figure 7–20 Dot marking method to indicate inductor polarity: (a) inductors connected series aiding; (b) inductors connected series opposing.

Sometimes it is desirable that no mutual coupling be allowed to exist between series-connected inductors which are located close together. They can be placed perpendicular to each other or enclosed in metal cases. When placed perpendicularly, the magnetic flux lines will be moving parallel with the coils forming the adjacent inductor. Enclosing an inductor in a metal case and grounding the case prevents the magnetic field about the inductor from moving beyond the case and inducing an unwanted voltage across a nearby inductor. It also prevents unwanted voltages from being induced across the inductor from other nearby inductors. The total inductance for series-connected inductors where no mutual coupling exists can be determined from Equation (7–7).

$$L_T = L_1 + L_2 + L_3 + \cdots + L_N$$
where N equals
the number of inductors   (7–7)

7-1.7 **Parallel-connected Inductors.** Inductors can also be connected in parallel with each other, as indicated in Figure 7–21. Equations (7–8) and (7–9) are used to determine the total equivalent inductance where no mutual coupling exists. Notice that the equations for both series and parallel inductors are in the same format as those for series- and parallel-connected resistors providing that no mutual coupling exists between the inductors.

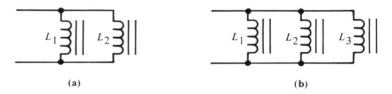

(a)   (b)

Figure 7–21 Inductors connected in parallel: (a) two inductors; (b) three inductors.

$$L_T = \frac{(L_1)(L_2)}{L_1 + L_2}$$ (7–8)

for two parallel-connected inductors

$$\frac{1}{L_T} = \frac{1}{L_1} + \frac{1}{L_2} + \frac{1}{L_3} + \cdots + \frac{1}{L_N}$$ (7–9)

for three or more series-connected inductors

7-2 INDUCTORS AND AC CIRCUITS

7-2.1 **Introduction.** Inductors are used in both DC and AC circuits. The discussion so far has been centered around inductors used in DC circuits. Their major application in DC circuits is to oppose changes in current which may occur due to variations in the source voltage or load resistance.

7-2.2 **Inductive Reactance.** In an AC circuit such as that shown in Figure 7–22, the current flowing through the inductor is continually changing. This causes the magnetic field about the inductor to be con-

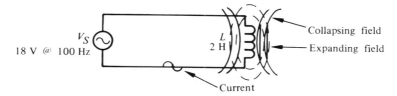

Figure 7–22   Inductor connected to an AC source.

stantly expanding and collapsing. This, in turn, causes a continuously changing voltage to be induced across the inductor, which opposes the source voltage. The opposing voltage reduces the intensity of the current flowing through the circuit and acts like an AC resistance. This "resistance" is called inductive reactance and is given the symbol X_L. Inductive reactance is a function of both the frequency of the current flowing through the inductor and size of the inductor, as indicated by Equation (7–10).

$$X_L = 2\pi f L \quad \text{in ohms}$$

(7–10)

The unit of measurement is the ohm just as it is for resistance. As the equation indicates, frequency and inductance are both directly proportional to inductive reactance. The greater either of these values, the larger the resulting inductive reactance. The current flowing in the circuit appearing in Figure 7–22 is limited in intensity only by the inductive reactance value. As indicated in Example 7–6, Ohm's law is used to compute the circuit current and voltage just as it is used for resistors. Kirchhoff's law also applies to such a circuit. The slight error between the voltage dropped across the inductor and the source voltage occurred when the inductive reactance was computed. If a more exact value for pi was used, instead of the 3.14 value, the resulting current would have been slightly higher, causing the inductor voltage to more closely approach the source potential. For most applications, a pi value of 3.14 is sufficient.

As mentioned previously, inductive reactance is directly related to frequency. If the source frequency is increased, inductive reactance increases, which in turn reduces the intensity of the circuit current. When the source frequency is decreased, inductive reactance decreases, which causes the current flow to increase. If, in the circuit shown in Figure 7–22, the source frequency is increased from 100 to 1000 Hz, the reactance increases from 1256 to 12,560 Ω as shown in Example 7–7. This causes the

Example 7–6   Ohm's law applied to an inductive circuit

Problem
For the circuit shown in Figure 7–22, calculate the value of the inductive reactance, the current flowing through the circuit, and the voltage induced across the inductor.

Solution
$$X_L = 2\pi \, fL = (2)(3.14) \, (100) \, (2) = 1256 \ \Omega$$

$$I_T = \frac{V_S}{X_L} = \frac{18 \text{ V}}{1256 \ \Omega} = 0.0143 \text{ A} = 14.3 \text{ mA}$$

$$V_L = (I_T)(X_L) = (0.0143 \text{ A}) \, (1256 \ \Omega) = 17.96 \text{ V}$$

Example 7–7   Effect of frequency on inductive reactance and current

Problem
For the circuit appearing in Figure 7–22, compute the inductive reactance and current flow if
a. the source frequency is increased to 1000 Hz
b. the source frequency is decreased to 10 Hz

Solution
a. $X_L = 2\pi fL = (2)(3.14)(1000)(2) = 12{,}560 \ \Omega$

$$I_T = \frac{V_S}{X_L} = \frac{18 \text{ V}}{12{,}560 \ \Omega} = 0.00143 \text{ A} = 1.43 \text{ mA}$$

b. $X_L = 2\pi fL = (2)(3.14)(10)(2) = 125.6 \ \Omega$

$$I_T = \frac{V_S}{X_L} = \frac{18 \text{ V}}{125.6 \ \Omega} = 0.143 \text{ A} = 143 \text{ mA}$$

current to decrease to 0.00143 A. On the other hand, if the frequency is decreased from 100 to 10 Hz, the reactance decreases to 125.6 Ω. This causes the current to increase to 0.143 A as indicated in Example 7–7.

One should realize that an inductor connected to a DC source has no reactance. This is because the frequency of a DC source is 0 Hz.

7-2.3 Voltage-Current Relationship in an Inductive Circuit.   When an inductor is connected to an AC source, the voltage induced across the inductor leads the current flowing through it by 90°, as illustrated in Figure 7–23. This is caused by the self-induced voltage across the inductor being maximum when the current intensity increases from zero to its peak value. This is shown in vector format in Figure 7–24.

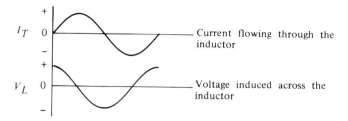

Figure 7–23   Voltage-current relationship in an inductive circuit.

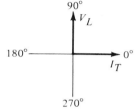

Figure 7–24   Vector representation of the *V-I* relationship
in an inductive circuit.

7-2.4 Inductor Q.   The inductors encountered thus far have been
"ideal" inductors. That is, they have had no resistance. An actual inductor does have resistance, however. An inductor is constructed by wrapping wire around a core. The resistance of the wire represents a resistance (R), which is in series with the inductance, as shown in Figure
7–25. Depending upon the type and size of the inductor, this resistance
may range from a low of a few ohms to a high of several hundred ohms.

Inductor resistance is usually an undesired phenomenon as it represents a power loss. An ideal inductor stores energy but does not consume it. An actual inductor, on the other hand, does dissipate some energy because of its resistance. A quantity used to judge the quality of an
inductor is the quality factor whose symbol is Q. Inductor quality factor
is the ratio of the reactance of the inductor, at a particular frequency, to
its DC series resistance. As indicated in Equation (7–11), Q is unitless

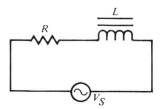

Figure 7–25   Inductor and its DC series resistance.

since the ohms unit appears in both the numerator and denominator of the equation.

$$Q = \frac{X_L}{R} \quad \text{(in ohms)} \tag{7-11}$$

Inductors having a Q of less than 10 are called low-Q inductors. Inductors having a Q of 10 or above are called high-Q inductors. R is that value of resistance that an ohmmeter would measure if placed across the inductor. It is often referred to as a DC resistance because it remains the same, regardless of the frequency of the current flowing through the inductor. Inductive reactance, on the other hand, cannot be measured with an ohmmeter and is frequency dependent. The inductor appearing in Example 7–8 has a Q of 157 and is considered to have a high Q when connected to a 5000-Hz source.

Example 7–8 Calculating inductor Q

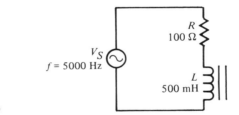

Figure 7–26

Problem
Determine the Q of the inductor shown in Figure 7–26.

Solution

$$Q = \frac{X_L}{R} = \frac{15{,}700 \ \Omega}{100 \ \Omega} = 157$$

$$X_L = 2\pi f L = (2)(3.14)(5000)(0.5) = 15{,}700 \ \Omega$$

7-2.5 Applications of Inductors. As previously mentioned, inductors are used in DC circuits to oppose changes in current. In AC circuits, they are primarily used as filters for a variety of applications. As a filter,

an inductor will pass DC and low-frequency AC currents but will attenuate higher frequency currents. The only effect an inductor has in a DC
circuit, under steady-state conditions, is its low DC resistance. The device
acts like a higher value resistor in an AC circuit. This "AC resistance" is
called reactance and is frequency dependent.

7-3 TRANSFORMERS

7-3.1 Physical Construction. Transformers have many applications in electrical and electronic circuits. In general, they are used to increase or decrease the amplitude of AC voltage, increase or decrease the
current capacity of a circuit, and match source and load resistances for
maximum power transfer. As illustrated in Figure 7–27, they are manufactured in a variety of sizes.

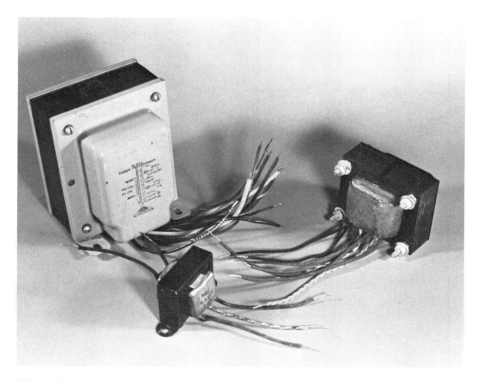

Figure 7–27   Some representative types of transformers.

The schematic symbol of a transformer appears in Figure 7–28. Physically the device consists of two inductors wound on the same core. Energy is transferred from one inductor to the other by mutual inductance. As depicted in Figure 7–29, the windings are placed on a common core whose shape is such that the coefficient of coupling between the two windings is one. One winding of the transformer is usually connected to an AC voltage source, as shown in Figure 7–30. This winding is called the primary winding. The other winding is called the secondary winding and is connected to a circuit which can be considered to be a load.

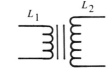

Figure 7–28 Schematic symbol for a basic transformer.

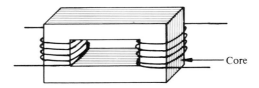

Figure 7–29 Physical construction of a transformer.

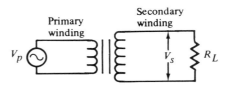

Figure 7–30 Circuit connections for a basic transformer.

7-3.2 Principles of Operation.   When the primary winding is connected to an AC source, the changing current flowing through the winding produces a magnetic field that is continually expanding and collapsing. This causes a voltage to be induced across the secondary winding. The amplitude of the induced voltage depends upon the turns ratio between the primary and secondary windings. If the secondary winding has more turns than the primary winding, the secondary voltage will be greater than the primary voltage and the transformer is called a voltage step-up transformer. Conversely, if the secondary winding has fewer turns than the primary winding, the secondary voltage is less than the primary voltage. This is called a voltage step-down transformer.

The turns ratio can be found by using Equation (7–12).

$$\text{Turns ratio} = a = \frac{N_p}{N_s} = \frac{V_p}{V_s} \qquad\qquad (7\text{–}12)$$

Notice that the symbol for turns ratio is the letter a. Turns ratio is unitless, as either the number of turns or voltage appear in both the numerator and denominator of the equation. For the circuit shown in Figure 7–31, the turns ratio is 1:6, or 0.167. The secondary voltage can be computed by using Equation (7–13).

Figure 7–31   Relationship between primary and secondary voltage.

$$V_s = \frac{V_p}{a} \qquad\qquad (7\text{–}13)$$

As indicated, the secondary voltage is the quotient of the primary voltage and turns ratio. For the circuit appearing in Example 7–9, the secondary voltage is 16.7 V.

Example 7–9   Calculating transformer secondary voltage

Problem
For the circuit shown in Figure 7–32, compute the secondary voltage.

Solution

$$V_s = \frac{V_p}{a} = \frac{100 \text{ V}}{6} = 16.67 \text{ V}$$

$$a = \frac{N_p}{N_s} = \frac{300}{50} = 6:1 = 6$$

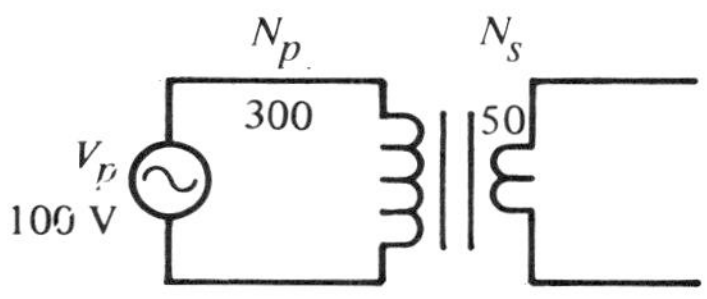

Figure 7–32

The power transfer between the primary and secondary circuits is constant. This means that if the primary voltage is 100 V and the current is 1 A, 100 W of power are available in the primary circuit. The maximum power which can be transferred from the primary circuit to the secondary circuit is 100 W. If a voltage step-up transformer is being used, the current available to the load in the secondary circuit is less than 1 A. Thus a voltage step-up transformer is automatically a current step-down transformer. The current available to the secondary circuit can be found by using Equation (7–14).

$$I_s = (I_p)\ (a)\quad \text{in amperes}\tag{7–14}$$

In the circuit appearing in Example 7–10, the current available to the secondary circuit is 0.2 A. The actual secondary current is determined by the load connected to the secondary winding. The load resistance must not be such that it allows a current greater than 0.2 A of current to flow. Since power is the product of voltage and current, if the secondary current exceeds 0.2 A, the secondary voltage will decrease in order to maintain a secondary power of 200 W. The transformer is overloaded when this occurs.

Example 7–10   Calculating available secondary current

Problem
Calculate the available secondary current for the circuit shown in Figure 7–33.

Solution

$$I_s = (I_p)(a) = (2\ \text{A})(0.1) = 0.2\ \text{A}$$

$$a = \frac{N_p}{N_s} = \frac{100}{1000} = 1:10 = 0.1$$

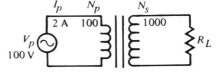

Figure 7–33

7-3.3 Resistance Matching.   Energy is transferred from the primary circuit to the secondary circuit by mutual induction. If a load is connected to the secondary winding, the resulting current flowing in the secondary circuit will create a magnetic field about the secondary winding, which induces a voltage across the primary winding. This causes the primary current to change in the same fashion that a change in resistance in the primary circuit causes the primary current to change. This has the effect of transferring the secondary resistance back into the primary circuit if the proper turns ratio is used. A transformer is often used to match the resistance of a load (secondary circuit) to that of the source (primary circuit) to obtain maximum power transfer from the source to a load. Equation (7–15) is used to determine the required turns ratio to match the load resistance.

$$a = \sqrt{\frac{\text{Source resistance}}{\text{Load resistance}}} = \sqrt{\frac{R_S}{R_L}} \qquad (7\text{–}15)$$

For the circuit appearing in Example 7–11, the required turns ratio is 19.36:1, which means that for every 19.36 turns of the primary winding, there is one secondary winding.

Example 7–11   Calculating the turns ratio required to match the load resistance with the source resistance

Problem
For the circuit shown in Figure 7–34, compute the transformer turns ratio required to match the load resistance with the source resistance.

Solution

$$a = \sqrt{\frac{R_S}{R_L}} = \sqrt{\frac{1500}{4}} = 19.36 : 1 = 19.36$$

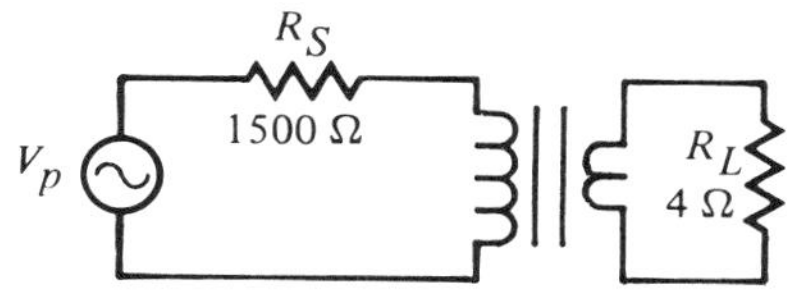

Figure 7–34

DC voltage cannot be directly applied to the primary winding of a transformer. For a DC source, the magnetic field about the primary is stationary and a voltage cannot be induced across the secondary winding. In addition, there is no inductive reactance in the primary circuit to help limit primary current intensity. Primary current will be limited only by the DC resistance of the primary winding and any other resistance which may be in the circuit. The excessive current flowing through the primary winding may burn the winding out in a very short period of time. DC voltage can be applied to a transformer primary if it is broken, or "chopped" up. This is the purpose of the ignition points in the older, nonelectronic automobile ignitions.

Some transformers may have more than one secondary or primary winding. Some examples of various winding schemes appear in Figure 7–

35. The polarity between the primary and secondary voltages is usually 180°. Some transformers are manufactured which have no phase inversion, however. Dot markings apply for transformers just as they do for inductors where polarity is important.

Notice that one of the secondary windings for the transformer appearing in Figure 7–35(c) has a center tap (CT). The voltages between the center tap and either end of the secondary winding are equal. A 180° phase shift exists across the two secondary winding connections. Transformers having a center-tapped secondary are often used where two equal amplitude voltages which are 180° out of phase are required.

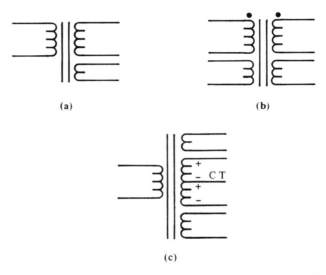

Figure 7–35   Assorted transformer winding schemes: (a) two secondary windings; (b) two primary and two secondary windings; (c) three secondary windings.

SUMMARY

1. Inductance is that property of an electric circuit which stores energy in an electromagnetic field and opposes a change in current.
2. An inductor is a device which is used to give a circuit a particular amount of inductance.
3. An inductor is formed by wrapping wire around a core.
4. There are two general kinds of inductors, iron-core and air-core.
5. The unit of measurement for inductance is the henry.
6. Iron-core inductors range in value from a low of a few hundred millihenries to a high of about 15 H. Air-core inductors range in value from a low of a few microhenries to a high of a few hundred millihenries.

7. The inductance value of an inductor is directly proportional to the number of turns squared, core permeability, and cross-sectional area of the core. It is inversely proportional to the length of the core.

8. An inductor opposes changes in the current flowing through it by electromagnetic induction. The changing current produces a moving magnetic field which induces a voltage across the inductor's windings. The polarity of the induced voltage either aids or opposes the source so that the intensity of the current flowing through the inductor remains constant.

9. Inductors are used in both DC and AC circuits. The L/R time constant is important in DC circuits. It identifies the time required for the current to its full, or steady-state, value.

10. One L/R time constant is the time required for the current to reach 63 percent of its full value. Five time constants are required for the current to finally approach its full value.

11. The energy stored by an inductor can be determined by using the equation $W_L = LI^2/2$ and is measured in joules.

12. Inductors, like resistors, can be connected in series. When mutual coupling exists, and two inductors are connected series aiding, the total inductance is determined by the equation $L_T = L_1 + L_2 + 2L_M$.

13. If two inductors are connected in a series-opposing configuration, $L_T = L_1 + L_2 - 2L_M$.

14. When inductors are connected in series with no mutual coupling present, the total inductance is the sum of the individual inductance values.

15. Inductors may also be connected in parallel with one another. The total, or equivalent, inductance for two parallel-connected inductors is given by the equation $L_T = (L_1)(L_2)/(L_1 + L_2)$. For three or more inductors, $1/L_T, = 1/L_1 + 1/L_2 + 1/L_3$. Both equations assume no mutual coupling between the inductors.

16. An inductor connected to an AC source has a voltage induced across it which continuously opposes the source voltage. This creates an AC "resistance" called inductive reactance. The equation for determining inductive reactance is $X_L = 2\pi f L$.

17. In an AC circuit containing inductance, the voltage induced across the inductor leads the current flowing through it by 90°.

18. An inductor has a series resistance (R) associated with it. This represents the resistance of the wire wrapped around the core. The resistance represents an energy loss, and even though it cannot be avoided, it should be kept to a minimum. The figure of merit, or quality factor (Q), of an inductor is the ratio of X_L to R ($Q = X_L/R$). Inductors having a Q which is less than 10 are called low-Q inductors. Devices having Q values of 10 or greater are called high-Q inductors.

19. Inductors are sometimes called chokes. An inductor operating in a high frequency circuit is often called a radio frequency choke (RFC).

20. Transformers are formed by mounting two inductors on the same core. The inductor which is connected to a source is called the primary winding and the inductor connected to a load is called the secondary winding.

21. Transformers are used to step voltage up or down, step current capacity up or down, or match a load resistance to a source resistance.

22. A voltage step-down transformer is automatically a current step-up transformer and vice versa.
23. The turns ratio (*a*) of a transformer may be determined by dividing the primary voltage by the secondary voltage or by dividing the number of turns forming the primary winding by the number of turns forming the secondary winding.
24. The secondary voltage of a transformer can be computed by dividing the primary voltage by the turns ratio.
25. The resistance of a load can be matched to the resistance of a source by using a transformer which has a particular turns ratio. The turns ratio can be determined by the equation $a = \sqrt{R_S/R_L}$.

PRACTICE EXERCISES

1. Define the term *inductance* and identify its symbol and its unit of measurement.
2. Describe how an inductor opposes a change in current.
3. A DC circuit contains a 25-mH inductor and a 10,000-Ω resistor connected in series with each other. The devices are connected to a 10-V battery. Calculate the time required for the current to approach its steady-state value. What is the intensity of the steady-state current?
4. Define the term *inductive reactance.*
5. A 0.03-H choke is connected to an AC source which has an rms value of 50 mV and a frequency of 1.6 MHz. Compute the inductive reactance of the inductor.
6. For the circuit described in exercise 5, compute the value of the current flowing in the circuit.
7. What is the phase relationship between the current flowing through, and the voltage induced across, an inductor?
8. Describe the difference between self-inductance and mutual inductance.
9. A 30-mH choke is connected in series aiding with a 50-mH choke. If the coefficient of coupling is 0.8, compute the value of the total inductance.
10. An 8-H inductor is connected in parallel with a 2-H inductor. Determine the total inductance for the parallel combination.
11. A transformer has 200 primary turns and 600 secondary turns. If the primary is connected to a 50-V rms source, what is the secondary voltage?
12. A 7-H inductor and a 3-H inductor are connected in a series-opposing configuration. If the coefficient of coupling is 0.6, calculate the total inductance of the circuit.
13. An inductor is connected to an AC source which has a frequency of 3000 Hz. If 7.5 V is induced across the inductor and the current flowing through the circuit is 35 mA, what is the inductance value of the device?
14. A transformer is to be used to match a 5500-Ω source resistance to a 250-Ω load resistance. What is the turns ratio requirement?
15. An inductor having a value of 300 μH is connected to a 3-V AC source which has a frequency of 1.5 MHz. If the choke has a series DC resistance of 510 Ω, what is its *Q?*

16. A transformer has a turns ratio of 15. If the primary voltage is 117 V and the primary current is 600 mA, what is the current available in the secondary circuit?
17. What is an RFC?
18. Why is it sometimes important to match the resistance of a load to that of a source?
19. Four inductors are connected in parallel with one another. No mutual coupling exists between the devices. If the values of the inductors are 3, 7, 10, and 8 H, what is the total inductance of the network?
20. Why are inductors sometimes mounted in metal enclosures?
21. A 7-H choke has 350 mA of current flowing through it. If the DC series resistance is 27 Ω, how much energy is the device storing?
22. Why can't DC voltage be directly applied to the primary of a transformer?

ANSWERS TO PRACTICE EXERCISES

1. Inductance is that property of a circuit which opposes a change in current and which stores energy in an electromagnetic field. Its symbol is the letter L and its unit of measurement is the henry.
2. An inductor opposes a change in current by producing a self-induced voltage across itself which either aids or opposes the source voltage.
3. $1\tau = L/R = 0.025$ H/10,000 $\Omega = 2.5$ μs. Since it takes five time constants for the current to approach full value, then (5) $(\tau) = (5)(2.5$ μs$) = 12.5$ μs, $I = V/R = 10$ V/10,000 $\Omega = 0.001$A.
4. Inductive reactance (X_L) is the opposition to the flow of current an inductor offers to an AC source.
5. $X_L = 2\pi fL = (2)(3.14)(1,600,000)(0.03) = 301,440$ Ω.
6. $I_t = V_s/X_L = 0.05$ V/301,440 $\Omega = 0.166$ μA.
7. The voltage induced across an inductor leads the current flowing through it by 90°.
8. Self-inductance is that property of an inductor which causes a voltage to be induced across itself whenever a changing current flows through it. Mutual inductance is that phenomenon associated with an inductor which causes a voltage to be induced across an inductor whenever a moving magnetic field produced by another inductor passes through it.
9. $L_T = L_1 + L_2 + 2L_M = 30 + 50 + 61.96 = 141.96$ mH
   $L_M = k\sqrt{L_1 L_2} = 0.8\sqrt{(0.03)(0.05)} = 0.03098$ H $= 30.98$ mH
10. $L_T = (L_1)(L_2)/L_1 + L_2 = (8)(2)/8 + 2 = 1.6$ H
11. $V_s = \dfrac{V_p}{a} = \dfrac{50 \text{ V}}{0.333} = 150.15$ V

    $a = \dfrac{N_p}{N_s} = \dfrac{200}{600} = 1:3 = 0.333$
12. $L_T = L_1 + L_2 - 2L_M = 7 + 3 - 5.5 = 4.5$ H
    $L_M = k\sqrt{L_1 L_2} = 0.6\sqrt{(3)(7)} = 2.75$ H

13. $X_L = 2\pi fL; \quad L = \dfrac{X_L}{2\pi f}; \quad X_L = \dfrac{V_L}{I_T}$

$X_L = \dfrac{7.5 \text{ V}}{0.035 \, a} = 214.29 \ \Omega; \quad L = \dfrac{214.29 \ \Omega}{(2)(3.14)(3000)} = 11.37 \text{ mH}$

14. $a = \sqrt{\dfrac{R_S}{R_L}} = \sqrt{\dfrac{5500}{250}} = 4.69, \text{ or } a = 4.69:1$

15. $Q = X_L/R_S = 2826/510 \ \Omega = 5.54$

$X_L = 2\pi fL = (2)(3.14)(3 \times 10^{-4})(1.5 \times 10^6) = 2826 \ \Omega$

16. $I_s = (I_p)(a) = (0.6 \text{ A})(15) = 9 \text{ A}$

17. An RFC is an air-core inductor used in a high-frequency circuit.

18. It is necessary to match the load resistance with the source resistance when maximum power transfer from the source (primary circuit) to the load (secondary circuit) is desired.

19. $\dfrac{1}{L_T} = \dfrac{1}{L_1} + \dfrac{1}{L_2} + \dfrac{1}{L_3} + \dfrac{1}{L_4} = \dfrac{1}{3} + \dfrac{1}{7} + \dfrac{1}{10} + \dfrac{1}{8}$

$\dfrac{1}{L_T} = 0.333 + 0.143 + 0.1 + 0.125 = 0.701; \quad L_T = \dfrac{1}{0.701} = 1.43 \text{ H}$

20. An inductor is sometimes mounted in a metal enclosure, or case, to prevent the magnetic field from leaving the inductor and to keep unwanted magnetic fields away from it.

21. $W_L = \dfrac{LI^2}{2} = \dfrac{(7)(0.1225)}{2} = 0.429 \text{ J}$

22. DC voltage cannot be directly connected to the primary winding of a transformer because the magnetic field about the primary is stationary and cannot cause a voltage to be induced across the secondary winding. In addition, there is no reactance present in the primary circuit, and excessive current may flow which may ruin the transformer.

CHAPTER EXAMINATION

1. A 4-H inductor and an 8-H inductor are connected in parallel. Neglecting any mutual coupling between the devices, the total inductance is _____ H.

    a. 1   **c.** 0.437
    b. 12   **d.** 2.667

2. If the two inductors identified in question 1 are connected in a series-aiding arrangement and L_M is zero, then L_T is equal to _____ H.

    a. 6   **c.** 24
    b. 12   **d.** 2.667

3. If the two inductors identified in question 2 have a mutual inductance of 6 H, the total inductance equals _____ H.

   a. 6   c. 24
   b. 12   d. 2.667

4. A 10-V battery, 10-Ω resistor, and 1-H choke are all connected in series. What is the time required for the current to reach 63 percent of its steady-state value?

   a. 10 s   c. 0.63 s
   b. 0.1 s   d. 47.7 s

5. For the circuit described in question 4, what is the intensity of the current at the end of one time constant?

   a. 1 A   c. 0.63 A
   b. 0.37 A   d. none of the above

6. How much time is required for the current to approach its full value for the circuit identified in question 4?

   a. 5 s   c. 0.63 s
   b. 10 s   d. none of the above

7. A transformer has 20 primary turns and 400 secondary turns. Its turns ratio is

   a. 0.05   c. 40
   b. 20   d. none of the above

8. If the primary of the transformer identified in question 7 is connected to a 100-V rms source, the secondary voltage is

   a. 20 V   c. 2000 V
   b. 200 V   d. none of the above

9. If the current flowing in the primary circuit of the transformer described in question 7 is 1.25 A, the maximum current available in the secondary circuit is

   a. 10 mA   c. 62.5 mA
   b. 22.25 mA   d. none of the above

10. Two 250-μH chokes connected in series and which have no mutual coupling have a total inductance of _____ μH.

    a. 125   **c.** 500
    b. 250   **d.** 400

11. The same two inductors that are identified in question 10 are connected in parallel. Again, considering no mutual coupling, what is the total inductance?

    a. 125 μH   **c.** 500 μH
    b. 250 μH   **d.** 400 μH

12. Two chokes having 8 H of inductance each are connected in a series-opposing arrangement. If the mutual inductance between the two is 4 H, the total inductance is _____ H.

    a. 4   **c.** 16
    b. 8   **d.** 24

13. An inductor opposes a change in

    a. farads   **c.** current
    b. henries   **d.** voltage

14. To induce a voltage across an inductor, there must be a

    a. moving field   **c.** current of large value
    b. stationary field   **d.** voltage of large value

15. A 1-mH choke is connected to an AC source which has a frequency of 1 MHz and a potential of 10 V rms. What is its inductive reactance value?

    a. 1 Ω   **c.** 1935 Ω
    b. 10 Ω   **d.** 6280 Ω

16. For the circuit described in question 15, what is the current flow?

    a. 1.59 mA   **c.** 1.000 mA
    b. 5.17 mA   **d.** 10.000 A

17. The unit of measurement for inductive reactance is the

    a. ohm   **c.** hertz
    b. farad   **d.** henry

18. Three inductors are connected in parallel. Their values are 500, 250, and 100 mHs. If no mutual coupling exists between them, what is their equivalent inductance?

a. 31.25 mH   c. 850.00 mH
b. 62.50 mH   d. none of the above

19. The unit of measurement for inductance is the

    a. ohm   c. hertz
    b. farad   d. henry

20. The phase relationship between the voltage induced across an inductor and the current flowing through it is

    a. 0°   c. 90°
    b. 45°   d. 180°

21. A 2-H inductor connected to a source which has an rms value of 50 V and a frequency of 250 MHz has an inductive reactance value of

    a. 250,000 Ω   c. 314,000 Ω
    b. 251,000 Ω   d. none of the above

22. A transformer is to be used to match a 5000 Ω load resistance to a 500 Ω source resistance. The transformer must have a turns ratio of

    a. .1   c. 10
    b. 0.316   d. none of the above

8

Capacitance

OBJECTIVES

Upon completion of this chapter you should be able to do the following:

1. Define the term *capacitance*.
2. Describe the physical construction of a capacitor.
3. Discuss the physical factors which affect the capacity of a capacitor.
4. Identify the unit of measurement used for capacitance.
5. Describe the charging and discharging action of a capacitor.
6. Define the term *RC time constant*.
7. Calculate the time required to charge a capacitor.
8. Compute the total capacitance for capacitors connected in series.
9. Calculate the total capacitance for parallel connected capacitors.
10. Define the term *capacitive reactance*.
11. Calculate the value of capacitive reactance when frequency and capacitance are both known.
12. Calculate the current flowing through a circuit containing a capacitor connected to an AC sinusoidal source.
13. Identify the phase relationship between the voltage across a capacitor and the current flowing through it.
14. Identify six types of capacitors with respect to the type of dielectric used.
15. Describe what is meant by the DC working voltage of a capacitor (WVDC).
16. Describe the effect of a capacitor when connected to a DC source and to an AC source.
17. Identify two applications for capacitors.

8-1 CAPACITORS IN DC CIRCUITS

8-1.1 Introduction. Like the resistor and the inductor, the capacitor is another device frequently used in electrical and electronic circuits. Capacitance is that property of an electric circuit which stores energy in an electrostatic field and which opposes a change in voltage. Although all circuits exhibit capacitance, which is primarily caused by adjacent parallel running conductors, it is usually small enough to be ignored except in high frequency circuits. When the effect of capacitance is desired, a device called a capacitor is connected into the circuit.

The statement appearing above which was used to define capacitance is similar to that used in the previous chapter to define inductance. What inductors are to current, capacitors are to voltage. Inductors oppose a change in current. Capacitors oppose a change in voltage. Both are energy-storing devices. An inductor stores energy in an electromagnetic field whereas a capacitor stores energy in an electrostatic field.

8-1.2 Physical Construction of Capacitors. A capacitor consists of two conductors or plates separated by a dielectric as illustrated in Figure 8–1. The unit of measurement for capacitance is the farad (abbreviated F). The letter C is used to denote capacitance. The farad is a very large unit of measurement. Almost all capacitors are rated in microfarads or picofarads.

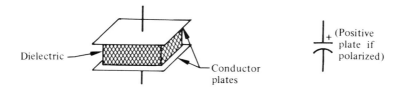

Dielectric — Conductor plates — + (Positive plate if polarized)

Figure 8–1   Physical construction of a capacitor.

The physical factors which determine the capacity of a capacitor include the cross-sectional area of the plates, the distance between the plates, and the dielectric constant of the material from which the dielectric is made. As indicated by Equation (8–1), capacity is directly related to the cross-sectional area of the plates (A) and the dielectric constant of the material (k), and is inversely proportional to the distance between the plates (d).

$$C = \frac{kA}{d} \quad \text{in farads} \qquad\qquad (8\text{–}1)$$

In the equation A is the area of one plate in square meters; k is obtained from a table similar to Table 8–1; and d is measured in meters.

Table 8–1   Dielectric Constants of Commonly Used Capacitor Dielectrics

Material	Dielectric Constant (k)
Vacuum	1
Air	1.0006
Teflon	2
Polyesters	4
Paper (wax coated)	4
Mica	5
Ceramic (porcelain)	7
Tantalum oxide	25

If a capacitor is formed from plates which have a cross-sectional area of 0.005 m² each, which are separated by a distance of 2 mm, and utilizes mica as its dielectric, it will have a capacity of 12.5 F as illustrated in Example 8–1.

Example 8–1   Calculating the capacity of a capacitor

Problem
Calculate the capacity of the capacitor described above.

Solution

$$C = \frac{(k)(A)}{d} = \frac{(5)(0.005)}{0.002} = 12.5 \text{ F}$$

8-1.3 Principles of Operation. Capacitors have various applications in both DC and AC circuits. The action of a capacitor can best be described by connecting it to a DC source and resistor as shown in Figure 8–2. It is assumed that initially the capacitor has no charge across its plates.

When the switch is closed, as indicated in Figure 8–3, electrons are pulled from the top plate due to the attracting force of the voltage source.

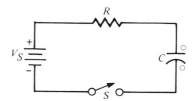

Figure 8–2   DC circuit containing a capacitor.

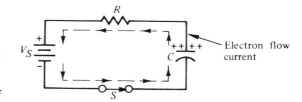

Figure 8–3   Charging action of
a capacitor.

This leaves that plate with a deficiency of electrons, or positively charged. At the same time, electrons are repelled and pushed through the conductor from the negative terminal of the voltage supply to the bottom of the capacitor. This results in the bottom plate becoming negatively charged. The capacitor is taking energy from the voltage source during this time. This process continues until the voltage across the capacitor, created by the charged plates, is equal to the supply voltage, as shown in Figure 8–4.

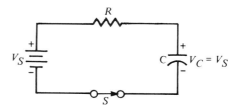

Figure 8–4   Capacitor in the charged state.

At this time the capacitor is fully charged and is storing a potential equal to the supply voltage. The switch can be opened and the capacitor will retain this charge. An electrostatic field exists across the plates and through the dielectric as illustrated in Figure 8–5. The energy taken from the source and stored by the capacitor is stored in the electrostatic field.

Although the capacitor has charged to the source potential, the purpose of the voltage source is to cause electrons from one plate to be transferred to the other plate. If the source causes a charge of -5 C to be transferred from the top plate to the bottom one, the transfer charge on

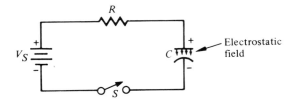

Figure 8–5 Electrostatic field across the plates of a charged capacitor.

the plates of the capacitor is 5 C, as indicated in Figure 8–6. Although a net difference in charge of 10 C exists across the two plates, transfer charge is the charge used in discussing capacitor charge.

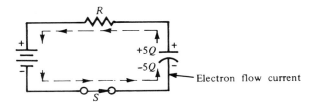

Figure 8–6 Capacitor transfer charge.

As shown by Equation (8–2), transfer charge is dependent upon the size of the capacitor (in farads) and the voltage across the plates.

$$Q = (C)(V_C) \quad \text{in coulombs} \tag{8–2}$$

The equation can be rearranged, as shown in Equation (8–3).

$$C = \frac{Q}{V_C} \quad \text{in farads} \tag{8–3}$$

This equation indicates that capacitance is equal to the ratio of transfer charge to capacitor voltage and is the basis of the definition of the farad: 1 F is equal to 1 C of charge divided by 1 V. The charge equation appearing in Equation (8–2) indicates that 1 C of charge has been transferred between plates if the capacitor has a value of 1 F and a potential of 1 V exists across the plates.

If a resistor is connected across a charged capacitor, as shown in Figure 8–7, the capacitor begins to discharge. As the capacitor discharges, it acts like a voltage source for R_2, causing a current to flow through it. During this time the capacitor is releasing the energy that it was storing. After a period of time, there is no longer a charge on the plates and the capacitor is in the discharged state, as indicated in Figure 8–8.

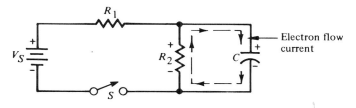

Figure 8–7   Discharging action of a capacitor.

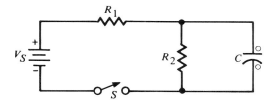

Figure 8–8   Capacitor in the discharged state.

During the time that a capacitor charges, the voltage across the device increases at a rate illustrated by the graph appearing in Figure 8–9. This is the same universal time constant curve used to depict the current buildup in an inductive circuit. It takes five time constants (TCs) for the capacitor to approach full charge. One time constant (τ) is the time re-

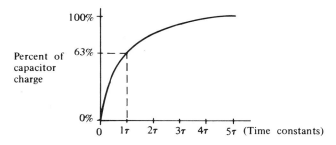

Figure 8–9   Capacitor charging curve.

quired for the capacitor to reach 63 percent of the applied voltage and is obtained by multiplying the value of the capacitance (in farads) by the series resistance in the circuit as indicated by Equation (8–4).

$$1 \text{ TC } (\tau) = (R)(C) \quad \text{in seconds} \tag{8–4}$$

For the circuit appearing in Example 8–2, one time constant is equal to 15 μs. This is the time required for the capacitor to charge to 63 percent of the source voltage. The time required for the capacitor to approximately reach full charge is five times this value, or 75 μs.

Example 8–2   Application of the *RC* time constant formula

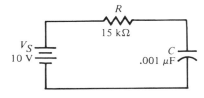

Figure 8–10

Problem
For the circuit shown in Figure 8–10, calculate the following:

    a. time required for the capacitor to charge to 63 percent of the source voltage
    b. the voltage across the capacitor at one time constant
    c. time required for the capacitor to approach full charge

Solution

    a. $\tau = (R)(C) = (15,000)(0.000000001) = 15$ μs
    b. $V_c = (0.63)(V_s) = (0.63)(10) = 6.3$ V
    c. five time constants $= (5)(\tau) = (5)(15 \text{ μs}) = 75$ μs

In addition to showing the rate at which a capacitor charges, the universal time constant curve can also be used to show the rate at which current flows in the circuit as the capacitor charges. As illustrated in Figure 8–11, the current flowing through the conductors connecting the source to the capacitor is initially high as electrons are taken from the positive plate and deposited on the negative plate. As the charge across

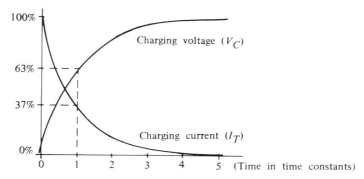

Figure 8–11 Universal time constant curve.

the plates approaches the source voltage in amplitude, the current begins to decrease rapidly. At the end of the first time constant, the current has decreased to 37 percent of its initial value. The current has decayed to zero by the end of the fifth time constant. This illustrates one application of a capacitor. Capacitors block DC current. Current flows in the conductors connecting the DC source to the capacitor while the capacitor charges. As soon as the capacitor has charged, current intensity is zero and the capacitor behaves like an open switch in the circuit.

8-1.4 Opposition to a Change in Voltage. A capacitor can be placed in a DC circuit to help maintain a steady or constant load voltage. If a capacitor is connected across the load resistance in the circuit appearing in Figure 8–12, the capacitor will almost instantaneously charge to the potential of the source. After the capacitor has charged, the load voltage and the capacitor voltage are both equal to the source potential. If, for some reason, the source voltage decreases in amplitude, the capacitor will discharge through the load as illustrated in Figure 8–13. The discharging current (I_C) aids the source current (I_S). The extra current flowing through the load will prevent the load voltage from decreasing while the capacitor is discharging.

Figure 8–12 Charging action of a capacitor connected to a load.

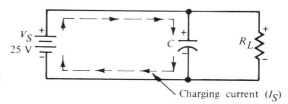

Charging current (I_S)

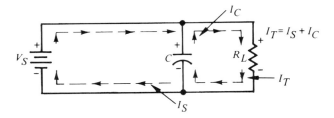

Figure 8–13 Discharging action of a capacitor connected to a load.

If the source voltage should increase after the circuit has been operating for a period of time, the capacitor will charge to the amplitude of the new potential. During this time the voltage across the load remains at the former source potential, as indicated in Figure 8–14. The effect that changes in source potential have upon the load depends upon the length of time that the voltage varies and the RC time constant of the load resistance and capacitance.

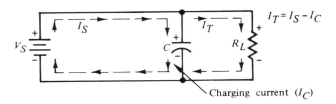

Figure 8–14 Charging action of a capacitor connected across a load when the source potential increases.

8-1.5 Capacitors Connected in Series. Capacitors can be connected together in series just as resistors and inductors can similarly be connected. Two capacitors are shown connected together in series in the circuit appearing in Figure 8–15.

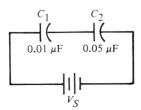

Figure 8–15 Circuit containing two capacitors connected in series.

The equation used to compute the total capacitance for two series-connected capacitors is

$$C_T = \frac{(C_1)(C_2)}{C_1 + C_2}$$ (8–5)

For the capacitors appearing in Figure 8–15, the total capacitance is 0.00833 μF, as calculated in Example 8–3.

Example 8–3   Determining the total capacitance for two series-connected capacitors

Problem
Calculate the total capacitance in the circuit appearing in Figure 8–15.

Solution

$$C_T = \frac{(C_1)(C_2)}{C_1 + C_2} = \frac{(0.01)(0.05)}{0.01 + 0.05} = 0.00833 \ \mu F$$

The diagram of a circuit containing three capacitors connected in series is shown in Figure 8–16. The equation for determining the total circuit capacitance for three or more series connected capacitors is

$$\frac{1}{C_T} = \frac{1}{C_1} + \frac{1}{C_2} + \frac{1}{C_3} + \cdots + \frac{1}{C_N}$$ (8–6)

As you have no doubt noticed, the equation used to calculate the total capacitance for two series connected capacitors is in the same format as that used for resistors or inductors connected in parallel. In similar

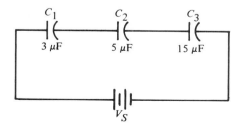

Figure 8–16   Circuit containing three capacitors connected in series.

fashion, the formula used for three or more series connected capacitors is the same as that used for three or more parallel connected resistors or inductors. For the capacitors used in the circuit appearing in Figure 8–16, the total capacitance is 1.67 μF as calculated in Example 8–4.

Example 8–4   Determining the total capacitance for three series-connected capacitors

Problem
Determine the total capacitance in the circuit appearing in Figure 8–16.

Solution

$$\frac{1}{C_T} = \frac{1}{C_1} + \frac{1}{C_2} + \frac{1}{C_3} = \frac{1}{3} + \frac{1}{5} + \frac{1}{15} = \frac{9}{15}$$

$$C_T = \frac{15}{9} = 1.67 \ \mu F$$

8-1.6 Capacitors Connected in Parallel.   The equation used to compute the total capacity of capacitors connected in parallel is

$$C_T = C_1 + C_2 + C_3 + \cdots + C_N \tag{8–7}$$

As indicated, the total capacitance for parallel-connected devices is merely the sum of the individual capacitor values. In the circuit appearing in Example 8–5, the total capacitance is 40 μF.

Example 8–5   Determining the total capacity for capacitors connected in parallel

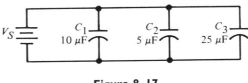

Figure 8–17

Problem
Calculate the total capacitance of the three capacitors connected in the circuit shown in Figure 8–17.

Solution

$$C_T = C_1 + C_2 + C_3$$
$$C_T = 10 + 5 + 25 = 40 \ \mu F$$

8-1.7 **Energy Stored by Capacitors.** Capacitors are energy-storing devices as are inductors. Unlike an inductor, which releases its energy as soon as the circuit is deenergized, a charged capacitor will retain its energy for a relatively long period of time. The energy stored by a capacitor can be determined from Equation (8–8).

$$W_C = \frac{(C)(V_C)^2}{2} \quad \text{in joules} \tag{8–8}$$

For the capacitor shown in the circuit appearing in Example 8–6, the energy stored is 0.001125 J.

Example 8–6 Determining the energy stored in a capacitor

Figure 8–18

Problem
Determine the energy (E) stored by the capacitor shown in the circuit of Figure 8–18.

Solution

$$E = \frac{(C)(V_C)^2}{2} = \frac{(10 \times 10^{-6})(15)^2}{2} = 0.001125 \text{ J}$$

Theoretically, a capacitor will retain its energy and charge indefinitely. However, leakage losses, in the form of small surface currents flowing across the dielectric, will cause it to discharge over a period of time.

8-1.8 **Working Voltage (WVDC).** Whenever a capacitor is placed in a circuit, such as the one appearing in Figure 8–19, it must be able to withstand the voltage across its plates when it is charged, without the dielectric breaking down and allowing current to flow. Capacitors, in addition to their capacity rating, have a voltage rating. This is called the DC working voltage or WVDC rating. For the capacitor appearing in the circuit of Figure 8–19, the WVDC rating must be at least 100 V. It is better to use a capacitor which has a moderately higher voltage rating to pro-

Figure 8–19 Capacitor connected to a DC voltage source.

vide for a safety factor in the event the supply voltage fluctuates and increases in value. Choosing a capacitor with a working voltage 25 percent above the actual applied voltage is rather common. This means that for the circuit shown in Figure 8–19 a capacitor having a minimum WVDC rating of 125 V should be used. When a capacitor is connected to an AC source, the WVDC rating should be at least 25 percent greater than the peak value of the applied voltage.

8-2 CAPACITORS IN AC CIRCUITS

8-2.1 Introduction. Capacitors are used in AC circuits just as they are in DC circuits. In a DC circuit, once the capacitor has charged, after five time constants, there is no longer any current flowing in the circuit. This is not true in AC circuits which employ capacitors. In an AC circuit a capacitor continually charges and discharges through the voltage source causing current to continually flow through the conductors connecting the capacitor to the source.

8-2.2 Capacitive Reactance. A sinusoidal voltage source is connected to a capacitor to form a circuit such as that shown in Figure 8–20. During the positive alternation the capacitor charges to the peak value of the source potential which occurs at 90°. As the source potential begins to decrease from 90 to 180°, the capacitor begins to discharge, causing a discharging current (I_C) to attempt to flow back through the source which

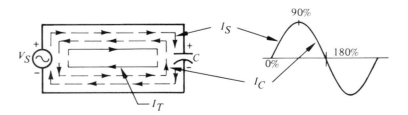

Figure 8–20 Capacitor action during the positive alternation.

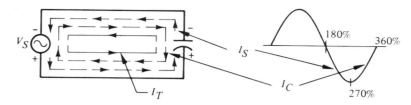

Figure 8–21   Capacitor action during the negative alternation.

opposes the source current (I_S). The net current (I_T) flowing in the circuit is the difference between the charging and discharging current.

During the negative alternation the capacitor begins to charge in the opposite direction, as shown in Figure 8–21, reaching the peak value of the source at 270°. As the source potential begins to decrease from 270 to 360°, the capacitor begins to discharge. The discharging current again opposes the source current, causing the net circuit current to be less than if the capacitor was not in the circuit. The charging and discharging current produced by the capacitor behaves like an "AC resistance." The intensity of the source current is decreased because of the opposition of the current supplied by the capacitor. The opposition to the flow of sinusoidal current is called capacitive reactance (X_C). The equation for computing capacitive reactance is

$$X_C = \frac{1}{2\pi fC} = \frac{0.159}{fC} \quad \text{in ohms} \qquad\qquad (8\text{–}9)$$

As indicated, capacitive reactance is inversely proportional to both frequency and the size of the capacitor. Ohm's law applies to AC circuits containing capacitance just as it does for circuits containing inductance, as illustrated in Example 8–7.

If the frequency of the source shown in Example 8-7 is increased from 1000 to 10,000 Hz, the capacitive reactance decreases and the intensity of the current increases, as indicated in Example 8–8. The voltage drop across the capacitor remains the same and is equal to the source voltage. The reactance of a capacitor becomes less and less as the frequency of the source is increased and may even appear as a short circuit. For low-frequency sources the reactance is much greater and the capacitor tends to act like an open circuit.

Example 8–7   Calculating capacitive reactance

Problem
Given the circuit shown in Figure 8–22, calculate the following:

a. capacitive reactance (X_C)
b. circuit current (I_T)
c. voltage across the capacitor (V_C)

Figure 8–22

Solution

a. $X_C = \dfrac{0.159}{fC} = \dfrac{0.159}{(1 \times 10^3)(1 \times 10^{-5})} = 15.9 \ \Omega$

b. $I_T = \dfrac{V_S}{X_C} = \dfrac{25 \text{ V}}{15.9 \ \Omega} = 1.57 \text{ A}$

c. $V_C = (I_T)(X_C) = (1.57 \text{ A})(15.9 \ \Omega) = 24.96 \text{ V}$

Example 8–8   Effect of frequency on capacitive reactance and current

Problem
If the frequency of the voltage source is increased to 10,000 Hz for the circuit appearing in Example 8–7, determine the new value of

a. capacitive reactance
b. circuit current
c. voltage across the capacitor

Solution

a. $X_C = \dfrac{0.159}{fC} = \dfrac{0.159}{(1 \times 10^4)(1 \times 10^{-5})} = 1.59 \ \Omega$

b. $I_T = \dfrac{V_S}{X_C} = \dfrac{25 \text{ V}}{1.59 \ \Omega} = 1.57 \text{ A}$

c. $V_C = (I_T)(X_C) = (15.7 \text{ A})(1.59 \ \Omega) = 24.96 \text{ V}$

8-2.3 Voltage-Current Phase Relationship.   When a voltage source is first applied to an uncharged capacitor, there is initially a high surge current flowing through the circuit as the device charges. As the charge across the capacitor approaches the peak value of the source potential, the current flow decreases, reaching zero at the time that the charge across the capacitor is equal to the source potential. This has the effect of causing the voltage across the capacitor (V_C) to lag the current flowing through the circuit (I_T) by an angle of 90°, as illustrated in Figure 8–23.

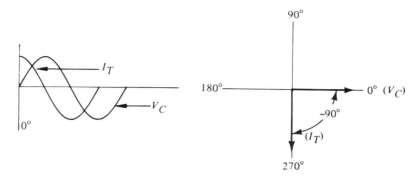

Figure 8–23   Capacitor voltage-current phase relationship.

8-3 THE CAPACITOR AS A CIRCUIT ELEMENT

8-3.1 Types of Capacitors.   There are approximately 20 different types of capacitors. Different types are required for different circuit applications. Some of the more commonly used types include ceramic, plastic film, paper, mica, electrolytic, and air. Capacitors obtain their name from the type of dielectric used between the conductive plates.

Ceramic capacitors are probably the most versatile of all the different types. They are available with a wide range of dielectric constants and are suitable for miniaturized circuits. They can operate over a broad range of frequencies and can function within a wide temperature range. They can be molded into various sizes and shapes which give them electrical and mechanical advantages when compared to many other capacitors. Some representative types of ceramic disc capacitors appear in Figure 8–24.

There are a wide variety of plastic film capacitors available for various circuit applications. Some of the more commonly used types include polystyrene, polypropylene, polyester, and polycarbonate. These capacitors are constructed from two parallel-plate conductors with the plastic dielectric placed between the plates. The material is then formed into a roll and leads are attached to each end. The roll is then encapsulated in plastic. Some typical types are shown in Figure 8–24.

The construction of paper capacitors is quite simple. They consist of two metal foils separated by kraft paper. Leads are attached to the foil conductors and the material is formed into a roll and encapsulated. Some commonly used types appear in Figure 8–25.

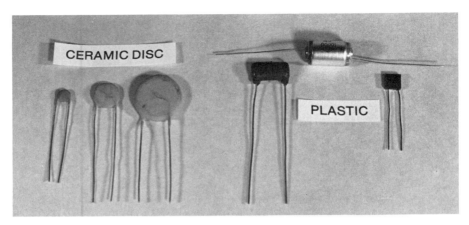

Figure 8–24 Representative types of ceramic and plastic capacitors.

Mica is one of the few natural dielectrics used in the manufacture of capacitors. These capacitors are formed by interweaving alternate layers of mica and conductors. Leads are attached and the mica and conductor layers are encapsulated. Some typical examples appear in Figure 8–25.

With the exception of ceramic capacitors, electrolytic capacitors are the most widely used of all the other types. They have the distinct advantage of having a high electrical capacity for a relatively small physical size. There are two general types—aluminum and tantalum. Although there are some nonpolarized electrolytic capacitors, most are polarized.

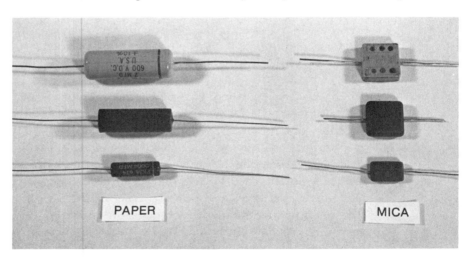

Figure 8–25 Representative types of paper and mica capacitors.

Polarity must be observed when connecting them into a circuit. If connected into a circuit backwards, the dielectric (which is in the form of an electrolyte) becomes hot and expands and the capacitor may explode.

Ideally, no current flows through the dielectric of the electrolytic capacitor when it is fully charged. In practice, however, all electrolytics allow a small DC current, called a leakage current, to pass. The lower the leakage current value, the higher the quality of the capacitor. Three quantities are used to indicate the quality factor of an electrolytic capacitor. One of these is the equivalent series resistance (ESR). This is a measure of the internal resistance of the capacitor. Another is the dissipation factor (DF). This is the ratio of the equivalent series resistance to the capacitive reactance at a specified frequency. The third quantity which is sometimes used as a figure of merit is the power factor (PF). Power factor is the ratio of the equivalent series resistance to the impedance of the capacitor at a specified frequency. Impedance is the vector sum of resistance and reactance and is discussed in a future chapter. Some representative types of electrolytic capacitors appear in Figure 8–26.

Figure 8–26 Some common types of electrolytic capacitors.

Figure 8–27 Variable capacitors.

The capacitors identified to this point all have had fixed capacity values. Those whose capacity can be changed often use air as a dielectric. There are two kinds of capacitors whose capacity can be changed—the variable and the adjustable. The variable capacitor is one which is made up of two sets of plates. One set of plates is stationary while the other is mounted on a shaft as shown in Figure 8–27. The capacity of the capacitor is varied by rotating the shaft. Although you may not be aware of it, you have no doubt rotated the shaft on this type of capacitor hundreds of times. This is what is used to change the channels, or stations, on most radio receivers.

Adjustable capacitors are those whose capacitance is changed with a screwdriver. Two typical examples of adjustable capacitors appear in Figure 8–28. These types of capacitors are also often found in radio receivers and are called padders or trimmers, depending upon how they are used.

The types of dielectric materials used in the various capacitors, in addition to the plate area size and plate spacing, affect the capacity of capacitors. Capacity ranges for commonly used capacitors appear in Table 8–2.

8-3.2 Capacitor Applications. Capacitors have many applications. In DC circuits they are often connected across conductors carrying DC current to bypass stray unwanted AC signals. Electromagnetic fields

Figure 8–28   Adjustable capacitors.

TABLE 8–2   Capacity Ranges for Selected Capacitors

Capacitor Type	Capacity Range
Air	10–365 pF
Mica	300 pF–0.05 μF
Ceramic	1 pF–1 μF
Paper	0.001–1 μF
Plastic	0.001–60 μF
Electrolytic	0.1–500,000 μF

caused by 60-cycle energy, strong radio waves, and sources of arcing all may cause AC voltages to be induced across conductors. To prevent this AC voltage from appearing at the load in a DC circuit, a capacitor is connected across the line, as illustrated in Figure 8–29. Connected in this fashion, capacitors are called bypass capacitors. The capacitor provides a less resistive path for the AC signal than the load, yet, at the same time, prevents the DC current from bypassing the load. The capacity of a capacitor used in this fashion must be large enough so that the reactance at the AC signal frequencies being bypassed is much less than the resistance of the load.

Many circuits contain both DC and AC currents. Usually, in such cases, it is desirable to block the DC current and pass the AC current. As depicted in Figure 8–30, the capacitor allows the AC current to pass from

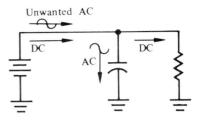

Figure 8–29 Bypass capacitor application.

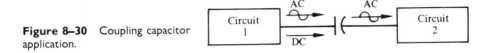

Figure 8–30 Coupling capacitor application.

circuit 1 to circuit 2 but blocks the DC and keeps it from appearing at circuit 2. A capacitor used in this fashion is called a coupling capacitor.

Another application of a capacitor is shown in Figure 8–31. A capacitor used in this fashion was discussed earlier in the chapter and is called a filter capacitor. Its purpose is to maintain a constant voltage across the load when the source voltage fluctuates. Actually, for all the applications just identified, the capacitor acts like a filter just as the inductor does. Filters will be discussed in greater detail in a future chapter.

One should exercise caution when servicing equipment containing capacitors, especially large ones. After a capacitor has been charged, it can retain the charge for several days or even weeks. Turning the equipment off does not necessarily mean that the charge stored on the plates is gone. Before servicing equipment containing large capacitors, they should be discharged by placing a well-insulated jumper lead across its terminals after the power has been turned off. The charge on large capacitors is great enough to be lethal if one comes in contact with it.

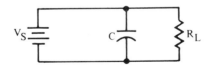

Figure 8–31 Filter capacitor application.

SUMMARY

1. A capacitor is a device consisting of two conductors separated by a nonconductor.
2. The capacity of a capacitor is directly affected by the cross-sectional area of the plates and the dielectric constant of the insulating material. It is inversely proportional to the distance between the plates.

3. The farad is the unit of measurement used for capacitance.
4. Capacitors are used in both DC and AC circuits. It takes five time constants for a capacitor to approximately reach full charge when connected to a DC source. After the capacitor has fully charged, current ceases to flow.
5. One time constant is the time required for a capacitor to charge to 63 percent of the applied source voltage. This time is obtained by multiplying the capacity value of the capacitor by any resistance which is in series with its charging path.
6. A capacitor is an energy-storing device. It takes energy from the source during the time that it is charging, stores the energy in the electrostatic field existing across its plates, and releases it back to the circuit when it is discharging.
7. A capacitor opposes changes in voltage. It is often placed in parallel with a load to prevent fluctuations in the voltage source from appearing across the load.
8. Capacitors may be connected in series and in parallel with each other.
9. The total capacitance for two capacitors connected in series can be computed from the formula $C_T = (C1)(C2)/(C_1) + (C_2)$.
10. The total capacity for three or more series-connected capacitors can be determined from the formula

$$\frac{1}{C_T} = \frac{1}{C_1} + \frac{1}{C_2} + \frac{1}{C_3} + \cdots + \frac{1}{C_N}$$

11. The total capacitance for capacitors connected in parallel is the sum of the individual capacitor values.
12. The energy stored by a capacitor is given by the formula $W_C = (C)(V_C)^2/2$ and is measured in joules.
13. Capacitors, like inductors, have reactance when connected in a circuit driven by a sinusoidal source.
14. Capacitive reactance is inversely proportional to both frequency and capacity and may be determined by the formula $X_C = 0.159/fC$. According to this equation, capacitive reactance decreases for higher frequencies and greater capacity sizes.
15. When a capacitor is operating in a circuit containing a sinusoidal source, the current flowing through the circuit leads the voltage across the capacitor (or voltage lags current) by an angle of 90°.
16. Capacitors obtain their names by the type of dielectric used in their construction. Although plate area size and plate separation distance affect capacity size, the dielectric constant of the dielectric determines, to a large extent, the capacity of the device.
17. Capacitors have various circuit applications. Like the inductor, its basic function is that of a filter. Capacitors pass high-frequency AC currents, attenuate lower-frequency currents, and block DC currents. They are used in circuits to prevent voltage fluctuations from appearing across loads, to prevent AC voltages induced across DC lines from appearing across loads, and to block DC current when both AC and DC currents are present in a circuit.

PRACTICE EXERCISES

1. Define the term *capacitance*.
2. Describe the physical construction of a capacitor.
3. Identify the factors which affect the capacity of a capacitor.
4. Identify six types of capacitors.
5. A 5000Ω resistor is connected in series with a 0.01μF capacitor. If the circuit is connected to a 15V DC source, calculate the time for one time constant, the voltage across the capacitor at the end of the first time constant, and the time required to charge the capacitor.
6. A 0.05μF capacitor is connected in series with a 0.02μF capacitor. What is the value of the total capacitance in this circuit?
7. If the two capacitors identified in exercise 6 are connected in parallel, what is the total circuit capacitance?
8. If a third capacitor having a value of 0.01 μF is connected in series with the two series-connected capacitors identified in exercise 6, what is the resulting total capacitance?
9. A 20μF capacitor is connected to a 50V rms source which has a frequency of 150 Hz. Calculate the capacitive reactance, the circuit current, and voltage across the capacitor and identify the phase angle between the voltage and current.
10. A 50μF capacitor is connected to a 25V DC source. When fully charged, how much energy is being stored by the capacitor?
11. A 0.001μF capacitor is connected in series with another which has a value of 0.002 μF. If an AC source having an amplitude of 25 mV and a frequency of 10,000 Hz is connected to the devices, what is the current flowing through, and the voltage drop across, each device?
12. What kind of capacitor is polarized?
13. What does polarization refer to?
14. What is meant by the WVDC rating of a capacitor?
15. For the capacitor used in the circuit described in exercise 9, what is the minimum WVDC value?
16. What is the effect on the capacity of a capacitor if the distance between its plates is doubled?
17. A 25μF capacitor is connected in series with a battery and a light bulb which has a resistance of 50 Ω. What is the voltage across the bulb after five time constants? Will the bulb light?
18. A 60pF capacitor and a 30pF capacitor are connected in series with each other. If a 20pF capacitor is connected in parallel with the series network, what is the total capacitance of the network?

ANSWERS TO PRACTICE EXERCISES

1. Capacitance is that phenomenon associated with a device or circuit which opposes a change in voltage and which stores energy in an electrostatic field.
2. A capacitor consists of two conductor plates separated by a dielectric.

3. The capacity of a capacitor is directly affected by the cross-sectional area of the plates and the kind of dielectric used and is inversely proportional to the distance between the plates.

4. Six types of capacitors include paper, mica, ceramic, plastic, air, and electrolytic.

5. **a.** $1 \tau = (R)(C) = (5 \times 10^3)(1 \times 10^{-8}) = 5 \times 10^{-5} \text{s} = 50 \ \mu\text{s}$
   b. $V_C = (0.63)(V_s) = (0.63)(15) = 9.45 \text{ V}$
   c. $(5)(50 \ \mu\text{s}) = 250 \ \mu\text{s}$

6. $C_T = (C_1)(C_2)/(C_1 + C_2) = (0.05)(0.02)/(0.05 + 0.02) = 0.0143 \ \mu\text{F}$

7. $C_T = C_1 + C_2 = 0.05 + 0.02 = 0.07 \ \mu\text{F}$

8. $\dfrac{1}{C_T} = \dfrac{1}{C_1} + \dfrac{1}{C_2} + \dfrac{1}{C_3} = \dfrac{1}{0.02} + \dfrac{1}{0.05} + \dfrac{1}{0.01} = 0.0059 \ \mu\text{F}$

9. $X_C = \dfrac{0.159}{(f)(C)} = \dfrac{0.159}{(150)(0.00002)} = 53 \ \Omega$

   $I_T = \dfrac{V_S}{X_C} = \dfrac{50 \text{ V}}{53 \ \Omega} = 0.943 \text{ A}$

   $V_C = (I_T)(X_C) = (0.943)(53) = 49.98 \text{ V}$

   Current leads voltage by 90°.

10. $W_C = \dfrac{(C)(V_C)^2}{2} = \dfrac{(50 \times 10^6)(625)}{2} = 0.0156 \text{ J}$

11. $I_T = \dfrac{V_S}{X_{CT}} = \dfrac{0.025}{23{,}839} = 1.05 \ \mu\text{A}$

    $X_{CT} = \dfrac{0.159}{(f)(C_T)} = \dfrac{0.159}{(1 \times 10^4)(6.67 \times 10^{-10})} = 23{,}839 \ \Omega$

    $C_T = \dfrac{(C_1)(C_2)}{C_1 + C_2} = \dfrac{(0.001)(0.002)}{0.001 + 0.002} = 0.000667 \ \mu\text{F}$

    $X_{C1} = \dfrac{0.159}{(f)(C_1)} = \dfrac{0.159}{(1 \times 10^4)(1 \times 10^{-9})} = 15{,}900 \ \Omega$

    $X_{C2} = \dfrac{0.159}{(f)(C_2)} = \dfrac{0.159}{(1 \times 10^4)(2 \times 10^{-9})} = 7950 \ \Omega$

    $V_{C1} = (I_T)(X_{C1}) = (1.05 \times 10^{-6})(1.59 \times 10^4) = 0.0167 \text{ V}$
    $V_{C2} = (I_T)(X_{C2}) = (1.05 \times 10^{-6})(7.95 \times 10^3) = .00835 \text{ V}$

    Note that Kirchhoff's law holds true for capacitive circuits. $V_S = V_{C1} + V_{C2} = 0.0167 + 0.00835 = 0.025 \text{ V}$. Notice that the smaller capacitor has the greatest reactance and drops the larger voltage.

12. The electrolytic capacitor is polarized.

13. On a polarized capacitor, one terminal is positive and the other is negative.

14. The DC working voltage of a capacitor (WVDC) refers to the maximum voltage which can be applied to a capacitor without the dielectric breaking down and excessive leakage current occurring.

15. The minimum WVDC rating of the capacitor used in exercise 9 is approximately 70 V. This value should be overrated by 25 percent, making the final

value about 88 V. WVDC ratings are standardized; the closest available value would be 100 V.

16. If the distance between the plates is doubled, the capacity of a capacitor is reduced by a factor of one-half.

17. After five time constants the capacitor is fully charged and the current flowing in the circuit is zero. The light bulb has no voltage across it and will not light.

18. The total capacity of the series-connected capacitors is 20 pF $[C_T = C_1C_2/(C_1 + C_2) = (60)(30) + (60 + 30) = 20 \text{ pF}]$. When a 20pF capacitor is connected across this network the total capacitance is the sum of the series-connected capacitances and the parallel device, or $20 + 20 = 40$ pF.

CHAPTER EXAMINATION

1. A capacitor consists of

   a. two dielectrics separated by a conductor
   b. two conductors separated by a dielectric
   c. two dissimilar metals separated by a dielectric
   d. two dissimilar metals immersed in an electrolyte

2. The time required for a capacitor to charge to 63 percent of the applied voltage is called a

   a. farad   c. coulomb
   b. henry   d. time constant

3. A capacitor has a (an) ――――――――― reactance at low frequencies.

   a. low   c. zero
   b. high   d. infinite

4. The total capacitance for a 5 and a 10μF capacitor connected in series is

   a. 15 μF   c. 3.33 μF
   b. 2.18 μF   d. none of the above

5. An 8V battery, a 4.7 Ω resistor, and a 0.001μF capacitor are all connected in series. At the end of the first time constant, the voltage across the capacitor is approximately ――――――― V.

   a. 2   c. 8
   b. 5   d. 3.8

6. For the circuit described in question 5, the time for one *RC* time constant is

   a. 8 ms   c. 4.7 μs
   b. 4.7 ns   d. 37.6 ms

7. A 0.47μF and a 0.047μF capacitor are connected in parallel. The total capacity is _____ μF.

   a. 2.28   c. 0.517
   b. 6.24   d. 0.00477

8. The _____ is the unit of measurement for capacitance.

   a. ohm   c. henry
   b. farad   d. coulomb

9. A 500V DC source is connected to a 3000μF capacitor. How much energy is stored by the capacitor?

   a. 375 J   c. 150,000 J
   b. 32 nJ   d. none of the above

10. A 15μF capacitor is connected to a 50V rms source. If the frequency of the source is 2500 Hz, the reactance of the capacitor is

    a. 4.24 Ω   c. 56,743 Ω
    b. 2780 Ω   d. none of the above

11. The current flowing in the circuit identified above is

    a. 2 A   c. 0.881 mA
    b. 17.9 mA   d. 11.79 A

Choose true or false for questions 12 to 23.
12. T F   The capacity of a capacitor is directly related to the distance between the plates.
13. T F   All capacitors are polarized with the exception of electrolytics.
14. T F   The reactance of a capacitor decreases as the source frequency is increased.
15. T F   The AC current flowing through a circuit, containing capacitance as a load, leads the voltage across the capacitor by 90°.
16. T F   For a fixed frequency, increasing the capacitor size decreases the capacitive reactance value.
17. T F   In an AC circuit, capacitive reactance behaves somewhat like resistance.
18. T F   The unit of measurement for capacitive reactance is the farad.
19. T F   The cross-sectional area of the plates inversely affects the capacity of a capacitor.
20. T F   The reactance of a capacitor to DC current is infinite.
21. T F   In a circuit containing both DC and AC current, a capacitor can be used to pass the DC current and block the AC current.
22. T F   The capacitor is an energy-storing device. As such, it stores energy in an electrostatic field.
23. T F   The mica capacitor has the distinction of providing a large electrical capacity for a small physical size.

9

RL and *RC* Circuits

OBJECTIVES

Upon completion of this chapter you should be able to do the following:

1. Describe what is meant by an imaginary number.
2. Discuss what is meant by a complex number (rectangular coordinate number).
3. Explain what is meant by a polar number (vector).
4. Multiply and divide polar numbers.
5. Convert numbers in rectangular form to equivalent numbers in polar form.
6. Define the term *impedance.*
7. Define the term *phasor.*
8. Calculate the impedance, current flow, and individual voltage drops appearing in a series *RL* circuit.
9. Compute the impedance, current flow, and individual voltage drops in a series *RC* circuit.
10. Determine the impedance and current flowing in a parallel *RL* circuit.
11. Calculate the impedance and current flowing in a parallel *RC* circuit.

9-1 INTRODUCTION

The principle of reactance was developed in the last two chapters. Inductors and capacitors are both reactive devices. The energy released by their respective fields opposes the sources connected to circuits in which these devices appear. This type of opposition to the flow of sinusoidal current is called reactance. There are two types of reactance—inductive and capacitive. Seldom do reactive devices appear by themselves in circuits. For example, they are often connected in series or in parallel with resistors. The circuit analysis process is somewhat different for these types of circuits. In a circuit containing only resistance, the voltage and current phase relationship in the circuit is 0°. For a circuit containing only inductance or capacitance, the voltage and current phase relationship is 90°. Voltage either leads or lags current. Because of this difference in phase relationship, the total opposition to the flow of current in a circuit containing both resistance and reactance is the vector sum of the resistance and reactance values. The resistance and reactance values cannot be directly added together.

9-2 THE _j_ OPERATOR

Numbers are used to indicate the quantity of something. Both positive and negative numbers exist, as indicated in Figure 9–1. The only difference between the two is their direction. Whole numbers are called integers. Numbers appearing between adjacent integers are called fractions. Various kinds of arithmetic functions can be performed on this system of numbers.

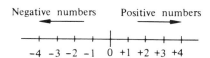

Figure 9–I   Portion of the real numbering base.

An interesting phenomenon occurs when the square root of a negative number is taken. As indicated in Example 9–1, the square root of a positive integer can have either a positive or negative base. However,

Example 9–I   The square root of a positive integer

Problem
Determine the base of $\sqrt{9}$.

Solution
$\sqrt{9} = +3$ or -3
$(+3)(+3) = +9$
$(-3)(-3) = +9$

when the square root of a negative number is taken, as shown in Example 9–2, no base exists in the normal numbering system. To facilitate the handling of this type of number, an imaginary *(i)* numbering base was developed; *i* is defined as being the square root of minus one ($i = \sqrt{-1}$). Because *i* is used to designate the current variable in electricity, the letter *j* is used to identify an imaginary number, as shown in Example 9–3, and is called the *j* operator. As indicated, the square root of $\sqrt{-9}$ is $j3$. Some other *j* variables appear in Example 9–4.

Example 9–2   The square root of a negative integer has no base

Problem
Determine the base of $\sqrt{-9}$.

Solution

$\sqrt{-9}$ cannot be $+3$ or -3

$(+3)(+3) = +9$

$(-3)(-3) = +9$

Example 9–3   The square root of a negative number

Problem
Find the base of $\sqrt{-9}$.

Solution

$$\sqrt{-9} = \sqrt{(-1)(9)} = \sqrt{-1}\,\sqrt{9} = j3$$

Example 9–4   Some commonly used *j* variables

Problem
Determine the values of j^2, j^3, and j^4.

Solution

$j^2 = (j)(j) = (\sqrt{-1})(\sqrt{-1}) = -1$

$j^3 = (j)(j^2) = (j)(-1) = -j$

$j^4 = (j^2)(j^2) = (-1)(-1) = 1$

Imaginary numbers appear on the vertical axis of a graph like that depicted in Figure 9–2. Imaginary numbers appearing above the horizontal axis are positive, whereas those numbers appearing below the horizontal axis are negative.

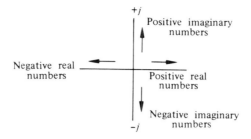

Figure 9–2 Relationship between real and imaginary numbers.

9-3 COMPLEX NUMBERS

A complex number is one which contains both a real component and an imaginary component, as illustrated in Example 9–5. This number is located in the upper right-hand quadrant of the graph appearing in Figure 9–3.

Example 9–5 A complex number

Problem
Identify the real and imaginary components of the number $2 + j3$.

Solution
$$2 + j3$$
real   imaginary

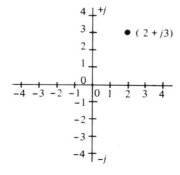

Figure 9–3 Location of a complex number on a graph.

9-4 THE RECTANGULAR COORDINATE SYSTEM

A complex number is a method of identifying a quantity which has both a real and an imaginary component. A rectangular coordinate system is used to represent the magnitude of the complex number. The magnitude represents a point located somewhere in the system. As indicated in Figure 9–4, the rectangular system of coordinates is formed by two axes which are perpendicular to one another. The horizontal axis represents real numbers and is called the R axis. Imaginary numbers are represented by the vertical axis which is called the j axis. The intersection of the R and j axes forms the zero reference for both real and imaginary numbers. All numbers appearing on the horizontal axis to the right of the intersecting lines are positive real numbers and those appearing to the left are negative. Positive imaginary numbers appear on the vertical axis above the intersecting lines and negative imaginary numbers appear below the intersecting axes. The coordinate system is divided into four quadrants. A complex number having a magnitude of $4 + j3$ appears in the first quadrant, as illustrated in Figure 9–5. If a number has a magnitude of $-3 - j2$, it appears in the third quadrant.

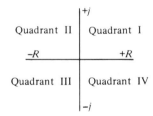

Figure 9–4 Rectangular system of coordinates.

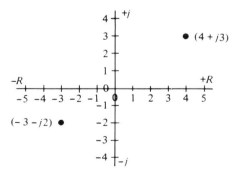

Figure 9–5 Complex numbers located on a rectangular system of coordinates.

9-5 THE POLAR COORDINATE SYSTEM

If the axes of the rectangular coordinate system appearing in Figure 9–4 are labeled in degrees, as depicted in Figure 9–6, a polar coordinate system is formed. This system is used to represent numbers in vector form just as the rectangular coordinate system is used to represent a complex number. A vector is a force which has both magnitude and direction. Its magnitude is given as a coefficient and its direction by an angle. The vector $8\angle130°$ appears in the second quadrant of the polar chart appearing in Figure 9–6.

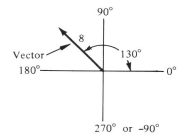

Figure 9–6   Polar system of coordinates.

9-6 CONVERTING FROM RECTANGULAR COORDINATES TO POLAR COORDINATES

Electrical variables in AC circuits can be written either in rectangular (complex) or polar (vector) format. One must be able to convert from one form of coordinates to the other. The complex number $3+j4$ appears in Figure 9–7 in the rectangular system of coordinates. The number repre-

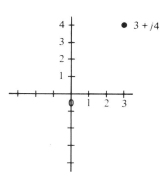

Figure 9–7   Number located in the rectangular system of coordinates.

sents a point located three units on the positive real axis and four units on the positive imaginary axis and appears in the first quadrant.

The complex number appearing in Figure 9–7 can be converted into a vector by constructing a right triangle as shown in Figure 9–8. The hypotenuse is formed by drawing a line segment from the intersection of the two axes through the point identified by the number $3 + j4$. A vertical line drawn perpendicular to the horizontal axis forms the opposite side of the triangle. The hypotenuse represents the magnitude of the vector. The angle (θ) is obtained from the arc tangent ($\tan^{-1}$) function. The arc tangent is the inverse function of the tangent and represents the angle whose tangent is the ratio of the opposite side to the adjacent side of the angle. The arc tangent is usually written $\tan^{-1}$.

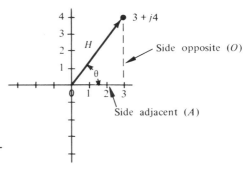

Figure 9–8 Converting a complex number into an equivalent polar number.

A complex number can be converted into a polar number by using the Pythagorean theorem and the arc tangent function as shown by Equation (9–1).

$$\text{Vector} = \sqrt{(R)^2 + (j)^2} \angle \tan^{-1}\frac{j}{R}$$

(9–1)

As indicated, the magnitude of the vector is equal to the square root of the sum of the squares and its direction is the angle whose tangent is the ratio of j to R. The rectangular number appearing in Figure 9–7 is equal to $5\angle 53.1°$ in polar form as shown in Example 9–6.

Example 9–6   Converting a rectangular number into a polar number

Problem

Convert the complex number $3 + j4$ into an equivalent polar number.

Solution

$$3 + j4 = \sqrt{(R)^2 + (j)^2} \angle \tan^{-1} \frac{j}{R} = \sqrt{(3)^2 + (4)^2} \angle \tan^{-1} \frac{4}{3}$$

$$= \sqrt{9 + 16}\, \tan^{-1} 1.33 = 5 \angle 53.1°$$

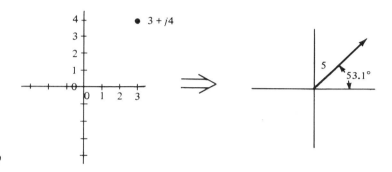

Figure 9–9

9-7 ARITHMETIC OPERATIONS USING POLAR COORDINATES

Polar coordinates may be multiplied together and divided as illustrated in Example 9–7. The coefficients are multiplied together and the angle values added for the multiplication process. The coefficients are divided

Example 9–7   Multiplication and division of polar numbers

Problem

Perform the following multiplication and division operations.

Solution

Multiplication

$$(15 \angle 13°)(4 \angle 17°) = 60 \angle 30°$$
$$(\ 7 \angle 45°)(8 \angle -15°) = 56 \angle 30°$$

Division

$$\frac{72 \angle 45°}{9 \angle 30°} = 8 \angle 15°; \quad \frac{47 \angle 53°}{5 \angle -17°} = 9.4 \angle 70°$$

and the angle in the denominator is subtracted from the angle appearing in the numerator for the division process.

9-9 IMPEDANCE

Resistive and reactive devices can be connected in series, parallel, or series-parallel with each other. The total opposition to the flow of current when an AC sinusoidal source is connected to these kinds of circuits is called impedance. A circuit containing both resistance and reactance is called a complex circuit because the circuit impedance represents a complex number. A circuit containing a resistor and an inductor connected in series appears in Figure 9–10. Since the voltage across the inductor leads the current flowing through it, inductive reactance (X_L) is displaced 90° and appears on the positive portion of the imaginary axis. The voltage developed across the resistor is in phase with the current flowing through it and appears on the positive portion of the real axis of a rectangular system of coordinates, as shown in Figure 9–10(b).

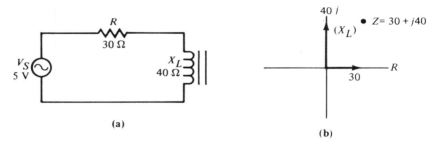

(a)

(b)

Figure 9–10 Circuit containing a resistor connected in series with an inductor and the resulting impedance

The symbol used to represent impedance is the letter Z and its unit of measurement is the ohm. The impedance of the circuit appearing in Figure 9–10 is $30 + j40$. Impedance has only limited application when written in the rectangular coordinate format. Instead, impedance is almost always written in polar form. Equation (9–2) is used to obtain the impedance when resistive and inductive devices are connected in series.

$$Z = \sqrt{(R)^2 + (X_L)^2} \angle \tan^{-1} \frac{X_L}{R} \qquad\qquad (9\text{–}2)$$

This is the same equation used to convert a rectangular number into a polar number in Equation (9–1) except that the resistor and inductive reactance variables have been substituted for the real and imaginary components of the complex number. The impedance of the circuit appearing in Figure 9–10 is 50 Ω ∠53.1° as computed in Example 9–8.

Example 9–8   Calculating the impedance of a series resistive-inductive circuit

Problem
Compute the impedance of the circuit shown in Figure 9–12.

Solution

$$Z = \sqrt{(R)^2 + (X_L)^2} \angle \tan^{-1}\frac{X_L}{R}$$

$$Z = \sqrt{(30)^2 + (40)^2} \angle \tan^{-1}\frac{40}{30} = 50\ \Omega \angle 53.1°$$

The resulting impedance is shown in Figure 9–11. The impedance represents the polar sum of the resistance and inductive reactance values.

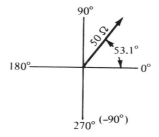

Figure 9–11   Impedance depicted in polar format

9-9 SERIES *RL* CIRCUITS

A series *RL* circuit is a circuit made up of one or more resistors connected in series with one or more inductors as illustrated in Figure 9–12. This type of circuit can be analyzed in much the same fashion as series resis-

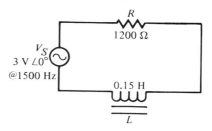

Figure 9–12   Series *RL* circuit

tive circuits. The major difference between analyzing resistive circuits and complex circuits is the voltage and current relationships which exist within the circuits. In a complex circuit the impedance, current flow, and voltage drops across the individual circuit components are computed using numbers in phasor format. A phasor is a polar number, or vector, whose magnitude is in rms units. The impedance of a series *RL* circuit may be determined by using Equation (9–2). The impedance of the circuit shown in Figure 9–12 is 1853 Ω ∠49.66° as calculated in Example 9–9.

Example 9–9   Calculating the impedance of a series *RL* circuit

Problem
Calculate the impedance of the circuit shown in Figure 9–12.

Solution

$$Z = \sqrt{(R)^2 + (X_L)^2} \angle \tan^{-1} \frac{X_L}{R}$$

$$Z = \sqrt{(1200)^2 + (1413)^2} \angle \tan^{-1} \frac{1413}{1200} = 1853 \ \Omega \angle 49.66°$$

$$X_L = 2\pi f L$$

$$X_L = (2)(3.14)(1500)(0.15) = 1413 \ \Omega$$

The current flowing through the circuit is computed by using Ohm's law. As indicated in Example 9–10, the current flowing in the circuit is 1.62 mA ∠−49.66°. The source voltage is used as a reference and has an angle of 0°. The circuit current is lagging the source voltage by 49.66°.

Example 9–10   Calculating the current flowing in a series *RL* circuit

Problem
Calculate the current flowing in the circuit shown in Figure 9–12.

Solution

$$I_T = \frac{V_S}{Z} = \frac{3 \ V \angle 0°}{1853 \ \Omega \angle 49.66°} = .00162 \ A \angle -49.66°$$

Ohm's law is used to compute the voltage drop across both the resistor and the inductor, as shown in Example 9–11. The resulting potentials can be checked by using Kirchhoff's voltage law. If the sum of the individual voltage drops equals the applied voltage, the impedance, current, and voltage calculations were performed properly. Since the two voltages are out-of-phase, they must be added together vectorally. The

Example 9–II   Calculating the voltage drops in a series *RL* circuit

Problem

Compute the voltage drop across the resistor and the inductor for the circuit appearing in Figure 9–12.

Solution

$$V_R = (I_T)(R) = (.00162 \text{ A} \angle -49.66°)(1200 \ \Omega \angle 0°) = 1.94 \text{ V} \angle -49.66°$$
$$V_L = (I_T)(X_L) = (.00162 \text{ A} \angle -49.66°)(1413 \ \Omega \angle 90°) = 2.29 \text{ V} \angle 40.34°$$

Check:

$$V_S = V_R + V_L = \sqrt{(V_R)^2 + (V_L)^2} = \sqrt{(1.94)^2 + (2.29)^2} = 3 \text{ V}$$

relationship between the electrical variables are depicted in phasor format in Figure 9–13. Notice that the voltage across the inductor is leading the current flowing through it by an angle of 90° and the current flowing through the resistor is in phase with the voltage dropped across it. They have been shifted by the angle of impedance, but the relationships are the same as when these devices are used by themselves in a circuit.

A common application of a series *RL* circuit is that of a phase shift network. This is a circuit used to introduce a phase difference between the source voltage and circuit current.

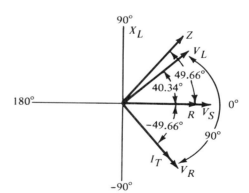

Figure 9–I3 Phasor relationship of variables appearing in a series *RL* circuit

9-I0 SERIES *RC* CIRCUITS

A series *RC* circuit is one containing one or more resistors connected in series with one or more capacitors. The variables associated with this type of circuit are calculated in the same manner as those computed for a series *RL* circuit. The impedance is obtained from Equation (9–3).

$$Z = \sqrt{(R)^2 + (X_C)^2} \angle \tan^{-1} \frac{-X_C}{R} \qquad (9-3)$$

This equation is similar to the one used to obtain the impedance of a series *RL* circuit except that X_C has been substituted for X_L. The phase angle of the impedance in a series *RC* circuit is always negative as indicated by the negative sign associated with X_C in the arc tangent function.

A series *RC* circuit appears in Example 9–12. In this circuit a 0.05-µF

Example 9—12 Determining the variables associated with a series *RC* circuit

Problem
Compute the following for the circuit appearing in Figure 9–14:

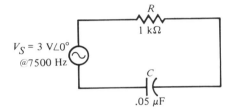

$V_S = 3\ V\angle 0°$
@7500 Hz

R
1 kΩ

C
.05 µF

Figure 9–14

    a. capacitive reactance (X_C)
    b. impedance (Z)
    c. current (I_T)
    d. voltage across the resistor (V_R)
    e. voltage across the capacitor (V_C)

Solution

a. $X_C = \dfrac{0.159}{fC} = \dfrac{1.59 \times 10^{-1}}{(7.5 \times 10^3)(5 \times 10^{-8})} = 424\ \Omega$

b. $Z = 1000 - j424$ in rectangular form; in polar form

$Z = \sqrt{(R)^2 + (X_C)^2} \angle \tan^{-1} \dfrac{-XC}{R} = \sqrt{(1000)^2 + (424)^2} \angle \tan^{-1} \dfrac{-424}{1000}$

$Z = 1086.17\ \Omega \angle -22.98°$

c. $I_T = \dfrac{V_S}{Z} = \dfrac{3\ V \angle 0°}{1086.17\ \Omega \angle -22.98°} = 0.00276\ A \angle +22.98°$

d. $V_R = (I_T)(R) = (0.00276\ A \angle 22.98°)(1000\ \Omega \angle 0°) = 2.76\ V \angle 22.98°$

e. $V_C = (I_T)(X_C) = (0.00276\ A \angle 22.98°)(424\ \Omega \angle -90°) = 1.17\ V \angle -67.02°$

Check:

$V_S = V_R + V_C = \sqrt{(V_R)^2 + (V_C)^2} = \sqrt{(2.76)^2 + (1.17)^2} = 3\ V$

capacitor is connected in series with a 1000-Ω resistor. The capacitor has a reactance of 424 Ω at a source frequency of 7500 Hz. The current flowing in the circuit is limited by the impedance of the resistor and the capacitor.

In rectangular form this value is $1000 - j424$; in polar format the impedance is equal to $1086.17\ \Omega \angle -22.98°$. Capacitive reactance is located on the negative portion of the imaginary axis. This axis has an angle of 270°, or $-90°$. Since this represents the $-j$ axis, capacitive reactance is negative. This causes the angle associated with the impedance phasor to be negative.

The current flowing through the circuit is leading the applied voltage. The voltage across the resistor leads the source voltage and is in phase with the circuit current, whereas the voltage across the capacitor lags the source voltage.

Kirchhoff's voltage law can be used to verify the individual voltage drops. Since they are out of phase, the voltages must be added together vectorally. One can observe from the phasor diagram shown in Figure 9–15 that the current flowing through the circuit leads the voltage across the capacitor by 90° and is in phase with the voltage developed across the resistor. Like the series *RL* circuit, the series *RC* circuit is often used to introduce a phase shift between the source voltage and circuit current.

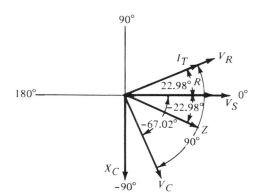

Figure 9–15 Phasor relationship of variables appearing in a series *RC* circuit

9-12 PARALLEL *RL* CIRCUITS

A parallel *RL* circuit is one which contains two or more branches. Each branch contains either an inductor or a resistor. The diagram of a parallel *RL* circuit appears in Figure 9–16. Several variables are of interest in this type of circuit. These include the total, or series equivalent, impedance (Z_T), the individual branch currents (I_1 and I_2), and the total current (I_T).

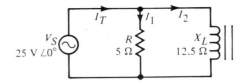

Figure 9–16 Parallel *RL* circuit

The branch currents may be obtained by the use of Ohm's law. The phasor results appear in Example 9–13.

Example 9–13 Calculating the branch currents in a parallel *RL* circuit

Problem
Calculate the current flowing through each branch in the circuit shown in Figure 9–16.

Solution

$$I_1 = \frac{V_S}{R} = \frac{25 \text{ V} \angle 0°}{5 \text{ } \Omega \angle 0°} = 5 \text{ A} \angle 0° \qquad I_2 = \frac{V_S}{X_L} = \frac{25 \text{ V} \angle 0°}{12.5 \text{ } \Omega \angle 90°} = 2 \text{ A} \angle -90°$$

The total current is obtained by vectorally adding together the two branch currents as shown in Example 9–14. Since the circuit is inductive, the current lags the source voltage.

Example 9–14 Computing the total current in a parallel *RL* circuit

Problem
Determine the total current flowing in the circuit which appears in Figure 9–16.

Solution

$$I_T = \sqrt{(I_1)^2 + (I_2)^2} \angle \tan^{-1} \frac{-I_2}{I_1} = \sqrt{(5)^2 + (2)^2} \angle \tan^{-1} \frac{-2}{5}$$
$$I_T = 5.385 \text{ A} \angle -21.8°$$

Ohm's law can be used to calculate the circuit impedance. The phasor result appears in Example 9–15.

Example 9–15 Determining the impedance of a parallel *RL* circuit

Problem
Compute the impedance of the circuit shown in Figure 9–18 by using Ohm's law.

Solution

$$Z_T = \frac{V_S}{I_T} = \frac{25 \text{ V} \angle 0°}{5.385 \text{ A} \angle -21.8°} = 4.64 \text{ } \Omega \angle 21.8°$$

9-12 PARALLEL *RC* CIRCUITS

A parallel *RC* circuit is a circuit which contains two or more branches. Each branch contains either a resistor or a capacitor.

The diagram of a two-branch parallel *RC* circuit appears in Example 9–16. The current supplied by the source is limited by the impedance of the parallel resistor and capacitor combination. The method just discussed for the parallel *RL* circuit can be applied to the parallel *RC* circuit when the circuit impedance must be determined, as illustrated in Example 9–16.

Example 9–16   Determining the impedance of a parallel *RC* circuit

Problem
Calculate the impedance of the circuit appearing in Figure 9–17.

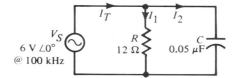

Figure 9–17

Solution

$$I_1 = \frac{V_S}{R} = \frac{6 \text{ V} \angle 0°}{12 \text{ }\Omega \angle 0°} = 0.5 \text{ A} \angle 0° \qquad I_2 = \frac{V_S}{X_C} = \frac{6 \text{ V} \angle 0°}{31.8 \text{ }\Omega \angle -90°} = 0.189 \text{ A} \angle 90°$$

$$X_C = \frac{0.159}{fC} = \frac{1.59 \times 10^{-1}}{(1 \times 10^5)(5 \times 10^{-8})} = 31.8 \text{ }\Omega \angle -90°$$

$$I_T = \sqrt{(I_1)^2 + (I_2)^2} \angle \tan^{-1} \tfrac{I_2}{I_1} = \sqrt{(0.5^2 + (0.189)^2} \angle \tan^{-1} \tfrac{0.189}{0.5}$$

$$I_T = 0.535 \text{ A} \angle 20.7°$$

$$Z_T = \frac{V_S}{I_T} = \frac{6 \text{ V} \angle 0°}{0.535 \text{ A} \angle 20.7°} = 11.21 \text{ }\Omega \angle -20.7°$$

SUMMARY

1. There are two types of numbering systems—the real and the imaginary. The real numbering system includes those numbers located on the horizontal axis of the rectangular system of coordinates. The imaginary system are those numbers which appear on the vertical axis.
2. The imaginary numbering system is based on the *j* operator which is defined as the $\sqrt{-1}$.
3. A number which is composed of a real component and an imaginary component is called a complex number.

4. There are two systems of coordinates—the rectangular and the polar.
5. The rectangular system of coordinates is used to represent a number written in complex, or rectangular, form.
6. The polar coordinate system is used to represent a polar number (vector) or phasor.
7. A vector is a force which has both magnitude and direction.
8. Circuits which contain both resistance and reactance (either inductive or capacitive) are called complex circuits. This is because the resistance unit of measurement is located on the real axis and the reactance unit of measurement is located on the imaginary, or *j,* axis of the rectangular system of coordinates.
9. The total opposition to the flow of current that a complex circuit offers to a sinusoidal AC source is called impedance.
10. Impedance is usually expressed in phasor format and represents the polar sum of the circuit resistance and reactance.
11. A phasor is a vector whose magnitude is represented in rms units.
12. Resistors and inductors can be connected together in series with each other. When connected in this fashion, a circuit is called a series *RL* circuit.
13. A series *RC* circuit is one containing resistance connected in series with capacitance.
14. The electrical variables associated with both series *RL* and series *RC* circuits are calculated in similar fashion. In a series *RL* circuit the source voltage leads the current flowing through the circuit, whereas in a series *RC* circuit the applied voltage lags the circuit current.
15. Inductors and resistors, and capacitors and resistors, can also be connected in parallel with one another. These are called parallel *RL* and parallel *RC* circuits respectively.

PRACTICE EXERCISES

1. Define the term *impedance.*
2. How is the impedance magnitude determined?
3. What determines the impedance angle?
4. What is a phasor?
5. A 7H inductor is connected in series with a 50kΩ resistor. The devices are connected to a 100mV rms voltage source which has a frequency of 2000 Hz. Calculate the impedance of the circuit, the current flowing through the circuit, and the voltage drop across the resistor and inductor.
6. A 0.47μF capacitor is connected in series with a 470Ω resistor. The devices are connected to a source which has a frequency of 500 Hz and an output peak voltage of 5 V. Calculate the impedance of the circuit, the current flow, and the voltage drop across each of the two devices.
7. A 20μF capacitor having a reactance of 100 Ω is connected in parallel with a 200Ω resistor. If the network is driven by a 10V rms source, what is the impedance of the circuit and the current flowing through it?

ANSWERS TO PRACTICE EXERCISES

1. Impedance is the opposition to the flow of current a complex circuit offers to an AC sinusoidal source. It can also be defined in terms of Ohm's law ($Z = V_S/I_T$). As such, impedance is considered to be a vector.

2. The magnitude of the impedance of a circuit depends upon the amount of resistance and reactance appearing in the circuit.

3. The impedance angle is also dependent upon the amount of resistance and inductance in the circuit. The angle is determined from the arc tangent function.

4. A phasor is a vector, or polar number, whose magnitude is in rms units.

5. $Z = \sqrt{(R)^2 + (X_L)^2} \angle \tan^{-1} \frac{X_L}{R} = \sqrt{(50{,}000)^2 + (87{,}920)^2} \angle \tan^{-1} \frac{87{,}920}{50{,}000}$

   $= 101 \text{ k}\Omega \angle 60.37°$

   $X_L = 2\pi FL = (2)(3.14)(2000)(7) = 87{,}920 \ \Omega$

   $I_T = \dfrac{V_S}{Z} = \dfrac{0.1 \text{ V} \angle 0°}{101{,}000 \ \Omega \angle 60.37°} = 0.99 \ \mu\text{A} \angle -60.37°$

   $V_R = (I_T)(R) = (9.9 \times 10^{-7} \angle -60.37°)(5 \times 10^4 \angle 0°) = 49.5 \text{ mV} \angle -60.37°$

   $V_L = (I_T)(X_L) = (9.9 \times 10^{-7} \angle -60.37°)(8.792 \times 10^4 \angle 90°) = 87 \text{ mV} \angle 29.63°$

   Check:

   $V_S = \sqrt{(V_R)^2 + (V_L)^2} = \sqrt{(0.0495)^2 + (0.087)^2} = 0.1 = 100 \text{ mV}$

6. $Z = \sqrt{(R)^2 + (X_C)^2} \angle \tan^{-1} \frac{-X_C}{R} = \sqrt{(470)^2 + (677)^2} \angle \tan^{-1} \frac{-677}{470}$

   $= 824.15 \ \Omega \angle -55.23°$

   $X_C = \dfrac{0.159}{fC} = \dfrac{1.59 \times 10^{-1}}{(5 \times 10^2)(4.7 \times 10^{-7})} = 677 \ \Omega$

   $I_T = \dfrac{V_S}{Z} = \dfrac{(5 \text{ V})(0.707) \angle 0°}{824.15 \ \Omega \angle -55.23°} = 0.00429 \text{ A} \angle 55.23°$

   $V_R = (I_T)(R) = (0.00429 \ \text{A} \angle 55.23°)(470 \ \Omega \angle 0°) = 2.016 \text{ V} \angle 55.23°$

   $V_C = (I_T)(X_C) = (0.00429 \text{ A} \angle 55.23°)(677 \ \Omega \angle -90°) = 2.9 \text{ V} \angle -34.77°$

   Check:

   $V_S = \sqrt{(V_R)^2 + (V_C)^2} = \sqrt{(2.016)^2 + (2.9)^2} = 3.5 \text{ V}$

   $5 \text{ V pk} = 3.5 \text{ V rms}$

7. $I_T = \sqrt{(I_1)^2 + (I_2)^2} \angle \tan^{-1} \frac{I_2}{I_1} = \sqrt{(0.05)^2 + (0.1)^2} \angle \tan^{-1} \frac{0.1}{0.05} = 0.112 \text{ A} \angle 63.43°$

   $I_1 = \dfrac{V_S}{R} = \dfrac{10 \text{ V} \angle 0°}{200 \ \Omega \angle 0°} = 0.05 \text{ A} \angle 0° \qquad I_2 = \dfrac{V_S}{X_C} = \dfrac{10 \text{ V} \angle 0°}{100 \ \Omega \angle -90°} = 0.1 \text{ A} \angle 90°$

   $Z = \dfrac{V_S}{I_T} = \dfrac{10 \text{ V} \angle 0°}{0.112 \text{ A} \angle 63.43°} = 89.28 \ \Omega \angle -63.43°$

CHAPTER EXAMINATION

1. An inductor having a reactance of 72 Ω is connected in series with a 56 Ω resistor. What is the impedance of the circuit?

2. If the devices identified in question 1 are connected to a 200 mV rms source, calculate the voltage dropped across the resistor.

3. A 0.15 H inductor is connected in parallel with a 1500 Ω resistor. The parallel combination is connected to a 1 V rms source which has a frequency of 2000 Hz. What is the impedance of the circuit?

4. How much current is supplied by the source for the circuit described in question 3?

Choose true or false for questions 5 to 13.

5. T F   A phasor is a force which has both magnitude and direction.

6. T F   In a series *RL* circuit, the current flowing through the circuit lags the applied voltage.

7. T F   A complex number is one which is either very large or very small.

8. T F   If the number $30 + j75$ represents the rectangular impedance of a series *RL* circuit, then R has a value of 30 Ω and L has a value of 75 H.

9. T F   Circuit impedance is usually represented in phasor format.

10. T F   A phasor can be a polar number whose length is indicated in rms units.

11. T F   When using Ohm's law to calculate impedance, the source voltage must be in rms units.

12. T F   In any type of AC circuit, the voltage dropped across a resistor is always in phase with the current flowing through it.

13. T F   In a complex circuit containing an inductor, the current flowing through the inductor is in phase with the source voltage.

10

RLC Circuits

OBJECTIVES

Upon completion of this chapter you should be able to do the following:

1. Calculate the current flowing in a series *RLC* circuit.
2. Compute the impedance of a series *RLC* circuit.
3. Determine the voltage drops across the devices forming a series *RLC* circuit.
4. Calculate the instantaneous power consumed in an AC circuit.
5. Calculate the average power consumed in an AC resistive circuit.
6. Compute the average power consumed in a complex AC circuit.
7. Determine the apparent power consumed in a complex circuit.
8. Calculate the power factor associated with a complex circuit.
9. Describe the significance of the power factor.
10. Define the term *resonance*.
11. Calculate the resonant frequency of a series resonant circuit.
12. Describe the relationship between impedance, current, and frequency in a series resonant circuit.
13. Calculate the bandwidth of a series resonant circuit.
14. Compute the resonant frequency of a parallel resonant circuit.
15. Describe the relationship between impedance, current, and frequency in a parallel resonant circuit.
16. Identify two applications for resonant circuits.
17. Identify four general types of filters and describe the characteristics of each.

10-1 INTRODUCTION

It was determined in the last chapter that resistors and inductors or resistors and capacitors can be connected together either in series or in parallel. Some AC circuits contain all three of these types of devices connected

219

together in series. A circuit containing resistance, inductance, and capacitance connected together in series is called a series *RLC* circuit.

The first part of this chapter deals with the analysis of series *RLC* circuits. The next portion of the chapter is concerned with the power consumed by devices connected in a circuit which is energized by an AC sinusoidal source. Resonant circuits are considered next. These are special types of *RLC* circuits. The last portion of the chapter deals with filters, which are a common application of reactive devices and resonant circuits.

10-2 SERIES *RLC* CIRCUITS

A schematic diagram of a series *RLC* circuit appears in Figure 10–1. The impedance of the circuit is the phasor sum of the individual resistance

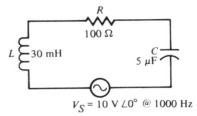

Figure 10–1   Series *RLC* circuit.

and reactive values. As indicated in Example 10–1 the inductive reactance of the inductor is 188.4 Ω and the reactance of the capacitor is 31.8 Ω. Since the reactance of the inductor has a phase angle of $+90°$ and the

---

Example 10–1   Computing inductive and capacitive reactance

Problem

Calculate the reactances of the inductor and capacitor shown in Figure 10–1.

Solution

$$X_L = 2\pi fL = (2)(3.14)(1000)(0.03) = 188.4\ \Omega \angle 90°$$

$$X_C = \frac{0.159}{fC} = \frac{0.159}{(1000)(0.000005)} = 31.8\ \Omega \angle -90°$$

---

phase angle of the reactance of the capacitor is $-90°$, the angular displacement between the two reactances is 180°, as shown in Figure 10–2.

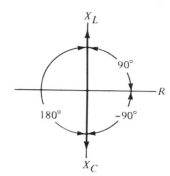

Figure 10–2 Angular displacement between inductive and capacitive reactance.

The impedance of the circuit can be determined from Equation (10–1).

$$Z = \sqrt{(R)^2 + (X_L - X_C)^2} \angle \tan^{-1} \frac{X_L - X_C}{R}$$

(10–1)

If the capacitive reactance was larger than the reactance of the inductor, Equation (10–2) would be used. As calculated in Example 10–2, the impedance of the circuit appearing in Figure 10–1 is 185.8 Ω ∠ 57.44°.

$$Z = \sqrt{(R)^2 + (-X_C + X_L)^2} \angle \tan^{-1} \frac{-X_C + X_L}{R}$$

(10–2)

Example 10–2 Calculating the impedance of a series *RLC* circuit.

Problem

For the circuit shown in Figure 10–1, calculate the impedance.

Solution

$$Z = \sqrt{(R)^2 + (X_L - X_C)^2} \angle \tan^{-1} \frac{X_L - X_C}{R}$$

$$Z = \sqrt{(100)^2 + (156.6)^2} \angle \tan^{-1} \frac{156.6}{100} = 185.8 \ \Omega \angle 57.44°$$

Since the reactance of the inductor is larger than that of the capacitor, the circuit behaves inductively and the impedance phasor appears in the first quadrant as depicted in Figure 10–3.

The current flowing in the circuit is computed by using Ohm's law as shown in Example 10–3. The voltage drops across the individual devices are obtained by application of Ohm's law as shown in Example 10–4.

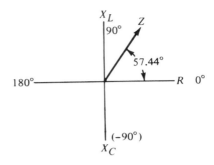

Figure 10–3 Impedance phasor.

Example 10–3 Calculating the current flowing in a series *RLC* circuit
___

Problem
Determine the current flowing in the circuit appearing in Figure 10–1.

Solution

$$I_T = \frac{V_S}{Z} = \frac{10 \text{ V} \angle 0°}{185.8 \text{ } \Omega \angle 57.44°} = 0.0538 \text{ A} \angle -57.44°$$
___

Example 10–4 Calculating the voltage drops in a series *RLC* circuit
___

Problem
Compute the voltage across each device in the circuit shown in Figure 10–1.

Solution
$$V_R = (I_T)(R) = (0.0538 \text{ A} \angle -57.44°)(100 \text{ } \Omega \angle 0°) = 5.38 \text{ V} \angle -57.44°$$

$$V_L = (I_T)(X_L) = (0.0538 \text{ A} \angle -57.44°)(188.4 \text{ } \Omega \angle 90°) = 10.14 \text{ V} \angle 32.56°$$

$$V_C = (I_T)(X_C) = (0.0538 \text{ A} \angle -57.44°)(31.8 \text{ } \Omega \angle -90°) = 1.71 \text{ V} \angle -147.44°$$
___

The phasors for the variables appear in Figure 10–4. Notice that the voltages across the inductor and capacitor are 180° out of phase. The voltage across the inductor leads the current flowing through the circuit by 90° and the voltage across the capacitor lags the circuit current by 90°. The voltage dropped across the resistor is in phase with the current flowing through it.

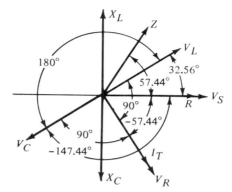

Figure 10–4   Phasor relationship for the variables associated with the circuit appearing in Figure 10–1.

If the capacitor was smaller, or the frequency of the source lower, the circuit would behave capacitively and the current flowing through the circuit would lead the source voltage, as illustrated in Example 10–5.

Example 10–5   Calculating the variables associated with a series _RLC_ circuit

Problem
If the frequency of the source for the circuit appearing in Figure 10–1 is decreased to 100 Hz, calculate the impedance, current, and voltage drops across the resistor, inductor, and capacitor.

Solution

$$X_L = 2\pi f L = (2)(3.14)(100)(0.03) = 18.84 \ \Omega$$

$$X_C = \frac{0.159}{fC} = \frac{0.159}{(100)(0.000005)} = 318 \ \Omega$$

$$X = \sqrt{(R)^2 + (-X_C + X_L)^2} \ \angle \ \tan^{-1} \frac{-X_C + X_L}{R}$$

$$Z = \sqrt{(100)^2 + (-318 + 18.84)^2} \ \angle \ \tan^{-1} \frac{-318 + 18.84}{100}$$

$$Z = 315.43 \ \Omega \ \angle \ -71.52°$$

$$I_T = \frac{V_S}{Z} = \frac{10 \ V \angle 0°}{315.43 \ \Omega \angle -71.52°} = .0317 \ A \angle 71.52°$$

$$V_R = (I_T)(R) = (0.0317 \ A \angle 71.52°)(100 \ \Omega \angle 0°) = 3.17 \ V \angle 71.52°$$

$$V_L = (I_T)(X_L) = (0.0317 \ A \angle 71.52°)(18.84 \ \Omega \angle 90° = .597 \ V \angle 161.52°$$

$$V_C = (I_T)(X_C) = (0.0317 \ A \angle 71.52°)(318 \ \Omega \angle -90°) = 10.08 \ V \angle -18.48°$$

Check:

$$V_S = \sqrt{(V_R)^2 + (V_C - V_L)^2} = \sqrt{(3.17)^2 + (10.08 - .597)^2} = 10 \ V$$

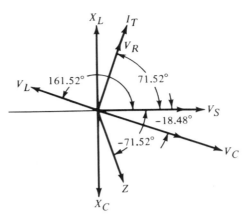

Figure 10–5

Decreasing the frequency of the source changed the variables in the circuit considerably. The reactance of the inductor decreased and that of the capacitor increased. The resulting impedance increased and its angle became negative, indicating that the circuit had taken on the characteristics of an *RC* circuit.

10-3 POWER IN AC CIRCUITS

10-3.1 Introduction. Whenever an AC sinusoidal source is connected to a circuit, or load, current flows through the circuit and power is consumed. There are several different types of power associated with different kinds of AC circuits. The more common types are discussed in the sections that follow.

10-3.2 Instantaneous Power. This is the power consumed by a resistive circuit, or load, at any instant of time. Instantaneous power is the product of instantaneous voltage and current which occurs at a particular angle. Since the voltage and current are in phase in a resistive circuit, the angle is the same for both the voltage and the current. For the circuit appearing in Example 10–6, the power consumed by the load when the voltage and current is at 60° is 7.5 W. The resulting power has two positive alternations. The first is a graph of the product of the voltage and current which occurred during the positive alternation. The second alternation is a graph of the voltage and current during the negative alternation. Since both are negative, the resulting power curve is positive. A positive power curve indicates that a device is consuming power.

Example 10–6   Calculating instantaneous power

Problem

Calculate the instantaneous power consumed by the load for the circuit in Figure 10–6 when the voltage and current are at 60°.

Solution

p = instantaneous power in watts

$p = [(V_{pk}\sin\,\theta)][(I_{pk}\sin\,\theta)] = [(10\ V)(\sin\,60°)][(1\ A)(\sin\,60°)]$

$p = [(10\ V)(0.866)][(1\ A)(0.866)] = 7.5\ W$

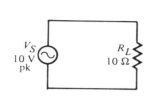 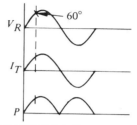

Figure 10–6

10-3.3 Average Power in Resistive Circuits.

This type of power is sometimes called true, real, or effective power and represents the actual power consumed by a circuit, or load, over a full cycle of sinusoidal voltage and current. Average power is the product of voltage, current, and the cosine of the angle between the voltage and current as indicated by Equation (10–3). The voltage and current must both be in rms units.

$$P = (V_{rms})(I_{rms})(\cos\,\theta)\quad \text{in watts} \tag{10–3}$$

Since the current flowing through a resistive circuit is in phase with the source voltage, the cosine factor is equal to one and may be omitted. The average power consumed by the load appearing in Example 10–7 is 5 W.

10-3.4 Average Power in Reactive Circuits.

Circuits containing pure reactance, such as the one appearing in Example 10–8, consume no power. A reactor, such as a capacitor or an inductor, stores energy but does not consume it. Since the voltage and current are displaced 90° in a reactor, the product of one cycle of voltage and current results in two

Example 10–7 Calculating the average power in a resistive circuit

Problem
Compute the average power dissipated by the load in the circuit of Figure 10–7.

Solution

$$P = (V)(I)(\cos \theta) = (7.07 \text{ V})(0.707 \text{ A})(1) = 5 \text{ W}$$
$$V_S = (0.707)(10 \text{ V}_{pk}) = 7.07 \text{ V} \quad I = \frac{V_S}{R_L} = \frac{7.07 \text{ V}}{10 \text{ Ω}} = 0.707 \text{ A}$$

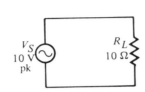

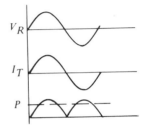

Figure 10–7

Example 10–8 Calculating the average power in a reactive circuit

Problem
Calculate the average power consumed by the circuit shown in Figure 10–8.

Solution
$$P = (V)(I)(\cos \theta) = (7.07 \text{ V})(.707 \text{ A})(\cos 90°) = (5)(0) = 0 \text{ W}$$

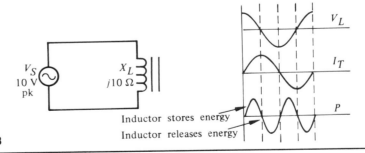

Inductor stores energy
Inductor releases energy

Figure 10–8

cycles of power. The reactor is taking energy from the source and storing it during the positive half-cycle. The energy is returned to the source during the negative half-cycle. Therefore, the net power dissipated by the reactor is zero. The formula for average power confirms this.

10-3.5 **Average Power in Complex Circuits.** Circuits containing both resistance and reactance consume power. However, the only devices which dissipate power are the resistive elements within the circuit. A load having an impedance of $30 + j40$ is connected to an AC source in the circuit appearing in Example 10–9. The power dissipated by the load is the power consumed by the resistor, which is 0.6 W. Either Equation (10–3) or the I^2R form of Watt's law can be used to compute the power consumed in a complex circuit.

Example 10–9 Calculating the average power in a complex circuit

Problem
Calculate the average power consumed by the load appearing in the circuit of Figure 10–9.

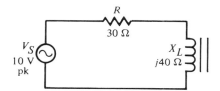

Figure 10–9

Solution

$$P = (V)(I)(\cos \theta) = (7.07 \text{ V})(0.1414 \text{ A})(0.6) = 0.6 \text{ W}$$
$$V = (V_{pk})(0.707) = 7.07 \text{ V}$$
$$I = \frac{V_S}{Z} = \frac{7.07 \text{ V} \angle 0°}{50 \ \Omega \angle 53.1°} = 0.1414 \text{ A} \angle -53.1°$$
$$Z = \sqrt{(R)^2 + (X_L)^2} \angle \tan^{-1} \frac{X_L}{R} = \sqrt{(30)^2 + (40)^2} \angle \tan^{-1} 1.33$$
$$= 50 \ \Omega \angle 53.1°$$
$$\text{or } P = (I)^2(R) = (0.1414)^2(30) = 0.6 \text{ W}$$

10-3.6 **Apparent Power.** Although average power is the power actually consumed by a load, apparent power is often used as a power unit in complex circuits. Apparent power is the product of rms voltage and current without regard to the phase angle between voltage and current, as indicated by Equation (10–4).

$$P_a = (V_{rms})(I_{rms}) \quad \text{in volt-amperes (VA)} \tag{10–4}$$

The unit of measurement for apparent power is the volt-ampere (VA). This is the power the circuit, or load, is apparently consuming. However, for loads containing reactance, the energy stored is eventually returned to the source. The only power consumed is that which is dissipated by the resistive elements in the load. The apparent power consumed by the load in the circuit appearing in Figure 10–9 is 1 VA, as indicated in Example 10–10.

Example 10–10   Calculating the apparent power in a complex circuit

Problem
Compute the apparent power dissipated by the load in the circuit appearing in Example 10–9.

Solution
$P_a = (V)(I) = (7.07 \text{ V})(0.1414 \text{ A}) = 1 \text{ VA}$

10-3.7 Power Factor.   The ratio of the average power consumed by a circuit to the apparent power defines power factor (PF). As indicated by Equation (10–5), power factor is also equal to the cosine of the angular displacement between the voltage and current in a complex circuit.

$$\text{PF} = \frac{\text{Average Power}}{\text{Apparent Power}} = \cos \theta \qquad \text{(10–5)}$$

The power factor may range from a low of zero in a pure reactive circuit to a high of one in a circuit containing only resistance. Power factor is important in high-power circuits. Although a highly reactive load consumes little power, the conductors connecting the source to the load must be large enough to carry the current. To reduce conductor size and to make the system more efficient, it is desirable to maintain the power factor as close to one as possible. This means that the average and apparent powers are nearly equal. In manufacturing plants where large electric motors are often loads, capacitance is often switched into the load circuits to counterbalance the inductive effect of the motors.

The power factor for the circuit shown in Example 10–9 is 0.6 as indicated in Example 10–11.

Example 10–11   Calculating the power factor in a complex circuit

Problem
Compute the power factor of the circuit appearing in Example 10–9.

Solution

$$PF = \frac{\text{Average Power}}{\text{Apparent Power}} = \frac{0.6}{1} = 0.6$$

$$\text{or } PF = \cos\theta = \cos 53.1° = 0.6$$

10-4 RESONANT CIRCUITS

10-4.1 Introduction.   A resonant circuit is one containing an inductor, capacitor, and sometimes a resistor all connected in series or in parallel with each other, and an AC source. The frequency of the source is such that the reactance values of the inductor and capacitor are equal.

10-4.2 Series Resonant Circuits.   Both inductive and capacitive reactance vary with frequency. Inductive reactance is directly proportional to frequency, whereas capacitive reactance varies inversely with frequency. When connected in series with each other and to an AC source, there is some unique frequency which causes both reactances to be equal. This frequency is called the resonant frequency (f_R). The formula for determining the frequency of resonance is derived in Equation (10–6).

$$X_L = 2\pi f L \qquad X_C = \frac{1}{2\pi f C}$$

at resonance $X_L = X_C$

Therefore $2\pi f L = \dfrac{1}{2\pi f C} = 4\pi^2 f^2 LC$

$$f = f_R = \frac{1}{2\pi\sqrt{LC}} = \frac{0.159}{\sqrt{LC}} \qquad \text{in hertz} \qquad\qquad (10\text{--}6)$$

The phase relationship between inductive and capacitive reactance is 180°. Since the reactances are equal at the frequency of resonance, and displaced 180°, they cancel one another, and the only opposition to the flow of current is the resistance in the circuit.

The relationship between frequency, current, and impedance is shown in Figure 10–10. The impedance decreases as the resonant frequency is approached, reaching a minimum at the resonant frequency. As the frequency is increased, the impedance again increases. For frequencies below the frequency of resonance, capacitive reactance is domi-

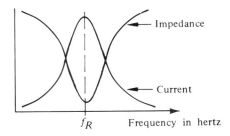

Figure 10–10 The relationship between frequency, impedance, and current in a series resonant circuit.

nant and the circuit behaves capacitively. Inductive reactance is greater than capacitive reactance for frequencies above resonance, and the circuit acts inductively.

The current curve is the inverse of the impedance curve. As the source frequency is increased toward resonance, current increases and reaches its maximum intensity at resonance since the only opposition to the flow of current is resistance. The current decreases for frequencies above resonance.

A series *RLC* circuit appears in Example 10–12. The circuit is resonant at 290.305 kHz and has 0.67 A of current flowing through it. The current has an angle of 0° indicating that the circuit behaves resistively when it is resonant.

Example 10–12 Calculating the resonant frequency and current for a series *RLC* circuit

Problem
Calculate the resonant frequency for the circuit shown in Figure 10–11. Determine the current flowing through the circuit when it is resonant.

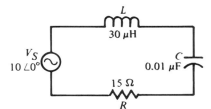

Figure 10–11

Solution

$$f_R = \frac{0.159}{\sqrt{LC}} = \frac{1.59 \times 10^{-1}}{\sqrt{(3 \times 10^{-5})(1 \times 10^{-8})}} = 290{,}305 \text{ Hz}$$

$$I_T = \frac{V_S}{R} = \frac{10 \text{ V} \angle 0°}{15 \text{ } \Omega \angle 0°} = 0.67 \text{ A} \angle 0°$$

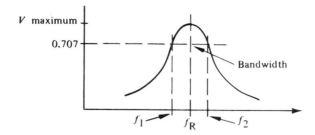

Figure 10–12   Bandwidth for a series resonant circuit.

Although an *RLC* circuit is resonant for a particular frequency, in actual practice it is resonant for a band of frequencies. For the frequency response curve appearing in Figure 10–12, the circuit is considered to be in resonance for those frequencies between f_2 and f_1. Frequencies f_2 and f_1 are called cutoff frequencies and are defined as being those frequencies where the amplitude of the curve is 0.707 times the maximum amplitude value. The difference between the cutoff frequencies is called the bandwidth. Bandwidth is a function of the circuit Q and can be computed using Equation (10–7).

$$\text{Bandwidth (BW)} = f_2 - f_1 = \frac{f_R}{Q} \quad \text{in hertz} \tag{10–7}$$

The circuit depicted in Example 10–13 has a resonant frequency of 503 kHz and has a bandwidth of 15,917.72 H.

Example 10–13   Calculating the bandwidth of a resonant circuit

Problem

Calculate the bandwidth of the circuit appearing in Figure 10–13.

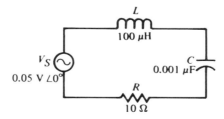

Figure 10–13

Solution

$$f_R = \frac{0.159}{\sqrt{LC}} = \frac{1.59 \times 10^{-1}}{\sqrt{(1 \times 10^{-4})(1 \times 10^{-9})}} = 503 \text{ kHz}$$

$$Q = \frac{X_L}{R} = \frac{316 \ \Omega}{10 \ \Omega} = 31.6$$

$$X_L = 2\pi fL = (2)(3.14)(5.03 \times 10^5)(1 \times 10^{-4}) = 316 \ \Omega$$

$$BW = \frac{f_R}{Q} = \frac{503,000}{31.6} = 15,917.72 \text{ Hz}$$

The upper and lower cutoff frequencies can be calculated from Equations (10–8) and (10–9).

$$f_1 = f_R - \frac{BW}{2} \quad \text{(lower cutoff frequency)} \qquad \textbf{(10–8)}$$

$$f_2 = f_R + \frac{BW}{2} \quad \text{(upper cutoff frequency)} \qquad \textbf{(10–9)}$$

For the circuit shown in Figure 10–13, the lower and upper cutoff frequencies are 495.0411 and 510.9588 kHz, respectively (see Example 10–14).

Example 10–14   Calculating the bandwidth of a series resonant circuit

Problem

Determine the lower and upper cutoff frequencies for the circuit appearing in Figure 10–13. Draw the frequency response curve and identify the cutoff frequencies on the curve (see Figure 10–14).

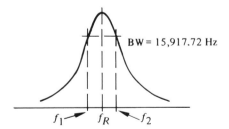

Figure 10–14

Solution

$$f_1 = f_R - \frac{BW}{2} = 503,000 - \frac{15,917.72}{2} = 495,041.1 \text{ Hz}$$

$$f_2 = f_R + \frac{BW}{2} = 503,000 + \frac{15,917.72}{2} = 510,958.8 \text{ Hz}$$

When a series *RLC* or *LC* circuit is in resonance, the voltages developed across both the inductor and capacitor are amplified by a factor of *Q* as illustrated in Example 10–15. With a 50-mV source applied to the circuit, the voltages across the inductor and capacitor are both 31.6 times larger than the source potential. This is one of the desirable features of a series resonant circuit.

Example 10–15   Calculating the voltages across the capacitor and inductor in a series resonant circuit

Problem

Calculate the voltages dropped across both the inductor and capacitor for the circuit appearing in Figure 10–13.

Solution

$$V_L = (I_T)(X_L) = (0.005 \text{ A} \angle 0°)(316 \text{ }\Omega \angle 90°) = 1.58 \text{ V} \angle 90°$$

$$X_L = 2\pi f L = (2)(3.14)(5.03 \times 10^5)(1 \times 10^{-4}) = 316 \text{ }\Omega$$

$$I_T = \frac{V_S}{R} = \frac{0.05 \text{ V} \angle 0°}{10 \text{ }\Omega \angle 0°} = 0.005 \text{ A} \angle 0°$$

or $V_L = (Q)(V_S) = (31.6)(0.05 \text{ V}) = 1.58 \text{ V}$

$$V_C = (I_T)(X_C) = (0.005 \text{ A} \angle 0°)(316 \text{ }\Omega \angle -90°) = 1.58 \text{ V} \angle -90°$$

$$X_C = \frac{1.59 \times 10^{-1}}{(5.03 \times 10^5)(1 \times 10^{-9})} = 316 \text{ }\Omega$$

or $V_C = (Q)(V_S) = (31.6)(0.05 \text{ V}) = 1.58 \text{ V}$

As indicated by Equation (10–7), the bandwidth of a resonant circuit is dependent upon the *Q* of the circuit. Since *Q* represents the ratio of the reactance of the inductor to the circuit resistance, the smaller the circuit resistance, the more narrow the resulting bandwidth. If the resistance of the circuit appearing in Figure 10–13 is reduced to 1 Ω, the circuit *Q* increases to 316. This causes the bandwidth to decrease from 15,917.72 to 1591.77 Hz as indicated in Example 10–16.

Example 10–16   Effect on bandwidth when resistance is decreased

Problem

If the 10-Ω resistor appearing in the circuit shown in Figure 10–13 is replaced with a 1-Ω resistor, calculate the resulting bandwidth of the circuit.

Solution

$$Q = \frac{X_L}{R} = \frac{316 \text{ }\Omega}{1 \text{ }\Omega} = 316$$

$$\text{BW} = \frac{f_R}{Q} = \frac{503,000 \text{ Hz}}{316} = 1591.77 \text{ Hz}$$

If the circuit resistance is increased, the Q of the circuit decreases and the bandwidth increases as shown in Example 10–17.

Example 10–17   Effect on bandwidth where resistance is increased

Problem

Compute the bandwidth of the circuit shown in Figure 10–13 if the 10–Ω resistor is replaced with one having a value of 100 Ω.

Solution

$$Q = \frac{X_L}{R} = \frac{316\ \Omega}{100\ \Omega} = 3.16$$

$$\text{BW} = \frac{f_R}{Q} = \frac{503,000\ \text{Hz}}{3.16} = 159,177.22\ \text{Hz}$$

Resonant circuits are often used as filters. A filter is a circuit which passes electrical signals within a desired frequency band and rejects all others. When a resonant circuit is used as a filter, the signal frequencies to be passed are those appearing between the upper and lower cutoff frequencies. This bandwidth is directly affected by the amount of resistance in the circuit. The smaller the resistance, the narrower the bandwidth. When it is desired to pass a wider band of frequencies, a larger value of resistance is required. The amplitude of the signals to be passed will be less for resonant circuits having a wide bandwidth because the Q has been reduced.

10-4.3 Parallel Resonant Circuits.   A parallel resonant circuit is a circuit consisting of an inductor connected in parallel with a capacitor and whose reactances are equal. The parallel-connected devices are connected to an AC source, as illustrated in Figure 10–15. Because both reactances vary with frequency, there is one particular frequency at which the two reactances are equal. This frequency is called the resonant frequency of the circuit. As indicated in Equation (10–10), the same equation is used to determine the resonant frequency of a parallel circuit as is used to determine the frequency of resonance for a series circuit.

Unlike a series resonant circuit, in which the impedance is minimum and current is maximum at resonance, current is minimum and

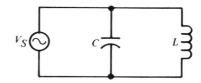

Figure 10–15   Parallel resonant circuit.

$$f_R = \frac{1}{2\pi\sqrt{LC}} = \frac{0.159}{\sqrt{LC}} \quad \text{in hertz} \qquad (10\text{--}10)$$

impedance is maximum in a parallel resonant circuit. This is caused by the two branch currents being displaced 180°, as shown in Figure 10–16 (see Example 10–18). The current flowing through the capacitive branch (I_1) is leading the source voltage by 90°, whereas the current flowing through the inductive branch (I_2) is lagging the source potential by 90°. The net source current (I_T) at points A and B is zero, since the two branch currents are equal in amplitude and 180° apart. The impedance of the network is infinite at the frequency of resonance. In actual circuits, due to the resistance of the inductor and leakage losses of the capacitor, there is a small amount of current flowing from the source. The circuit imped-ance is high but not infinite.

Example 10–18 Calculating the variables associated with a parallel resonant circuit

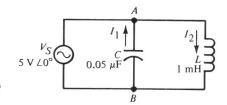

Figure 10–16

Problem

Calculate the resonant frequency, total current flow, and impedance of the parallel LC circuit shown in Figure 10–16.

Solution

$$f_R = \frac{0.159}{\sqrt{LC}} = \frac{0.159}{\sqrt{(1\times10^{-3})(5\times10^{-8})}} = 22{,}500 \text{ Hz}$$

$$I_T = I_1 + I_2 = 35.4 \text{ mA} \angle -90° + 35.4 \text{ mA} \angle 90° = -j35.4 \text{ mA} + j35.4 \text{ mA} = 0$$

$$I_1 = \frac{V_S}{X_C} = \frac{5 \text{ V} \angle 0°}{141.3 \ \Omega \angle -90°} = 35.4 \text{ A} \angle 90°$$

$$I_2 = \frac{V_S}{X_L} = \frac{5 \text{ V} \angle 0°}{141.3 \ \angle 90°} = 35.4 \text{ mA} \angle -90°$$

$$X_L = 2\pi f_R L = (2)(3.14)(0.001)(22{,}500) = 141.3 \ \Omega$$

$$X_C = \frac{0.159}{(f_R)(C)} = \frac{1.59 \times 10^{-1}}{(2.25 \times 10^4)(5 \times 10^{-8})} = 141.3 \ \Omega$$

$$Z_T = \frac{V_S}{I_T} = \frac{5 \text{ V}}{0 \text{ A}} = \text{infinite}$$

The graph of frequency versus current and impedance appears in Figure 10–17. This graph is the inverse of the one shown in Figure 10–10.

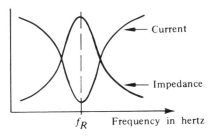

Figure 10–17 Relationship between frequency, impedance, and current in a parallel resonant circuit.

The bandwidth characteristics associated with series resonant circuits also apply for parallel resonant circuits. Parallel resonant circuits have numerous applications. Like series resonant circuits, they are often used as filters. They are also frequently used in the output circuits of amplifier stages and are essential to the operation of sinusoidal oscillators.

10-5 *LC* FILTERS

10-5.1 Introduction. *LC* filters are inductors, capacitors, and sometimes resistors connected together in some configuration to pass certain bands of signal frequencies and attenuate or bypass all others. There are four general types of filters: low-pass, high-pass, band-stop, and band-pass filters.

10-5.2 Low-Pass Filters. Low-pass filters are used to pass low frequency signals and attenuate high frequency signals. A typical low pass filter is shown in Figure 10–18. The filter consists of the inductor and capacitor. The voltage source is one which has many AC signal frequencies present, such as an antenna. The filter will allow DC and low AC signal frequencies to pass to the load. Those electrical signals which have higher frequencies are attenuated and bypassed around the load. The action of the filter is based upon the reactances of the inductor and capacitor. The reactance of the inductor is minimal at low signal frequencies and drops very little voltage. The reactance of the capacitor is high at low signal frequencies, allowing very little low frequency signal current to bypass the load. The low frequency signal current travels through the load as indicated in Figure 10–19.

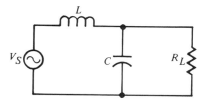

Figure 10–18   Low-pass filter.

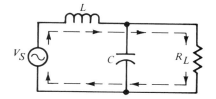

Figure 10–19   Circuit path for low frequency currents.

The reactance of the inductor is high for the higher AC signal frequencies coming from the source, causing a considerable portion of these to be dropped across the inductor. Those high frequency signals not dropped across the inductor are shunted around the load because of the low reactance of the capacitor, as shown in Figure 10–20.

The voltage across the load is depicted in Figure 10–21 and represents the frequency response of the filter. A low-pass *LC* filter does not have a sharp transition from low to high frequencies. Instead, a gradual transition occurs. The cutoff frequency (*f*) is used to identify those signal frequencies the filter will allow to pass. This is defined as being the frequency where the amplitude of the load voltage is down 0.707 from its maximum value.

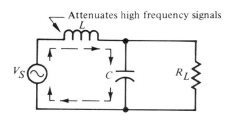

Figure 10–20   Circuit path for high frequency currents.

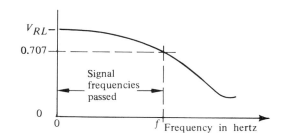

Figure 10–21   Frequency response for a low-pass filter.

10-5.3 High-Pass Filters.   High-pass filters are used to pass high frequency AC signals and attenuate or bypass low frequency electrical signals. A typical high-pass filter appears in Figure 10–22. The reactance of the capacitor is low, whereas the reactance of the inductor is high, for high frequency signals. This allows the high frequency signal currents to flow from the source through the load as indicated in Figure 10–23. On the other hand, the capacitance has a high reactance and the inductor has a low reactance for low frequency signals causing these signals to be at-

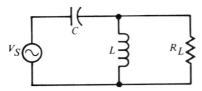
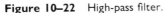

Figure 10–22   High-pass filter.

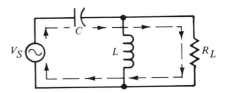

Figure 10–23   Circuit path for high freq uency currents.

tenuated and bypassed around the load, as shown in Figure 10–24. The frequency response curve for the high-pass filter is illustrated in Figure 10–25.

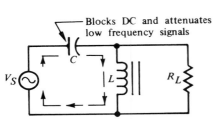

Figure 10–24   Circuit path for low frequency currents.

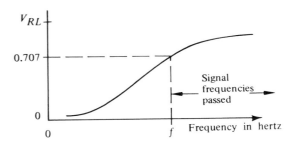

Figure 10–25   Frequency response for a high-pass filter.

10-5.4 Band-Stop (Reject) Filters.   A band-stop filter is one which rejects, by either attenuating or bypassing, a certain narrow band of signal frequencies and passes all others. The circuit diagram for this type of filter appears in Figure 10–26. Values for the inductor and capacitor form a series resonant circuit at the frequency band to be rejected. This offers a low impedance path which bypasses the load for that band of frequencies. The *LC* branch offers a high impedance path for all other signals causing them to flow through the load. The frequency response for this filter appears in Figure 10–27. This filter has two cutoff frequencies, a lower (f_1) and an upper (f_2). The *LC* branch is in resonance midway between the cutoff frequencies.

10-5.5 Band-Pass Filters.   A band-pass filter is shown in Figure 10–28. This filter consists of two resonant circuits: L_1 and C_1 form a series resonant circuit and L_2 and C_2 comprise a parallel resonant circuit. This filter will pass a particular band of signal frequencies and reject, or attenuate, all others. The values of the inductors and capacitors used in both

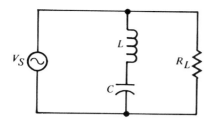

Figure 10–26   Band-stop filter.

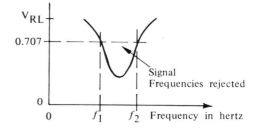

Figure 10–27   Frequency response for a band-stop filter.

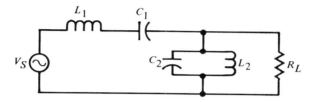

Figure 10–28   Band-pass filter.

resonant circuits are such that both circuits are resonant at the band of signal frequencies to be passed to the load. The series circuit offers little attenuation to the desired band of signal frequencies. At the same time the parallel circuit offers a high impedance to the desired band of signal frequencies, preventing them from bypassing the load. For signal frequencies above and below the desired ones, the series resonant circuit offers a high impedance, causing these signals to be attenuated. At the same time, the parallel resonant circuit provides a low impedance path for the unwanted signal frequencies, causing them to bypass the load. The frequency response for this type of filter is shown in Figure 10–29.

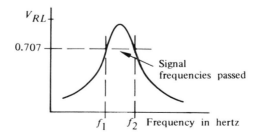

Figure 10–29   Frequency response for a band-pass filter.

SUMMARY

1. A series *RLC* circuit is one containing resistance, inductance, and capacitance, all connected in series.
2. The current flowing through a series *RLC* circuit can either lead or lag the applied voltage depending upon the reactance values of the inductor and capacitor.
3. Power is consumed whenever resistive or complex circuits are connected to an AC source.
4. Two different types of power are of interest in AC resistive circuits: instantaneous and average.
5. Instantaneous power is the product of instantaneous voltage and current and represents the power consumed by resistive devices at a particular voltage and current angle.
6. Average, or true, power represents the amount of power a resistive device consumes during one cycle of voltage and current. In a resistive circuit average power is the product of voltage and current, both in rms units.
7. Power is also consumed by resistive devices connected in complex circuits. Average power for these kinds of circuits is determined by multiplying the rms product of voltage and current by the cosine of the angle between the source voltage and circuit current.
8. In addition to average power, apparent power is sometimes of interest in AC complex circuits. Apparent power is obtained by multiplying the source voltage by the intensity of the current flowing in the circuit (both in rms units). Its unit of measurement is the volt-ampere (VA).
9. Power factor (PF) is the ratio of the actual (average) power consumed in a complex circuit to the power apparently consumed. Power factor is also equal to the cosine of the angle between the source voltage and circuit current. This ratio should be as close to one as possible for high power circuits.
10. A series *LC* or *RLC* circuit is resonant when the reactances of the inductor and capacitor are equal. The single unique frequency at which the reactances are equal is called the resonant frequency.
11. In a series resonant circuit the inductive and capacitive reactances cancel one another and the only opposition to the flow of current is the DC resistance appearing in the circuit. At resonance, the current flowing through the circuit is in phase with the source voltage.
12. In a series *LC* or *RLC* circuit, the impedance is minimum and the current flowing through the circuit is maximum at the resonant frequency of the circuit.
13. An inductor connected in parallel with a capacitor also has a resonant frequency. This type of circuit is called a parallel resonant circuit.
14. In a parallel resonant circuit the impedance is maximum and the source current is minimum at the resonant frequency.
15. Usually *LC* and *RLC* circuits will not resonate at frequencies below 10,000 Hz due to the large sizes of the inductor and capacitor required.
16. For all practical purposes, a resonant circuit is not resonant for a single frequency. Instead, it is resonant for a band of frequencies.

17. The frequencies at which an *LC* or *RLC* circuit is resonant represents the bandwidth of the circuit. The bandwidth of a resonant circuit represents those frequencies located between the upper and lower cutoff frequencies.
18. Bandwidth is a function of the *Q* of the circuit. This implies that the resistance of the circuit directly affects the bandwidth of a resonant circuit.
19. The voltages appearing across the inductor and capacitor of a series resonant circuit are amplified by a factor of *Q*.
20. There are four general categories of filters: low-pass, high-pass, band-stop, and band-pass filters.
21. A low-pass filter passes DC and low frequency AC electrical signals and attenuates or bypasses high frequency signals.
22. A high-pass filter passes high frequency electrical signals and attenuates or bypasses DC and low frequency signals.
23. A band-stop filter rejects a particular band of signal frequencies and allows signal frequencies below and above the rejected band of frequencies to pass.
24. A band-pass filter passes a particular band of signal frequencies and rejects all others.

PRACTICE EXERCISES

1. A series *RLC* circuit consists of a 10-kΩ resistor, a 2-H inductor, and a capacitor which has a value of 0.005 μF. If the circuit is connected to a 20-V rms source which has a frequency of 1000 Hz, calculate the impedance of the circuit.
2. What is the intensity of the current flowing through the circuit described in exercise 1?
3. Calculate the voltage across the resistor, inductor, and capacitor for the circuit identified in exercise 1.
4. A 50-Ω resistor, a 25-pF capacitor, and a 10-mH choke are all connected in series. Calculate the resonant frequency of the circuit.
5. Determine the current flowing in the circuit identified in exercise 4 if the source potential is 100 mV rms.
6. Calculate the voltage dropped across each of the devices in the circuit described in exercise 4.
7. Compute the bandwidth and the lower and upper cutoff frequencies for the circuit described in exercise 4.
8. In a series *RLC* circuit indicate the phase relationship between the applied voltage and circuit current when the circuit is
   a. in resonance
   b. below resonance
   c. above resonance
9. What is the relationship between frequency and current in a series resonant circuit?
10. What is the relationship between impedance and frequency in a series resonant circuit?
11. Describe the relationship between frequency and current in a parallel resonant circuit.

12. A 1-H inductor is connected in parallel with a 3-pF capacitor. Calculate the resonant frequency of the circuit.
13. A 100-Ω resistor is connected in series with a capacitor having a reactance of 100 Ω. The circuit is connected to a 200-V rms source. Calculate the average power consumed by the circuit.
14. Determine the apparent power consumed by the circuit described in exercise 13.
15. What is the power factor for the circuit identified in exercise 13?
16. A 47-Ω resistor is connected to a generator whose output voltage is 15 V rms. Determine the instantaneous power dissipated by the resistor when the current and voltage are at 83°.
17. List two applications for resonant circuits.
18. Define the term *resonance*.
19. What is the significance of the power factor in a complex circuit?
20. Identify the four general types of filters and describe the characteristics of each.

ANSWERS TO PRACTICE EXERCISES

1. $Z = \sqrt{(R)^2 + (-X_C + X_L)^2} \angle \tan^{-1} \frac{-XC + XL}{R}$

   $Z = \sqrt{(10,000)^2 + (-31,800 + 12,560)^2} \angle \tan^{-1} \frac{-19,240}{10,000} = 21,683 \ \Omega \angle -62.5°$

2. $I_T = \dfrac{V_S}{Z} = \dfrac{20 \text{ V} \angle 0°}{21,683 \ \Omega \angle -62.5°} = .922 \text{ mA} \angle 62.5°$

3. $V_R = (I_T)(R) = (0.000922 \text{ A} \angle 62.5°)(10,000 \ \Omega \angle 0°) = 9.22 \text{ V} \angle 62.5°$
   $V_L = (I_T)(X_L) = (0.000922 \text{ A} \angle 62.5°)(12,560 \ \Omega \angle 90°) = 11.58 \text{ V} \angle 152.5°$
   $V_C = (I_T)(X_C) = (0.000922 \text{ A} \angle 62.5°)(31,800 \ \Omega \angle -90°) = 29.32 \text{ V} \angle -27.5°$

4. $f_R = \dfrac{0.159}{\sqrt{LC}} = \dfrac{0.159}{\sqrt{(1 \times 10^{-2})(2.5 \times 10^{-11})}} = 318,000 \text{ Hz}$

5. $I_T = \dfrac{0.01 \text{ V} \angle 0°}{50 \ \Omega \angle 0°} = 0.002 \text{ A} \angle 0°$

6. $V_R = (I_T)(R) = (0.002 \text{ A} \angle 0°)(50 \ \Omega \angle 0°) = 0.1 \text{ V} \angle 0°$
   $V_C = (I_T)(X_C) = (0.002 \text{ A} \angle 0°)(20,000 \ \Omega \angle -90° = 40 \text{ V} \angle -90°$
   $X_C = \dfrac{0.159}{(f_R)(C)} = \dfrac{0.159}{(3.18 \times 10^5)(2.5 \times 10^{-11})} = 20,000 \ \Omega \angle -90°$
   $X_L = 2\pi f_R L = (2)(3.14)(318,000)(0.01) = 20,000 \ \Omega \angle 90°$
   $V_L = (I_T)(X_L) = (0.002 \text{ A} \angle 0°)(20,000 \ \Omega \angle 90°) = 40 \text{ V} \angle 90°$

7. $\text{BW} = \dfrac{f_R}{Q} = \dfrac{318,000 \text{ Hz}}{400} = 795 \text{ Hz}$

   $Q = \dfrac{X_L}{R} = \dfrac{20,000 \ \Omega}{50 \ \Omega} = 400$

$$f_1 = f_R - \frac{BW}{2} = 318{,}000 - \frac{795}{2} = 317{,}602.5 \text{ Hz}$$

$$f_2 = f_R + \frac{BW}{2} = 318{,}000 + \frac{795}{2} = 318{,}397.5 \text{ Hz}$$

8. **a.** The voltage and current are in phase at resonance.
   b. The circuit behaves capacitively below resonance. The current will lead the source voltage.
   c. Above resonance, the circuit acts inductively and the current flowing through the circuit leads the applied voltage.
9. The current increases as the source frequency approaches the resonant frequency of the circuit. At the frequency of resonance the current flowing through the circuit reaches its maximum value. As the source frequency is increased above the resonant frequency of the circuit, current begins to decrease.
10. As the source frequency approaches resonance, the impedance decreases, reaching a minimum at the resonant frequency of the circuit. The impedance increases as the source frequency is increased above the resonant frequency of the circuit.
11. In a parallel resonant circuit the source current decreases as the source frequency approaches the resonant frequency of the circuit. The current is minimum when the source frequency is equal to the resonant frequency of the circuit.

12. $f_R = \dfrac{0.159}{\sqrt{LC}} = \dfrac{1.59 \times 10^{-1}}{\sqrt{(1)(3 \times 10^{-12})}} = 91{,}907 \text{ Hz}$

13. $P = (I_T)(V_S)(\cos \theta) = (1.414 \text{ A})(200 \text{ V})(0.707) = 200 \text{ W}$

    $I_T = \dfrac{V_S}{Z} = \dfrac{200 \text{ V} \angle 0°}{141.4 \text{ } \Omega \angle -45°} = 1.414 \text{ A} \angle + 45°$

    $Z = \sqrt{(R)^2 + (Xc)^2} \angle \tan^{-1} \frac{-XC}{R} = \sqrt{(100)^2 + (100)^2} \angle \tan^{-1} -1 = 141.4 \text{ } \Omega \angle -45°$

14. $P_a = (V_S)(I_T) = (200 \text{ V})(1.414 \text{ A}) = 282.8 \text{ VA}$

15. $\text{PF} = \dfrac{P}{P_a} = \dfrac{200}{282.8} = 0.707$

16. $p = (V_{pk})(\sin 83°)][(I_{pk})(\sin 83°)]$

    $V_{pk} = \dfrac{15 \text{ V}}{0.707} = 21.22 \text{ V}; \ I_{pk} = \dfrac{21.22}{47 \text{ } \Omega} = 0.451 \text{ A}$

    $p = [(21.22 \text{ V})(0.992)][(0.451 \text{ A})(0.992)] = 9.41 \text{ W}$

17. Series and parallel resonant circuits are both often used as filters. A parallel resonant circuit is often used in the output circuit of a high-frequency amplifier.
18. Resonance occurs in an *LC* or *RLC* circuit when the reactances of the inductor and capacitor are equal.
19. Power factor represents the ratio of the power actually consumed in a complex circuit to the power apparently consumed. The apparent power is the

product of the source voltage and circuit current. When large values of reactance are present in the circuit, the conductors have to be large enough to
carry the extra current. The excessive current causes power losses along the
conductors, which decrease the efficiency of the system. It is important that
the apparent power have approximately the same value as the average
power.

20. Low-pass filters pass DC and low AC signal frequencies. They attenuate or
bypass AC signal frequencies.
High-pass filters pass high-frequency AC signals and attenuate or bypass DC
and low-frequency signals.
Band-stop filters attenuate or bypass a particular band of signal frequencies
and pass all others.
Band-pass filters pass a particular band of frequencies and reject all others.

CHAPTER EXAMINATION

1. A 50-Ω resistor is connected in series with an inductor which has a reactance
of 100 Ω. The circuit is connected to a 100-V rms source. Calculate the actual
power consumed by the circuit.
2. For the circuit described in question 2, compute the power apparently consumed by the circuit.
3. What is the power factor for the circuit identified in question 1?
4. A series *RLC* circuit is made up of a resistor having a value of 25 Ω, an inductor having a reactance of 70 Ω, and a capacitor which has a reactance of 40 Ω.
If the circuit is connected to a 2-V rms source, what is the impedance of the
circuit?
5. How much current is flowing in the circuit described in question 4?
6. For the circuit identified in question 4, calculate the voltage dropped across
the resistor, inductor, and capacitor.
7. A 250-mH choke is connected in parallel with a 0.005-μF capacitor. Calculate
the resonant frequency of the circuit.
8. A 25-Ω resistor is connected in series with a 0.0047-μF capacitor and a 100-μH
inductor. The circuit is connected to a 100-mV rms source. What is the resonant frequency of the circuit?
9. How much current is flowing in the circuit described in question 8 at
resonance?
10. What is the Q of the circuit identified in question 8?
11. What is the bandwidth of the circuit described in question 8?
12. How much power is dissipated by the circuit described in question 8?
13. A resistor having a value of 10 Ω is connected to an AC generator whose output voltage is 50 V peak. Calculate the instantaneous power dissipated by the
resistor at 60°.
14. What is the average power consumed by the load in the circuit described in
question 13?

Choose true or false for questions 15 to 22.
15. T   F   In a series resonant circuit the impedance is minimum and the current is maximum at the resonant frequency.

16. T F   The current flowing through a series *RLC* circuit is always in phase with the source voltage when the circuit is in resonance.
17. T F   A high-pass filter bypasses or attenuates all high-frequency electrical signals and passes DC and low frequency AC signals.
18. T F   Ideally, the only device which consumes power in an AC complex circuit is the resistor.
19. T F   An *LC* or *RLC* circuit is in resonance when the inductive or capacitive values are equal.
20. T F   For maximum efficiency, the power factor in a complex circuit should be as close to zero as possible.
21. T F   A series resonant circuit is often used to correct the power factor.
22. T F   The average power consumed by a complex circuit may be obtained by multiplying the product of rms voltage and current by the power factor of the circuit.

PART TWO

Linear Circuits

The *PN* Junction Diode
The Bipolar Junction Transistor
The Field-Effect Transistor
Special Semiconductor Devices
Rectifier Circuits
Voltage Amplifier Circuits
Linear Integrated Circuits
Power Amplifier Circuits
Oscillator Circuits

11

The *PN* Junction Diode

OBJECTIVES

Upon completion of this chapter you should be able to do the following:

1. Identify the two elements commonly used as semiconductor materials.
2. Describe what is meant by covalent bonding.
3. Discuss the purpose of doping semiconductor materials, identify the two general types of dopants, and list three elements used for each type.
4. Explain how a *PN* junction is formed.
5. Draw the energy diagram for a *PN* junction.
6. Describe how the barrier potential is formed about the *PN* junction.
7. Describe what a diode is.
8. Discuss the purpose of biasing a diode.
9. Draw the schematic diagram of a *PN* diode showing the proper biasing connections for both forward and reverse bias.
10. Describe, with the aid of diagrams, how current flows through the diode for both forward- and reverse-bias conditions.
11. Discuss how a diode operates as a switch.
12. Discuss the differences between an ideal diode and an actual one.
13. Identify the majority and minority current carriers for both *P*- and *N*-type semiconductor materials.
14. Describe the cause of reverse current flow in a reverse-biased diode circuit.
15. List two other names associated with reverse current.
16. Draw the volt-ampere curve for a diode for both forward- and reverse-bias conditions and identify the threshold and avalanche breakdown potentials on the curve.
17. Discuss the cause of avalanche breakdown.
18. Identify the amplitude of the bias potentials required to overcome the barrier potentials for both germanium and silicon diodes.

249

II-I INTRODUCTION

This begins the second part of the book. This section is concerned with solid-state (semiconductor) devices, circuits, and systems which have linear, or analog, applications. There are two general types of circuits—passive and active. Passive circuits are those included in Part One of the book. These circuits may contain resistors, capacitors, and inductors which are connected together to perform various functions. Active circuits contain devices such as transistors, integrated circuits, and electron tubes in addition to utilizing resistors, capacitors, and inductors. There are two subclassifications of active circuits—linear and digital. Linear circuits are those in which the active devices are operated in the linear region of their operating range. Although the terms *linear* and *analog* are sometimes used interchangeably, there is a slight difference in meaning between the two. An analog circuit is one whose input and output signals, for the most part, are linearly related. The chapters in this section deal with semiconductor devices and circuits which utilize these kinds of devices for linear purposes.

II-2 SEMICONDUCTOR PRINCIPLES

11-2.1 Covalent Bonding. Semiconductor materials are elements located in the fourth column of the Periodic Chart of the Elements. These elements all have four valence electrons. Although several elements are located in the fourth column, the two materials most often used in the manufacture of solid-state devices are germanium and silicon. Germanium has an atomic number of 32 and the atomic number of silicon is 14. Both of these materials have four valence electrons. The electron distribution for both the silicon and germanium atoms are shown in Figure 11–1.

The atom is a very small particle. Billions are required to form a substance large enough to be visible. Atoms are joined, or bonded, together with other atoms a number of different ways to form larger substances. Crystalline materials, which include semiconductors, utilize covalent bonding. Adjacent atoms share valence band electrons and are attached to one another by the electrostatic force existing between the electrons and nuclei of the atoms when covalent bonded. Both the germanium and silicon atoms require eight valence electrons for that band to be filled. As illustrated in Figure 11–2, adjacent atoms share electrons so that the individual atoms appear to have a full complement of eight electrons in their valence band.

Figure 11–1   Electron distribution for the silicon and germanium atoms: (a) silicon; (b) germanium.

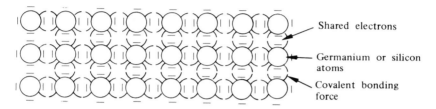

Shared electrons

Germanium or silicon atoms

Covalent bonding force

Figure 11–2   Covalent bonding diagram.

11-2.2 Energy Levels.   The paths in which electrons travel about the nucleus of an atom, as illustrated in Figure 11–1, represent energy levels within a single atom. Because of the overlapping of energy levels when individual atoms are attached together, a diagram such as the one appearing in Figure 11–3 is useful when referring to the energy levels of electrons in a substance composed of many millions of atoms. This type of diagram shows the energy levels for only the valence and conduction bands. A forbidden region exists between the two bands. For current flow to occur, energy has to be imparted to the material to raise electrons from the valence band into the conduction band. The width of the forbidden region varies, depending upon the type of material. It is wide for insulators, narrower for semiconductors, and slightly overlaps for conductors, as illustrated in Figure 11–4. This helps explain why less voltage is

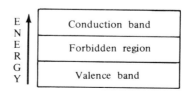

Figure 11–3   Energy diagram for a substance.

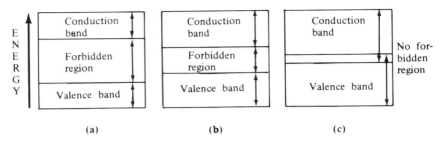

Figure 11–4   Energy diagrams for various classes of substances: (a) insulators; (b) semiconductors; (c) conductors.

required to cause current to flow through a conductor than through an insulator.

11-2.3 Semiconductor Materials.   Germanium and silicon in their pure state are called intrinsic semiconductors. They have a rather high resistance. Special impurities, called dopants, are added to the germanium or silicon during the manufacturing process to reduce their resistance by introducing additional current carriers. Impurities are elements whose atomic numbers appear in either the third or fifth columns of the Periodic Chart of the Elements.

Impurities located in the fifth column of the periodic chart are called donors. These elements have five valence band electrons. Elements often used as donors include arsenic, antimony, and phosphorous.

Dopant materials located in the third column of the periodic chart are called acceptors. They contain three valence electrons. Commonly used acceptor elements include aluminum, gallium, and indium.

Semiconductor crystals are grown in a vacuum under very tightly controlled conditions. During the manufacturing process small amounts of dopants, in gaseous form, are added to the germanium or silicon materials. For every approximately one million semiconductor atoms, 5 to 10 dopant atoms are added (5 to 10 ppm). As indicated in Figure 11–5, when a dopant atom which has five valence electrons (donor) is added to the semiconductor material, the atom enters into the material and becomes part of it. Four of the five electrons are shared with the adjacent germanium or silicon atoms. The remaining electron does not enter into the covalent bonding structure. Instead, it is loosely attached to the dopant atom. This electron can easily be raised into the conduction band and becomes a current carrier with the application of voltage. Semiconductor materials which have been doped with donor elements are called *N*-type semiconductors since current conduction is by negative charges (electrons).

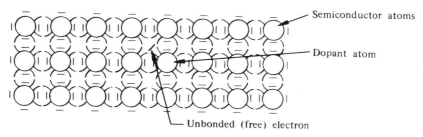

Semiconductor atoms

Dopant atom

Unbonded (free) electron

Figure 11–5 Covalent bonding diagram of a semiconductor material which has been doped with a donor atom.

Dopant materials which have three valence electrons are called acceptor dopants. An acceptor atom is shown in the covalent bonding diagram appearing in Figure 11–6. Since the atom has only three valence electrons, a hole which represents the absence of an electron appears in the bonding structure. Because the hole represents an absence of an electron, it represents a positive charge. With the application of voltage, an electron from a nearby atom can be attracted to the hole creating a hole where that electron was. An electron from a neighboring atom can fill this hole, creating yet another hole which can be filled. This process continues so that the hole "wanders" throughout the covalent-bonded structure. Semiconductor materials which have been doped with acceptor dopants are called *P*-type semiconductors because the current conduction is by holes or positive charges.

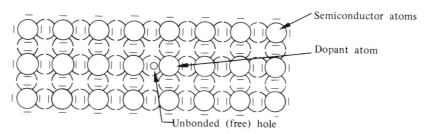

Semiconductor atoms

Dopant atom

Unbonded (free) hole

Figure 11–6 Covalent bonding diagram of a semiconductor material which has been doped with an acceptor atom.

11-2.4 Current Conduction in Semiconductors. Like any material through which current flows, a voltage source has to be connected to the doped semiconductor material to raise valence band electrons to the conduction band, as illustrated in Figure 11–7. Conduction in *N*-type semiconductors is very similar to conduction in conductors. The repelling

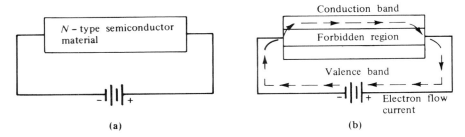

Figure 11–7 Current flow through an *N*-type semiconductor: (a) voltage source connected to donor-doped semiconductor; (b) current conduction in donor-doped semiconductor.

force between the negative terminal of the battery and the donor electrons and the attracting force between the positive terminal of the battery and electrons cause electrons to flow through the material from the negative to the positive end, as shown in Figure 11–7(b). The direction of electron flow in the external circuit is from the negative terminal of the battery, through the conductor connecting the negative terminal to the semiconductor, through the semiconductor, and back to the positive terminal of the battery via the conductor. The electrons which flow through the semiconductor are primarily those introduced by the donor atoms.

Current conduction is different for *P*-type material, as indicated in Figure 11–8. In this type of semiconductor current conduction consists of hole flow which occurs in the valence band. In the diagram appearing below an electron from the negative terminal of the battery recombines with a hole located at the left side of the material. As equilibrium has to be maintained, an electron leaves the right side of the material, creating a new hole. An electron will fill this hole, causing a new hole to be created. This process continues so that the movement of holes is opposite in direction to that of the electrons. Hole flow occurs only in semiconductor

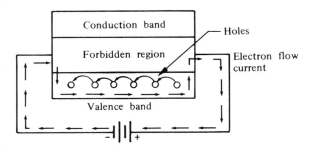

Figure 11–8 Current flow through a *P*-type semiconductor.

and other crystalline materials. It does not occur in conductors and should not be confused with conventional current. Hole flow occurs in the valence band of semiconductor materials.

11-3 THE *PN* JUNCTION DIODE

11-3.1 Forming the Junction. N- and P-doped semiconductor materials, by themselves, have only limited application. At best, they can be used as resistors where the resistivity of the material depends upon the amount of impurities added during the manufacturing process. To form a practical semiconductor device, a *P* section and an *N* section are both grown during the manufacturing process. This is accomplished by first introducing acceptor dopants during the growing process and, after a period of time, introducing donor impurities to the germanium or silicon material. This forms a semiconductor device such as that depicted in Figure 11–9. A *PN* junction is formed where the *P* section joins the *N* section. The *PN* junction is a molecular one formed during the growing process and is not merely a physical or mechanical coupling between the two sections. This two-section semiconductor device is called a diode.

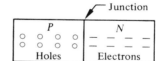

Figure 11–9 *PN* junction diode.

It is interesting to note the energy levels of the respective *P* and *N* sections of the diode as they appear in Figure 11–10. The *P*-section valence and conduction bands are at a higher energy level than those in the *N* section. A transistion occurs at the *PN* junction where the energy levels between the two sections come together.

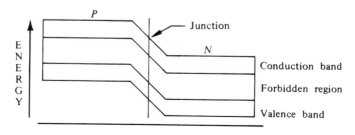

Figure 11–10 Energy levels for a *PN* junction diode.

During the growing process some of the mobile electrons in the N section move across the junction and recombine with holes in the P section. This results in the formation of positive ions in the immediate vicinity of the junction in the N section and the creation of negative ions in the vicinity of the junction in the P section, as illustrated in Figure 11–11. This forms a small voltage across the junction which is called the barrier, or junction, potential. This voltage is approximately 0.3 V for germanium semiconductor devices and 0.7 V for silicon.

As shown in Figure 11–12, the area in the immediate region of the junction is called the depletion region. This region is void of current carriers since the mobile electrons from the N section have crossed the junction and recombined with holes in the P section. The ions created on either side of the junction prevent further electron-hole recombinations from occurring. In addition to the barrier potential, a small junction capacitance made up of the P and N sections and the depletion region is associated with all PN junctions.

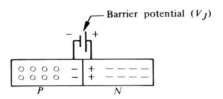

Figure 11–11   Formation of the barrier potential.

11-3.2 Purpose of Forward Bias.   An external voltage source, called a bias supply, must be connected across the ends of the two semiconductor sections to cause the device to conduct. The amplitude of the source must be great enough to overcome the barrier potential. The positive terminal of the bias supply is connected to the P section and the negative terminal is connected to the N section for forward-bias conditions to occur, as shown in Figure 11–13.

Forward bias establishes the conditions required for the diode to turn on, or conduct. The energy levels between the P and N sections are

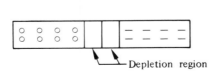

Figure 11–12   The depletion region.

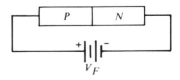

Figure 11–13   Forward biased *PN* junction diode.

brought into equilibrium and the width of the depletion region is reduced, as illustrated in Figure 11–14.

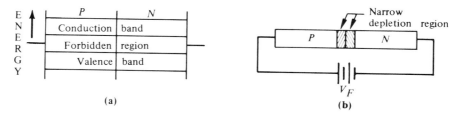

Figure 11–14   Energy levels in a forward biased *PN* junction diode: (a) energy levels; (b) depletion width.

As shown in Figure 11–15, current flow in the N section consists of electrons which travel through the conduction band. They cross the junction and drop into the valence band of the P section where they recombine with holes. Conduction through the P section is by hole flow. For every hole which is filled by an electron crossing the junction, a new one is produced by an electron in the P section being attracted to the positive terminal of the bias supply.

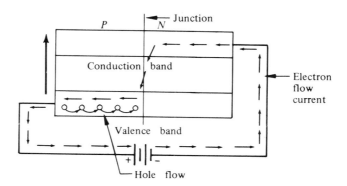

Figure 11–15   Current flow through a forward biased *PN* junction diode.

11-3.3 Purpose of Reverse-Bias.   The diode is reverse biased by the bias supply when the negative terminal of the source is connected to the P section and the positive terminal is connected to the N section, as shown in Figure 11–16. Reverse-bias increases the difference in energy levels between the N and P sections, as indicated in Figure 11–17. At the same time, current carriers in the vicinity of the junction are pulled, in opposite directions, away from the junction, as depicted in Figure 11–18.

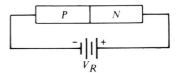

Figure 11–16   Reverse-biased *PN* junction diode.

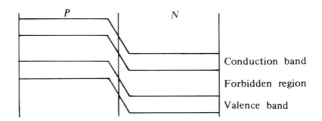

Figure 11–17   Energy levels in a reverse-biased *PN* junction diode.

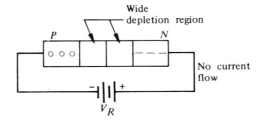

Figure 11–18   Depletion region in a reverse-biased *PN* junction diode.

This causes the depletion region to widen. There is no conduction through the diode because there are no electrons in the vicinity of the junction in the N section to cross the junction and recombine with holes in the P section. The purpose of reverse-bias is to ensure that the diode does not conduct.

    11-3.4 The Analogy of a Diode and a Switch.   The schematic symbol appearing in Figure 11–19 is used to represent the *PN* junction diode. The arrowhead is called the anode and the line touching the arrowhead is called the cathode. The *PN* semiconductor device is called a diode because it is made up of two sections—an anode and a cathode. The diode operates in a circuit as a switch. For the circuit appearing in Figure 11–20, when the switch is in the closed position, current flows through the load and the voltage drop across the load is equal to the source voltage (10 V).

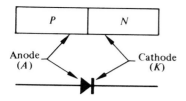

Figure 11–19 Schematic symbol for a *PN* junction diode.

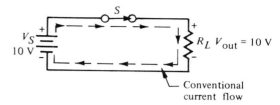

Figure 11–20 Current flows through a load when the switch is closed and the circuit is complete.

The switch has been replaced by a diode in Figure 11–21. The polarity of the bias supply is such that it forward biases the diode. Current flows through the circuit and the voltage drop across the load is again 10 V, just as it was for the circuit shown in Figure 11–20. As far as the voltage source and load were concerned, it didn't matter whether the switch or the diode were in the circuit; the results were the same. Notice the direction of current flow in the circuit. Current flows in the direction of the anode arrow through the diode.

The switch is opened for the circuit whose diagram appears in Figure 11–22. Since current cannot flow through the circuit, the voltage across the load is zero. The switch has been replaced by a diode in Figure 11–23. The polarity of the supply voltage is such that it reverse biases the

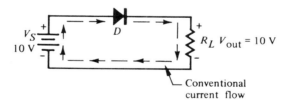

Figure 11–21 Current flows through a load when the diode is forward biased.

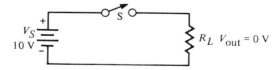

Figure 11–22 Current does not flow through a load when the switch is open and the circuit is incomplete.

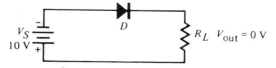

Figure 11–23 Current does not flow through a load when the diode is reverse-biased.

diode so that current does not flow through the circuit. The load voltage is zero just as it was for the open switch in the circuit appearing in Figure 11–22. By observing the circuits appearing in Figures 11–20 through 11–23, one can see that the diode behaves as a switch. Current flows through the circuit when the diode is forward biased and the device operates as a switch in the closed position. When the diode is reverse biased, it acts like a switch in the open position and current cannot flow through the load.

The term *semiconductor* comes from the idea that the diode allows current to flow through a circuit when it is forward biased and doesn't allow current to pass when it is reverse biased. It passes current in one direction but not the other.

The circuits whose diagrams appear in Figures 11–21 and 11–23 utilized a DC source to forward and reverse bias the diode. Actually, the bias voltage does not have to be a constant source. Any voltage source high enough in amplitude to overcome the barrier potential will cause the diode to conduct. A sinusoidal voltage is connected to the circuit appearing in Figure 11–24. During the positive alternation the diode is forward biased and current flows through the load producing a voltage equal in amplitude to the input voltage. The diode is reverse biased during the negative half-cycle. Current cannot flow through the circuit and the voltage across the load is zero. Comparing the input and output voltages in Figure 11–25, it becomes apparent that a series of sinusoidal voltages will alternately forward and reverse bias a diode. The negative alternations do not appear across the load.

Figure 11–24 Diode biased by a sinusoidal voltage source.

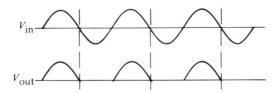

Figure 11–25 Comparison of the input and output voltages of a diode biased with a sinusoidal source.

11-3.5 Diode Analysis.   It was found in the previous section that a diode will function as a switch in a circuit if it is properly biased. In this section the electrical properties of a diode will be considered in greater detail. Although a diode does indeed perform the functions of a switch, it operates as an imperfect one. One must be aware of those electrical properties which are unique to *PN* junction devices.

It is advantageous to approach the analysis of the *PN* junction diode from an "ideal" diode point of view, develop some approximations for the device, and then consider the device as it actually exists. An ideal diode and a switch have the same electrical characteristics. As indicated in Figure 11–26, a switch has 0 Ω resistance and 0 V across its contacts in the closed position. The applied voltage is dropped across the load and not the switch. This is illustrated by the volt-ampere curve appearing in Figure 11–27. Volt-ampere curves are graphs of the voltage across and the current flowing through electrical devices. They are often useful in analyzing components.

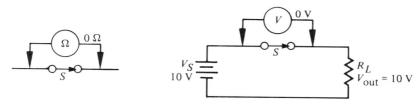

Figure 11–26   Electrical characteristics of a closed switch.

Figure 11–27   The volt-ampere curve for a switch in the closed position.

When the switch is opened, it exhibits an infinite resistance, no current flows through the circuit, and the source voltage appears across the switch, as indicated in Figure 11–28. The volt-ampere curve for this condition appears in Figure 11–29.

The switch shown in the circuit appearing in Figure 11–26 has been replaced by a forward biased diode in the circuit shown in Figure 11–30. The volt-ampere curve is the same as that for the closed switch.

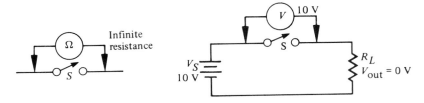

Figure 11–28   Electrical characteristics of an open switch.

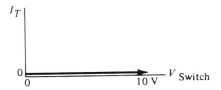

Figure 11–29   Volt-ampere curve for a switch in the open position.

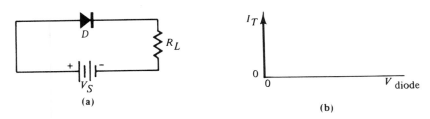

Figure 11–30   (a) Forward-biased diode; (b) volt-ampere curve for a forward-biased ideal diode closed switch.

The diode is shown reverse-biased in Figure 11–31. As such, no current flows through the circuit, the voltage across the load is zero, and the source voltage appears across the diode. The volt-ampere curve is exactly like that of the open switch.

Although the ideal diode is useful in explaining the basic operation of the diode, it does not take into account the electrical variables which exist in actual devices. The ideal diode allows one to approximate the action of a diode in a circuit. An actual diode has variables which cause it to deviate from the ideal. One of these is the junction, or barrier, potential. This value is approximately 0.3 V for germanium diodes and 0.7 V for silicon devices. To conduct, the junction potential must be overcome by the bias supply. The operation of the diode can be more closely approximated by taking into account the junction potential. The resulting equivalent diagram and volt-ampere curve appear in Figure 11–32.

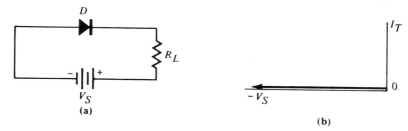

Figure 11–31   (a) reverse-biased diode; (b) volt-ampere curve for a reverse-biased ideal diode.

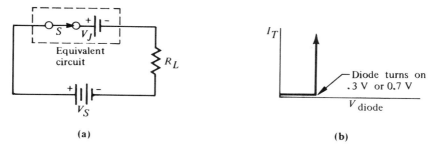

Figure 11–32   (a) Equivalent circuit and (b) volt-ampere characteristic for a forward biased diode with junction potential indicated.

Another variable which sometimes has to be considered is resistance. An ideal diode has no resistance. An actual diode, on the other hand, does have resistance, as illustrated in Figure 11–33. The *P* and *N* sections both exhibit resistance. The two resistances can be combined and formed into one lumped resistance, as shown in Figure 11–33(b). This single resistance is called a bulk resistance and is dependent upon the dopant level and size of the semiconductor material. Resistance modifies the volt-ampere curve so that it appears as depicted in Figure 11–34. The resulting equivalent circuit consists of a switch, battery, and resistance, all connected in series. The diode will not turn on until the bias supply

Figure 11–33   Diode resistance: (a) *P* and *N* section resistance; (b) lumped bulk resistance.

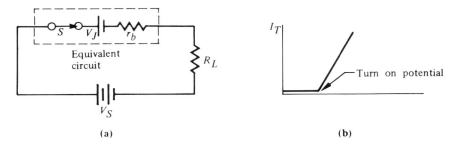

Figure 11–34   (a) Equivalent circuit and (b) volt-ampere curve for a forward biased diode.

reaches the barrier potential. After the diode turns on, current increases linearly as it does through a resistor.

The resistance of an actual diode is somewhat nonlinear and depends upon the amount of current flowing through the device. This causes the volt-ampere curve to appear as that shown in Figure 11–35. There is a significant amount of nonlinearity in the region where the device turns on. After the diode begins conducting, the resistance is rather constant as indicated by the slope of the volt-ampere curve. The voltage at which the diode turns on is sometimes referred to as the threshold potential.

The third and last variable which must be considered when comparing an ideal diode with an actual device is reverse current. The ideal diode has no current flowing through it when it is reverse-biased. It behaves like an open switch. In an actual diode the depletion region widens under reverse-bias conditions. Although this region is depleted of free-current carriers created by the dopant elements, a few silicon or germanium electrons absorb enough heat energy to be elevated from the valence band into the conduction band. This creates current carriers—electrons in the conduction band and holes in the valence band, as illustrated in Figure 11–36. These are called minority current carriers. The minority carriers in the *P* section are electrons while those in the *N* section are holes. All diodes will have some minority current carriers when operated in an environment above absolute zero. The amount of minority current carriers created depends upon the temperature; the warmer the environ-

Figure 11–35   Volt-ampere characteristic for a forward-biased diode.

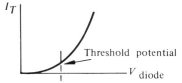

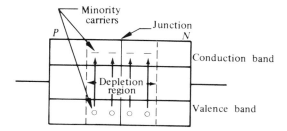

Figure 11–36 Creation of minority current carriers.

ment in which the diode operates, the greater the amount of minority carriers created. When the diode is reverse-biased, the polarity of the bias supply is such that reverse current flows through the circuit, as shown in Figure 11–37. For a given temperature, reverse current is rather constant. Reverse current, sometimes called leakage or cutoff current, is small for most diodes. It is usually in the range of a few microamperes.

If the reverse-bias supply appearing in Figure 11–37 is increasingly made more negative, a potential is finally reached where the reverse current begins to increase very rapidly, as shown in Figure 11–38. The potential of the reverse-bias supply is great enough at this point to cause the covalent bonding force in the semiconductor material to break apart. This effect is called avalanche breakdown. Most diodes should never be operated with reverse-bias potentials large enough to cause them to go into the avalanche breakdown region. This will usually destroy the device very rapidly. *Zener breakdown* is another term used to refer to the reverse breakdown region. The reverse breakdown voltage ratings of diodes vary. They range from a low of a few volts for some diodes to a high of several thousand volts for others.

The complete volt-ampere curve, or characteristic, for a diode appears in Figure 11–39. The forward and reverse curves are located on a system of rectangular coordinates. The forward volt-ampere curve is lo-

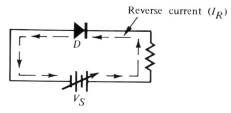

Figure 11–37 Reverse current flowing through a reverse-biased diode.

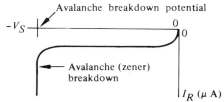

Figure 11–38 Volt-ampere characteristic for a reverse-biased diode.

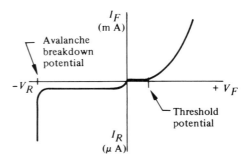

Figure 11–39   Volt-ampere curves for a diode.

cated in the first quadrant and the reverse curve is located in the third quadrant. Notice that the intensity of the reverse current is much smaller than that of the forward current.

11-3.6 Diode Ratings and Characteristics.   There are hundreds of different kinds of diodes available for various types of circuit applications. As shown in Figure 11–40, they are manufactured in a variety of

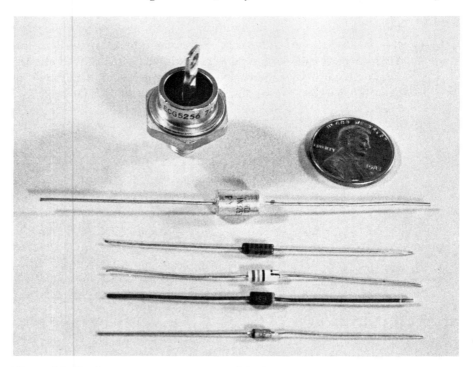

Figure 11–40   Some representative types of diodes.

sizes and shapes. Each different kind of diode has its own unique ratings and characteristics. The engineer or technician who designs circuits which utilize diodes selects a device type which meets that circuit's requirements. Ratings are maximum values which should not be exceeded. There are four ratings which should be given careful consideration when designing a circuit: maximum peak reverse voltage (PRV), maximum forward DC current ($I_{F(\text{avg})}$), maximum repetitive peak forward current ($I_{FM(\text{rep})}$), and maximum peak surge current ($I_{FM(\text{surge})}$).

Characteristics are different from ratings. Ratings are values that must not be exceeded. If they are, the diode may be ruined, or at best, its life expectancy will be shortened. Characteristics are values that the manufacturer guarantees will not be exceeded. These tend to describe how closely a particular diode approaches the operation of an ideal type of device. Three important characteristics are average DC reverse current ($I_{R(\text{DC})}$), peak reverse current ($I_{R(\text{pk})}$), and the average DC forward voltage ($V_{F(\text{DC})}$). Ratings and characteristics are found in the manufacturer's specification sheet, which is often included with the device when it is purchased. They may also be found in most diode and transistor manuals.

The technician who repairs electronic equipment should replace a defective diode with the same type. If an exact replacement is not available, a diode should be used whose ratings equal or exceed those of the diode being replaced. The characteristics should be equal to, or less than, those for the defective diode.

11-3.7 Diode Nomenclature.   Most diodes are registered by the Joint Electron Device Engineering Council (JEDEC). This means that any company which manufacturers diodes may manufacture any particular diode. The ratings and characteristics for the diode must be identical, no matter who manufactures it. JEDEC-registered diodes usually have a 1N prefix followed by two, three, or four numbers. Examples include the 1N34, 1N249, and 1N2516. In addition to producing JEDEC-registered diodes, many semiconductor companies manufacture diodes which have their own unique company nomenclature.

11-3.8 Determining Diode Polarity.   Diodes, of course, are polarized. They have an anode and cathode. It is important to connect the device into a circuit properly if it is to function as it should. The diode is usually connected for forward bias operation. This means that the anode potential is more positive than the potential at the cathode. Most diodes have some type of markings on their case to indicate the anode, cathode, or both. Figure 11–41 serves to illustrate some of the ways in which diode

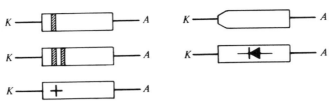

Figure 11–41 Typical methods of identifying diode polarity (A = anode; K = cathode).

polarity is identified. Usually, if one or more bands appear on the case, the end nearest the bands is the cathode side of the diode. Some diodes are marked with a plus sign at one end. This indicates that the cathode is located at that end. The EIA color code is used to determine the type of diode when two or more colored bands are located at one end of the device. For example, if a diode has two bands which are orange and yellow in color, it is a 1N34 type.

11-3.9 Testing Diodes. Diodes do, on occasion, become defective. There are many ways of testing the devices. Several specialized test instruments exist for this purpose. One of the quickest and easiest methods is to test it with an ohmmeter. This is accomplished by measuring the resistance of the diode in the forward direction and noting the resistance value. Next the resistance is measured with the ohmmeter reverse biasing the device. The ratio of the forward to reverse resistance should be at least 1 to 10. Usually it will be much greater than this. If it is less than this value, the diode is defective and must be replaced. If one obtains the same low resistance for both measurements, the diode is shorted and must be discarded. If both measurements are extremely high and equal, the diode is open and must be replaced.

SUMMARY

1. Semiconductor materials are elements located in the fourth column of the Periodic Chart of the Elements. Germanium and silicon are the elements most often used in the manufacture of semiconductor devices.
2. Semiconductor substances are formed from individual semiconductor atoms held together by a covalent bonding process.
3. Small amounts of impurities, called dopants, are added to semiconductor materials during the growing, or manufacturing, process to create current carriers in the substance.

4. There are two general types of dopants—donors and acceptors. Donor elements have five valence band electrons. When they enter into the covalent bonding structure an electron is free to become a current carrier.

5. Acceptor elements have three valence electrons. When they become covalent bonded with semiconductor atoms, a hole is created which becomes a current carrier.

6. A semiconductor substance which has been doped with a donor element is called an N-type semiconductor. A semiconductor substance which has been doped with an acceptor element is called a P-type semiconductor.

7. Current conduction through an N-type semiconductor is by the movement of electrons in the conduction band. Conduction through P-type material is by the movement of holes in the valence band.

8. P and N semiconductor substances are joined together to form practical electronic devices. A section of P material which is molecularly attached to a section of N material forms a PN junction diode.

9. A PN junction diode performs the same function as a switch in a circuit. When forward biased, the diode behaves like a switch in the closed position. The diode acts like a switch in the open position when it is reverse biased.

10. Forward biasing a diode causes it to turn on, or conduct, by causing the junction barrier potential to be overcome, by bringing the energy levels into equilibrium, and by reducing the width of the depletion region.

11. Current flows easily through a forward biased diode. Conduction occurs by electrons in the conduction band of the N section crossing the junction and recombining with holes in the valence band of the P section.

12. Diodes have both majority and minority current carriers. In the P section the majority carriers are holes and the minority carriers are electrons. Electrons constitute the majority carriers in the N section and holes form the minority carriers.

13. Although the diode performs the function of a switch in a circuit, it operates as an imperfect one. A switch has no resistance and voltage across its contacts in the closed position. In the open position it has an infinite resistance and no current flows through its contacts. A diode, on the other hand, has a junction potential and a bulk resistance which affect the current flowing through it when it is forward biased. When reverse-biased, a diode allows a small amount of current to flow.

14. Reverse current is sometimes referred to as cutoff current and leakage current. Reverse current is caused by the flow of minority current carriers created in the depletion region of a reverse-biased diode. Minority current carriers are electron-hole pairs which are caused by semiconductor valence band electrons being raised to the conduction band by thermal energy.

15. Diode ratings are electrical variables which must not be exceeded by the circuit in which the device is connected.

16. Diode characteristics identify the typical or maximum values of specific variables associated with a particular type of diode.

17. Diodes are identified by a number. Most numbers begin with a 1N prefix.

18. The polarity of most diodes is marked on their cases. If the diode contains one or more bands, the end nearest the band is usually the cathode.

PRACTICE EXERCISES

1. List the two elements from which most semiconductor devices are manufactured.
2. Describe what is meant by covalent bonding.
3. Draw the energy diagrams for an insulator, a semiconductor, and a conductor.
4. What is the purpose of doping semiconductor materials?
5. List two general types of dopants. How many valence electrons do each have?
6. Identify three elements often used as *P*-type dopants.
7. List three elements used as *N*-type dopant materials.
8. Identify the relative strength of the dopants added to the germanium or silicon semiconductor materials during the growing process.
9. List the majority and minority current carriers in both *P*- and *N*-type semiconductor materials.
10. Where do the majority current carriers come from in a *PN* junction diode?
11. Where do the minority current carriers come from in a diode?
12. Describe how a *PN* junction is formed.
13. Discuss how the barrier potential is formed across a *PN* junction. What is the approximate amplitude of this potential for both silicon and germanium semiconductor materials?
14. Discuss how the depletion region is formed in the vicinity of the *PN* junction.
15. What is the purpose of biasing a *PN* junction diode? Identify the two types of biasing schemes.
16. Give the effect of forward bias on
    a the energy levels in the *N* and *P* sections of the semiconductor materials
    b. the barrier potential
    c. the depletion region
17. Describe the effect of reverse bias on the depletion region of a diode.
18. Discuss the similarities between the ideal diode and a switch.
19. Identify three characteristics which cause an actual diode to differ from the ideal type.
20. What does the term *semiconductor* mean when referring to a semiconductor device?
21. Describe how current flows through a *PN* junction diode when it is forward biased.
22. Draw the equivalent circuit of a *PN* junction diode.
23. Draw the volt-ampere curves for a diode. Identify both the threshold and avalanche breakdown potentials.
24. What causes avalanche breakdown? What is another name for this effect?
25. Discuss the differences between *PN* junction diode ratings and characteristics.
26. What is the significance of the front-to-back resistance ratio of a diode? What is the minimum value for this ratio?

ANSWERS TO PRACTICE EXERCISES

1. Most semiconductor devices are made from silicon and germanium.

2. Covalent bonding is one of several bonding processes in which individual atoms are attached together to form substances. Crystalline materials, which include semiconductors, utilize this type of bonding method. Individual atoms are attached together by the sharing of valence band electrons.

3. See Figure 11–4.

4. Semiconductor materials are doped during the manufacturing process to introduce current carriers to the material. Individual valence electrons are tightly held to the nuclei of the atoms by the covalent bonding structure and are not easily raised to the conduction band to become current carriers. Dopant elements have three or five valence band electrons. Each dopant atom has one electron or hole which does not become bonded with adjacent germanium or silicon atoms. These are free to become current carriers.

5. Acceptors and donors are the two general types of dopants. Acceptor elements have three valence electrons and donor elements have five electrons in their valence band.

6. Aluminum, gallium, and indium are elements which are often used as acceptor dopants.

7. Elements commonly used as donor dopants include arsenic, antimony, and phosphorous.

8. Approximately 5 to 10 dopant atoms are added to every one million germanium or silicon atoms. This represents a mixture of about 5 to 10 ppm.

9. In *P*-type semiconductor substances, the majority current carriers are holes and the minority carriers are electrons. The majority carriers are electrons in *N*-type material and the minority current carriers are holes.

10. Majority current carriers come from the electrons or holes associated with the dopant elements.

11. Minority current carriers are generated when some of the semiconductor (germanium or silicon) valence electrons absorb enough thermal (heat) energy to be elevated into the conduction band. When this occurs, a hole is created in the valence band where the elevated electron was formerly located. The elevated conduction band electron and its associated hole is called an electron-hole combination.

12. A *PN* junction is formed during the growing, or manufacturing, process. Acceptor dopant elements are added to the pure semiconductor material for a period of time and then donor elements are introduced to the material. The junction represents the transistion which occurs between the acceptor doped (*P*) and donor doped (*N*) semiconductor materials.

13. The junction, or barrier potential, is formed when free electrons (introduced by the donor dopants) in the *N* section travel across the junction and recombine with holes in the *P* section. This creates negative ions in the *P* section in the immediate vicinity of the junction and positive ions in the *N* section. The barrier potential represents the difference in charge which exists on either side of the junction. The amplitude of this potential is approximately 0.3 V for germanium-doped material and 0.7 V for silicon-doped material.

14. The depletion region is a small area located on either side of the junction which is void of free current carriers. Electrons in the N section of the material have crossed the junction and have recombined with holes in the P section.

15. A PN junction diode is biased so that the device can be turned on and off. There are two types of biasing schemes—forward and reverse.

16. Forward bias brings the energy levels into equilibrium, overcomes the barrier potential, and reduces the width of the depletion region. The effect of all of this is to allow current to easily flow through the device.

17. Reverse-bias causes the depletion region of the diode to become wider.

18. The ideal diode has the same characteristics as a switch.

19. The three electrical characteristics which cause an actual diode to differ from an ideal device are
    a. barrier potential
    b. bulk resistance
    c. reverse current

20. A semiconductor allows current to flow in one direction (when forward biased) and not in the other direction (when reverse biased).

21. When a diode is forward biased, electrons in the conduction band cross the junction, drop into the valence band, and recombine with holes. One electron leaves the negative terminal of the bias supply and enters the N section of the diode for every electron which crosses the junction and recombines with a hole. For every hole which is filled in the P section of the device, a new one is created by an electron leaving the P section and traveling to the positive terminal of the bias source.

22. See Figure 11–34.

23. See Figure 11–39.

24. Avalanche breakdown occurs when the reverse-bias potential is great enough to break the covalent bonding force holding the individual atoms together. This is sometimes called zener breakdown.

25. Ratings are electrical variables which must not be exceeded by the circuit in which the diode is connected. Characteristics are those variables, such as reverse current and voltage drop that tend to describe the quality of a diode.

26. A diode functions as a switch. A switch has a zero-to-infinity closed-to-open (front-to-back) resistance ratio. Although a diode will never have the exact characteristics of a switch, it will approach this ideal when the front-to-back resistance ratio is very high. The minimum ratio is 1 to 10.

CHAPTER EXAMINATION

Choose true or false.
1. T F A diode is biased to cause it to be turned on and off.
2. T F Covalent bonding is the type of bonding structure which occurs in semiconductor materials.
3. T F A PN junction is formed when a diode is forward biased.
4. T F Holes constitute the minority current carriers in P-type semiconductor material.

5. T   F   The energy levels for the valence and conduction bands are higher in *P*-type semiconductor material than those in *N*-type material.
6. T   F   Reverse current is sometimes called leakage current.
7. T   F   Peak reverse voltage (PRV) is a diode rating.
8. T   F   Reverse current (I_R) is a diode characteristic.
9. T   F   Forward voltage (V_F) is a diode rating.
10. T   F   Avalanche breakdown occurs when excessive forward bias is applied to a diode.
11. T   F   The threshold potential for a silicon diode is approximately 0.3 V.
12. T   F   Diode characteristics are electrical variables which must not be exceeded in the circuit in which the diode is connected.
13. T   F   Reverse current occurs when the covalent bonding force holding the atoms together is broken.
14. T   F   When forward biasing a diode, the positive terminal of the bias supply is connected to the cathode and the negative terminal is connected to the anode.
15. T   F   A semiconductor diode is a device which allows current to flow through it equally well in either direction.
16. T   F   Forward current in a diode is caused by the movement of minority current carriers moving through the device.
17. T   F   Gallium is sometimes used as a donor element.
18. T   F   Arsenic can be used as a donor dopant.
19. T   F   Semiconductor materials are doped during the manufacturing process to form a *PN* junction.
20. T   F   The major differences between an ideal diode and an actual one is that the actual device contains resistance, will allow a small amount of current to flow when reverse-biased, and has a barrier potential across its junction.
21. T   F   The avalanche breakdown potential for silicon diodes is approximately 0.7 V.
22. T   F   Indium is sometimes used as an acceptor dopant.
23. T   F   A *PN* junction is formed when free electrons in the *N* section cross the junction and combine with holes in the *P* section.
24. T   F   The width of the depletion region about the junction is reduced when a diode is reverse biased.
25. T   F   Diodes may be manufactured from either silicon or germanium materials.

12

The Bipolar Junction Transistor

OBJECTIVES

Upon completion of this chapter you should be able to do the following:

1. Identify the two kinds of bipolar junction transistors and list the names of the two junctions and three sections forming the devices.
2. Identify the majority and minority current carriers associated with each section of a bipolar junction transistor.
3. Draw or recognize the schematic symbol for each of the two types of bipolar junction transistors.
4. Describe how each junction is biased and draw or recognize the proper bias connections for each type of bipolar transistor.
5. Identify the three currents associated with the bipolar transistor and describe the mathematical relationship between them.
6. Describe how current flows through the bipolar junction transistor.
7. List the three circuit configurations in which bipolar junction transistors can be connected and draw or recognize each from a schematic diagram.
8. Differentiate between the three circuit configurations by describing the input impedance, output impedance, current gain, voltage gain, and input-output phase relationship for each.
9. Identify the operating variables which may be obtained from the family of volt-ampere characteristics.
10. Describe how a bipolar transistor is able to control or amplify a current.
11. Discuss the cause of reverse current in a bipolar transistor and list the various terms used to identify this variable.
12. Define transistor current gain, identify the two types of gain, and calculate the value of either.
13. Draw the DC load line and locate the operating point for a transistor connected in the common emitter configuration.

14. Describe the effect of temperature on transistor Q-point current and identify a method used to produce temperature stability.
15. Identify the three types of emitter-base self-bias associated with the common-emitter connector transistor.
16. Calculate the DC variables associated with a transistor connected in the common-emitter configuration and employing any one of the three self-biasing methods.

12-1 INTRODUCTION

Transistors are capable of being used for a variety of applications. They are, however, primarily used in amplifier, oscillator, and switching circuits. Transistors are made from semiconductor materials and are manufactured in a fashion much like that of diodes. The transistor was developed by scientists working at Bell Laboratories in 1948 as a replacement for the less efficient electron tube.

There are two types of transistors. Each utilizes a different kind of technology. These include the bipolar junction transistor (often called the BJT) and the field effect transistor (often referred to as the FET). Of the two, the bipolar junction device was developed first and is the one which has the most applications. Bipolar junction transistors are manufactured in several different sizes and shapes for various circuit applications. Examples of some typical devices appear in Figure 12–1.

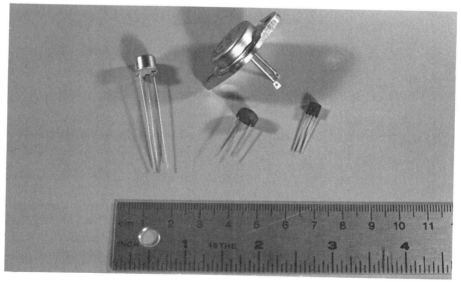

Figure 12–1   Typical bipolar junction transistors.

12-2 PRINCIPLES OF OPERATION

The bipolar transistor is an extension of the semiconductor junction diode. Manufactured from a single semiconductor crystal, it has three sections and two *PN* junctions, as shown in Figure 12–2. The three sections include the emitter, base, and collector. The junction separating the emitter and base is called the emitter-base junction and the junction separating the base and collector is known as the base-collector junction.

As illustrated in Figure 12–3, there are two types of bipolar transistors—*PNP* and *NPN*. The *PNP* transistor has the emitter and collector sections made of *P*-type material and the base is composed of *N*-type material. In the *NPN* transistor the emitter and collector sections are composed of *N*-type material and the base is made from *P*-type material. The schematic symbols for the bipolar transistor appear in Figure 12–4.

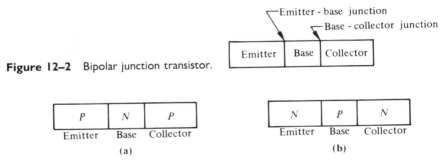

Figure 12–2 Bipolar junction transistor.

Figure 12–3 Types of bipolar junction transistors: (a) *PNP* transistor; (b) *NPN* transistor.

Figure 12–4 Schematic symbols for the bipolar junction transistor: (a) *PNP* transistor; (b) *NPN* transistor.

The energy levels for both the *PNP* and *NPN* transistors are depicted in Figure 12–5. The energy levels for the *P* sections are higher than those for the *N* sections. The transistors cannot operate in this fashion. Like the diode, the transistor must be biased to change the energy levels between the sections. Since the transistor has two *PN* junctions, both

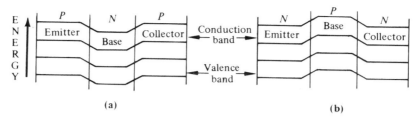

Figure 12–5   Energy levels for (a) the PNP transistor and (b) the NPN transistor.

have to be biased. The emitter-base junction is forward biased and the base-collector junction operates with reverse bias. The circuit diagrams appearing in Figure 12–6 illustrate how the two bias supplies are connected to properly bias both the *PNP* and *NPN* devices. In both circuits the emitter-base junctions are forward biased and the base-collector junctions are reverse biased. Double subscripts are used to denote the bias supplies, V_{BB} and V_{CC}. Double subscripts which contain the same letters usually identify a voltage source. V_{BB} forward biases the emitter-base junctions and V_{CC} reverse biases the base-collector junctions. The V_{CC} supply is usually larger than the V_{BB} source. The only difference between the *PNP* and *NPN* biasing schemes is the polarity of the bias sources. In both cases the emitter-base junction is forward biased and the base-collector junction reverse biased.

   When properly biased, the energy levels for the two transistors appear as shown in Figure 12–7. Forward bias applied across the emitter-base junction causes the energy levels to equalize between the emitter-base junctions. Reverse biasing the collector-base junction increases the energy levels between the base and collector and allows current to flow through the base-collector junction.

   The current flowing through a *PNP* device is shown in Figure 12–8. The positive charge created by the positive terminal of the V_{BB} supply

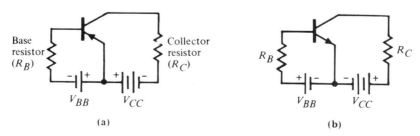

Figure 12–6   Bias connections for the bipolar junction transistor: (a) *PNP* transistor; (b) *NPN* transistor.

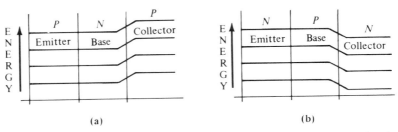

Figure 12-7 Energy levels in a biased bipolar junction transistor: (a) energy levels for a biased *PNP* transistor; (b) energy levels for a biased *NPN* transistor.

forces holes in the valence band of the *P*-type emitter to cross the emitter-base junction. A few (approximately 1 to 5 percent) of the electrons in the conduction band of the *N*-type base drop into the valence band and recombine with holes which have crossed the emitter-base junction. The remaining holes travel through the base and cross the base-collector junction. The holes drift through the collector and are attracted by the negative potential of the V_{CC} supply.

For each hole which is filled by an electron when traveling through the base, an electron is supplied by the V_{BB} source. This forms a recombination current which is called base current (I_B).

An electron recombines with every hole which crosses the collector-base junction and travels through the collector section. These electrons are supplied by the V_{CC} source and form a current which is called collector current (I_C).

Electrons attracted from the *P*-type emitter to the positive terminal of the V_{BB} supply create the holes which travel from the emitter into the base and collector sections and form a current which is called the emitter current (I_E). This current is the sum of the base and collector currents.

Current conduction in the *NPN* bipolar device is similar to that of the *PNP* transistor. As shown by the diagram appearing in Figure 12-9,

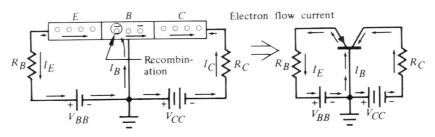

Figure 12-8 Current flow in a PNP bipolar junction transistor.

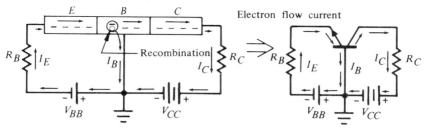

Figure 12–9 Current flow in an NPN bipolar junction transistor.

the emitter-base junction is forward biased and the base-collector junction is reverse biased. Electrons in the conduction band of the emitter are forced through that section and cross the emitter-base junction because of the negative charge on the emitter produced by the V_{BB} supply. A few (approximately 1 to 5 percent) of the electrons which cross the junction drop down into the valence band and recombine with holes in the base section. The remaining electrons travel through the base, cross the base-collector junction, and drift through the collector where they are attracted by the positive charge produced by the V_{CC} source.

For every electron that recombines with a hole in the base section, a new hole is produced by an electron attracted from the base by the positive charge produced by the V_{BB} supply. The recombination current which flows from the base to the V_{BB} bias supply is called base current (I_B). The base is made very thin and is more lightly doped in comparison to the emitter in bipolar transistors. This prevents most of the carriers which cross the emitter-base junction from combining with the carriers in the base section.

The electrons which travel through the collector are attracted by the positive charge produced by the V_{CC} bias supply. For every electron which crosses the base-collector junction, an electron leaves the collector and travels to the V_{CC} supply. This current is called collector current (I_C).

For each electron which crosses the emitter-base junction, an electron is supplied by the V_{BB} bias supply. This current is called emitter current (I_E). Emitter current is the sum of the base and collector currents.

Resistor, R_B, is called the base resistor. It, along with the forward bias supply, V_{BB}, determines the intensity of the base current. The resistor appearing in the collector circuit, R_C, is called the collector resistor. Its purpose is to establish a load in the collector circuit which is used to develop the output signal voltage when a signal is applied to the input of the transistor.

Electron flow current was utilized in the circuits just discussed to

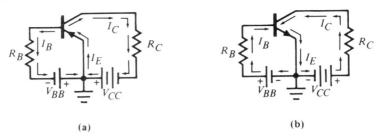

(a)   (b)

Figure 12–10 Conventional current flow in a bipolar junction transistor: (a) in a *PNP* transistor; (b) in a *NPN* transistor.

facilitate the analysis of the *PNP* and *NPN* devices. When conventional current is used, the emitter current flows in the direction of the emitter arrow as indicated in Figure 12–10.

The mathematical relationships between the currents which flow through the bipolar junction transistor appear in Equations (12–1) to (12–3). They are the same for both the *PNP* and *NPN* devices.

$$I_E = I_B + I_C \qquad (12–1)$$

$$I_C = I_E - I_B \qquad (12–2)$$

$$I_B = I_E - I_C \qquad (12–3)$$

12-3 CIRCUIT CONFIGURATIONS

One of the more common applications of the bipolar junction transistor is its use in an amplifier circuit. An amplifier is a circuit which amplifies an electrical current or voltage called a signal. The signal is applied to the input of the amplifier and an enlarged reproduction appears at the amplifier output. The ratio of the output signal amplitude to the input signal amplitude is called gain. The input and output signals have both current and voltage components. Therefore, an amplifier can have a current gain, a voltage gain, and a power gain.

Bipolar junction transistors used in amplifier circuits can be connected in one of three different circuit configurations: common-emitter, common-base, and common-collector circuits. The circuits are identified by the transistor section which is common to both the input and output circuits of the transistor. A transistor connected in the common-emitter configuration is depicted in Figure 12–11. The input signal is applied be-

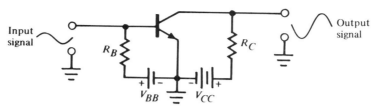

Figure 12–11 Transistor connected in the common-emitter (CE) configuration.

tween the base of the transistor and ground and the output signal is obtained from the collector with respect to ground. Since the emitter is at ground potential, it is correct to say that the input signal is applied between the base and emitter and the output is taken from the collector and emitter. Notice that the emitter terminal is common to both the input and output signals.

A transistor connected in the common-base configuration is shown in Figure 12–12. In this circuit the signal is applied between the emitter terminal and ground and is taken from the collector with respect to ground. Since the base is at ground potential, it is proper to state that the input signal is applied between the emitter and base terminals and the output signal is obtained from the collector and base terminals. The base terminal is common to both the input and output signals.

A common-collector connected transistor is shown in Figure 12–13. Unlike the common-emitter and common base circuits which employed a collector resistor to develop the output signal, this circuit uses an emitter resistor to develop the output signal. The V_{CC} supply provides a low-impedance path to ground for the signal. The input signal is applied between the base and ground and the output signal is taken from the emitter with respect to ground. Since the collector is at signal ground potential, the input signal is actually applied between the base and collector and the output signal is obtained across the emitter and collector terminals. Hence, the collector is common to both the input and output sig-

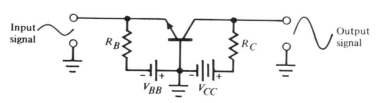

Figure 12–12 Transistor connected in the common-base (CB) configuration.

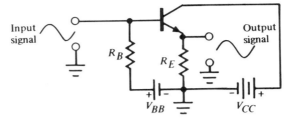

Figure 12–13 Transistor connected in the common-collector (CC) configuration.

nals. The signal developed across the emitter resistor is in phase with the input signal. For this reason, this circuit is often called an emitter follower.

The requirements of the circuit in which the transistor operates determines which one of the three circuit configurations is to be used. Transistor circuits have several operating variables which have to be met to satisfy the conditions of a particular circuit. Some of these include input impedance, output impedance, current gain, voltage gain, and input-output phase relationship. These variables are summarized for the three circuit configurations in Table 12–1. One can observe that the input impedance is low when the transistor is connected in the common-base configuration, medium when connected in the common-emitter arrangement, and high when connected in the common-collector configuration. On the other hand, the output impedance is high for a transistor connected in the common base circuit, medium for the common-emitter, and low when used as an emitter follower. Current gain is less than one when the transistor is operated in the common-base circuit and will vary, depending upon the transistor type, for transistors connected in the common emitter and common-collector configurations. The voltage gain is al-

TABLE 12–1   A Comparison of the Variables Associated with the Common-Emitter, Common-Base, and Common-Collector Circuit Configurations

Variable	Circuit Configuration		
	CE	*CB*	*CC*
Input impedance	300–12,000 Ω	30–250 Ω	2500 Ω–1 M Ω
Output impedance	500–100 k Ω	100 k Ω–1 M Ω	25 Ω–5 k Ω
Current gain	20–800	0.8–0.99	20–800
Voltage gain	high	medium	0.5–0.99
Input-output phase	180°	0°	0°

ways greater than one for transistors connected in the common base and common-emitter configurations and less than one when connected as an emitter follower. The exact values of the electrical variables depend upon the type of transistor used and values of the resistors and other devices connected to the transistor. The vast majority of transistor circuits are connected in the common-emitter configuration. This method of operation has medium input and output impedances and provides for rather significant current and voltage gains.

12-4 DC OPERATING CONDITIONS

12-4.1 The Volt-Ampere Characteristics. A transistor is usually used to control or amplify the current flowing through a circuit. Probably the easiest way to describe how these functions are accomplished is by the use of the volt-ampere curves for the device. Since the common emitter circuit is the one most often used, the discussion which follows describes how the curves are obtained and used for this type of circuit arrangement.

The curves are obtained by connecting the transistor in the common-emitter configuration, as shown in Figure 12–14. The V_{BB} and V_{CC} bias supplies are variable so that the base current (I_B) and the collector-to-emitter voltage (V_{CE}) can be adjusted in small increments. V_{BB} is adjusted to zero so that the base current is initially zero. V_{CC} is adjusted singularly so that V_{CE}, as indicated by the voltmeter connected between the collector and emitter, measures 0, 0.2, 0.4, 2, 8, and 10 V. Collector current is recorded for each of the V_{CE} values and appears in Table 12–2. V_{CC} is next reduced to zero and V_{BB} is increased until base current is 100 µA as indicated by the ammeter in the base circuit. Collector current is again measured and recorded for V_{CE} values of 0, 0.2, 0.4, 2, 8, and 10 V as V_{CC} is increased. V_{CC} is returned to 0 V and V_{BB} is increased until base current is 200 µA. Collector current is recorded for V_{CE} values of 0, 0.2, 0.4, 2, 8,

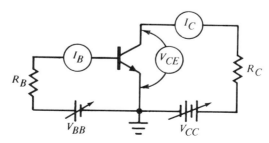

Figure 12–14 Common-emitter circuit used to obtain the volt-ampere characteristics.

and 10 V. This process is repeated for base current values of 300 and 400 μA.

The data appearing in Table 12–2 are used to plot a series of graphs, or curves, called a family of volt-ampere characteristics, as depicted in Figure 12–15. A separate volt-ampere curve is shown for each value of base current. Each curve shows the effect on collector current when the collector-emitter voltage is increased while the base current is held constant.

TABLE 12–2   Data Required to Plot the Volt-Ampere Characteristics

I_B (μA)	V_{CE} (V)						
	0	0.2	0.4	2	8	10	
0	0	0.2	1	2	4	5	I_C (mA)
100	0	0.21	42	16	20	22	
200	0	0.28	11	28	30	32	
300	0	0.3	18	38	40	42	
400	0	0.31	28	48	50	52	

One can observe from the curves appearing in Figure 12–15 that, for a given value of base current, collector current increases rapidly in intensity as the collector-to-emitter voltage is increased from 0 to approximately 1 V. As V_{CE} is increased above this value, the collector current increases very little. This suggests that the collector voltage has little effect on collector current after the transistor has been turned on.

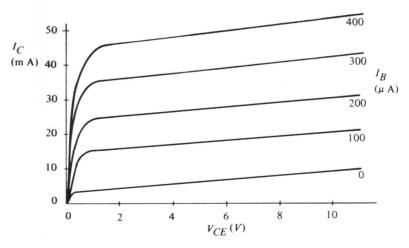

Figure 12–15 Family of volt-ampere characteristics for an *NPN* common-emitter connected transistor.

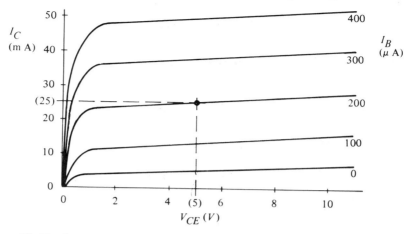

Figure 12–16 Base current determines the intensity of the collector current.

Base current has a much greater effect on collector current than does the collector-to-emitter voltage. For example, if V_{CE} is adjusted for 5 V and the base-emitter supply adjusted for a base current of 200 μA, the resulting collector current is approximately 25 mA as obtained from the family of characteristic curves appearing in Figure 12–16. If V_{CE} is maintained at a 5-V potential and the base current is increased from 200 to 300 μA, as depicted in Figure 12–17, the collector current increases from 25 to 37 mA. This means that a change in base current of 100 μA $(300 - 200$ μA$)$

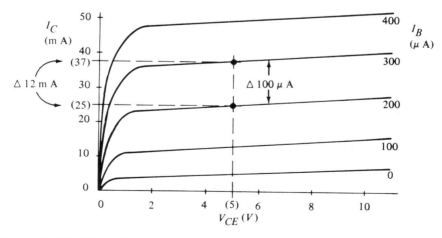

Figure 12–17 Effect of base current on collector current.

has caused the collector current to change 12 mA (37 − 25 mA). The change in the output, or collector, current is 120 (12 mA/100 μA) times larger than the change in the input, or base, current. *This is the key to the operation of the bipolar junction transistor when connected in the CE configuration. A small change in base current causes a much larger change in collector current to occur.* Base current has much more effect and control on collector current than does the collector-to-emitter voltage.

The characteristic curves plotted in Figure 12–15 were those for an *NPN* transistor. Volt-ampere curves are plotted for *PNP* devices in the same fashion as they are for *NPN* devices. As shown in Figure 12–18, the only difference between the family of volt-ampere characteristics is the polarity of the collector bias source.

The family of the volt-ampere characteristic curves for a transistor connected in the common-base configuration can be graphed from the data obtained from a circuit similar to that appearing in Figure 12–19. The resulting curves are shown in Figure 12–20. The major difference between these curves and those associated with the common-emitter circuit is the input current. Base current represents the input current for a transistor connected in the common-emitter configuration, whereas emitter current is the input current for a transistor connected in the common-base configuration. Transistors connected in the common-collector configuration utilize the common-emitter characteristic curves.

Usually ones does not have to plot the curves for a transistor. Many

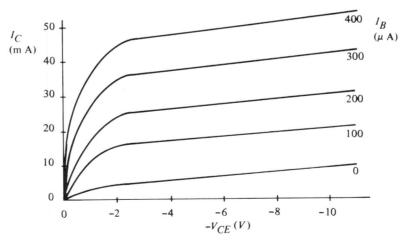

Figure 12–18 Family of volt-ampere characteristics for a PNP common-emitter connected transistor.

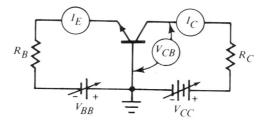

Figure 12-19 Common-base circuit used to obtain the volt-ampere characteristics.

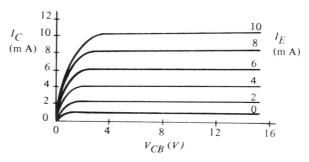

Figure 12-20 Family of volt-ampere characteristics for an NPN common-base connected transistor.

transistor manuals and most specification sheets include the curves as part of the data shown for the transistor.

12-4.2 Reverse Current.   One would not expect collector current to flow when the emitter-base junction is not forward biased. However, for the circuit appearing in Figure 12-14, collector current was present when the base current was zero, as indicated by the data appearing in Table 12-2. The current which flows in the collector circuit when the emitter-base junction is not forward biased is reverse current. Since the base collector junction is operated with reverse-bias, conditions for reverse current exist in the collector section just as they exist for reverse-biased diodes. Reverse current, which is the flow of minority current carriers, forms part of the collector current of bipolar junction transistors. Reverse current is sometimes called cutoff or leakage current. If the transistor is connected in the common-emitter configuration, reverse current is often referred to as I_{CEO}. This is the current which flows from the collector to the emitter with the base connection open circuited. An open base connection ensures that the emitter-base junction is not forward biased. This is the method used by transistor manufacturers to measure reverse current. Reverse current is sometimes called I_{CBO} for a transistor operated in the common-base configuration. In this case the emitter is open circuited.

The bipolar junction transistor obtains its name from the fact that both majority and minority current flow occurs in the device.

12-4.3 Transistor Current Gain. One of the more important transistor characteristics is current gain. Transistor current gain is the ratio of the output current to the input current for a fixed value of collector voltage. There are two current gains associated with transistors—alpha and beta. Alpha current gain is the current gain of a transistor connected in the common-base configuration. Beta current gain is associated with transistors connected in the common-emitter and common-collector configurations.

There are two types of alpha and beta current gain: DC and AC alpha and beta current gain. Equations (12–4) to (12–7) are used to calculate the current gains associated with the bipolar junction transistor.

$$\text{DC beta gain } (\beta_{DC}) = \frac{I_C}{I_B} \qquad V_{CE} \text{ constant} \qquad (12\text{–}4)$$

$$\text{AC beta gain } (\beta_{AC}) = \frac{\Delta I_C}{\Delta I_B} \qquad V_{CE} \text{ constant}, \qquad \Delta = \text{a change in} \quad (12\text{–}5)$$

$$\text{DC alpha gain } (\alpha_{DC}) = \frac{I_C}{I_E} \qquad V_{CB} \text{ constant} \qquad (12\text{–}6)$$

$$\text{AC alpha gain } (\alpha_{AC}) = \frac{\Delta I_C}{\Delta I_E} \qquad V_{CB} \text{ constant} \qquad (12\text{–}7)$$

Beta current gain, for most transistors, can be found in transistor specification sheets and transistor manuals. Usually, either the DC or AC value will be given, but not both. AC beta is usually provided for transistors which are to be operated as small signal, or voltage, amplifiers. DC beta is usually given for transistors which are to be operated as large signal (power) amplifiers and in switching circuits. Although alpha current gain is usually not provided in most transistor manuals, it can be calculated from Equation (12–8).

$$\alpha = \frac{\beta}{1 + \beta} \qquad (12\text{–}8)$$

As indicated, alpha current gain will always be less than one. This can be verified by Equations (12–6) and (12–7). Alpha current gain is the ratio of

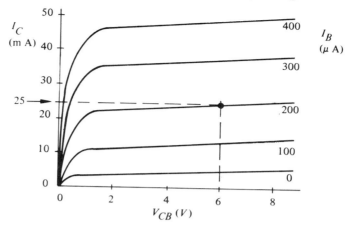

Figure 12–21 Determining the value of DC beta.

collector current to emitter current. Since emitter current is always larger than collector current, this ratio will always be less than one. This is one of the characteristics associated with the common base transistor which was listed in Table 12–1.

Although beta current gain is often listed in transistor manuals, it can also be determined from the family of volt-ampere characteristics. For the transistor whose curves appear in Figure 12–21, DC beta is equal to 125. This means that the output current (I_C) is 125 times larger than the input current (I_B). It also means that the transistor is able to amplify a current signal by a factor of 125. The same transistor has an AC beta value of 70, as shown in Figure 12–22. If the transistor were connected in

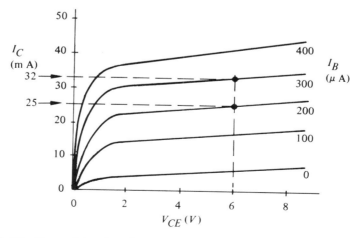

Figure 12–22 Determining the value of AC beta.

the common-base configuration, its DC current gain would be 0.992, as calculated in Example 12–1.

Example 12–1 Determining the value of DC alpha

Problem

Determine the DC alpha gain of the transistor whose characteristic curves appear in Figure 12–21 if its DC beta value is 125 when $V_{CE} = 6$ V and $I_B = 200$ μA.

Solution

$$\alpha_{DC} = \frac{\beta}{1 + \beta} = \frac{125}{126} = 0.992$$

12-4.4 The DC Load Line. It is important that the bias potentials have the amplitude to cause the transistor to operate properly. One may determine the approximate value of the collector supply (V_{CC}) from a transistor manual. Since this source reverse biases the base-collector junction, it should not be large enough to cause that junction to operate in the avalanche breakdown region. However, the V_{CC} supply does not have a great effect on the intensity of the collector current.

The forward-biased emitter-base junction is more critical. The forward-bias supply (V_{BB}), along with the base resistor (R_B), establishes the base current. The collector current is dependent upon the amount of current flowing in the base current. If the base current is too high, the resulting collector current may be large enough to damage the transistor due to the excessive heat which is produced at the base-collector junction. Improper base current will also cause distortion to occur in the output circuit of the transistor when it is operated as an amplifier. The DC base current required for proper circuit operation is obtained from the DC load line. The DC load line is a line segment superimposed over the family of characteristic curves. The load line allows one to describe how the transistor will operate under any emitter-base biasing conditions.

A line segment is defined as two points connected by a line. For the DC load line, the first point represents the voltage and current conditions which exist if the transistor is open circuited. With this condition, collector current is zero and the reverse-bias potential, V_{CC}, is felt across the collector and emitter, causing that voltage, V_{CE}, to be equal to V_{CC}. This condition is identified as point A on the graph appearing in Example 12–2.

The second point located on the graph represents the conditions which exist if the transistor is short circuited. This results in the collector-to-emitter voltage being equal to zero. The collector current is limited in

Example 12–2 Drawing the DC load line for a transistor connected in the common emitter configuration

---

Problem

Draw the DC load line for the transistor appearing in the circuit of Figure 12–23.

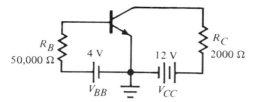

Figure 12–23

Solution

1. Locate point A. $V_{CE} = V_{CC} = 12$ V. $I_C = 0$.

2. Locate point B. $I_C = \dfrac{V_{CC}}{R_C} = \dfrac{12 \text{ V}}{2000 \text{ }\Omega} = 6$ mA. $V_{CE} = 0$.

3. Connect points A and B (see Figure 12–24).

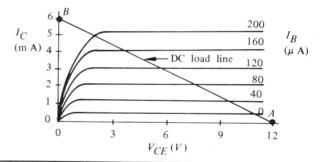

Figure 12–24 *V-I curves.*

---

intensity only by the resistance of the collector load resistor, R_C. This is identified as point B on the graph and is obtained by dividing V_{CC} by R_C. This represents the current flowing in the circuit if the transistor is short circuited. The voltage across the transistor, V_{CE}, is zero for this condition. The DC load line is completed by drawing a line connecting point A with point B as shown in Example 12–2.

The operating point is located on the DC load line next. This represents the DC voltage and current conditions when no signal is applied to the transistor. This point is often called the resting point, or quiescent point (Q-point). The Q-point is located at the intersection of a base current curve and the DC load line. The base current value is obtained by dividing the emitter-base voltage supply, V_{BB}, by the base resistance. For the circuit shown in Example 12–3, the base current is 80 μA. This is the same circuit used in Example 12–2 to obtain the DC load line.

Example 12–3 Locating the operating point for a transistor connected in the common emitter configuration

Problem

Locate the operating (Q) point for the circuit shown in Figure 12–25.

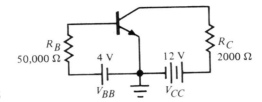

Figure 12–25

Solution

1. $I_B = \dfrac{V_{BB}}{R_B} = \dfrac{4\ V}{50,000\ \Omega} = 80\ \mu A.$

2. Place the point on the DC load line (see Figure 12–26).

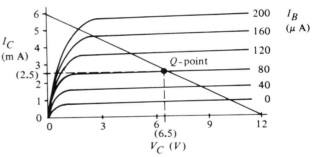

Figure 12–26 V-I curves.

The resulting collector current and collector-to-emitter voltage can be determined after the Q-point has been located. The collector current represents that current on the volt-ampere curves which is identified by the line projected horizontally from the Q-point, as shown in Example 12–3. The collector-to-emitter voltage is obtained by projecting a vertical line from the Q-point to the horizontal voltage axis. The resulting collector current is 2.5 mA and the collector-to-emitter voltage is approximately 6.5 V. Thus, before connecting the circuit, the circuit designer can predict what the collector current and the collector-to-emitter voltage will be for a given value of base current. The circuit designer can also determine the effect on collector current and collector-emitter voltage if the base current is varied. For example, if the base current is increased, the collector current will increase and the collector-emitter voltage will decrease. Similarly, if the base current is decreased, collector current will decrease and the collector-to-emitter voltage will increase.

The DC load line identifies three regions of operation for a transistor, which are represented by the area on the volt-ampere curves below the DC load line. As shown in Figure 12–27, these include the cutoff, active (or linear), and saturation regions. Most amplifiers are operated in the midsection of the active region, hence the name linear circuits. When the transistor is used as a switch, its Q-point goes from the cutoff region to the saturation region as the transistor is turned on and off.

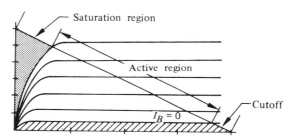

Figure 12–27 Operating regions for a bipolar junction transistor.

12-5 THERMAL STABILITY

Thermal stability is defined as the ability of a transistor to maintain a constant operating point when changes in ambient temperature occur. The bipolar junction transistor has a negative temperature coefficient. The internal resistance of the device decreases with increases in temperature. This is caused by electrons in the valence band of the germanium or silicon material being elevated into the conduction band by heat energy. This creates additional minority current carriers. Reverse current doubles for each 10 °C increase in temperature, base-emitter voltage decreases 2.5 mV for every 1 °C increase in temperature, and transistor current gain increases when the temperature increases. These factors cause the operating point of the transistor to change, as illustrated in Figure 12–28. In addition to creating distortion, the transistor may be ruined because of thermal runaway. When the ambient temperature increases, the collector current increases and additional heat is produced at the base-collector junction. This creates additional collector current which produces yet more heat at the base-collector junction. This process is called thermal runaway.

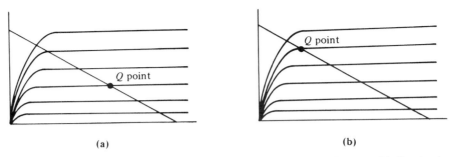

(a)   (b)

Figure 12–28 Effect of heat on the operating point: (a) normal *Q*-point; (b) *Q*-point has shifted because of increase in temperature.

Because transistors in most circuits have to operate in changing temperature environments, some means must be provided to maintain thermal stability to prevent the operating point from shifting. Although various schemes are used, all employ a self-correcting negative feedback system. Negative (also called degenerative) feedback is the process of feeding a portion of the output signal back into the input circuit 180° out-of-phase with the input signal. A common method used to achieve this is to place a resistor (R_E) in the emitter circuit as shown in Figure 12–29.

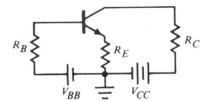

Figure 12–29 Transistor employing an emitter resistor to provide for thermal stability.

The emitter resistor introduces negative feedback into the circuit. As the collector and emitter currents increase with an increase in temperature, the voltage drop produced by the emitter resistor reduces the base current which causes the collector and emitter currents to become less. This is verified by Kirchhoff's voltage law. Loop equations for the input circuit are shown for the emitter resistor being both in and out of the circuit. As indicated by Equation (12–10), the base current is reduced when a resistor is used in the emitter circuit.

12-6 TRANSISTOR BIASING SCHEMES AND DC ANALYSIS

12-6.1 Introduction. The need for transistor bias has been firmly established in the previous sections of this chapter. As a reminder, the

Input loop and base current equations for the circuit shown in Figure 14–29 without R_E:

$$-V_{BB} + V_{RB} + V_{BE} = 0$$
$$-V_{BB} + (I_B R_B) + V_{BE} = 0$$

$$I_B = \frac{V_{BB} - V_{BE}}{R_B}$$

(12–9)

Loop and base current equations for the input circuit with R_E:

$$-V_{BB} + V_{RB} + V_{BE} + V_{RE} = 0$$
$$-V_{BB} + (I_B R_B) + V_{BE} + V_{RE} = 0$$

$$I_B = \frac{V_{BB} - V_{BE} - V_{RE}}{R_B}$$

(12–10)

emitter-base junction must be forward biased and the base-collector junction reverse biased. The forward biased emitter-base junction is the more critical of the two junctions. Not only does it produce the base current which turns the transistor on, it also establishes the operating point which determines how the transistor will operate. Although a separate emitter-base bias supply (V_{BB}) was used to develop the base current in the previous sections, most transistors employ a single bias source to provide both the forward and reverse-bias potentials. These are called self-biasing methods. Three different schemes are used to develop self-bias: the fixed, the collector feedback, and the voltage divider.

The mathematical analysis associated with each different type of circuit allows one to determine the various DC voltages and currents associated with the transistor without having to use the volt-ampere characteristics. This is particularly important to the engineer who designs circuits and the technician who troubleshoots and repairs them.

Transistor analysis can become rather rigorous. The procedure can be simplified considerably by making the following two approximations:

1. Let $I_C = I_E$.
2. Let $V_{BE} = 0.3$ V for germanium transistors and 0.7 V for silicon transistors.

The collector and emitter currents differ only by the value of the base current. Since this current is usually very small when compared to the collector and emitter currents, the error introduced is minimal. The actual voltage dropped across the emitter-base junction is a function of several factors including the dopant level and the ambient temperature. For most transistor applications the values listed above are close to being exact. Neither of the approximations will greatly affect the results of the calculated variables since most circuits utilize resistors which have 10 percent tolerances and transistors which have even higher tolerances.

Various subscripts are used to denote the different currents and voltages which appear in transistor circuits. When double subscripts are used to identify voltages, the last subscript identifies the reference with which the voltage measurement is made. For example, the voltage V_{CE} is the potential which exists between the collector and the emitter with the emitter being the reference. A voltage variable utilizing a single subscript implies that the reference is chassis ground. For instance, the collector-to-ground voltage is identified as V_C. Uppercase letters indicate DC or steady-state variables. Lowercase letters represent AC or signal voltages which change in amplitude with respect to time.

12-6.2 Fixed Bias. A diagram of a transistor connected in the common-emitter configuration and employing fixed bias appears in Figure 12–30. The collector is reverse biased by the V_{CC} supply. The base-emitter junction is forward biased by the same supply which is connected to the base by R_B. Both junctions are properly biased. The base is approximately 0.3 to 0.7 V (depending upon the type of transistor) positive with respect to the emitter.

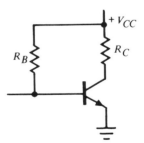

Figure 12–30 Common-emitter connected transistor employing fixed-base bias.

Equations can be derived to determine the DC variables associated with the circuit by wiring loop equations for both the input and output circuits. Base current is determined first. As indicated in Equation (12–11), this current is primarily determined by the value of R_B.

As shown in Equation (12–12), the collector current is the product of beta and base current. The loop equation is written for the output circuit to determine V_{CE} in Equation (12–13).

For the circuit shown in Example 12–4, the base current is 37.2 μA, the collector current is 8.37 mA, and the collector-emitter voltage is 5.815 V. These represent the DC variables at the Q-point.

Loop equation for input circuit:

$$V_{RB} + V_{BE} - V_{CC} = 0$$
$$(I_B R_B) + V_{BE} - V_{CC} = 0$$
$$I_B R_B = V_{CC} - V_{BE}$$
$$I_B = \frac{V_{CC} - V_{BE}}{R_B} \qquad (12\text{–}11)$$

I_B
+
−
R_B
R_C
V_{CC}
V_{BE}
I_E

Figure 12–31 Circuit for deriving Equation (12–12).

Loop equation for the output circuit of Figure 14–32:

$$I_C = (\beta)(I_B) \qquad (12\text{–}12)$$
$$I_C R_C + V_{CE} - V_{CC} = 0$$
$$V_{CE} = V_{CC} - I_C R_C \qquad (12\text{–}13)$$

V_{CC}
I_C
R_B
R_C
Output
circuit
V_{CE}
I_E

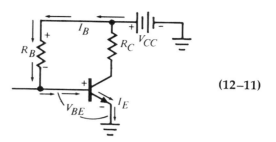

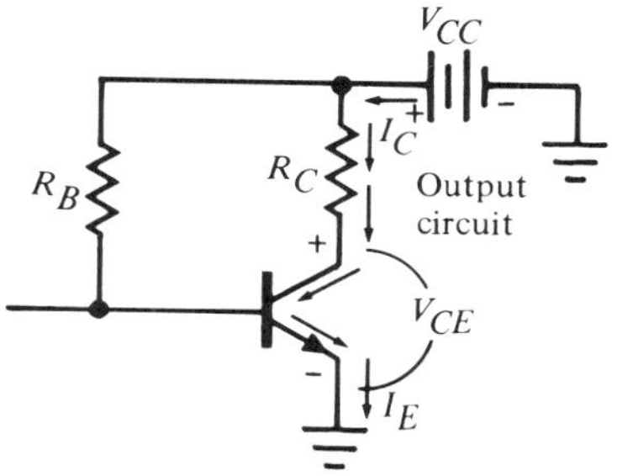

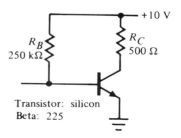

Figure 12–32 Circuit for deriving Equations (12–13) and (12–14).

Example 12–4 Calculating the DC variable associated with a fixed bias circuit employing an emitter resistor

---

Problem

Calculate I_B, I_C, and V_{CE} for the circuit appearing in Figure 12–33.

+10 V
R_B
250 kΩ
R_C
500 Ω
Transistor: silicon
Beta: 225

Figure 12–33

Solution

$$I_B = \frac{V_{CC} - V_{BE}}{R_B} = \frac{10 - 0.7\ \text{V}}{250\ \text{k}\Omega} = 37.2\ \mu\text{A}$$
$$I_C = (\beta)(I_B) = (37.2\ \mu\text{A})(225) = 8.37\ \text{mA}$$
$$V_{CE} = V_{CC} - I_C R_C = 10 - 4.185 = 5.815\ \text{V}$$

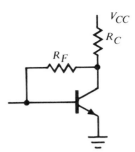

Figure 12–34 Common-emitter connected transistor employing collector feedback bias.

12-6.3 Collector Feedback Bias. One disadvantage of the fixed-bias scheme is that it does not provide for stabilization of the operating point base current when changes in temperature occur. A resistor placed in the emitter circuit reduces this problem somewhat by providing a self-correcting negative feedback potential which reduces base current when the ambient temperature increases.

Another biasing technique which utilizes negative feedback to provide thermal stabilization is the collector feedback circuit. Forward bias for the emitter-base junction is obtained by connecting a resistor (R_F) between the collector and base, as shown in Figure 12–34. The base bias is dependent upon the collector-emitter voltage. In this circuit, when the collector current increases due to an increase in temperature, the voltage drop across R_C increases which causes V_{CE} to decrease. Since the base is connected to the collector, the base voltage decreases causing the base current to decrease. This scheme provides the negative feedback required to maintain a constant operating point for changes in operating temperature. The equation for computing base current is derived from the loop equation for the input circuit, as shown in Equation (12–14).

Loop equation for the input circuit of Figure 12–35:

$$V_{RC} + V_{RF} + V_{BE} - V_{CC} = 0$$
$$I_E R_C + I_B R_F + V_{BE} - V_{CC} = 0$$

Since $I_E = I_C = (\beta)(I_B)$, then

$$(\beta I_B)(R_C) + I_B R_F = V_{CC} - V_{BE}$$
$$I_B \, (\beta R_C + R_F) = V_{CC} - V_{BE}$$

$$I_B = \frac{V_{CC} - V_{BE}}{R_F + \beta R_C}$$

(12–14)

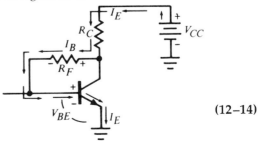

Figure 12–35 Circuit for deriving Equation (12–14).

The equation for determining the collector-emitter voltage is derived by writing the loop equation for the output circuit as shown below.

Loop equation for the output circuit of Figure 12–36:

$$V_{RC} + V_{CE} - V_{CC} = 0$$

$$V_{CE} = V_{CC} - V_{RC}$$

$$V_{CE} = V_{CC} - I_E R_C$$

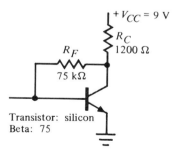

(12–15)

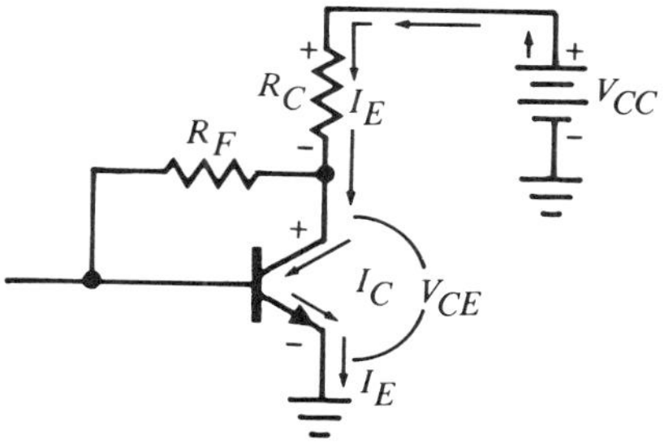

Figure 12–36   Circuit for deriving Equation (12–16).

For the collector feedback circuit appearing in Example 12–5, the base current at the Q-point is 50.3 μA; the collector current is 3.77 mA; and the collector-emitter voltage is 4.476 V.

Example 12–5

Problem

Calculate I_B, I_C, I_E, and V_{CE} for the circuit shown in Figure 12–37.

$+V_{CC} = 9$ V

R_C
1200 Ω

R_F
75 kΩ

Transistor: silicon
Beta: 75

Figure 12–37

Solution

$$I_B = \frac{V_{CC} - V_{BE}}{R_F + \beta R_C} = \frac{9 - 0.7 \text{ V}}{75,000 \text{ Ω} + (75)(1200 \text{ Ω})} = 50.3 \text{ μA}$$

$$I_C = I_E = (\beta)(I_B) = (75)(0.0000503 \text{ A}) = 0.00377 \text{ A} = 3.77 \text{ mA}$$

$$V_{CE} = V_{CC} - I_C R_C = 9 \text{ V} - (0.00377 \text{ A})(1200 \text{ Ω}) = 4.476 \text{ V}$$

12-6.4 Voltage Divider Bias.   There are two types of bias instability associated with bipolar junction transistors. One of these, thermal, or temperature, has already been identified. The other is current, or beta, gain instability. Temperature instability is not a major problem in the voltage feedback biasing circuit or in the fixed-bias circuit if an emitter resistor is used.

Current gain instability refers to the variations in beta gain which occur in the same type of transistors. This gain may vary by several hundred percent. This is caused by the method by which transistors are manufactured and cannot be avoided. Transistors are made from doped semiconductor crystals. Several thousand transistors can be cut from the same crystal. These will all have the same electrical characteristics. Another crystal which is doped to the same extent, and grown under the exact same conditions to produce the same type of transistor, may have electrical characteristics which are considerably different. For this reason, transistor specification sheets and manuals usually identify typical or minimum and maximum values of the various characteristics, including beta.

Beta instability in transistors presents a special problem for circuit designers. The collector current at the Q-point is equal to the product of beta and base current. If several thousand circuits are to be produced over a period of time, the beta values of the transistors used in the circuits may vary several hundred percent. This will cause the collector current at the Q-point to vary from circuit to circuit, which may create problems such as distortion.

The problem is so serious that it would prevent the widespread use of the bipolar transistor if there was no way to compensate for it. Fortunately, however, there is. The solution lies in a biasing technique which is called voltage divider bias. Voltage divider bias allows the transistor to operate independently of beta. In addition, placing a resistor in the emitter circuit allows the transistor to be free from the effects of temperature variations. For these reasons, this is the type of biasing technique used for most bipolar junction transistors.

The schematic diagram of a transistor using voltage divider bias appears in Figure 12–38. Resistors R_{B1} and R_{B2} form a voltage divider network which is in parallel with the transistor. Three different currents are associated with the voltage divider network. Current I_1 is the sum of currents I_B and I_2. The resistance values of the network are chosen so that the resistance of R_{B2} is considerably less than the input resistance to the transistor. This causes the base current, I_B, to be much less than I_2. Current I_2 is called a bleeder current. For the bias circuit to be effective, I_2

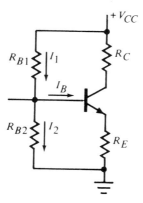

Figure 12–38 Common-emitter connected transistor employing voltage divider bias.

should be at least 10 times greater than I_B. The forward voltage applied to the base of the transistor is developed by the current flowing through R_{B2} and is affected very little by the intensity of the base current component of I_1 which flows through R_{B1}.

The transistor base voltage can be calculated by using the voltage divider rule, as shown in Equation (12–16).

$$V_B = V_{CC}\left(\frac{R_{B2}}{R_{B1} + R_{B2}}\right)$$

(12–16)

The emitter voltage is equal to the difference between the base and base-emitter potentials and the emitter current is determined from Ohm's law as indicated in Equations (12–17) and (12–18).

$$V_E = V_B - V_{BE}$$

(12–17)

$$I_E = \frac{V_E}{R_E}$$

(12–18)

In the output circuit the collector voltage is equal to the difference between the V_{CC} supply and the voltage drop across R_C and the collector-emitter voltage is equal to the difference between V_C and V_E, as shown in the following equations.

$$V_C = V_{CC} - I_C R_C \qquad\qquad (12\text{–}19)$$

$$V_{CE} = V_C - V_E \qquad\qquad (12\text{–}20)$$

or $V_{CE} = V_{CC} - I_C R_C - I_E R_E$ where $I_C = I_E$

When one compares Equation (12–18) with those derived for the fixed and collector feedback circuits, it becomes apparent that, unlike the other circuit equations which utilized beta, beta does not appear in any of the formulas just developed. The voltage divider bias circuit causes the transistor to operate independently of beta current gain.

For the circuit shown in Example 12–6, I_E is equal to 2.6 mA, V_C is equal to 6.8 V, and V_{CE} is 6.41 V.

Example 12–6 Calculating the DC variables associated with a common-emitter-connected transistor which uses voltage divider bias

Problem

Calculate V_B, V_E, I_E, V_C, and V_{CE} in the circuit appearing in Figure 12–39.

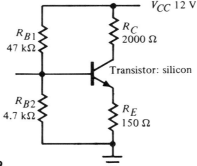

Figure 12–39

Solution

$$V_B = V_{CC}\left(\frac{R_{B2}}{R_{B1} + R_{B2}}\right) = (12\text{ V})\left(\frac{4700\ \Omega}{51,700\ \Omega}\right) = 1.09\text{ V}$$

$$V_E = V_B - V_{BE} = 1.09 - 0.7 = 0.39\text{ V}$$

$$I_E = \frac{V_E}{R_E} = \frac{0.39\text{ V}}{150\ \Omega} = 0.0026\text{ A} \qquad I_C = I_E$$

$$V_C = V_{CC} - I_C R_C = 12 - 5.2 = 6.8\text{ V}$$

$$V_{CE} = V_C - V_E = 6.8 - 0.39 = 6.41\text{ V}$$

The biasing circuits just discussed establish the DC operating conditions which allow the transistor to be operated as an amplifier or an oscillator circuit. These types of circuits will be discussed in subsequent chapters. Transistors used for these types of applications can be connected in either the common-emitter, common-collector, or common-base configurations. A load is required in all three circuit configurations to develop the output signal voltage when a signal is applied to the input of the transistor. This is often a resistor; however, it can be an inductor or the primary winding of a transformer. The load is connected in the collector circuit (R_C) when the transistor is operated in the common-base and common-emitter circuit configurations and is located in the emitter circuit (R_E) when the transistor is operated in the common-collector circuit configuration.

The output signal is coupled from the output terminals of the transistor. These are the collector and emitter terminals for a transistor connected in the common-emitter configuration ($v_{out} = v_{ce}$). The output signal voltage is 180° out-of-phase with the input signal voltage (v_{be}) in a common-emitter connected transistor. When the input signal applied to the base becomes more positive, the base current (i_b) increases. This causes the collector current (i_c) to increase ($i_c = \beta i_b$). The increase in collector current causes the voltage drop across the collector load resistor (v_{rc}) to increase and the output signal voltage to decrease ($v_{ce} = V_{CC} - v_{rc}$).

12-7 THE HYBRID TRANSISTOR MODEL

The hybrid (h) transistor model is an equivalent circuit which is often used as an aid in analyzing bipolar junction transistors. Although other models are sometimes used, the hybrid equivalent circuit is used for most transistor applications. The hybrid equivalent circuit appears in Figure 12–40. The circuit consists of a Thevenin equivalent circuit on the input side which is made up of an input resistance (h_i) connected in series with a voltage source ($h_r v_0$). A Norton equivalent circuit appears on the output

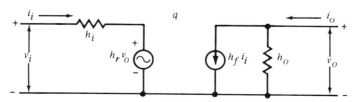

Figure 12–40   Hybrid equivalent circuit.

side. This circuit contains an output resistance (h_0) which is connected in parallel with a current source ($h_f i_i$). The equivalent circuit is called a hybrid since it is made up of two different equivalent circuits—a Thevenin circuit on the input side and a Norton circuit on the output side. A Norton circuit does for a circuit containing a current source what a Thevenin circuit does for a circuit containing a voltage source.

The equivalent circuit can be used to represent all three circuit configurations. A second subscript is added to the h variable to identify the type of circuit configuration. The hybrid model is used to derive four variables which form the criteria for developing standardized specifications for bipolar transistors. Each of these is identified below for the common-emitter configuration.

1. Input resistance (h_{ie}): This represents the input resistance (r_i) to the transistor without any external devices connected to it. Derived from Ohm's law, h_{ie} is equal to the ratio of the input signal voltage to the input signal current with the output signal voltage set to zero. The unit of measurement associated with h_{ie} is the ohm.
2. Output conductance (h_{oe}): This variable is defined as the ratio of the output signal current to the output signal voltage with the input signal current set to zero. This variable is usually stated in microsiemens (μS) or microamperes/volt (μA/V).
3. Reverse transfer voltage ratio (h_{re}): This value is obtained by dividing the input signal voltage by the output signal voltage with the input signal current set to zero. This variable is unitless.
4. Forward transfer current ratio (h_{fe}): Commonly called AC beta in the common emitter configuration, this represents the ratio of the output signal current to the input signal current with the output signal voltage being set to zero. This variable is unitless.

The output signal voltage is set to zero for the h_{ie} and h_{fe} variables by short-circuiting the output terminals. The input current is set to zero by open-circuiting the input terminals. In addition to being used as the criteria for developing standardized transistor specifications, or parameters as they are sometimes called, the variables appearing above are used to develop equations used by circuit designers for determining such items as input impedance, output impedance, current gain, voltage gain, and power gain for bipolar transistor circuits. Transistors may be divided into two categories—small signal and large signal. The hybrid parameters are useful only for analyzing bipolar junction transistors fabricated for small-signal applications. Large-signal transistors are analyzed by using a graphical method of analysis. Equations (12–27) through (12–30) define each of the four parameters for the transistor connected in the common-emitter configuration. Equivalent equations exist for transistors connected in the common-base and common-collector circuit configurations and can be found in most circuit design handbooks.

$$h_{ie} = \frac{v_{be}}{i_b} ; \qquad v_{ce} = 0 \tag{12-21}$$

$$h_{re} = \frac{v_{be}}{v_{ce}} ; \qquad i_b = 0 \tag{12-22}$$

$$h_{oe} = \frac{i_c}{v_{ce}} ; \qquad i_b = 0 \tag{12-23}$$

$$h_{fe} = \frac{i_c}{i_b} ; \qquad v_{ce} = 0 \tag{12-24}$$

12-8 *BJT* SPECIFICATIONS

Most transistors are registered with JEDEC. These devices utilize a nomenclature that begins with a 2N prefix followed by a series of numbers. An example is the 2N3904 transistor. In addition, most semiconductor companies manufacture transistors which have their own "in house" numbering scheme. One cannot tell from the number whether the transistor is made from silicon or germanium or whether it is an *NPN* or *PNP* device. A transistor data book must be consulted for this information. Most transistors today are *NPN* silicon devices. *NPN* transistors respond to higher frequencies better than *PNP* devices.

Transistors have ratings and characteristics as did the diodes discussed in the last chapter. Two important transistor characteristics include reverse current (I_{CO}) and beta current gain (h_{fe}). Important ratings include maximum base and collector currents, maximum power dissipation, and maximum reverse bias values.

Transistors are encapsulated in various types of cases. The emitter, base, and collector leads coming from the case are positioned in one of several possible types of configurations. One should consult a transistor data book to identify both the type of case and the lead configuration used for a particular type of transistor.

SUMMARY

1. The bipolar junction transistor is a three-section two-junction device: the emitter, base, and collector sections and the emitter-base and base-collector junctions.

2. The junctions must be biased for the transistor to operate. The emitter-base junction is normally forward biased whereas the base-collector junction is usually reverse-biased.

3. There are two types of bipolar transistors—*PNP* and *NPN*.

4. The bipolar junction transistor utilizes both majority and minority current carriers. The majority carriers are electrons in the N section and the minority carriers are holes. In the P section, holes form the majority current carriers and electrons constitute the minority carriers.

5. The three currents associated with the bipolar junction transistor include the emitter (I_E), base (I_B), and collector (I_C) currents. The emitter current is the sum of the other two currents.

6. Transistors can be connected in three different circuit configurations—the common-base, the common-emitter, and the common-collector.

7. The electrical variables associated with the transistor are quite different for each of the circuit configurations.

8. The common-emitter circuit is the type of configuration most often used.

9. The bipolar transistor is a current-controlled device. A change in the input current causes the output current to change.

10. Two types of current gain are associated with the transistor, alpha and beta. Alpha current gain (h_{fb}) is the gain achieved when the transistor is connected in the common-base configuration. This gain is equal to the ratio of collector current to emitter current and is always less than one. Beta current gain (h_{fe}) is the gain obtained when the transistor is connected in the common-emitter and common-collector circuit configurations. This gain is the ratio of collector current to base current and may be as high as several hundred.

11. Each type of transistor has its own unique family of volt-ampere curves. The curves show the relationship between the input current, output current, and output voltage.

12. A load line superimposed over the volt-ampere characteristics allows the circuit designer to locate an operating (Q) point. This permits the designer to determine the collector current and output voltage for a particular Q-point base current.

13. Three major operating regions are located on the family of volt-ampere curves: the active (linear), cutoff, and saturation regions. Transistors, when connected as amplifiers, usually are biased to operate in the active region. When connected as a switch, they are biased to operate in saturation when in the on state. In the off condition, the transistor is biased at cutoff.

14. Transistors have a negative temperature coefficient. The internal resistance decreases as the ambient temperature increases. This causes the operating point currents to increase. To stabilize the Q-point, a resistor is often connected to the emitter. This establishes a self-correcting feedback circuit.

15. Most transistor circuits utilize a single voltage source to provide both the forward and reverse-bias potentials required to operate the transistor. Usually the bias supply is for the reverse-biased collector junction and some means is provided to obtain the forward bias potential required to bias the emitter-base junction. This method of providing forward bias is called self-bias.

16. There are three self-biasing techniques: fixed, collector feedback, and voltage divider.

17. One may determine the DC operating conditions for a transistor circuit by applying the formulas which are derived from the loop equations written for the input and output circuits. This allows the circuit designer to determine how the circuit will perform before it is ever connected. It allows the circuit troubleshooter to determine if the circuit is operating properly by establishing computed data which can be compared with the measured variables.

18. The hybrid (h) model, or equivalent circuit, is a useful tool in analyzing and designing bipolar transistor circuits. Four formulas, or h parameters, are derived from the circuit which serve as criteria for developing specifications for the transistor. These include the input resistance (h_i), reverse transfer voltage ratio (h_r), output conductance (h_o), and forward transfer current ratio (h_f).

19. Transistors have several operating characteristics and ratings which may be obtained from a transistor manual (data book). Reverse current and beta current gain are the two most important characteristics. The maximum base and collector currents, maximum reverse-bias potentials, and maximum power dissipation constitute some of the more important ratings.

PRACTICE EXERCISES

1. Draw the schematic symbols for both the *PNP* and *NPN* transistor devices. Identify the collector, base, and emitter connections.

2. Draw the schematic diagrams for both the *PNP* and *NPN* transistors connected in the common-emitter configuration. Show the proper bias connections for both junctions in each circuit and identify the direction of the currents which flow through the circuits.

3. What is the mathematical relationships between the emitter, base, and collector currents in a bipolar junction transistor?

4. Identify the three methods in which transistors can be connected.

5. Draw the schematic diagram of an *NPN* transistor connected in the common-base configuration.

6. Draw the diagram of an *NPN* transistor connected in the common-emitter configuration.

7. Repeat exercise 6 for a transistor connected in the common-collector configuration.

8. Compare the relative input and output impedances, current and voltage gains, and input-output phase relationships between the common-emitter, common-base, and emitter follower circuit connections.

9. What is the effect of a change in input current (I_B) on output current (I_C) in a common-emitter-connected transistor?

10. What is the effect of a change in input current (I_E) on output current (I_C) in a common-base circuit?

11. What is the cause of reverse current?

12. What is the significance of the term *bipolar junction transistor*?

13. Identify the two general types of transistor current gain and discuss their differences.

14. What is the formula for computing alpha current gain?

15. How is beta current gain calculated?

16. What is the difference between DC and AC current gain?
17. Draw the DC load line for the circuit shown in Figure 12–41 and identify its operating point.

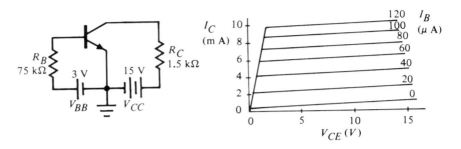

Figure 12–41

18. What is the collector current and collector-emitter voltage for the circuit appearing in exercise 17?
19. What are the three transistor-operating regions which are located on the family of volt-ampere curves?
20. What is the effect of a change in temperature on the operation of a transistor?
21. What type of method is used to bias the transistor shown in Figure 12–42?

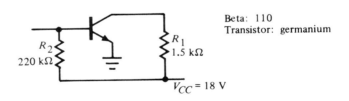

Figure 12–42

22. What device(s) determines the Q-point bias in the circuit shown in exercise 21?
23. Calculate I_B, I_C, and V_{CE} for the circuit appearing in exercise 21.
24. What type of biasing scheme is used in the circuit appearing in Figure 12–43?

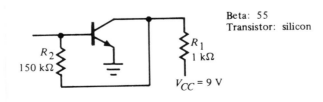

Figure 12–43

25. Calculate I_B, I_C, and V_{CE} for the circuit depicted in exercise 24.
26. What type of biasing system is used by the circuit shown in Figure 12–44?

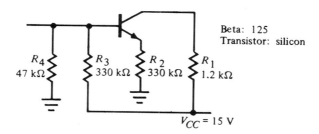

Beta: 125
Transistor: silicon

R_4
47 kΩ

R_3
330 kΩ

R_2
330 kΩ

R_1
1.2 kΩ

V_{CC} = 15 V

Figure 12–44

27. Determine the values of V_B, I_C, V_E, V_C, and V_{CE} for the circuit appearing in exercise 26.
28. Identify two characteristics associated with the BJT.
29. List three ratings which should be observed when selecting a transistor for a particular circuit application.
30. How is reverse current identified for the bipolar transistor connected in the common-base configuration?

ANSWERS TO PRACTICE EXERCISES

1. See Figure 12–4.
2. See Figure 12–10.
3. $I_E = I_B + I_C$; $I_C = I_E - I_B$; $I_B = I_E - I_C$.
4. Transistors can be connected in the common-base, common-emitter, and common-collector circuit configurations.
5. See Figure 12–12.
6. See Figure 12–11.
7. See Figure 12–13.
8. See Table 12–1.
9. A small change in base current creates a large change in collector current.
10. A change in emitter current causes a slightly smaller change in collector current to occur.
11. Reverse current (I_{CO}) is caused by minority current carriers which are primarily created in the reverse-biased base-collector junction.
12. "Bi" means two. Two types of current carriers flow in a bipolar junction transistor—majority and minority. The device is formed having junctions.
13. The two types of current gain are alpha and beta. Alpha gain is associated with the transistor when it is connected in the common-base configuration and is always less than one. Beta is the current gain produced by a transistor when it is connected in the common-emitter and common-collector circuit configurations. Beta is always greater than one.

14. $\alpha = \dfrac{I_C}{I_E}(V_{CB}$ constant)

15. $\beta = \dfrac{I_C}{I_B}(V_{CE}$ constant)

16. The input and output currents used in the current gain formulas are obtained from the same point for DC current gain. AC current gain is the ratio of a change in output and input currents.

17.

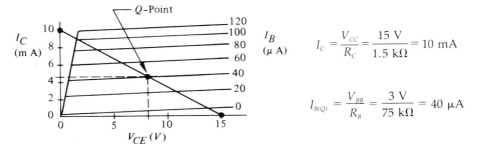

$$I_C = \frac{V_{CC}}{R_C} = \frac{15\ V}{1.5\ k\Omega} = 10\ mA$$

$$I_{B(Q)} = \frac{V_{BB}}{R_B} = \frac{3\ V}{75\ k\Omega} = 40\ \mu A$$

Figure 12–45

18. The collector current is approximately 4.5 mA and the collector-emitter voltage is approximately 8.5V.

19. The three volt-ampere regions include the active, saturation, and cutoff regions.

20. Temperature variations cause the operating point to shift.

21. Fixed-base bias is employed.

22. The Q-point is determined by the V_{CC} supply and R_2.

23. $I_B = \dfrac{V_{CC} - V_{BE}}{R_2} = \dfrac{17.7\ V}{220,000\ \Omega} = 80.5\ \mu A$

$I_C = (\beta)(I_B) = (110)(0.0000805\ A) = 8.85\ mA$

$V_{CE} = V_{CC} - I_C R_C = 18\ V - (0.00885\ A)(1500\ \Omega) = 4.725\ V$

24. Collector feedback bias is employed.

25. $I_B = \dfrac{V_{CC} - V_{BE}}{R_2 + \beta R_1} = \dfrac{9 - 0.7\ V}{205,000\ \Omega} = 40.4\ \mu A$

$I_C = (\beta)(I_B) = (55)(0.0000404\ A) = 2.22\ mA$

$V_{CE} = V_{CC} - I_C R_C = 9\ V - (0.00222\ A)(1000\ \Omega) = 6.78\ V$

26. Voltage divider bias is used.

27. $V_B = (V_{CC})\left(\dfrac{R_4}{R_3 + R_4}\right) = (15\ V)\left(\dfrac{47k}{377k}\right) = 1.87\ V$

$V_E = V_B - V_{BE} = 1.87 - 0.7 = 1.17\ V$

$I_E = \dfrac{V_E}{R_E} = \dfrac{1.17\ V}{330\ \Omega} = 3.55\ mA;\ I_C = I_E$

$$V_C = V_{CC} - I_C R_C = 15 \text{ V} - (0.00355 \text{ A})(1200 \ \Omega) = 10.74 \text{ V}$$
$$V_{CE} = V_C - V_E = 10.74 - 1.17 = 9.57 \text{ V}$$

28. Two characteristics associated with the BJT are reverse current and beta current gain.
29. Three BJT ratings which must be considered by the circuit designer are maximum base and collector currents, maximum power dissipation, and the maximum bias potentials the junctions can withstand without going into avalanche breakdown.
30. Reverse current in a common-base circuit is referred to as I_{CBO}.

CHAPTER EXAMINATION

1. Current gain is less than 1 in the _____ circuit.
   a. common-base   c. emitter follower
   b. common-emitter   d. common-collector
2. The _____ connection has the lowest output impedance of the three possible circuit configurations.
   a. common-base   c. common-emitter
   b. base-follower   d. common-collector
3. The _____ configuration has the lowest input impedance of the three methods of connecting transistor circuits.
   a. common-base   c. emitter follower
   b. common-emitter   d. common-collector
4. The output signal is 180° out of phase with the input signal for a transistor connected in the _____ circuit.
   a. common-base   c. emitter follower
   b. common-emitter   d. common-collector
5. The _____ configuration is by far the type of circuit connection most frequently used with BJTs.
   a. common-base   c. emitter follower
   b. common-emitter   d. common-collector
6. The different regions on the volt-ampere curves where the transistor can be operated (i.e., the Q-point located) are the
   a. active, linear, and cutoff
   b. active, linear, and saturation
   c. active, cutoff, and saturation
   d. active, linear, cutoff, and saturation
7. Which of the following is not a method of self-bias?
   a. fixed   c. voltage divider
   b. separate   d. collector feedback
8. The emitter-base junction in an NPN transistor must be _____ biased.
   a. forward   c. positive
   b. reverse   d. negative
9. For the circuit shown in Figure 12–46, calculate the Q-point base current.

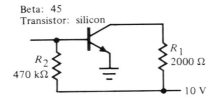

Beta: 45
Transistor: silicon

R_2
470 kΩ

R_1
2000 Ω

10 V

Figure 12–46

10. Calculate the current flowing through R_1 in the circuit shown in question 9.
11. What is the amplitude of the voltage appearing at the collector of the transistor depicted in question 9?
12. What type of biasing technique is used in the circuit shown in question 9?
13. What is the purpose of connecting a resistor to the emitter of a BJT?
14. What type of biasing method is used in the circuit shown in Figure 12–47?
15. What is the value of the base current flowing in the circuit of question 14?
16. Calculate the collector-to-ground voltage in the circuit appearing in question 14.
17. Determine the intensity of the collector current flowing in the voltage divider biased circuit of Figure 12–48.

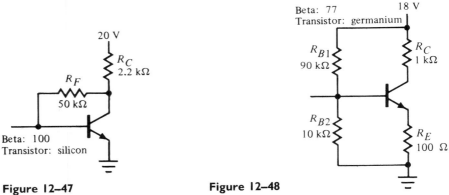

20 V

R_C
2.2 kΩ

R_F
50 kΩ

Beta: 100
Transistor: silicon

Figure 12–47

Beta: 77
Transistor: germanium

18 V

R_{B1}
90 kΩ

R_C
1 kΩ

R_{B2}
10 kΩ

R_E
100 Ω

Figure 12–48

18. What is the collector-emitter voltage value for the circuit appearing in question 17?

Choose true or false for questions 19 to 34.

19. T   F   Minority current carriers are created in the depletion region of the forward biased emitter-base junction of a BJT.
20. T   F   A BJT has a positive temperature coefficient and exhibits an increase in resistance for an increase in temperature.
21. T   F   Beta current gain is less than 1 for a transistor connected in the common-base configuration.
22. T   F   The input impedance of a transistor connected in the common-collector configuration is higher than that for the same transistor connected in the common-emitter configuration.
23. T   F   Cutoff, or reverse, current is considered to be a transistor characteristic.

24. T F I_{C0}, I_{CB0}, and I_{CE0} are all used to denote reverse current.

25. T F   If the beta current gain of a transistor is 242, its alpha gain is 0.973.

26. T F   In a common-emitter connected transistor, base current has a much greater effect on determining the value of collector current than does the collector-emitter voltage.

27. T F   A major advantage of using voltage divider bias to provide the forward bias to the emitter-base junction of a transistor is that the transistor is beta independent.

28. T F   Variations in beta current gain have little effect on a circuit which has a transistor which utilizes collector feedback bias.

29. T F   The circuit shown in Figure 12–49 is that of a transistor connected in the common-collector configuration.

30. T F   Both junctions of the transistor shown in Figure 12–50 are properly biased.

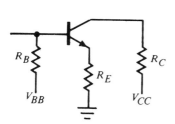

Figure 12–49

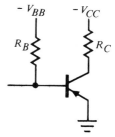

Figure 12–50

31. T F   In the voltage divider biased transistor appearing in Figure 12–51, resistor R_{B1} is primarily responsible for establishing the Q-point bias.

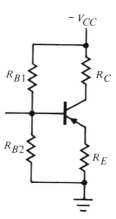

Figure 12–51

32. T F   The Q-point bias for the circuit shown in Figure 12–52 is approximately 25 μA.

33. T   F   The collector current at the Q-point for the circuit shown in Figure 12–52 is approximately 6 mA.

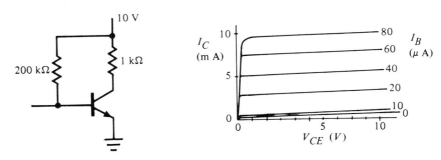

Figure 12–52

34. T   F   The DC beta (β_{DC}) for the transistor shown in question 32 is approximately 120.

13

The Field-Effect Transistor

OBJECTIVES

Upon completion of this chapter you should be able to do the following:

1. Identify the two general types of field-effect transistors.
2. Draw a sectioned diagram of either an N- or P-channel JFET and identify the parts within the structure.
3. Draw, or recognize, the schematic symbols for both the N- and P-channel JFETs.
4. Describe the effect of gate-to-source voltage (V_{GS}) on channel width.
5. Discuss the effect of gate-to-source voltage on output current (I_D).
6. Identify the three circuit configurations in which JFETs can be operated.
7. Draw the DC load line and locate the Q-point for a JFET connected in the common-source configuration.
8. Calculate the Q-point DC variables associated with the source resistor and voltage divider methods of self-bias.
9. Identify the two types of MOSFETs according to their mode of operation and describe the effect of gate bias on each.
10. Draw the schematic symbols for either the N- or P-channel depletion and enhancement mode MOSFETs.

13-1 INTRODUCTION

As mentioned in the last chapter, there are two kinds of transistors—bipolar junction types and field effect transistors. The bipolar device was discussed in the last chapter. This chapter is concerned with the field effect type. The field effect transistor, often called the FET, is the newer of the two devices. This transistor began appearing in circuits during the 1960s. There are two types of field effect devices which include the junction field effect transistor (JFET) and the metal oxide semiconductor field-effect transistor (MOSFET).

The field effect transistor is a unipolar device. Current flow through the transistor is by majority carriers only—either holes or electrons. Unlike the bipolar junction transistor which is current controlled, the field-effect transistor is a voltage controlled device. The input voltage controls the output current. The input resistance to a FET is extremely high with a 100 MΩ value being typical.

13-2 THE JUNCTION FIELD-EFFECT TRANSISTOR

13-2.1 Principles of Operation. A cross-sectional view of the JFET is shown in Figure 13–1. The device consists of a piece of either N- or P-type silicon semiconductor material, called the channel, which has an electrode, or lead, attached to each end. One electrode is called the source and the other is called the drain. These connections are not junctions. Instead, they are electrical (ohmic) connections which attach the leads to the channel. A small band of either P- or N-doped semiconductor material, called the gate, appears about the midsection of the channel. The semiconductor material forming the gate has a polarity opposite that of the channel. A PN junction is created where the gate connects to the channel.

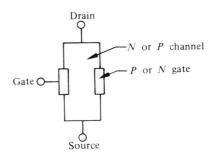

Figure 13–1 Cross-sectional view of a JFET.

Since the channel can be made from either N or P-type semiconductor, there are two types of JFETs—N channel and P channel. The circuit operation for both are identical. The only differences between them are the current carriers in the channel, the polarity of the gate, and the polarity of the bias and source voltages.

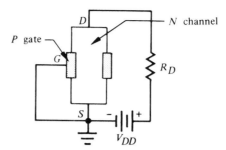

Figure 13–2   N-channel JFET.

An N-channel JFET appears in Figure 13–2. The drain voltage supply, V_{DD}, furnishes the voltage required to cause current to flow through the channel. The positive terminal of the supply is connected to the drain through resistor R_D. The negative terminal of the supply is connected to the source terminal. The gate and source terminals are connected together.

With the FET connected as illustrated in Figure 13–2, current begins to flow through the channel as shown in Figure 13–3. Like any semiconductor material, the channel has resistance. The resistance is divided so that R_1 represents the resistance from the drain to the gate and R_2 represents the gate-to-source resistance. Current flows from the positive terminal of V_{DD}, through R_D, downward through the channel and back to the negative terminal of V_{DD}. As the current flows through the channel, it produces voltage drops across the distributed channel resistance, as indicated in Figure 13–4. The top of R_2 is positive with respect to the

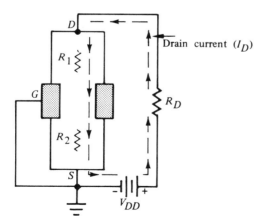

Figure 13–3   Current flow in an N-channel JFET.

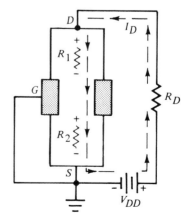

Figure 13–4   Voltage drops across the distributed resistance in an N-channel JFET.

source. Since the gate is at the source potential (ground), the *PN* junction formed by the gate and channel is reverse-biased. The voltage drop across the channel resistance decreases as the source terminal is approached. The depletion region formed becomes wider near the drain end because of a lack of negative charges in this region, whereas the potential difference is less near the source end of gate, which has basically a uniform distribution of charges, as illustrated in Figure 13–5. This reduces the intensity of the current flowing through the channel. The current flowing through the channel and external output circuit is called drain current I_D.

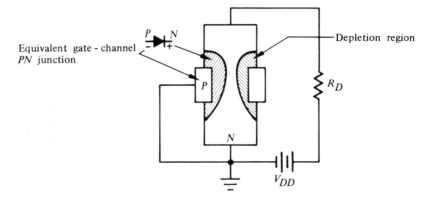

Figure 13–5 Effect of reverse-bias on the gate-channel junction and channel width.

The effect of reverse bias on drain current can further be illustrated by the volt-ampere curve for the JFET. As V_{DD} is increased from 0 to 8 V for the circuit shown in Figure 13–6(a), drain current increases from 0 to 15 mA, as indicated in Figure 13–6(b). The current does not increase continually as the voltage is increased. The drain current rises from 0 to 15 mA as the drain voltage is increased from 0 to 2 V. Increasing V_{DD} further does not cause the drain current to increase; instead, it remains rather constant. This is caused by the depletion region about the reverse-biased gate-channel junction. The depletion region has reduced the width of the channel and all the current carriers within the channel are being utilized. As indicated in Figure 13–6(b), the point at which I_D ceases to increase is called the pinch-off point. The drain-to-source voltage at which this occurred is called the pinch-off potential. This is the maximum drain current which will flow through the transistor.

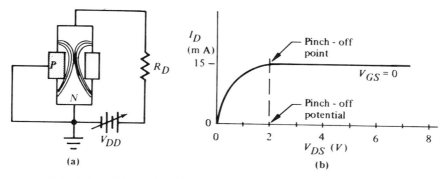

Figure 13–6 Effect of increasing V_{DD} on drain current: depletion region widens as V_{DD} is increased; (b) volt-ampere curve.

The schematic symbols used to represent the N- and P-channel JFET devices are shown in Figure 13–7. The gate arrow points toward the channel for the N-channel transistor and away from the channel for the P-channel device.

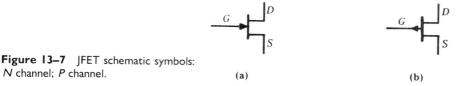

Figure 13–7 JFET schematic symbols:
N channel; P channel.

(a)

(b)

13-2.2 JFET Volt-Ampere Characteristics. The field effect transistor has only limited application when connected as shown in Figure 13–6. To make it a more useful device, some means must be provided so that the input circuit controls the output current. In practical circuits an external voltage, called a gate supply (V_{GG}), is connected between the gate and source to reverse bias the PN gate-to-channel junction. This aids the reverse-bias established by the drain current flowing through the channel. A family of volt-ampere curves can be graphed for the JFET just as they were for the BJT. These can be used to illustrate how the input (gate) voltage controls the output (drain) current.

The data required to plot the volt-ampere curves for an N-channel JFET can be obtained from the circuit whose diagram appears in Figure 13–8. V_{DD} is variable so that V_{DS} may be adjusted. A variable gate supply is used so that the gate-to-source (V_{GS}) can be adjusted.

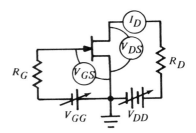

Figure 13–8   Circuit used to obtain the family of volt-ampere curves.

Data are obtained by adjusting V_{GG} for a V_{GS} value of 0 V. V_{DD} is singularly adjusted for V_{DS} values of 1, 2, 4, 12, and 16 V and the drain current measured and recorded for each of these values. The results appear in Table 13–1. V_{DD} is reset to zero and V_{GG} is adjusted for a V_{GS} value of -1 V. V_{DD} is again adjusted for individual V_{DS} voltages of 1, 2, 4, 12, and 16 V. Drain current is measured for each of these values and recorded. This process is continued for V_{GS} values of -2 and -3 V.

When the data appearing in Table 13–1 are plotted, a family of curves results as shown in Figure 13–9. The curves depict the effect of V_{DS} on I_D for a given V_{GS} potential. For example, if V_{GS} is adjusted to -1 V, as V_{DS} is increased from 0, I_D increases from 0 to 4 mA and then levels off and remains constant as V_{DS} is increased. This serves to illustrate the principle that the output voltage (V_{DS}) has little effect on the output current (I_D) after the pinch-off potential has been reached.

However, the input voltage (V_{GS}) has considerable effect on the output current (I_D). For example, when V_{DS} is 4 V and V_{GS} is -2 V, I_D is 1.7 mA. When the gate is made less negative by decreasing V_{GS} from -2 V to -1 V, I_D increases to 4 mA as shown in Figure 13–10. This serves to demonstrate the fact that the input, or gate, voltage is able to control the

TABLE 13–1   Data Used to Plot the Family of Volt-Ampere Curves

V_{GS} (V)	V_{DS}		(V)			
	0	1	2	4	12	16
0	0	3	5.5	6	6	6
-1	0	1.5	3.5	4	4	4
-2	0	0.75	1.7	1.7	1.7	1.7
-3	0	0.5	0.5	0.5	0.5	0.5
		I_D (mA)				

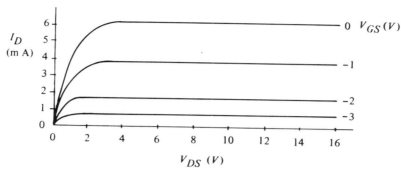

Figure 13–9   Family of volt-ampere curves for the JFET shown in Figure 13–8.

output current. A change of -1 V in the input circuit caused a 2.3 mA change to occur in the drain current. The field effect transistor is considered to be a voltage controlled device because the input voltage controls the output current. Like all semiconductor devices, the field effect transistor is not entirely linear. As illustrated in Figure 13–10, a change in V_{GS} from -2 to -1 V caused a 2.3-mA change in I_D to occur. A smaller change in I_D occurs when V_{GS} is changed from -2 to -3 V.

The gate-to-source voltage supply can turn the transistor completely off ($I_D = 0$). Since increasing the gate potential causes the drain current to decrease, V_{GS} can be increased to the point where the channel is completely pinched closed because of the resulting depletion region created by the reverse-biased gate-to-channel junction. For the transistor whose curves are shown in Figure 13–10, approximately -3.5 V will turn the device off.

Unlike the bipolar junction transistor which has to have an input current to operate, the field effect transistor does not utilize an input cur-

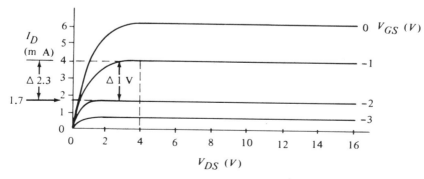

Figure 13–10   Effect of V_{GS} on I_D.

rent. Ideally, the input (gate) current is zero in a circuit such as that shown in Figure 13–8. This is due to the high input resistance caused by the reverse-biased gate-to-channel junction. In an actual circuit, however, there may be a slight amount of gate current (I_G). This represents the reverse current which flows in the reverse-biased junction. The resistor, R_G, used in the input, or gate, circuit usually has a very large value to further reduce any current flowing in this circuit. For most applications, input current is so small, it can be ignored.

13-2.3 The DC Load Line.   A DC load line can be superimposed over the volt-ampere characteristic curves for a JFET just as it can for the curves of a bipolar transistor. An N-channel JFET is shown in Figure 13–11. V_{DD} supplies the voltage required for current to flow through the channel and drain circuit. V_{GG} provides the potential required to reverse bias the gate-to-channel PN junction. Drain resistor, R_D, limits the intensity of the drain current to a certain extent and serves as a load to develop the output voltage V_{DS}. Gate resistor R_G helps insure that gate current is zero. The two points (cutoff and saturation) required to draw the DC load line are obtained in the same manner as they were for the BJT. As indicated in Figure 13–12, point A represents the condition which would exist if the transistor were open and point B represents the short-circuit conditions. The DC load line is the line segment connecting the two points.

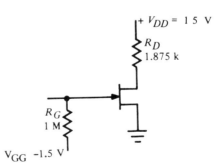

Figure 13–11   *N*-channel JFET.

The operating (Q) point can be located next. This is located at the intersection of the curve representing the gate-to-source potential and the DC load line. Since no current flows in the input circuit ($I_G = 0$), V_{RG} is zero and V_{GS} is equal to V_{GG}. Therefore, the operating point is located at the intersection of the -1.5-V V_{GS} curve and the DC load line, as illustrated in Figure 13–13. The Q-point establishes the DC operating conditions. As indicated in Figure 13–13, I_D is approximately 2.5 mA and V_{DS} is about 10.5 V.

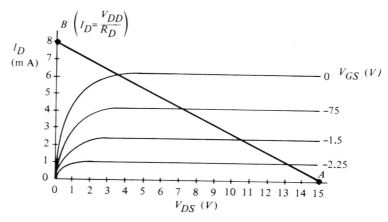

Figure 13–12   DC load line for the JFET appearing in Figure 13–11.

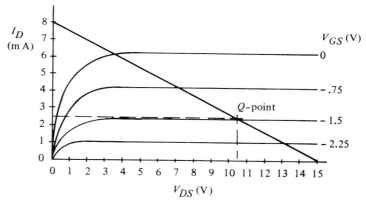

Figure 13–13   Q-point and DC operating conditions for the JFET shown in Figure 13–11.

13-2.4 JFET Circuit Configurations.   Like the bipolar junction transistor, the field effect transistor can be connected in three different circuit configurations—the common-gate, the common-drain, and the common-source. The diagram of the common-gate connection is shown in Figure 13–14. In this circuit the gate is common to both the input and output circuits. The input resistance to the transistor connected in this arrangement is less than it is when the device is connected in the other two circuit configurations. When a signal is applied to the circuit, the resulting output signal is in-phase with the input signal.

The device connected in the common-drain configuration is illustrated in Figure 13–15. This circuit is easily recognized by its lack of a load

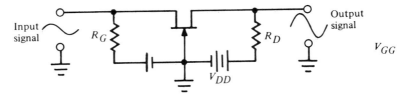

Figure 13–14   Common gate configuration.

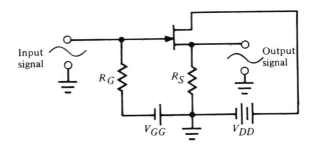

Figure 13–15   Common drain configuration.

resistor in the drain circuit. The drain is operated at ground potential for the signal. The source resistor, R_S, serves as the load to develop the output voltage. Of the three different circuit configurations, this one has the lowest output resistance. The output signal is in phase with the input signal. Since the output signal is developed by the source resistor and is in phase with the input, this circuit is often called a source follower.

A JFET connected in the common-source configuration appears in Figure 13–16. This is, by far, the most common method of operating the device. This is the type of circuit connection that has been used in the previous sections to develop the principles of operation for the JFET. When used as an amplifier, the output signal is 180° out-of-phase with the input signal.

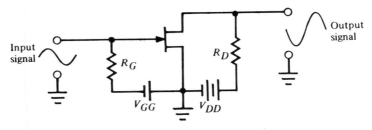

Figure 13–16   Common source configuration.

13-2.5 JFET Biasing Methods.   The gate-to-channel *PN* junction must be reverse-biased. The reverse-biased junction controls the amount of current flowing through the drain circuit and channel. Although a separate V_{GG} supply can be used to provide the bias, usually a single voltage source is used to provide both the drain potential and the gate-channel reverse-bias.

One method used to provide the bias is to connect a resistor (R_S) to the source as shown in Figure 13–17. The drain current flowing through the channel causes a voltage to be developed across R_S. This places the source above ground potential. Since no gate current flows in the input circuit, there is no voltage drop across R_G. This causes the gate to be at ground potential which means that the gate is negative with respect to the source. The polarity of the potential developed between the gate and the source V_{GS} is such that it reverse biases the input junction. The size of the source resistor and the intensity of the drain current both determine the amplitude of the Q-point bias (V_{GS}). The bias can be determined from Equation (13–1).

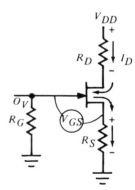

Figure 13–17   Self-bias obtained from a source resistor.

$$V_{GS} = V_{RG} - V_{RS}$$

Since $V_{RG} = 0$,
then $V_{GS} = -V_{RS}$
or $V_{GS} = -I_D R_S$

$$V_{GS} = -I_D R_S$$

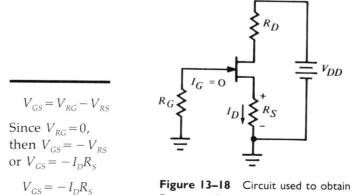

Figure 13–18   Circuit used to obtain Equation (13–1).

(13–1)

The output voltage, V_{DS}, can be determined from the equation derived from the loop equation written for the output circuit, as follows.

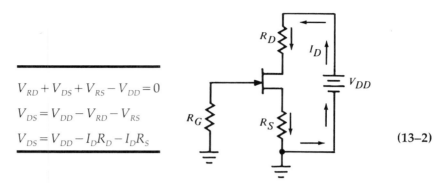

$$V_{RD} + V_{DS} + V_{RS} - V_{DD} = 0$$

$$V_{DS} = V_{DD} - V_{RD} - V_{RS}$$

$$V_{DS} = V_{DD} - I_D R_D - I_D R_S$$

(13–2)

Figure 13–19 Circuit used to derive Equation (13–2).

For the circuit shown in Example 13–1, V_{GS} equals -3.2 V and V_{DS}, at the operating point, is equal to 3 V.

Example 13–1 Calculations to determine the Q-point bias and output voltages for a JFET utilizing source resistor bias

Problem
Calculate the Q-point bias and output voltage for the circuit shown in Figure 13–20 if the drain current is 4 mA at the Q-point.

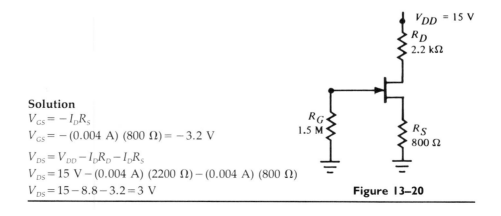

Solution
$$V_{GS} = -I_D R_S$$
$$V_{GS} = -(0.004 \text{ A}) (800 \text{ } \Omega) = -3.2 \text{ V}$$

$$V_{DS} = V_{DD} - I_D R_D - I_D R_S$$
$$V_{DS} = 15 \text{ V} - (0.004 \text{ A}) (2200 \text{ } \Omega) - (0.004 \text{ A}) (800 \text{ } \Omega)$$
$$V_{DS} = 15 - 8.8 - 3.2 = 3 \text{ V}$$

Figure 13–20

Voltage divider bias is another method of providing self-bias to the JFET. As illustrated in Figure 13–21, resistors R_1 and R_2 form a voltage divider biasing network. A source resistor is often used with this type of

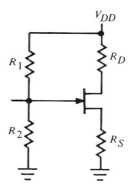

Figure 13–21   Voltage divider self bias.

circuit to provide negative feedback for reasons discussed in a later chapter. The Q-point bias potential (V_{GS}) is the difference between V_{R2} and V_{RS}, as indicated by Equation (13–3).

$$V_{GS} = V_G - V_{RS}$$

$$V_G = V_{R2} = (V_{DD}) \left(\frac{R_2}{(R_1 + R_2)} \right)$$

$$V_{RS} = (I_D R_S)$$

$$V_{GS} = V_{R2} - I_D R_S \tag{13–3}$$

The output voltage at the Q-point can be calculated from Equation (13–2).

The Q-point bias is -1.95 V for the circuit appearing in Example 13–2 and the output voltage is 10 V.

N-channel devices have been used to develop the theory of operation and to illustrate the biasing techniques associated with the JFET. P-channel transistors operate and are biased in the same manner as the N-channel devices. The only difference between circuits for the two devices is the polarity of the V_{DD} supply, the polarity required to reverse-bias the gate-channel junction, and the direction in which current flows through the channel, as illustrated by the circuit appearing in Figure 13–23.

Problem

Determine the Q-point bias and output voltage values for the circuit appearing in Figure 13-22 if $I_D = 5$ mA.

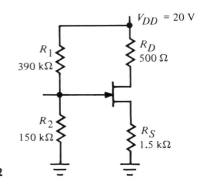

Figure 13–22

Solution

$$V_G = V_{R2} = (V_{DD}) \left(\frac{R_2}{R_1 + R_2}\right) = (20 \text{ V}) \left(\frac{150\text{k}}{540\text{k}}\right) = 5.55 \text{ V}$$

$$V_{GS} = V_{R2} - I_D R_S = 5.55 \text{ V} - (0.005 \text{ A})(1500 \text{ }\Omega) = -1.95 \text{ V}$$

$$V_{DS} = V_{DD} - I_D R_D - I_D R_S = 20 - 2.5 - 7.5 = 10 \text{ V}$$

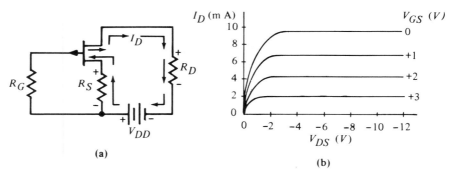

Figure 13–23   (a) *P*-channel JFET employing source resistor self-bias; (b) volt-ampere characteristics for a *P*-channel JFET.

13-3 THE MOSFET

The other type of field effect transistor is the metal oxide semiconductor field effect transistor (MOSFET). This transistor is sometimes called the insulated-gate field effect transistor (IGFET). There are two different types of MOSFETs. Each is constructed and operated differently. The method of FET operation is called a mode. There are two modes of operation—enhancement and depletion. In an enhancement mode MOSFET, the device is cut off without application of any gate potential. Application of gate voltage causes the transistor to turn on. Drain current can be controlled by increasing or decreasing the gate potential. Maximum drain current will flow through a depletion mode MOSFET without any potential applied to the gate just as it does in the JFET. (In fact, the JFET operates in the depletion mode.) Drain current is reduced as a voltage is applied to the gate. If the potential is great enough, the device will become cut off. Both the enhancement and depletion mode devices can be manufactured from substrates made of either N-type or P-type semiconductor material.

The MOSFET does not utilize a PN junction between the gate and channel as does the JFET. The enhancement mode transistor doesn't have a channel until voltage is applied to the gate. Gate voltage develops, or induces, the channel which allows drain current to flow between the drain and source connections. A cross-sectional view of the enhancement mode device is depicted in Figure 13–24.

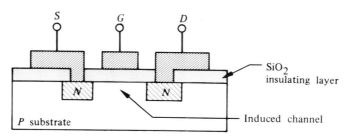

Figure 13–24 Cross-sectional view of an N-channel enhancement mode MOSFET.

A sectioned view of an N-channel depletion mode MOSFET is shown in Figure 13–25. This device does have a channel without the application of a gate potential. Channel width for both types of MOSFETs is controlled by the electrostatic field existing across the gate-to-channel capacitance created when a voltage is applied to the gate terminal. Both types of MOSFETs have very little current in the input circuit because of the high insulating qualities of the SiO_2 material. This means that the input resistance to these devices is extremely high, higher even than that of the JFET.

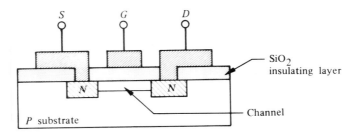

Figure 13–25 Cross-sectional view of an *N*-channel depletion mode MOSFET.

The schematic symbols used to represent the enhancement mode transistor are shown in Figure 13–26. Like the JFET, MOSFETs can be connected in the common-source, common-gate, and common-drain circuit configurations. The circuit (see Figure 13–27) shows an *N*-channel enhancement mode device connected in the common-source configuration. Resistor R_G serves to self-bias the device. This is a common method of providing gate (V_{GS}) potential.

The symbols used to represent the depletion mode transistors appear in Figure 13–28. An *N*-channel depletion mode MOSFET connected in the common source configuration is illustrated in Figure 13–29 along

Figure 13–26 Schematic symbols used to represent the enhancement mode MOSFET: (a) *N* channel; (b) *P* channel.

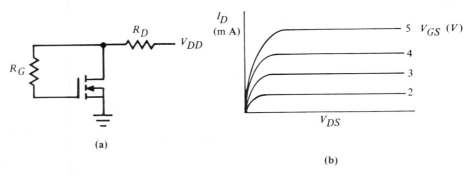

Figure 13–27 (a) *N*-channel enhancement mode MOSFET connected in the common-source configuration and (b) associated *V-I* curves.

Figure 13–28 Schematic symbols used to represent the depletion mode MOSFET: a) *N* channel; (b) *P* channel.

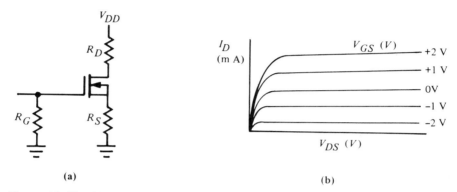

Figure 13–29 (a) *N*-channel depletion mode MOSFET connected in the common-source configuration and (b) associated *V-I* curves.

with its family of volt-ampere curves. Depending upon the location of the *Q*-point, this device can be operated with either positive or negative gate potentials. This implies that the depletion mode MOSFET can be operated either in the depletion or enhancement modes. This is not true of the enhancement mode MOSFET and the JFET. These devices operate only in the enhancement and depletion modes, respectively.

13–4 A COMPARISON OF THE FET WITH THE BJT

Field effect transistors are packaged much like their bipolar counterparts. Physically, it is usually impossible to distinguish between the two devices. Field effect transistors may be manufactured and packaged as separate (discrete) devices or in multiple format (integrated circuits). The integrated circuit format is an especially popular method of manufacturing MOSFETs. Field effect transistors employ the same kind of numbering scheme as is used to identify bipolar junction transistors. The FET may be identified by a 2N prefix which is followed by a series of digits or by an "in-house" manufacturer's number.

The BJT and FET have many similarities but they also have some obvious differences. Some of the more important differences are as follows:

1. the FET has a much higher input resistance; values as high as 100 MΩ are possible.
2. the FET is less noisy.
3. the FET does not utilize minority current carriers.
4. JFETs and MOSFETs are usually not used in power amplifier circuits. They are not capable of dissipating as much power as bipolar devices.

Field effect and bipolar junction transistors complement one another. The bipolar devices are better utilized in some circuits and field effect transistors in others. There are some circuits where both devices operate equally as well.

SUMMARY

1. There are two types of field effect transistors: the junction (JFET) and metal oxide semiconductor (MOSFET) devices.
2. The junction field effect transistor consists of either an N or P-doped semiconductor channel around which exists a band of oppositely doped semiconductor material called the gate. There are two types of JFETs—N channel and P channel.
3. Ohmic connections attach the source and drain terminals to opposite ends of the channel. A lead is connected to the gate to form a third terminal.
4. In a JFET the oppositely doped gate and channel materials form a PN junction. The depletion region about the junction extends into the channel. Reverse bias (V_{GS}) applied to the junction causes the depletion region to widen which reduces the width of the channel.
5. An external voltage source (V_{DD}) connected between the source and drain terminals causes a current to flow through the channel.
6. The current flowing through the channel is called drain current (I_D). The intensity of the current is primarily affected by the width of the channel, which is determined by the amount of reverse bias applied between the gate and source terminals.
7. The input resistance to a JFET is very high due to the reverse-biased gate-channel PN junction. The resulting input current (I_G) is small enough to usually be ignored.
8. The field effect transistor is a voltage controlled device. The input voltage (V_{GS}) controls the output current (I_D).
9. JFETs can be connected in the common-source, common-gate, and common-drain circuit configurations. The common-source connection is the one most frequently used.

10. The gate-to-source voltage required to reverse-bias the gate-channel junction is usually developed by a self-biasing technique. Two popular means of developing this potential include the use of a resistor in the source circuit and the application of a voltage divider connected across the input circuit.

11. MOSFETs are manufactured to operate either in the enhancement or depletion modes.

12. The enhancement mode MOSFET is normally operated in the off state. Application of a gate-to-source voltage causes the device to be turned on and allows current to flow through the channel.

13. The depletion mode device is usually fully turned on. A potential applied to the gate reduces the current flowing through the channel.

14. Depletion mode MOSFETs may be operated either in the depletion or enhancement modes, depending upon the polarity of the voltage applied to the gate.

15. MOSFETs have a much higher input resistance than the junction field effect devices and have less input current. Like the JFETs, MOSFETs can be operated in the common-source, common-gate, and common-drain circuit configurations. The common-drain circuit is often called a source follower.

PRACTICE EXERCISES

1. Draw a cross-sectional view of an *N*-channel JFET. Identify the major parts of the device.

2. Discuss the effects of applying a reverse-bias potential (V_{GS}) to the gate-to-channel junction.

3. Draw the schematic symbols for the *N* and *P*-channel JFETs.

4. Draw the schematic diagram of an *N*-channel JFET connected in the common-source circuit configuration.

5. Draw the DC load line for the circuit shown in Figure 13–30.

6. Locate the *Q*-point for the circuit appearing in Figure 13–30.

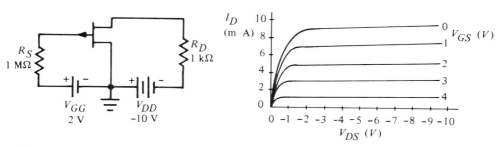

Figure 13–30

7. What are the drain current (I_D) and drain-to-source voltage (V_{DS}) values at the *Q*-point for the circuit shown in exercise 5?

8. Draw a diagram of an *N*-channel JFET connected in the common gate circuit configuration.
9. Draw a diagram of an *N*-channel JFET connected as a source follower.
10. Calculate the gate-to-source bias applied to the circuit appearing in Figure 13–31.
11. Determine the Q-point output voltage (V_{DS}) for the circuit shown in exercise 10.
12. What is the purpose of R_D in the circuit appearing in exercise 10?
13. What function does R_S perform in the circuit appearing in exercise 10?
14. Compute the V_{GS} and V_{DS} values in the circuit of Figure 13–32. $I_{D(Q)}$ is equal to 4 mA.

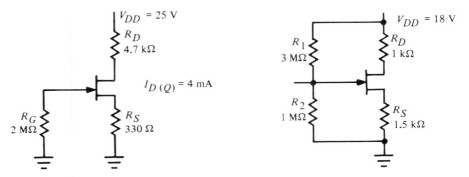

Figure 13–31   **Figure 13–32**

15. What is the purpose of resistors R_1 and R_2 in the circuit shown in exercise 14?
16. Identify the two types of MOSFETs.
17. What type of MOSFET does not have a channel until gate voltage is applied?
18. What controls the channel width and drain current in a MOSFET?
19. Draw the schematic symbols for the *N* and *P*-channel enhancement mode transistors.
20. Draw the schematic symbols for the *N* and *P*-channel depletion mode MOSFETs.
21. What is the major difference in the operation of the enhancement and depletion FET modes?
22. What type of MOSFET can be operated in either the enhancement or depletion modes?

ANSWERS TO PRACTICE EXERCISES

1. See Figure 13–1.
2. As V_{GS} is increased, the depletion region becomes wider and the channel becomes narrower, as illustrated in Figure 13–5.
3. See Figure 13–7.
4. See Figures 13–16, 13–17, or 13–11.

5.

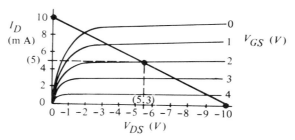

Figure 13–33

6. See Figure 13–33.
7. $I_D(_Q) = 5$ mA; $V_{DS}(_Q) = -5.3$ V
8. See Figure 13–14.
9. See Figure 13–15.
10. $V_{GS} = -1.32$ V; $V_{GS} = -I_D R_S = -(0.004$ A$)(330$ Ω$) = -1.32$ V
11. $V_{DS(Q)} = 4.88$ V; $V_{DS} = V_{DD} - V_{RD} - V_{RS} = 25 - 18.8 - 1.32 = 4.88$ V
12. Resistor R_D is the load resistor. It develops the output voltage.
13. Resistor R_S develops the bias voltage required to reverse-bias the gate-to-channel junction.
14. $V_{GS} = V_{R2} - I_D R_S = 4.5$ V $- (0.004$ A$)(1500$ Ω$) = -1.5$ V

$$V_{R2} = (V_{CC}) \left(\frac{R_2}{R_1 + R_2} \right) = (18 \text{ V}) \left(\frac{1 \text{ M}\Omega}{4 \text{ M}\Omega} \right) = 4.5 \text{ V}$$

$$V_{DS} = V_{DD} - I_D R_D = I_D R_S = 18 - 4 - 6 = 8 \text{ V}$$

15. Resistors R_1 and R_2 form a voltage divider network which, along with R_S, biases the *PN* gate-to-channel junction.
16. The two types of MOSFETs are the enhancement and depletion mode devices.
17. The enhancement mode MOSFET does not have a channel until voltage is applied to the gate of the device.
18. The electrostatic lines of force existing across the SiO_2 dielectric controls the channel width and drain current in a MOSFET.
19. See Figure 13–26.
20. See Figure 13–28.
21. In enhancement mode operation, the transistor is turned off until V_{GS} is applied. The transistor is fully turned on until V_{GS} is applied in the depletion mode.
22. The depletion mode MOSFET can be operated in either the depletion or enhancement modes.

CHAPTER EXAMINATION

Choose true or false for questions 1 to 15.
1. T   F   JFETs operate in the depletion mode.
2. T   F   The *PN* junction formed by the gate and channel in a JFET must be forward biased.

3. T   F   Conduction through the channel of a *P*-channel JFET is by hole flow.

4. T   F   Enhancement mode MOSFETs can be operated in either the enhancement or depletion modes.

5. T   F   The gate potential must be negative with respect to the source to properly bias a *P*-channel JFET.

6. T   F   Channel width is primarily affected by the amplitude of the V_{DD} supply in a JFET.

7. T   F   The input resistance to a MOSFET is higher than that of a JFET.

8. T   F   The most common type of FET circuit configuration is the common-drain circuit.

9. T   F   The enhancement mode MOSFET is normally in the off state. It is turned on when a voltage is applied to the gate.

10. T   F   The depletion mode MOSFET does not have a channel until a potential is applied to the gate.

11. T   F   Drain current is directly proportional to the amplitude of the gate-to-source bias potential in a JFET.

12. T   F   The common-drain circuit is often called a source follower.

13. T   F   The symbol shown in Figure 13–34 is for an N-channel enhancement mode MOSFET.

14. T   F   The symbol in Figure 13–35 represents a *P*-channel depletion mode MOSFET.

Figure 13–34   **Figure 13–35**

15. T   F   The MOSFET is a current-controlled device. A small change in the input current creates a larger change in output current.

16. For the circuit shown in Figure 13–36, draw the DC load line, locate the operating point, and determine $I_{D(Q)}$ and $V_{DS(Q)}$.

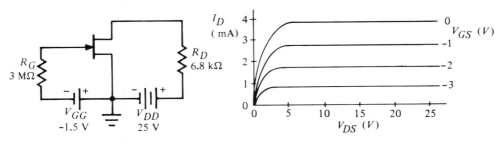

Figure 13–36

17. If I_D is 4.2 mA in the circuit appearing in Figure 13–37, determine the gate-to-source potential.

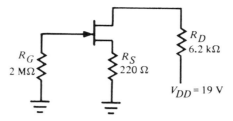

Figure 13–37

18. Calculate the V_{GS} value for the circuit appearing in Figure 13–38 if $I_D = .85$ mA.
19. Compute the output voltage (V_{DS}) for the circuit shown in question 18.

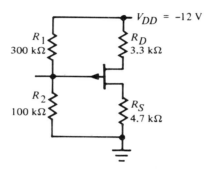

Figure 13–38

14

Special Semiconductor Devices

OBJECTIVES

Upon completion of this chapter, you should be able to do the following:

1. Draw or recognize the schematic symbol and the volt-ampere characteristic curve for the zener diode.
2. Identify the normal biasing state for the zener diode and describe a general application for the device.
3. Draw or recognize the schematic symbol and the volt-ampere characteristic curve for the tunnel diode.
4. Identify the normal biasing state for the tunnel diode and discuss two general applications for the device.
5. Draw or recognize the schematic symbol for the voltage variable capacitor (VVC) diode; describe how the diode is normally biased, and discuss a general application for the device.
6. Draw or recognize the schematic symbol for the photodiode, identify its normal biasing state, and describe a general application for the diode.
7. Draw or recognize the schematic symbol for the LED and describe a general application for the device.
8. Draw or recognize the schematic symbol for the SCR; describe how the device is turned on, identify two methods which can be used to turn it off, discuss the effect of gate current on the turn-on potential, and describe a general application for the device.

14-1 INTRODUCTION

The material presented in the last three chapters has dealt with the more common types of semiconductor devices. There are other types of semiconductor components, although not as commonly used as those previously encountered, that are essential to the operation of many circuits. Some of the more commonly used types include the zener diode, tunnel diode, voltage variable capacitor diode, photodiode, light-emitting diode, and silicon-controlled rectifier. These devices are introduced and discussed in this chapter.

14-2 THE ZENER DIODE

The semiconductor diode was introduced in Chapter 11. In that chapter it was found that a diode operates much like a switch. When forward biased, the diode had little resistance and current flowed through it and the external circuit very easily. Reverse biasing the diode caused it to have a very high resistance, and the very little current which flowed was due to the minority carriers created in the depletion region. The volt-ampere characteristic curves for both the forward and reverse-bias conditions are shown in Figure 14–1. In the forward bias state forward current (I_F) is very small until the threshold potential is reached. At that point the bias supply overcomes the barrier potential, and the device begins to conduct.

As indicated by the reverse-biased curve, reverse current (I_R) is very small (and can be ignored in many applications). If the amplitude of the reverse-bias potential is increased, a point is reached where the reverse-biased junction breaks down, and reverse current begins to increase very rapidly. This point is called avalanche or zener breakdown. The potential at which breakdown occurs depends upon the dopant level of the semiconductor material. Most diodes must not be operated in this region of the volt-ampere curve.

Actually, there is a difference between zener and avalanche breakdown. The phenomenon which creates each is somewhat different.

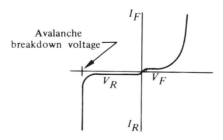

Figure 14–1   *V-I* curves for a diode.

Breakdown in diodes at 5 V or less is caused by the zener effect, whereas the avalanche effect causes breakdown to occur in diodes which are manufactured to breakdown with reverse-bias potentials in excess of 5 V. Usually, no distinction is made between the two types of breakdown, and the two terms refer to the same effect.

A zener diode is one which has been doped to breakdown at a specific reverse-bias potential. The device is normally connected so that it operates with reverse bias in the avalanche or zener breakdown region. The schematic symbol for the device is shown in Figure 14–2. Physically, the device looks like any other diode of comparative size. Zener diodes are manufactured with breakdown (reference) potentials ranging from a low of approximatelty 2 or 3 V to a high of several hundred volts. The doping level controls the breakdown potential. The more heavily the diode is doped, the smaller its breakdown voltage.

One of the more frequent applications of zener diodes is the voltage regulator circuit. A voltage regulator is often part of a rectifier power supply circuit. A rectifier power supply is a circuit which converts AC voltage into DC voltage. A voltage regulator is sometimes connected to the output of a rectifier power supply as illustrated in Figure 14–3. The regulator, made up of resistor R_s and the zener diode, is used to maintain a constant output voltage where input voltage or load resistance variations might cause the output voltage to change. If, for example, the load requires a constant 10-V potential in the circuit appearing in Figure 14–3,

Anode (A)

Figure 14–2 Schematic symbol for a zener diode.   Cathode (K)

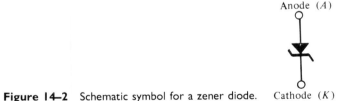

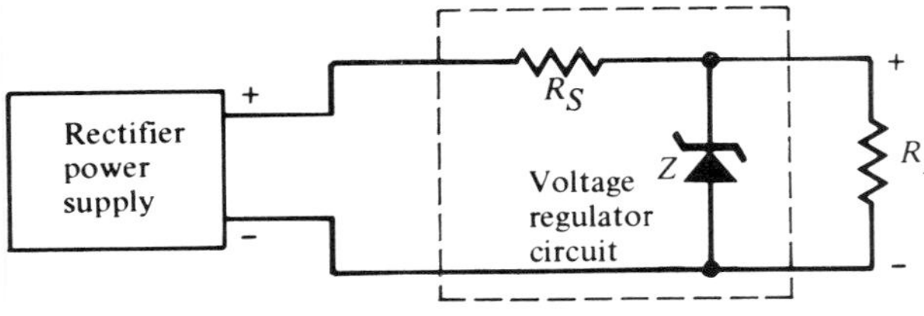

Figure 14–3 Zener diode connected as a voltage regulator.

the rectifier circuit is designed so that its output voltage is 3 or 4 V greater than the required load voltage. A 10V zener diode is connected in parallel with the load. The polarity of the diode is such that it is reverse biased. Since the diode is operating in its avalanche breakdown region, there will be 10 V dropped across it. Because the load is connected in parallel with the diode, the potential across it is also 10 V. The remaining voltage is dropped across the series resistor, R_s. If the voltage appearing at the output terminals of the rectifier circuit either increases or decreases (within certain limits), the load voltage remains stable because of the constant 10V drop across the zener diode. The change in voltage appears across R_s. It is important that the lowest possible rectifier voltage not be less than 10 V, however. The diode will no longer be operating in its avalanche breakdown region and the load voltage will be less than 10 V.

Two zener diodes can be connected back-to-back to form a square-wave generator. A sinusoidal voltage applied to the generator circuit will cause the diodes to go into avalanche breakdown, one at a time, on alternate half-cycles producing a square wave. Two 12V zeners will produce a 12V squarewave voltage, as indicated in Figure 14–4.

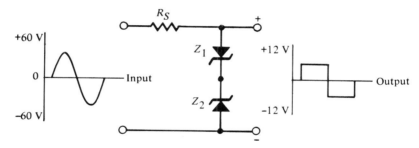

Figure 14–4   Zener diode square-wave generator.

14-3 THE TUNNEL DIODE

The tunnel diode has a forward volt-ampere curve which is quite unlike the curves associated with the semiconductor devices previously encountered. As illustrated in Figure 14–5, as the forward voltage (V_F), created by the bias supply, is increased, the forward current (I_F) flowing through the device rapidly increases when bias is first applied. When V_F is approximately 0.2 V, however, the current begins to decrease, and it continues to decrease as the V_F is increased to about 0.4 V. As the bias voltage is further increased, the forward current begins to increase in the same

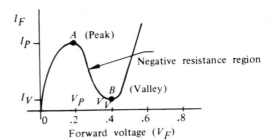

Figure 14–5 Forward volt-ampere curve for a tunnel diode.

manner as it does in any diode. That section of the curve which lies between points A and B, or the peak and valley, is called the negative resistance region because of the inverse relationship that exists between the applied voltage and resulting current.

The tunnel diode can be used as a high speed switch. It can be switched on and off between its peak and valley points, respectively, in a matter of a few nanoseconds or picoseconds. The device can also be operated as an oscillator where the positive feedback is obtained from the negative resistance region.

The symbol used to represent the tunnel diode is shown in Figure 14–6. Physically, the device looks much like any other diode and is available in a wide range of sizes.

Figure 14–6 Symbols used to represent the tunnel diode.

14-4 THE VOLTAGE VARIABLE CAPACITOR DIODE

The voltage variable capacitor (VVC) diode, often referred to as a varactor diode, is a variable capacitor whose capacity value is dependent upon the amplitude of an applied voltage. The VVC diode is a specially fabricated PN junction diode which is usually operated in the reverse-biased state. A capacitor, of course, is formed by two conductors separated by a dielectric. A junction diode has capacitance associated with its junction. The P and N sections represent the conductors of the capacitor while the depletion region forms the dielectric, as shown in Figure 14–7.

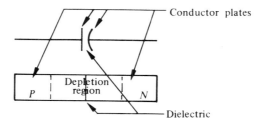

Figure 14–7   Capacitance associated with a *PN* junction diode.

The capacitance of a diode is affected by the width of the depletion region. The capacitance is greatest when the depletion region is very narrow and becomes smaller when the width is increased. The width of the depletion region can be controlled with the application of reverse-bias. As indicated in Figure 14–8, the capacitance decreases rapidly for low values of reverse bias. As the reverse-bias potential is increased, the capacitance decreases at a lower rate. The capacitance of a typical VVC diode ranges from a low of about 2 pF to a high of approximately 100 pF.

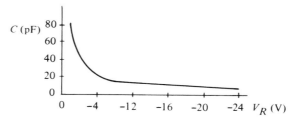

Figure 14–8   Relationship between reverse-bias and capacitance in a VVC diode.

Voltage variable capacitor diodes have some distinct advantages when compared to mechanically tuned variable capacitors. They are small; can be adjusted from a distance; can be adjusted very precisely; and have no moving parts. The schematic symbols used to represent the VVC diode appear in Figure 14–9.

Voltage variable capacitor diodes are often used in radio frequency (RF) circuits as the capacitor in series and parallel *LC* resonant circuits.

Figure 14–9   Symbols used to represent the VVC diode.

The *LC* circuit can be tuned by varying the DC potential, which reverse biases the VVC diode. An example of this type of application includes the electronic tuning technique used in some FM and television receivers.

14-5 THE PHOTODIODE

Electronics is a very versatile technology. Almost any physical phenomenon can be controlled by electronic means if suitable transducers are connected to convert the physical variables, or energy, into equivalent electrical variables. The inverse of this principle is also true. Electricity can be converted into other forms of energy through the use of appropriate transducers. Areas in which there is a considerable amount of activity in converting one form of energy into another are electricity and light. We are all familiar with electricity and the incandescent light bulb. However, there are a number of solid-state devices available that convert light energy into some form of electrical variable—resistance, current, or voltage—or that convert electricity into light. This section deals with one of the more common types of these devices, the photodiode.

A review of the nature of light is appropriate before commencing with the discussion of the photodiode. Light is composed of energy particles called photons. The energy level of a photon is dependent upon its frequency. When photons from a light source strike certain kinds of semiconductor materials, the energy released by the photons is absorbed by the valence electrons of the material, causing them to be elevated into the conduction band. This produces additional current carriers, which reduces the resistance of the material. This is the principle of operation of the photodiode.

The photodiode is a special kind of *PN* junction diode. The diode is operated in the reverse-biased state to create a wide depletion region. A lens is built into the case to focus light on the junction.

Photons, from a light source, enter the diode through the lens and strike the depletion region. The energy released by the photons causes covalent-bonded electrons to be elevated into the conduction band. This creates additional minority carriers which decreases the resistance of the diode and allows the reverse current to increase.

The amplitude of the reverse current flow is dependent upon the intensity of the light striking the diode, as shown in Figure 14–10. As indicated, there is a slight amount of current flow (dark current) when light is not present. This is due to the normal reverse current that flows in a reverse-biased diode circuit. The increase in reverse current is fairly linear for an increase in light intensity for a particular reverse-bias potential.

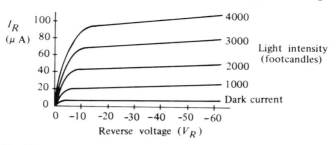

Figure 14–10   Volt-ampere curves for a photodiode.

Photodiodes are used in a variety of applications where light-activated switching is required or where it is desired to have the current flowing through a circuit proportional to the intensity of a particular light. A typical circuit is shown in Figure 14–11. The symbol used to represent the photodiode appears in Figure 14–12.

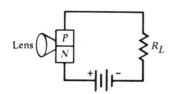

Figure 14–11   Photodiode circuit.

Figure 14–12   Symbol used to represent the photodiode.

14-6 THE LIGHT-EMITTING DIODE

The photodiode, just discussed, functions as a tranducer. It converts light energy into electrical current. There are occasions when it is desirable to convert electrical energy into light energy with a semiconductor transducer. This can be accomplished with the light-emitting diode (LED).

The principle of operation of the LED is identical to that of a normal *PN* junction diode. In a normal diode electron-hole recombinations occur as electrons cross the junction. The energy released by the electrons as they go from the higher energy conduction band to the lower energy valence band is mainly in the form of heat; however, a few photons are emitted. The frequency of the photons are such that they cannot be seen. If a diode is fabricated from a semiconductor material such as gallium arsenide phosphide (GaAsP), a greater number of photons are emitted. The frequency of the emitted photons are such that they produce a light which can be seen by the eye. A gallium arsenide phosphide LED produces a red light. Other light colors can be produced using other types of semiconductor materials. The symbol for the LED appears in Figure 14–13.

Figure 14–13   Symbol used to represent the LED.

14-7 THYRISTORS

14-7.1 Introduction.   In addition to the semiconductor devices just discussed, there exists a family of specially constructed four-section (*PNPN*) three-junction semicondcuctor devices called thyristors. They are often used in control circuits and have the capability of controlling relatively large amounts of power very efficiently. These devices include the silicon-controlled rectifier (SCR), the bidirectional triode thyristor (triac), the silicon unilateral switch (SUS), and the silicon bilateral switch (SBS).

14-7.2 The SCR.   The SCR is the oldest and most frequently used member of the thyristor family. It is basically a semiconductor diode whose conduction period can be controlled by an externally applied current. It performs the function of a switch and is used in applications such as motor speed control, light intensity control, phase control, time delay, battery charging, and power supply regulation.

The construction of the SCR is illustrated in Figure 14–14. It is fabricated as a *PNPN* device that has three junctions. The four semiconduc-

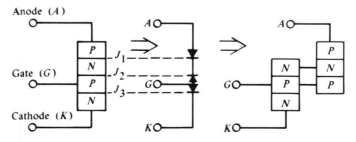

Figure 14–14   Composition of the SCR.

tor sections are equivalent to two transistors—a *PNP* and an *NPN* that share the center *N* and *P* sections.

The equivalent circuit of the SCR is shown in Figure 14–15. The device has three external terminals: an anode, cathode, and gate. The output of each transistor is connected to the input of the other, producing positive, or regenerative, feedback. This causes the conduction of the SCR to be self-sustaining after it is initially turned on. With the application of anode-to-cathode (V_{AK}) voltage, junctions J_1 and J_3 are forward biased and J_2 is reverse biased. The SCR will not conduct unless V_{AK} is large enough in amplitude to cause the diode associated with J_2 to reach its avalanche breakdown region. Usually, the SCR is not operated in this condition. Instead, a positive potential (V_G) is applied to the gate (base of Q_2). The resulting gate current (I_G) forward biases J_2 and provides the bias to turn Q_2 on. The resulting collector current (I_{C2}/I_{B1}) flows into the base of Q_1, turning that transistor on. The collector current (I_{C1}/I_{B2}) from Q_1 flows back into the base of Q_2, keeping that transistor conducting. The gate voltage can be removed from the base of Q_2 after the transistors have both been turned on. Conduction will be maintained by the feedback path provided between the collector of Q_1 and the base of Q_2.

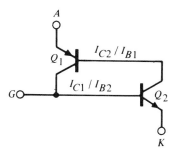

Figure 14–15 Equivalent circuit of the SCR.

The relationship between gate current and anode voltage is shown by the volt-ampere curves appearing in Figure 14–16. As indicated, the diode will conduct, or fire, without gate current if the anode-cathode potential is great enough to reach the forward breakover voltage, $V_{(BR)F}$. The forward breakover voltage represents the avalanche breakdown potential of J_2. After the SCR fires, its resistance decreases substantially, and the voltage across the anode-to-cathode decreases. The resulting anode current increases as V_{AK} is increased, just as it does for a conventional diode.

The anode-to-cathode potential required for forward breakover to occur decreases considerably with the application of gate current. The intensity of the gate current determines the anode potential required for the

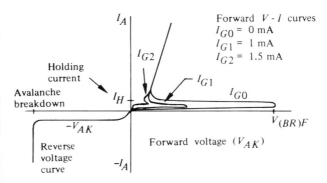

Figure 14–16 Volt-ampere characteristic curves for an SCR.

device to fire. The reverse characteristics for an SCR are similar to those of a regular diode. The symbol for the device appears in Figure 14–17.

Gate current is often applied in the form of narrow (trigger) pulses, as shown in Figure 14–18. Since the gate has no control over the SCR after it fires, there is no need to provide a continuous current to it. In addition, trigger pulses allow the SCR to be turned on at regular intervals.

The SCR cannot be turned off by simply removing the gate current or by reversing the gate source polarity. Instead, some means must be provided to cause the anode current to decrease below its holding current value (I_H), as identified by the volt-ampere curves appearing in Figure 14–16. Two techniques are used to accomplish this. One is called anode current interruption and involves momentarily disrupting the flow of anode current. Although several methods are employed to accomplish this, one simple method involves placing a switch in the anode circuit, as illustrated in Figure 14–19. After the diode is turned off, it will remain in that state until the switch is closed and another trigger pulse is applied to the gate.

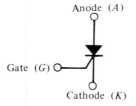

Figure 14–17 Symbol used to represent the SCR.

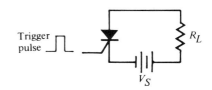

Figure 14–18 Turning the SCR on with a trigger pulse.

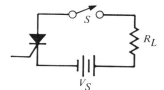

Figure 14–19 Anode current interruption method of turning an SCR off.

The other method of turning the SCR off is called forced commutation. Using this technique, an external current is forced to flow through the anode circuit in the opposite direction of the normal forward anode current flow. If the resulting anode current is less than the holding current value, the SCR will drop out of condition. One method of achieving this involves connecting a transistor across the SCR, as shown in Figure 14–20. While the SCR is conducting, the transistor is not forward biased and does not conduct. When it is desired to turn the SCR off, a positive pulse is momentarily applied to the base of the transistor, causing it to go into saturation. The resulting collector current opposes the SCR forward current, causing it to decrease below the holding current value.

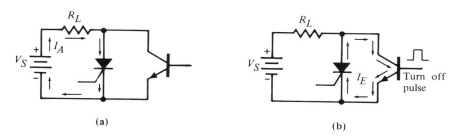

(a)   (b)

Figure 14–20 Forced commutation method of turning an SCR off: (a) SCR in conducting state; (b) turning off SCR.

Silicon-controlled rectifiers are manufactured in many different electrical and physical sizes and are packaged in a variety of cases, as illustrated in Figure 14–21.

14-7.3 The Triac. One of the major disadvantages of the SCR is that it can be turned on only in the first quadrant when the anode and gate signals are both positive. This means that the device can be turned on only during the positive alternations when used in AC applications. This problem can be overcome by connecting two SCRs together in an inverse parallel arrangement. Collectively, the two SCRs are capable of conducting with either polarity of the applied voltage. An alternative to

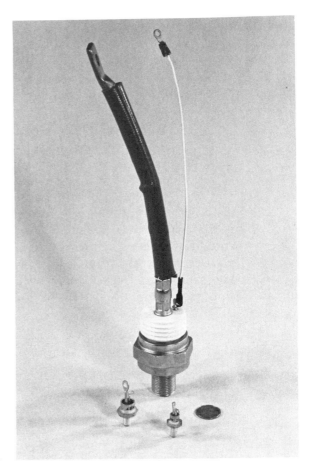

Figure 14–21   Typical SCRs.

this arrangement is to use a riac. This thyristor device can be operated with either positive or negative potentials and can conduct in either the first or third quadrants, as illustrated by the volt-ampere characteristics appearing in Figure 14–22. As indicated, operation is symmetrical for either positive or negative operation. The schematic symbol for the device is shown in Figure 14–23. Since the triac is a bidirectional device (conducts in either direction), it has no anode and cathode terminals. Instead, it has two main terminals (T_2 and T_1) in addition to the gate terminal. The operation of the triac is similar to that of the SCR in the first quadrant with one significant exception. The triac can be turned on in the first quadrant (T_2 positive) with either a positive or negative gate signal. Likewise, in the third quadrant (T_2 negative), the device can be turned on with the application of either a positive or negative signal.

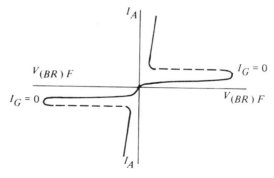

Figure 14–22 Volt-ampere characteristics for a triac.

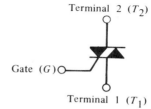

Figure 14–23 Schematic symbol for a triac.

14-7.4 The SUS and SBS. The silicon unilateral switch (SUS) and the silicon bilateral switch (SBS) are essentially miniature versions of the SCR and triac, respectively. The schematic symbols used to depict these devices appear in Figure 14–24.

The volt-ampere characteristic for the SUS is similar to that of the SCR except that it has a much lower breakover voltage. Like the triac, the SBS can be operated with either positive or negative potentials. Unlike the triac, a positive potential must be applied to the gate when anode 1

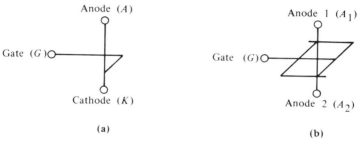

Figure 14–24 Schematic symbols for (a) the SUS and (b) the SBS.

is positive for conduction to occur. It will not conduct when a negative signal is applied to the gate.

The SUS is sometimes used in wave shaping circuits to reshape signals used to trigger other devices such as SCRs. The SBS can be used for the same purpose but, in addition, can provide trigger pulses for the triac as well.

SUMMARY

1. The zener diode is a device specially fabricated to be operated in the reverse breakdown region. The reverse breakdown voltage of the zener diode can be controlled by the doping levels of the P and N sections.
2. Zener diodes are often used as voltage regulators. They will provide a constant voltage to a load (within certain current limits) when connected in parallel with a load and operated in the reverse breakdown region.
3. The tunnel diode is a two-section semiconductor device which exhibits a negative resistance when slightly forward biased. The negative resistance effect allows the tunnel diode to be used as a high-speed switch. The device is also used in some oscillator circuits.
4. Voltage variable capacitor (VVC) diodes are designed to be operated in the reverse-biased state. These diodes exhibit a considerable amount of capacitance when reverse-biased. They can replace mechanical variable capacitors for many high frequency applications. They are especially useful when used as the capacitance in resonant LC circuits where the resonant frequency of the circuit can be varied by changing the reverse-bias potential on the diode.
5. Photodiodes are used in applications where it is necessary to convert light energy into an electrical current. The photodiode is operated in the reverse-biased state. The reverse current of the device is directly proportional to the intensity of the light striking the PN junction.
6. Light-emitting diodes (LEDs) are used to convert voltage into light energy. The diode is normally operated in the forward biased state. The color of the light emitted from the diode depends upon the type of semiconductor material from which the diode is fabricated. The LED is especially useful in display applications where the presence of a voltage causes the diode to light.
7. The silicon-controlled rectifier (SCR) has many applications in both industrial and consumer electronics. It is often used in light dimmer circuits and in small appliances and tools where it is desirable to control the speed of a motor.
8. The conduction period of an SCR can be controlled. The device is turned on by applying a positive potential to the gate. After the SCR begins conducting, or fires, the gate voltage can be removed. The only way the device can be turned off is to reduce the anode current below its holding current value. This can be accomplished by either momentarily interrupting the anode current or

by forcing current through the device in the opposite direction of normal current flow.

PRACTICE EXERCISES

1. Draw the schematic symbol of the zener diode.
2. Draw the forward and reverse volt-ampere characteristic curves of the zener diode and identify the breakdown potential on the reverse curve.
3. How is the zener diode usually biased in a circuit?
4. What primarily determines the breakdown voltage of a zener diode?
5. Identify an application of the zener diode.
6. Draw the symbol used to represent the tunnel diode.
7. Draw the forward V-I curve associated with the tunnel diode. Identify I_p, I_V, and the negative resistance region on the curve.
8. How is the tunnel diode usually biased?
9. Identify two general applications for the tunnel diode.
10. Draw the schematic symbols for the voltage variable capacitor diode.
11. How is the VVC diode normally biased?
12. What elements within the VVC diode form the capacitance of the device?
13. How is the capacitance varied in a VVC diode?
14. Describe a general application for the VVC diode.
15. Draw the symbol associated with the photodiode.
16. What is the major purpose of the photodiode?
17. How is the photodiode usually biased?
18. Draw the schematic symbol for the light-emitting diode.
19. What is the major purpose of the LED?
20. What determines the color of light emitted from the LED?
21. What are thyristor devices?
22. Identify four types of thyristors.
23. Draw the schematic symbol used to represent the SCR.
24. Draw the forward and reverse V-I characteristic curves for the SCR. Identify the breakover voltage and holding current values on the forward curve.
25. How is the SCR usually turned on?
26. How does the gate current affect the SCR after it has fired?
27. What is the effect of gate current on the breakover, or turn-on, potential of the SCR?
28. What is the significance of the holding current (I_H) in a SCR?
29. Identify two ways in which the SCR can be turned off.

ANSWERS TO PRACTICE EXERCISES

1. See Figure 14–2.
2. See Figure 14–1.
3. The zener diode is usually operated with reverse-bias.
4. The doping level basically determines the breakdown voltage of a zener diode.

5. A zener diode is often used as a voltage regulator. It can be used to provide a maximum voltage limit to a load.
6. See Figure 14–6.
7. See Figure 14–5.
8. The tunnel diode is usually operated with forward bias.
9. Two general applications of the tunnel diode are its uses as a switch and as an oscillator.
10. See Figure 14–9.
11. The VVC is normally connected for reverse-bias operation.
12. The *P* and *N* sections comprise the plates, and the depletion region represents the dielectric.
13. The capacitance is varied by changing the amplitude of the reverse-bias applied to the *PN* junction.
14. The VVC diode can be used almost any place where a small variable capacitance is required. It is often used in *LC* resonant circuits.
15. See Figure 14–12.
16. The photodiode is usually used as a transducer. It converts light energy into an equivalent electrical current.
17. The photodiode is usually reverse-biased.
18. See Figure 14–13.
19. The LED is a transducer which converts electrical energy into equivalent light energy.
20. The color of light emitted from an LED is determined by the type of semiconductor material from which the device is fabricated.
21. Thyristors are a group of semiconductor devices which are primarily used in applications where relatively large amounts of current must be controlled.
22. Four types of thyristors are the SCR, triac, SUS, and SBS.
23. See Figure 14–17.
24. See Figure 14–16.
25. The SCR is normally turned on by applying current to the gate.
26. The gate has no control on the SCR after the device has fired.
27. The intensity of the gate current determines the amplitude of the anode voltage required to cause the SCR to fire. The greater the value of gate current, the smaller the amplitude of the required anode voltage.
28. The holding current is the minimum value of anode current that can flow in the anode circuit and the SCR remain in the conduction state.
29. The SCR can be turned off by either the anode current interruption or forced commutation methods.

CHAPTER EXAMINATION

1. The symbol shown in Figure 14–25 is for the
   a. VVC diode
   b. photodiode
   c. zener diode
   d. tunnel diode

Figure 14–25

2. The symbol in Figure 14–26 represents the
   a. VVC diode
   b. photodiode
   c. zener diode
   d. tunnel diode

Figure 14–26

3. The symbol in Figure 14–27 is used to represent the
   a. VVC diode
   b. photodiode
   c. zener diode
   d. tunnel diode

Figure 14–27

4. The symbol shown in Figure 14–28 is of the
   a. LED
   b. SUS
   c. SBS
   d. SCR

Figure 14–28

5. The symbol in Figure 14–29 represents the
   a. LED
   b. photodiode
   c. zener diode
   d. tunnel diode

Figure 14–29

6. The symbol shown in Figure 14–30 is of the
   a. LED
   b. VVC diode
   c. photodiode
   d. tunnel diode

Figure 14–30

7. Which one of the following devices is normally operated in the forward biased condition?
   a. VVC   **c.** zener diode
   b. photodiode   **d.** tunnel diode

8. The volt-ampere characteristic curve shown in Figure 14–31 is for the
   a. SCR
   b. TRIAC
   c. zener diode
   d. tunnel diode

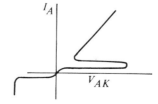

Figure 14–31

9. The volt-ampere characteristic curve shown in Figure 14–32 is of the
   a. SCR
   b. SUS
   c. zener diode
   d. tunnel diode

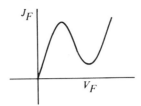

Figure 14–32

Choose true or false for questions 10 to 20.
10. T F   The SCR can be turned off by removing its gate current.
11. T F   The photodiode is a device which converts electrical energy into light energy.
12. T F   The zener diode is often used as a switch.
13. T F   The SCR is often used as a voltage regulator.
14. T F   The SCR exhibits a negative resistance effect immediately after it fires.
15. T F   The VVC diode is normally operated with forward bias.
16. T F   The LED is a transducer which converts light energy into an equivalent electrical current.
17. T F   The tunnel diode is normally operated with reverse bias.
18. T F   The tunnel diode can be used as a switch.
19. T F   The anode current interruption method can be used to turn an SCR off.
20. T F   The zener diode is normally operated with forward bias.

15

Rectifier Circuits

OBJECTIVES

Upon completion of this chapter you should be able to do the following:

1. Describe the purpose of a rectifier power supply; draw or recognize the diagrams for the half-wave, full-wave, and bridge rectifier circuits; describe the principles of operation for each of the three circuits; calculate the DC output voltage and load current for each of the circuits; identify the relationship between the AC input frequency and the output DC ripple frequency; and calculate the PRV across the nonconducting diodes for each of the three rectifier circuits.
2. Discuss the need for power supply filters; identify the general type of filter used in rectifier power supplies; and draw or recognize the diagrams of five variations of this type of filter.
3. Explain the purpose of a voltage regulator; recognize or draw the schematic diagrams of the zener diode and transistor-series-type voltage regulator circuits; and describe the circuit operation of each.

15-1 INTRODUCTION

The more commonly used semiconductor devices have been discussed in the last four chapters. Circuits which use these devices are covered in the next several chapters.

One of the most frequent applications of the diode is its use in rectifier power supply circuits. A rectifier power supply is a circuit that converts alternating voltage and current (AC) into direct voltage and current

(DC). The DC voltage is used to provide the potentials required to operate transistors, integrated circuits, and electron tubes (in older equipment) utilized in electronic equipment. Since electrical utility companies supply power in an AC format, almost all electronic equipment contains a rectifier power supply to convert this power into usable DC power, unless they are completely portable, or mobile, and utilize batteries. In its basic form a rectifier power supply contains only a rectifier circuit. In more advanced forms it contains the rectifier circuit and one or more of the following circuits: a filter, a regulator, and a voltage divider.

In addition to diodes, rectifier power supplies often employ relatively large power transformers, large electrolytic capacitors, and inductors. Because of the size of these devices, the power supply section is usually easily recognizable in most equipment, as illustrated in Figure 15–1.

There are two general types of rectifier circuits—the half-wave and the full-wave. Two types of full-wave rectifier circuits are available. These include the full-wave and the bridge.

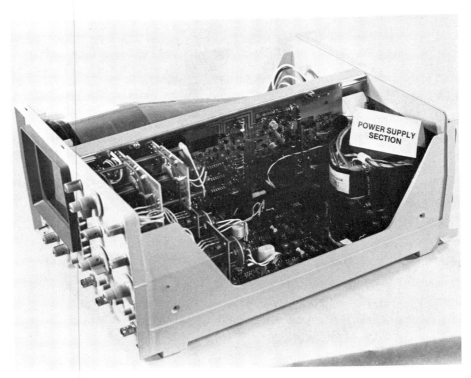

Figure 15–1 A rectifier power supply in an oscilloscope.

15-2 THE HALF-WAVE RECTIFIER CIRCUIT

The diagram of a half-wave rectifier circuit appears in Figure 15–2(a). During the positive half-cycle of the input source voltage, the anode is positive with respect to the cathode. This forward biases the diode, and current flows through the circuit. As the current flows through the load (R_L), a voltage (V_{RL}) is developed which follows the current, or is sinusoidal in shape, as shown in Figure 15–2(b). Although the diode does contain some forward resistance, it is usually small enough to be ignored in rectifier circuits. During the time that the diode is conducting, the voltage drop across the anode-cathode terminals (V_{AK}) is essentially zero and the source, or line, voltage is dropped across the load.

During the negative alternation, the diode is reverse, or back, biased. Current cannot flow through the circuit and the load voltage is zero. The source potential appears across the anode-cathode terminals, as indicated in Figure 15–2(b). The load, or output, voltage is called a pulsating DC voltage. The negative alternation has been eliminated. During the positive alternation, the amplitude of the output voltage increases at a sinusoidal rate from zero to approximately the peak input potential, after which it decreases back to zero. The output voltage does not cross the zero axis and become negative.

If a continuous sinusoidal voltage is applied to the rectifier circuit, the output will be a series of DC pulses. There is one output pulse cycle for each cycle of input voltage, as illustrated in Figure 15–3. The frequency of the rectified voltage is referred to as the DC ripple frequency. The DC ripple frequency of a half-wave rectifier is equal to the input AC voltage frequency.

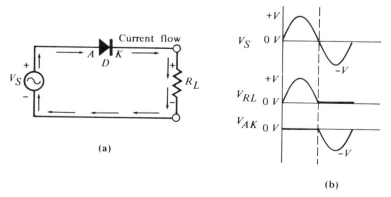

(a)

(b)

Figure 15–2   (a) Half-wave rectifier circuit and (b) its associated voltages.

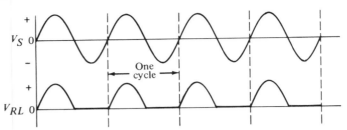

Figure 15–3   Relationship between input and output voltages in a half-wave rectifier circuit.

If the input voltage to the rectifier circuit appearing in Figure 15–2 has a peak value of 15 V, the output voltage developed across the load will be approximately 15 V if measured with an oscilloscope. A DC voltmeter connected across the load resistor would not indicate a potential of 15 V. Instead, a voltage of 4.77 V would be indicated, as shown in Figure 15–4. The voltage measured by a DC voltmeter is the average potential.

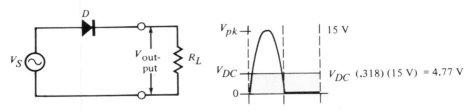

Figure 15–4   Relationship between peak and average voltage in a half-wave rectifier circuit.

Derived from calculus, the average, or DC, value is obtained from Equation 15–1.

$$V_{average} = V_{DC} = (0.318)(V_{pk})$$

(half-wave)

(15–1)

Although a resistor is often used to indicate the rectifier load, in actual equipment the load usually consists of the circuits connected to the output terminals of the rectifier circuit.

Transformers are sometimes used with rectifier circuits to step the input voltage up or down to provide a desired DC (average) output voltage from the rectifier, as illustrated in Figure 15–5.

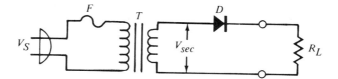

Figure 15–5 Transformer connected to a half-wave rectifier circuit.

Occasionally, it is necessary to calculate the DC voltages and current associated with a half-wave rectifier circuit. This process is illustrated in Example 15–1. In this circuit a voltage step-down transformer having a turns ratio of 10 : 1 is used to step down the 117-V rms input to 11.7 V, which is applied to the rectifier circuit. The average (DC) voltage which appears across the load can be determined by multiplying the peak value by 0.318. Because most AC voltage measurements are made in rms units, the rms value of the secondary voltage has to first be converted to peak

Example 15–1 DC voltage and current calculations associated with a half-wave rectifier circuit

Problem:
Given the circuit shown in Figure 15–6, calculate the DC voltage appearing across the load (V_{DC}), the DC current flowing through the load I_{DC}, and the peak reverse voltage (PRV) appearing across the diode.

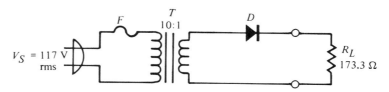

Figure 15–6

Solution

1. Calculate V_{sec}; $V_{sec} = \dfrac{V_S}{a} = \dfrac{117 \text{ V}}{10} = 11.7 \text{ V}$

2. Convert the rms secondary voltage to peak voltage.
   $V_{pk} = (V_{sec})(1.414) = (11.7 \text{ V})(1.414) = 16.5 \text{ V}$

3. Convert the peak voltage to average voltage to obtain V_{DC}.
   $V_{DC} = (V_{pk})(0.318) = (16.5 \text{ V})(0.318) = 5.25 \text{ V}$

4. Calculate I_{DC}; $I_{DC} = \dfrac{V_{DC}}{R_L} = \dfrac{5.25 \text{ V}}{173.3 \text{ }\Omega} = 30 \text{ mA}$

5. Determine the PRV; PRV $= (V_{sec})(1.414) = (11.7 \text{ V})(1.414) = 16.5 \text{ V}$

units before the average value can be calculated. These calculations result in a value of 5.25 V being developed across the load. The load current is obtained by dividing the DC load voltage by the load resistance.

When an AC voltage is applied to the diode, the diode is reverse-biased during the negative alternation. It must be capable of withstanding the peak negative voltage without going into avalanche breakdown. The diode used in the circuit must have a peak reverse voltage rating greater than 16.5 V.

Because a transformer is rather expensive and bulky, a resistor is sometimes connected in series with the diode to reduce the input voltage for load voltages that are less than the input voltage, as shown in Figure 15–7. The series resistor R_S is used to drop the input voltage down to a predetermined value. A fuse is provided to protect both the user and the circuit. If the load requires 45 mA of current and a DC potential of 9 V, R_S must have a value of 1000 Ω and a minimum power rating of 3 W, as indicated in Example 15–2.

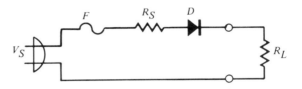

Figure 15–7   Transformerless half-wave rectifier utilizing a series dropping resistor.

Example 15–2   Calculating the size of the series dropping resistor used in a transformer-less half-wave rectifier circuit.

Problem
The half-wave rectifier shown in Figure 15–7 is connected to an audio cassette tape recorder. The recorder requires a DC voltage of 9 V and draws 45 mA of current. Calculate the required resistance value and minimum power rating of the series resistor required to deliver these variables to the recorder if the input line voltage is 117 V rms.

Solution

1. Convert $V_{RL\ DC}$ to $V_{RL\ pk}$; $V_{RL\ pk} = \dfrac{9\ V}{0.318} = 28.30\ V$

2. Convert V_S rms to $V_{S\ pk}$; (117 V)(1.414) = 165.44 V

3. Compute $V_{RS\ pk}$; $V_{RS\ pk} = V_{S\ pk} - V_{RL\ pk} = 165.44 - 28.30 = 137.14\ V$

4. Convert $V_{RS\ pk}$ to $V_{RS\ DC}$; (137.14 V)(0.318) = 43.61 V

5. Compute R_S; $R_S = \dfrac{V_{RS\ DC}}{I_{DC}} = \dfrac{43.61\ V}{0.045\ A} = 969.11\ \Omega$

6. Choose the closest standard EIA value. 1000 Ω
7. Compute the power rating. $P_{RS} = (I_{DC})(V_{RS\ DC})$
   $= (0.045\ A)(43.61\ V) = 1.96\ W$
8. Overrate by 25 percent. (1.96 W)(1.25) = 2.45 W
9. Choose the next largest standard size. 3 W

Therefore, R_S should have a resistance value of 1000 Ω and have a minimum power rating of 3 W.

15-3 THE FULL-WAVE RECTIFIER CIRCUIT

The diagram of a full-wave rectifier circuit is shown in Figure 15–8. This circuit requires two diodes and a transformer which has a center-tapped (CT) secondary. This kind of transformer has two equal amplitude voltages induced across its secondary that are 180° out-of-phase, as indicated in Figure 15–9.

During the positive alternation, diode D_1 is forward biased and D_2 is reverse biased. Current flows from the top half of the secondary, through D_1, downward through the load, and back to the center-tap of the transformer, as shown in Figure 15–10. The voltage developed across the load has approximately the same amplitude as the voltage appearing across the top half of the secondary.

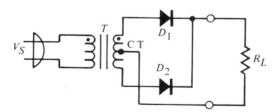

Figure 15–8   Full-wave rectifier circuit.

(a)   (b)

Figure 15–9   Voltages appearing across the secondary of a center-tapped transformer: (a) positive alternation; (b) negative alternation.

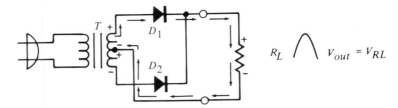

Figure 15–10 Current flow through a full-wave rectifier circuit during the positive alternation.

Diode D_1 is reverse-biased and D_2 is forward biased during the negative alternation. Current flows from the bottom of the secondary, through D_2, downward through the load, and back to the center-tap of the transformer, as indicated in Figure 15–11. The voltage developed across the load has the same polarity and amplitude as that produced during the positive alternation. Two cycles of DC voltage appear across the load for every one cycle of AC input voltage, as illustrated in Figure 15–12. Thus, the output DC ripple frequency is twice the input AC frequency.

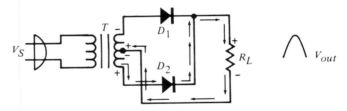

Figure 15–11 Current flow through a full-wave rectifier circuit during the negative alternation.

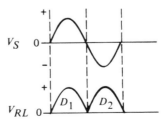

Figure 15–12 Relationship between input and output (load) voltages in a full-wave rectifier circuit.

The average, or DC, voltage that appears across the load of a full-wave rectifier is obtained by multiplying the peak amplitude by 0.636 as shown in Equation 15–2.

$$V_{average} = V_{DC} = (0.636)(V_{pk})$$

(full-wave)

(15–2)

This results in a DC output voltage that is twice that of a half-wave rectifier having the same secondary voltage. As indicated in Figure 15–13, an average value of 10.52 V appears across the load. This is approximately twice the voltage developed across the load in the circuit appearing in Example 15–1. The slight difference is caused by rounding off the values used in the calculations.

The nonconducting diode in a full-wave rectifier circuit must be capable of withstanding the peak reverse voltage applied across the entire secondary winding. The conducting diode acts like a short circuit. This places the full secondary voltage across the nonconducting diode, as shown in Figure 15–14. To calculate the peak reverse voltage appearing

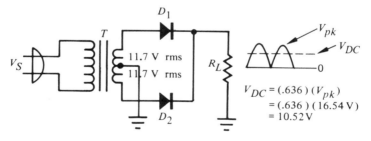

Figure 15–13 DC voltage appearing across the load of a full-wave rectifier circuit.

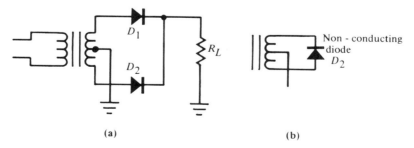

(a) (b)

Figure 15–14 Nonconducting diode appears across the end-to-end winding of a center-tapped secondary: (a) D_1 appears as a short; (b) D_2 appears across the entire secondary.

across the nonconducting diode, the end-to-end secondary rms voltage is multiplied by 1.414. This converts the secondary voltage to peak voltage. For the circuit shown in Figure 15–13, this results in a value of 33 V. The peak reverse voltage (PRV) rating of the diodes used in that circuit must be greater than 33 V.

The DC variables associated with a full-wave rectifier circuit can be calculated in a fashion similar to that used for half-wave rectifiers, as illustrated by the example shown in Example 15–3.

Example 15–3 DC voltage calculations associated with a full-wave rectifier circuit

Problem
The full-wave rectifier circuit appearing in Figure 15–15 is used to provide the DC voltage required to operate a small television receiver. If the input voltage is 117 V and the transformer turns ratio (*a*) is 3, determine the DC output voltage to the receiver.

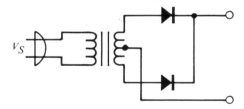

Figure 15–15

Solution
1. Determine the end-to-end secondary voltage.
$$V_{sec} = \frac{V_S}{a} = \frac{117 \text{ V}}{3} = 39 \text{ V}$$

2. Calculate the CT-to-end secondary voltage ($V_{1/2 \text{ sec}}$)
$$V_{1/2 \text{ sec}} = \frac{V_{sec}}{2} = \frac{39 \text{ V}}{2} = 19.5 \text{ V}$$

3. Convert the CT-to-end voltage to peak voltage.
$$V_{pk} = (V_{1/2 \text{ sec}})(1.414) = (19.5 \text{ V})(1.414) = 27.57 \text{ V}$$

4. Compute the DC output potential.
$$V_{DC} = (V_{pk})(0.636) = (27.57 \text{ V})(0.636) = 17.53 \text{ V}$$

5. Calculate the PRV.
$$\text{PRV} = (V_{sec})(1.414) = (39 \text{ V})(1.414) = 55.15 \text{ V}$$

15-4 THE BRIDGE RECTIFIER CIRCUIT

This is the second type of full-wave rectifier. As shown in Figure 15–16, this circuit requires four diodes. Although a transformer is usually required in this circuit, the secondary does not have to have a center-tap.

During the positive alternation, diodes D_1 and D_3 are forward biased and D_2 and D_4 are reverse biased. Current flows from the top of the transformer through D_1, downward through the load, through D_3, and back to the transformer, as illustrated in Figure 15–17. The current flowing through the load produces a voltage which is approximately equal to the peak value of the input potential.

Diodes D_2 and D_4 are forward biased and D_1 and D_3 are reverse-biased during the negative alternation. As shown in Figure 15–18, current flows from the bottom of the transformer through D_4, downward through the load, through D_2, and back to the top of the transformer to complete the circuit. Since current flows through the load in the same direction that it did during the positive alternation, the voltage developed across the load has the same polarity as it did for the positive alternation. Like the full-wave rectifier circuit, the DC ripple frequency is twice the input

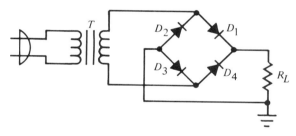

Figure 15–16 Bridge rectifier circuit.

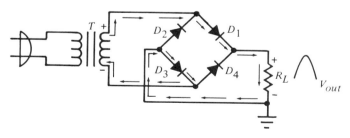

Figure 15–17 Current flow through a bridge rectifier circuit during the positive alternation.

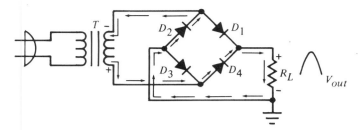

Figure 15–18 Current flow through a bridge rectifier circuit during the negative alternation.

AC frequency. Compared to a full-wave rectifier, the bridge rectifier circuit produces twice the DC output voltage if transformers having the same turns ratio are used. The transformer used in the circuit appearing in Example 15–4 has the same turns ratio as the one shown in Example 15–3. The DC output of the bridge circuit is twice as large as the voltage appearing across the load connected to the full-wave rectifier circuit in Example 15–3.

Although the bridge rectifier circuit utilizes four diodes instead of two, as the full-wave rectifier circuit does, the bridge rectifier is the more

Example 15–4 Calculating the DC output voltage of a bridge rectifier circuit

Problem
A bridge rectifier circuit is used to provide the DC voltage and current required to operate a relay. If 117 V is applied to the primary of the transformer and it has a turns ratio of 3 : 1, determine the DC potential applied to the relay coil.

Solution

    1. Calculate V_{sec}; $V_{sec} = \dfrac{117\ V}{3} = 39\ V$

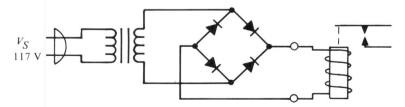

Figure 15–19

    2. Convert V_{sec} to V_{pk}; $V_{pk} = (V_{sec})(1.414) = (39\ V)(1.414) = 55.15\ V$
    3. Convert V_{pk} to V_{DC}; $V_{DC} = (V_{pk})(0.636) = (55.15\ V)(0.636) = 35.08\ V$

often used of the two. The main reason being that it does not require a transformer having a center-tapped secondary. The four diodes are often mounted in a single case.

The rectifier circuits discussed to this point all produce a positive potential across their output terminals. Sometimes a negative voltage is required by the transistors or integrated circuits employed in a circuit. A rectifier circuit can develop a negative voltage, with respect to ground, if the polarity of the diodes in the circuit are reversed, as illustrated in Figure 15–20.

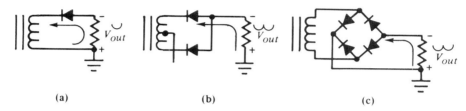

Figure 15–20   Rectifier circuits which produce negative voltages; (a) half-wave; (b) full-wave; (c) bridge.

15-5 RECTIFIER POWER SUPPLY FILTER CIRCUITS

The output voltage from a rectifier circuit consists of a series of DC pulses which must be converted into steady-state DC to be usable by most electrical loads. The output of a rectifier circuit contains two voltage components, as shown in Figure 15–21. One component is the average voltage (V_{DC}) and the other is the AC ripple voltage (V_r), which is a result of the voltage fluctuations which occur above and below the average value.

A term used to describe the relationship between the AC ripple voltage and the DC voltage is ripple factor. As shown in Equation 15–3, rip-

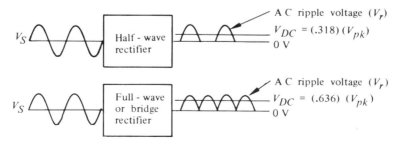

Figure 15–21   Voltage components associated with rectifier circuits.

ple factor (r) is the ratio of the rms value of the AC ripple voltage to the DC voltage.

$$\text{Ripple factor } (r) = \frac{\text{rms ripple voltage}}{\text{DC voltage}} = \frac{V_{r\,\text{rms}}}{V_{\text{DC}}} \qquad (15\text{–}3)$$

$$\text{Percent of ripple} = \frac{V_{r\,\text{rms}}}{V_{\text{DC}}} \times 100 \qquad (15\text{–}4)$$

This ratio is often expressed as a percentage as indicated by Equation 15–4, and is called percent of ripple. The smaller the percent of ripple value, the closer the output voltage of a power supply approaches pure (steady-state) DC. The percent of ripple values for the unfiltered rectifiers appear in Table 15–1.

TABLE 15–1   Percent of Ripple for Unfiltered Rectifier Circuits

Rectifier Circuit	Percent of Ripple
Half-wave	121
Full-wave	48
Bridge	48

A low-pass filter can be connected to the output of a rectifier circuit to reduce the percent of ripple. The voltage across, and the current flowing through, a load connected to a rectifier circuit consists of a series of DC pulses. The filter is made up of energy-storing devices (reactances), which store a portion of the energy being delivered to the load. The stored energy is then released to the load between the output pulses, as illustrated in Figure 15–22.

A capacitor connected in parallel with the load, or across the output terminals of a rectifier circuit, forms the most basic type of power supply low-pass filter, as shown in Figure 15–23. During the time from t_0 to t_1,

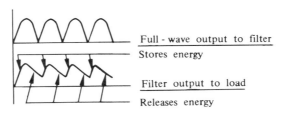

Full - wave output to filter
Stores energy

Filter output to load
Releases energy

Figure 15–22   Basic filter action.

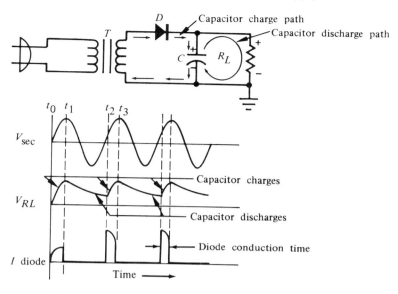

Figure 15–23   Action of a capacitor filter connected to a half-wave rectifier circuit.

the diode is forward biased and the capacitor charges to the peak value of the input voltage. From time t_1 to t_2, the cathode of the diode is at a higher potential than the anode due to the charge across the capacitor, and the diode becomes reverse-biased. During this time, the capacitor discharges through the load, releasing part of the energy that was stored during the charging process. The capacitor does not have time to fully discharge before the diode becomes forward biased and begins conducting again at time t_2. Since the capacitor does not have time to completely discharge, the diode remains reverse biased longer than it would if the capacitor was not in the circuit. This causes the conduction period of the diode to be considerably less than the normal 180° duration. The current flowing through the diode is different from that flowing through the load and consists of a series of narrow pulses. The amplitude of the diode current has a higher peak value since the diode still has to pass the same amount of average current.

The size of the capacitor and the resistance of the load both determine the extent to which the capacitor will discharge during the time the diode is cutoff. This, in turn, affects the amplitude of the AC ripple voltage appearing across the load, as shown in Figure 15–24. For a given capacitor value, a low resistance load causes the output voltage to vary considerably. A higher load resistance causes the AC voltage variations to be

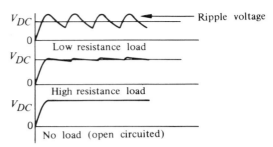

Figure 15–24 Effect of load resistance on AC ripple voltage.

less in amplitude. With no load connected to the output terminals of the filter (infinite resistance), the DC output voltage is constant and the ripple voltage is zero. Filters can be used with all three types of rectifier circuits. The full-wave and bridge rectifier circuits are easier to filter because of their higher-frequency ripple voltage. They require capacitor values of one-half the capacity of those used in half-wave rectifiers for the same load and ripple factor values. Half-wave rectifiers have only limited applications and are used primarily with high-resistance, low-current loads.

Several different types of low-pass filters are used with rectifier circuits. One of the most simple is the capacitor type just discussed. This one and some of the other more common types are shown in Figure 15–25. The DC output voltage and percent of ripple obtained from a particular filter depends upon whether the filter is connected to a half-wave or full-wave rectifier, the values of the components forming the filter circuit,

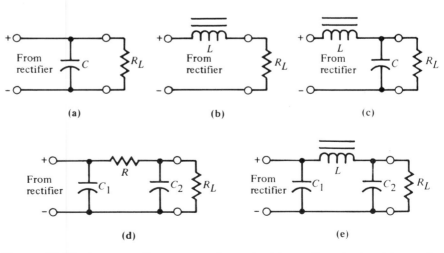

Figure 15–25 Low-pass filters commonly used with rectifier circuits: (a) capacitor; (b) inductor (c) "L" filter; (d) RC pi filter; (e) LC pi filter.

and the value of the load resistance. Because of their high electrical capacity, electrolytic capacitors are used in power supply filter circuits. Depending upon the desired percent of ripple, these may range from a low
of approximately 25 μF to a high of several thousand microfarads. Inductors used in power supply filters may range from a low of about 2 H to
a high of approximately 12 H.

For rectifier power supplies used in equipment such as radio and
television receivers, computers, and electronic test instruments, the transistors and integrated circuits in the equipment comprise the load for
their respective power supplies. Several different DC potentials may be
required to operate the circuits utilized in this kind of equipment. These
can be obtained from a single power supply by connecting a voltage divider network across the filter, as shown in Figure 15–26. In this circuit
three different voltages are developed across the output terminals with
respect to ground.

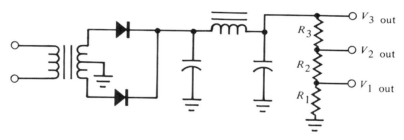

Figure 15–26 Voltage divider network connected to a rectifier power supply.

15-6 VOLTAGE REGULATOR CIRCUITS

The DC output voltage from a rectifier power supply may fluctuate from
time to time. This may be caused by either the amplitude of the AC input
voltage or the resistance of the load changing in value. The output variations are not great enough to affect the operation of most loads. There
are some applications, however, where a constant voltage is necessary.
These include applications where the power supply potential is being
used as a voltage reference or where the voltage is applied to a semiconductor device whose circuit operation is dependent upon a nonchanging
DC voltage value. A constant output voltage may be obtained from a rectifier power supply by connecting a voltage regulator circuit between the
filter and output terminals, as illustrated in Figure 15–27. There are sev-

eral types of voltage regulator circuits. One of the simplest, the zener diode voltage regulator, was discussed in the last chapter. It consists of a resistor and a zener diode, as shown in Figure 15–28. A zener diode having a breakdown voltage equal to the desired load voltage is connected across the output terminals. The turns ratio of the transformer is such that the input voltage to the regulator is slightly greater than the load and zener voltage requirements. The voltage difference is dropped across the resistor. As the load voltage attempts to increase or decrease, the changing voltage is absorbed by the resistor, and the voltage across the load remains constant.

Zener diodes can be connected in series with each other to form a voltage divider network to provide multiple regulated output voltages, as shown in Figure 15–29. The output potentials are the sum of the individual zener values as measured from the ground terminal.

Another type of voltage regulator appears in Figure 15–30. Called a transistor-series-type voltage regulator, this circuit employs a transistor

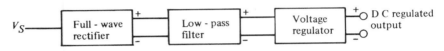

Figure 15–27   Rectifier power supply containing a voltage regulator.

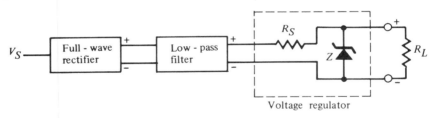

Figure 15–28   Zener diode voltage regulator circuit.

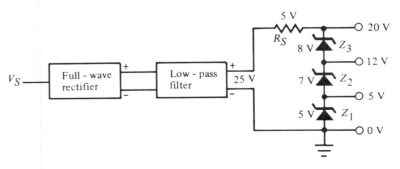

Figure 15–29   Multiple output zener diode voltage regulator circuit.

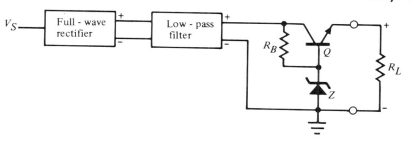

Figure 15–30 Transistor-series-type voltage regulator circuit.

which is connected in series with the load. The collector is connected to the output of the filter and the emitter is connected to the positive terminal of the load. A zener diode whose breakdown potential is somewhat greater than the load voltage provides a constant, or reference, voltage to the base. The emitter-base junction is forward biased by the difference of potential existing between the base and emitter. The transistor operates as a variable resistor. If the voltage across the load increases, the emitter becomes more positive. This decreases the emitter-base bias, causing the transistor to conduct less heavily. The resistance of the transistor increases causing the excess voltage to be dropped across the collector-emitter terminals. Thus, a constant-load voltage is maintained by the self-correcting feedback provided by the emitter-base circuit.

SUMMARY

1. Rectifier power supplies are used to convert AC voltage into DC voltage. Unless the equipment is completely portable and utilizes batteries, almost all electronic equipment requires rectifier power supplies to furnish the DC power required to operate their circuits.
2. The basic rectifier power supply consists of a rectifier circuit. This is usually followed by a filter, which is sometimes followed by a regulator circuit and/or a voltage divider circuit.
3. There are three types of rectifier circuits: the half-wave, full-wave, and bridge. The half-wave rectifier requires one diode; the full-wave rectifier has two diodes; and the bridge rectifier utilizes four diodes. The full-wave rectifier circuit requires a transformer that has a center-tapped secondary.
4. The DC output ripple frequency is equal to the frequency of the input AC voltage in the half-wave rectifier. The output ripple frequency is twice the input frequency for the full-wave and bridge rectifiers.
5. The full-wave and bridge rectifier circuits are both full-wave rectifiers. Two DC pulses appear across the output terminals for one cycle of AC input voltage.

6. The output of a rectifier circuit contains two voltage components: a DC and an AC; the DC voltage forms the reference for the AC component. The ripple factor (r) is used to describe the amount of ripple present at the output terminals of a power supply and is equal to the ratio of the rms value of the AC voltage to the DC voltage.

7. A low-pass filter is usually connected to the output of a rectifier circuit to reduce the ripple factor, or percent of ripple. The filter circuit contains one or more reactive devices which store energy during the conduction period of the diode(s) and releases it to the load during the nonconducting time.

8. A voltage regulator circuit is sometimes connected to the output of a filter to provide a constant voltage to a load. Two common types of voltage regulator circuits are the zener and the transistor-series-type.

9. The zener diode voltage regulator is the simpler of the two types of regulator circuits. In this circuit a zener diode is connected across the load which is to be regulated.

10. A bipolar transistor is connected in series with the load when the transistor-series-type voltage regulator is used. The transistor functions as a variable resistor whose resistance is dependent upon the conduction of the transistor. Transistor conduction is determined by the amplitude of the load voltage connected to the emitter.

PRACTICE EXERCISES

1. What is the purpose of a rectifier power supply?
2. Identify the three types of rectifier circuits.
3. Draw the diagram of a half-wave rectifier that utilizes a transformer.
4. Draw the circuit diagram of a full-wave rectifier circuit.
5. Draw the schematic diagram of a bridge rectifier circuit.
6. Compute the DC voltage across, and the current flowing through, the load for the circuit shown in Figure 15–31.
7. Calculate the DC load voltage and the current for the full-wave rectifier circuit in Figure 15–32.

Figure 15–31   **Figure 15–32**

8. Determine the DC load voltage and current conditions for the circuit shown in Figure 15–33.

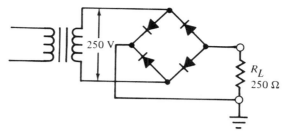

Figure 15–33

I I

9. Calculate the peak reverse voltage (PRV) which appears across the diode when it is reverse-biased for the circuit shown in exercise 6.
10. Determine the PRV for the nonconducting diode for the rectifier circuit appearing in exercise 7.
11. A transformerless half-wave rectifier circuit is to be used to supply 12 V to a 240 Ω load. Compute the resistance value and power rating of R_s if the input voltage is 120 V.
12. Define the term *ripple factor*.
13. Draw the diagrams of five types of low-pass filters that can be used with rectifier circuits.
14. What is the value of the ripple factor for an unfiltered bridge rectifier?
15. What constitutes a load for a rectifier power supply?
16. Identify two types of voltage regulator circuits.
17. Draw the diagram of the transistor-series-type voltage regulator circuit.
18. Describe the basic circuit operation of the transistor-series-type voltage regulator.
19. A bridge rectifier circuit connected to an *LC* pi filter is used to provide the DC voltage required to operate a microcomputer. The microcomputer requires regulated 5 and 12 V potentials to operate. Draw the schematic diagram of the power supply.

ANSWERS TO PRACTICE EXERCISES

1. A rectifier power supply converts AC voltage into DC voltage.
2. The three types of rectifier circuits are the half-wave, full-wave, and bridge.
3. See Figure 15–5.
4. See Figure 15–8.
5. See Figure 15–16.
6. $V_{sec} = \dfrac{V_{pri}}{a} = \dfrac{120 \text{ V}}{6} = 20 \text{ V}$

   $V_{pk} = (V_{sec})(1.414) = (20 \text{ V})(1.414) = 28.28 \text{ V}$

   $V_{DC} = (V_{pk})(0.318) = (28.28 \text{ V})(0.318) = 8.99 \text{ V}$

   $I_{DC} = \dfrac{V_{DC}}{R_L} = \dfrac{8.99 \text{ V}}{1000 \text{ }\Omega} = 8.99 \text{ mA}$

7. $V_{pk} = (V_{sec})(1.414) = (90 \text{ V})(1.414) = 127.3 \text{ V}$
$V_{DC} = (V_{pk})(0.636) = (127.3 \text{ V})(0.636) = 80.96 \text{ V}$
$I_{DC} = \dfrac{V_{DC}}{R_L} = \dfrac{80.96 \text{ V}}{5000 \ \Omega} = 16.2 \text{ mA}$

8. $V_{pk} = (V_{sec})(1.414) = (250 \text{ V})(1.414) = 353.5 \text{ V}$
$V_{DC} = (V_{pk})(0.636) = (353.5 \text{ V})(0.636) = -224.83 \text{ V}$ (voltage is negative because of the diode polarity)
$I_{DC} = \dfrac{V_{DC}}{R_L} = \dfrac{224.83 \text{ V}}{250 \ \Omega} = 0.899 \text{ A}$

9. $\text{PRV} = (V_{sec})(1.414) = 28.28 \text{ V}$

10. $\text{PRV} = (2)(V_{sec})(1.414) = (2)(90 \text{ V})(1.414) = 254.52 \text{ V}$

11.

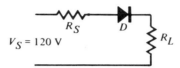

$V_S = 120 \text{ V}$

Figure 15–34

a. convert V_{DC} to V_{pk}; $V_{pk} = \dfrac{V_{DC}}{0.318} = \dfrac{12 \text{ V}}{0.318} = 37.74 \text{ V}$

b. convert $V_{S \ rms}$ to $V_{S \ pk}$; $V_{S \ pk} = (120 \text{ V})(1.414) = 169.68 \text{ V}$

c. calculate $V_{RS \ pk}$; $V_{RS \ pk} = 169.68 - 37.74 \text{ V} = 131.94 \text{ V}$

d. compute $V_{RS \ DC}$; $V_{RS \ DC} = (131.94 \text{ V})(0.318) = 41.96 \text{ V}$

e. compute I_{DC}; $I_{DC} = \dfrac{V_{DC}}{R_L} = \dfrac{12 \text{ V}}{240 \ \Omega} = 0.05 \text{ A}$

f. calculate R_S; $R_S = \dfrac{V_{RS \ DC}}{I_{DC}} = \dfrac{41.96 \text{ V}}{0.05 \text{ A}} = 839.2 \ \Omega.$

g. determine minimum power rating; $P_{RS} = (0.05 \text{ A})(41.96 \text{ V}) = 2.098 \text{ W}$
overrate by 25 percent; $(2.098)(1.25) = 2.662 \text{ W}.$

12. Ripple factor is a quantity which describes the ability of a power supply to produce a nonvarying voltage under constant input voltage and load conditions. It is the ratio of the rms value of the AC output voltage to the DC output voltage.

13. See Figure 15–25.

14. The ripple factor of an unfiltered bridge rectifier is 0.48.

15. A power supply load can be a single device or circuit that requires a DC voltage to operate. It can consist of several circuits or it can be an entire system such as a radio, television set, or computer.

16. Two types of voltage regulators are the zener diode and the transistor-series-type voltage regulator circuits.

17. See Figure 15–30.

18. The transistor-series-type voltage regulator functions as a variable resistor connected in series with the load. The resistance across the collector-emitter terminals depends upon the amount of transistor conduction which is controlled by the emitter-base bias. A zener diode connected to the base provides a reference potential. Voltage variations across the load are applied to the emitter, causing the transistor to conduct more or less heavily. The voltage drop across the transistor will vary, but the load voltage remains constant.

19.

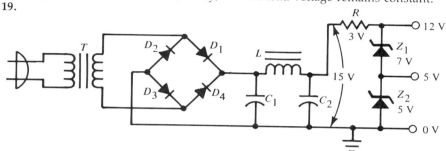

Figure 15–35

CHAPTER EXAMINATION

1. Draw the diagram of a half-wave rectifier circuit that will deliver a negative voltage to a load.
2. Determine the DC load voltage and current for the circuit in Figure 15–36.

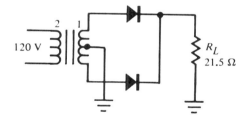

Figure 15–36

3. What is the amplitude of the peak reverse voltage appearing across the non-conducting diode in the circuit shown in question 2?
4. A bridge rectifier circuit has 41.5 V across its secondary winding. What is the value of the DC voltage appearing across the output terminals?
5. If 125 mA of current flows through a load connected to the rectifier circuit identified in question 4, what is the resistance of the load?

Choose true or false for questions 6 to 11.

6. T F   The PRV across the nonconducting diodes is the same for diodes connected in a full-wave rectifier circuit and a bridge rectifier circuit if both circuits have identical transformers and the input voltage is the same for both.
7. T F   The DC ripple frequency is twice the frequency of the input AC voltage in a bridge rectifier circuit.
8. T F   High-pass filters are usually connected to the output of a rectifier circuit to reduce the ripple factor of the output voltage.

9. T F   In a transistor-series-type voltage regulator, a change in the load voltage causes the collector-base bias potential to change, which causes the transistor to conduct either more or less heavily.

10. T F   The voltage appearing across the diode in a half-wave rectifier circuit is zero during the time that the diode is not conducting.

11. T F   The circuit shown in Figure 15–37 is that of a low-pass filter.

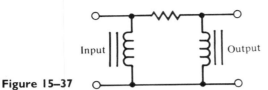

Figure 15–37

16

Voltage Amplifier Circuits

OBJECTIVES

Upon completion of this chapter you should be able to do the following:

1. Describe the purpose of an amplifier circuit.
2. Identify six methods in which amplifiers can be classified.
3. Calculate the total voltage gain of amplifiers connected in cascade.
4. Identify three methods of coupling amplifier stages together in cascade and discuss the frequency response of each.
5. Calculate the voltage gain, current gain, power gain, input impedance, and output impedance of an *RC*-coupled bipolar junction transistor amplifier stage.
6. Determine the transformer turns ratio required to match the output impedance of one stage to the input impedance of the next.
7. Describe the general application of tuned RF amplifiers.
8. Discuss the purpose of a follower circuit and identify its voltage gain and input-output phase characteristics.
9. Discuss the purpose of a paraphase amplifier circuit and identify its input-output signal phase relationship.
10. Identify the two general types of feedback and describe where each is used.

16-1 INTRODUCTION

The voltages and currents associated with electronic circuits represent various electrical and physical variables. They may represent sound (audio), sight (video), a modulated carrier, the output of an oscillator, or

381

strain. These voltages and currents are often called signals to differentiate them from the DC voltages and currents required to bias and operate transistors and integrated circuits.

Signal voltages are normally low in amplitude when first developed. Amplifier circuits are used to boost the amplitude to a usable value. For example, the modulated signal induced across the antenna of a radio receiver is amplified by a factor of approximately one million before the demodulated signal is applied to the terminals of the loudspeaker.

The major function of an amplifier circuit, or stage, is to increase the amplitude of the signal voltage, current, or power applied to its input terminals, as shown in Figure 16–1. Usually (there are exceptions), the output should be a replica of the input signal, although it may be inverted 180°. The triangular symbol appearing in Figure 16–1 is used to represent an amplifier. The gain of an amplifier is symbolized by the letter A, which is followed by a subscript identifying the type of gain. An amplifier may have a voltage gain, a current gain, and a power gain, as indicated by the equations appearing below. In all three cases the gain is defined as being the ratio of the output variable to the input variable.

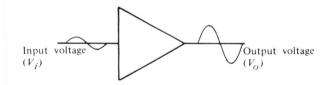

Figure 16–1 Schematic symbol for an amplifier.

$$\text{Voltage gain } (A_v) = \frac{v_o}{v_i} \tag{16–1}$$

$$\text{Current gain } (A_i) = \frac{i_o}{i_i} \tag{16–2}$$

$$\text{Power gain } (A_p) = \frac{p_o}{p_i} \tag{16–3}$$

16-2 METHODS OF CLASSIFYING AMPLIFIERS

There are many different types of amplifier circuits, each type having its own application and unique operating characteristics. Several methods are used to classify amplifiers for the purpose of describing their function. These include:

  1. signal size.
    a. small signal (voltage amplifiers)
    b. large signal (power amplifiers)

Small-signal, or voltage, amplifiers are used to amplify signals which are approximately less than 1 V in amplitude. Signals having amplitudes above this value are amplified by power amplifier circuits. Power amplifiers amplify signal current. They require an input signal having a relatively high voltage.

  2. frequencies handled.
    a. DC—0 Hz
    b. audio frequencies (AF)—20 to 20,000 Hz
    c. radio frequencies (RF)—frequencies above 20,000 Hz

Electrical signals may have frequencies which extend from a low of 0 Hz (DC) to a high of several gigahertz. No single amplifier is capable of amplifying signals whose frequencies may vary over this extremely wide range. Amplifiers are designed to amplify a band of signals whose frequencies lie within a particular range.

  3. bandwidth passed.
    a. tuned
    b. untuned

A tuned amplifier is an RF amplifier which amplifies a narrow band of RF signal frequencies. This is accomplished by connecting an LC resonant circuit to the input or output, or sometimes to both the input and output terminals of the amplifier. An untuned amplifier amplifies a relatively wide band of signal frequencies. An audio frequency (AF) amplifier is a type of untuned amplifier. Video and pulse amplifiers are examples of untuned RF amplifier stages.

  4. type of coupling.
    a. direct
    b. transformer
    c. resistance-capacitance *(RC)*

The type of coupling describes how the input signal is applied to the amplifier from the previous stage and how it is coupled from the amplifier and applied to the next stage.

5. class of operation (or conduction period).
   a. class *A*—output current flows 360° or for the duration of the input signal.
   b. class *AB*—output current flows for more than 180° but less than 360°.
   c. class *B*—output current flows for approximately 180°.
   d. class *C*—output current flows for less than 180°.

If the output signal is to be a reproduction of the input signal, output current must flow whenever a signal is applied to the input terminals of the amplifier. If it doesn't, distortion occurs. Special kinds of circuits are used with class *AB*, class *B*, and class *C* applications to prevent unwanted distortion.

6. circuit configuration.
   a. common-base or gate
   b. common-emitter or source
   c. common-collector or drain

Transistors can be connected in amplifier circuits in any one of the three configurations identified above. As discussed in Chapter 12, the configuration in which the transistor is used determines its input and output impedance, voltage, current, and power gain, and input-output phase relationship.

Any specific amplifier can be described by using the methods of classification identified above. For example, a particular amplifier in a radio receiver might be described as being a small-signal, RF, tuned, transformer-coupled, class *A* amplifier connected in the common-emitter configuration.

16-3 PRINCIPLES OF AMPLIFIER OPERATION

A common-emitter amplifier circuit is shown in Figure 16–2(a). Without a signal applied to the input, DC voltages and currents are present in the circuit, as discussed in Chapter 12. Resistors R_{B1} and R_{B2} are biasing resistors and establish the operating (Q) point, R_C provides the load, and R_E

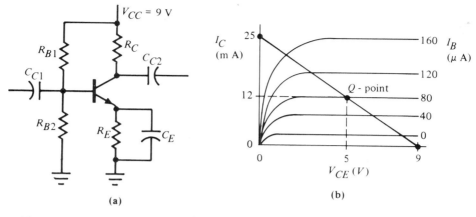

(a)   (b)

Figure 16–2   (a) Common-emitter amplifier circuit and (b) associated V-I output characteristic curves for the transistor.

prevents temperature changes from affecting the Q-point. Output current I_C and voltage V_{CE} can both be determined from the Q-point, as indicated in Figure 16–2(b).

When a signal is applied to the input of the amplifier, as shown in Figure 16–3(a), the base current (i_b) intensity increases and decreases above and below the Q-point (DC) value, as indicated in Figure 16–3(b). This causes collector current i_c to change at the input signal rate. If the Q-point base current (I_B) is 80 μA and the peak value of the input signal

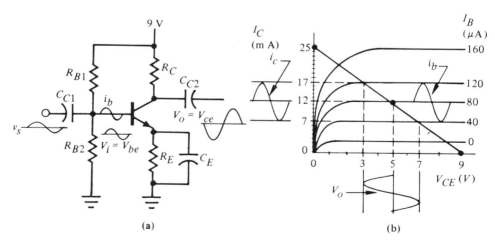

(a)   (b)

Figure 16–3   Effect of applying a signal to a common-emitter amplifier: (a) signal applied to amplifier; (b) resulting changes in current.

(i_b) is 40 μA, the resulting base current varies from a maximum value of 120 μA to a minimum value of 40 μA. The Q-point collector current (I_C) is 12 mA. The signal causes the collector current (i_c) to increase to a maximum value of 17 mA and decrease to a minimum value of 7 mA. Output current i_c is a replica of input signal i_b except that it is larger in amplitude. The input signal has a peak amplitude of 40 μA while the output current has a peak value of 5 mA. The collector current is 125 times larger than the base current. This implies that the amplifier has increased the amplitude of the input signal by a factor of 125.

The output voltage (v_{ce}) also varies as the base current changes. The output voltage (V_{CE}) is 5 V at the Q-point. When the signal is applied and the base current increases, the output voltage decreases to 3 V. During the negative alternation of the input signal, the output voltage increases to a value of 7 V. The output voltage is 180° out-of-phase with the input signal. This is true for both the bipolar and field effect transistors when they are connected in the common-emitter or common-source circuit configurations.

The base and collector currents and the collector-emitter voltage have two components associated with them when a signal is applied to the amplifier. These include the DC which comes from the power supply (V_{CC}) and the signal (AC) which comes from the signal source (v_S). The DC components form the reference for the AC values, as shown by the diagram appearing in Figure 16–4.

It has been shown that an amplifier circuit can amplify a signal. It was illustrated, through graphical analysis, that the output signal current was 125 times larger than the input signal current in the amplifier just discussed. This comes as no surprise, as this represents the AC beta gain discussed in Chapter 12. An amplifier connected in the common-emitter

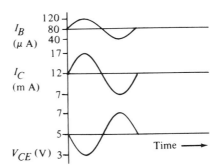

Figure 16–4 Synchrogram showing the phase relationships between the input and output currents and output voltage for an *NPN* common-emitter connected amplifier.

configuration also has a voltage gain. We have no method of determining voltage gain as of yet. This will be discussed in the following section.

The question often arises as to where the extra output power (current and voltage) comes from in an amplifier circuit. The answer is simple—it comes from the V_{CC} power supply. In a sense, an amplifier is a transducer which converts DC power into AC signal power. The input signal causes the DC current and voltage supplied by V_{CC} to vary at the signal rate.

16-4 CASCADE-CONNECTED AMPLIFIERS

16-4.1 Introduction.   More often than not, the gain achieved by a single amplifier is not sufficient to increase the amplitude of the signal to the level required for its application. When this is the case, amplifiers are connected in cascade (series) with each other, as illustrated in Figure 16–5. The amplitude of the signal is increased as it progresses through each amplifier stage. The total gain of the individual amplifiers is the product of the stage gain of the individual amplifiers, as indicated by the following equations.

$$A_{vt} = (A_{v1})(A_{v2})(A_{v3})$$ (16–4)

$$A_{it} = (A_{i1})(A_{i2})(A_{i3})$$ (16–5)

$$A_{pt} = (A_{vt})(A_{it})$$ (16–6)

When multiple amplifier stages are employed, the circuit designer must choose a coupling method to pass the signal from the output of one stage to the input of the next. Coupling methods must also be considered when coupling the signal from its place of origin (v_S) to the input of the first amplifier and when coupling the signal from the output of the last amplifier to its load. As identified previously, there are three methods of coupling amplifiers. Each of these are discussed in the following sections.

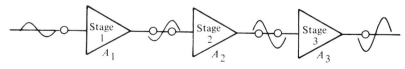

Figure 16–5   Cascade-connected amplifier stages.

16-4.2 Resistance-Capacitance (*RC*) coupling.   *RC* coupling is the most common method of coupling sources, amplifiers, and other circuits to one another. It can be used with BJT, FET, and electron tube amplifiers. This coupling method obtains its name from the biasing resistors and coupling capacitors used to couple the signal from one stage to the next. The diagram of an *RC*-coupled amplifier employing bipolar junction transistors connected in the common emitter configuration is shown in Figure 16–6. This amplifier represents the first stage of the cascade-connected amplifiers appearing in Figure 16–5.

Capacitors C_{C1} and C_{C2} are coupling capacitors. R_S represents the internal resistance of the signal source. The signal is coupled from v_S into the base through C_{C1}. The amplified signal is coupled from the collector to the base of the next stage through C_{C2}. To achieve maximum gain, the coupling capacitors should not drop any of the signal voltage. Both capacitors should be large enough in value that their reactances are low for the frequency of the signal to be coupled. If a band of signal frequencies are being amplified, the reactances must be small for the lowest signal frequency to be passed.

A capacitor (C_E) is connected across the emitter resistor. Called an emitter bypass capacitor, its function is to prevent degenerative (negative) feedback. When a signal is applied to the base of the amplifier, the emitter current changes at the base current rate. The resultant voltage developed across the emitter resistor opposes the input voltage and reduces its amplitude. This reduces the output voltage of the amplifier and is a type of degenerative, or negative, feedback. Although negative feedback is desired in some amplifiers, it is unwanted in most amplifiers. The bypass capacitor presents a low-reactance path around the emitter resistor for the signal current. Its size must be large enough that its reactance is

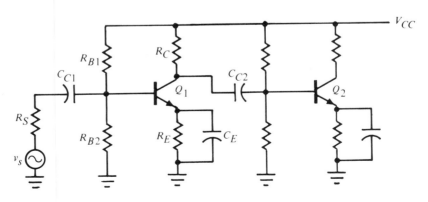

Figure 16–6   *RC*-coupled BJT amplifier.

low compared to the resistance of R_E. The bypass capacitor places the emitter at signal ground potential, as illustrated in Figure 16–7.

The V_{CC} power supply filter capacitors (or battery) also provide a low impedance path to ground for the signal. This places the top of R_{B1} at signal ground potential, as illustrated in Figure 16–8. Thus, resistors R_{B1} and R_{B2} are in parallel as the signal enters the transistor. These resistors and the coupling capacitor form the RC coupling network.

An amplifier has both an input impedance (Z_i) and an output impedance (Z_o). The impedance can be resistive or complex, depending upon the type of coupling used and the signal frequencies. In an RC-coupled amplifier using voltage divider bias and an emitter bypass capacitor, the input impedance is equal to the series equivalent resistance of the biasing resistors and the base-emitter input resistance (r_i) of the transistor, providing that the reactance of the coupling capacitor is very small for the signals to be amplified. For small-signal amplifiers, r_i is approximately equal to h_{ie}. Therefore, the input impedance appears as a single resistor as illustrated in Figure 16–9. The value of the impedance can be determined from Equation (16–7).

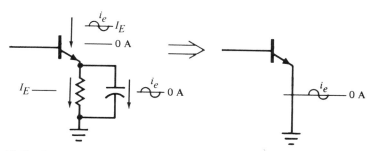

Figure 16–7   Bypass capacitor places the emitter at signal ground potential.

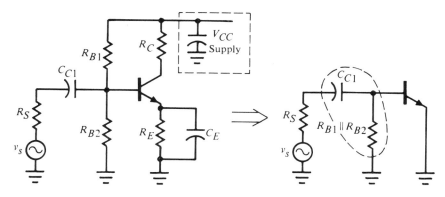

Figure 16–8   Base-biasing resistors and coupling capacitor form the RC coupling network.

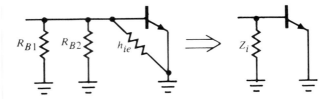

Figure 16–9 Input impedance (Z_i) to an *RC*-coupled BJT amplifier employing voltage divider bias.

$$\frac{1}{Z_i} = \frac{1}{R_{B1}} + \frac{1}{R_{B2}} + \frac{1}{h_{ie}}$$

(16–7)

The output impedance of an *RC*-coupled amplifier is equal to the series equivalent resistance of the parallel-connected resistances made up of R_C, r_o, and Z_i of the next stage. The top of the collector resistor (R_C) is at signal ground potential because of the filter capacitors in the V_{CC} supply. For small signal amplifiers, r_o is approximately equal to $1/h_{oe}$. If the output coupling capacitor has little reactance at the signal frequencies, the reactance can be ignored and the input impedance of the next stage appears in parallel with R_C and r_o. The resulting output circuit is depicted in Figure 16–10. The output impedance (Z_o) can be calculated from Equation (16–8).

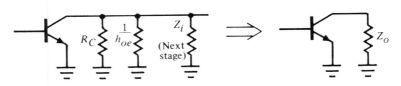

Figure 16–10 Output impedance (Z_o) of an *RC*-coupled BJT amplifier.

$$\frac{1}{Z_0} = \frac{1}{R_C} + h_{0e} + \frac{1}{Z_i} \quad \text{(next stage)}$$

(16–8)

The form of an *RC*-coupled amplifier appears differently for the signal (AC) voltages and currents than it does for the DC voltages and currents. The DC equivalent circuit appears in Figure 16–11(a). The capacitors are not shown since they block DC and appear as open circuits. The equivalent AC circuit is shown in Figure 16–11(b). In this circuit the ca-

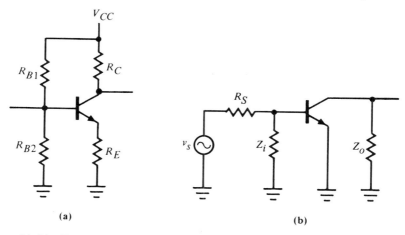

Figure 16–11   Equivalent circuits of an *RC*-coupled BJT amplifier: (a) DC equivalent circuit; (b) AC equivalent circuit.

pacitors are not included because they act like short circuits at the signal frequency.

The voltage gain of an amplifier is the ratio of the output voltage to the input voltage. The equation appearing below can be used to calculate the voltage gain of a bipolar junction transistor amplifier connected in the common emitter configuration.

$$\text{Voltage gain } (A_v) = \frac{-v_0}{v_i} = -\frac{-v_{ce}}{v_{be}} \cong \frac{-h_{fe}\,Z_0}{h_{ie}} \qquad\qquad \textbf{(16–9)}$$

The negative sign indicates that the output voltage is 180° out-of-phase with the input voltage.

The current gain (A_i) of an amplifier stage is somewhat less than the current gain (h_{fe}) of the transistor and can be determined from Equation (16–10).

$$\text{Current gain } (A_i) = \frac{h_{fe}}{1 + h_{0e}Z_0} \qquad\qquad \textbf{(16–10)}$$

In addition to voltage and current gain, amplifiers also have a power gain. Power gain (A_p) can be determined from Equation (16–11).

$$\text{Power gain } (A_p) = \frac{(A_i)^2 Z_0}{Z_i} \qquad\qquad (16\text{--}11)$$

The equations just presented can be used to determine the impedance and gain variables associated with an amplifier stage, as illustrated in Example 16–1.

The diagram of a two-stage field effect transistor amplifier appears in Figure 16–13. The coupling capacitor and gate resistor (R_{G2}) form the RC coupling network.

Example 16–1   Calculations for the impedance and gain variables for a BJT RC-coupled amplifier

Problem

The amplifier circuits appearing in Figure 16–12 represent a portion of the audio section of a citizens band radio. Determine Z_i, Z_o, A_v, A_i, and A_p for the first amplifier stage. The 2N3904 transistor is used in both stages.

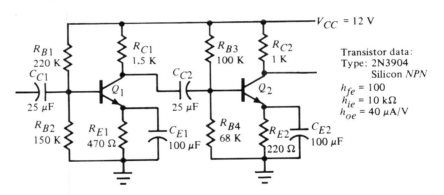

Figure 16–12

Solution

1. Calculate Z_i.

$$\frac{1}{Z_i} = \frac{1}{R_{B1}} + \frac{1}{R_{B2}} + \frac{1}{h_{ie(Q1)}}$$

$$\frac{1}{Z_i} = 0.0000045 + 0.0000067 + 0.0001 = 0.0001112$$

$$Z_i = \frac{1}{0.0001112} = 8992.8 \ \Omega$$

2. Calculate Z_0.

$$\frac{1}{Z_0} = \frac{1}{R_{C1}} + h_{0e} + \frac{1}{R_{B3}} + \frac{1}{R_{B4}} + \frac{1}{h_{ie(Q2)}}$$

$$\frac{1}{Z_0} = 0.000667 + 0.00004 + 0.00001 + 0.0000147 + 0.0001 = 0.0008317$$

$$Z_0 = \frac{1}{0.0008317} = 1202.36 \ \Omega$$

3. Calculate A_v.

$$A_v = \frac{-h_{fe} Z_0}{h_{ie}} = \frac{-(100)(1202.36)}{10,000} = -12.0236$$

4. Calculate A_i.

$$A_i = \frac{h_{fe}}{1 + h_{0e} z_0} = \frac{100}{1 + (0.00004)(1202.36)} = 95.42$$

5. Calculate A_p.

$$A_p = \frac{(A_i)^2 Z_0}{Z_i} = \frac{(9104.98)(1202.36)}{8992.8} = 1217.35$$

There are several factors which influence the circuit designer when selecting a coupling method. These include cost, size of the coupling devices, and the frequency and bandwidth of the signals to be amplified. Most amplifiers must be capable of amplifying a band of signal frequencies rather than a single frequency. Amplifiers in stereophonic receivers, for example, must be capable of amplifying signals which range from a low of just a few hertz to a high of approximately 20,000 Hz. Audio amplifiers in AM radio receivers must amplify a band of frequencies ranging

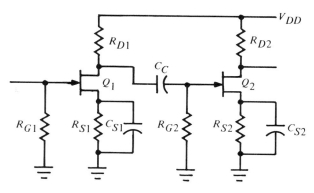

Figure 16–13 Two-stage FET *RC*-coupled amplifier.

from 50 to 5000 Hz. RF amplifiers in television receivers must be capable of amplifying a band of frequencies 6 MHz wide.

The coupling method selected is most affected by the frequency and bandwidth of the signals to be amplified. *RC* coupling cannot be used in amplifiers designed to amplify DC signals because the coupling capacitor will block the signal. In addition, the amplifier gain is not constant when *RC* coupling is used in amplifiers which amplify a band of frequencies. The reactance of the coupling capacitor becomes significant at low frequencies causing some of the input voltage to be dropped across the coupling capacitor. The emitter bypass capacitor is not as effective at low frequencies causing negative feedback to be produced. Transistors have input junction capacitance. At high frequencies, the low reactance of this capacitance decreases the input impedance of the amplifier, reducing the gain of the stage.

An aid which is often used to illustrate the effect of frequency on amplifier gain is the frequency response curve. A frequency response curve for an *RC*-coupled amplifier is shown in Figure 16–14. The gain of the amplifier is considered to be constant between frequencies f_1 and f_2. The gain has decreased to 0.707 times its maximum value at those frequencies. The bandwidth, or bandpass, of the amplifier is represented by the difference between the upper (f_2) and lower (f_1) frequencies. The low-frequency gain is reduced because of the reactance of the coupling and bypass capacitors. The high frequency gain is reduced because of the input junction capacitance of the transistor.

Even though *RC* coupling has the disadvantages of blocking DC and attenuating low frequency AC signals, it is widely used because of its simplicity, small size, and low cost. *RC* coupling can be used with any transistor or electron tube circuit configuration.

16-4.3 Transformer Coupling in AF Circuits. Transformer coupling is a method of coupling amplifier stages together in which the primary of the transformer is connected to the output of one stage and the secondary winding is connected to the input of the next, as shown in Fig-

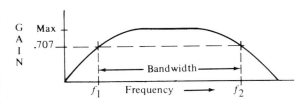

Figure 16–14 Frequency response curve of an *RC*-coupled amplifier.

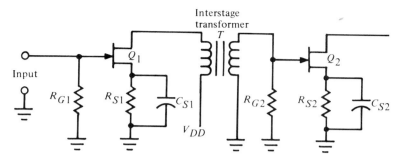

Figure 16–15   Two-stage transformer-coupled FET amplifier.

ure 16–15. Signal power is coupled from one stage to the next by mutual induction. Transformer coupling can be used in audio frequency (AF) and radio frequency (RF) amplifiers. It cannot be used in DC amplifiers, as there is no varying primary current to produce a changing magnetic field to create an induced voltage across the secondary winding. The transformer which couples one amplifier stage to another is often called an interstage transformer. The voltage across the secondary winding may be either less than or greater than the primary voltage. If a voltage step-up transformer is used, the transformer provides a voltage gain in addition to the voltage gain of the amplifier, as indicated in Figure 16–16. This is one of the reasons for using transformer coupling with voltage amplifiers.

Transformer coupling is often used in power amplifiers because of its impedance-matching characteristics. It is important to transfer maximum power from one stage to another in power amplifiers. According to the maximum power transfer theorem, the impedances must be matched for this to occur. The turns ratio of the interstage transformer causes the output impedance of the amplifier connected to the primary winding to equal the input impedance of the amplifier connected to the secondary winding. Since the output impedance of a transistor is usually larger than the input impedance, a voltage step-down transformer is often required. Equation (7–15) can be used to determine the transformer turns ratio. For

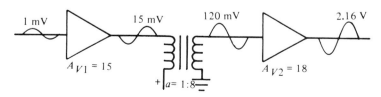

Figure 16–16   Transformer coupling used to increase voltage gain.

the circuit appearing in Example 16–2, a turns ratio of 1.73 is required. A coupling capacitor is often used, as shown in Figure 16–17, to prevent the bias voltage from being bypassed to ground through the secondary winding.

Transformer coupling is also used to couple the signal from the last amplifier in an amplifier section to a load such as a speaker, as illustrated in Figure 16–18. The transformer used for this type of application is called an output transformer. Usually this type of load has a low impedance. Most output transformers are voltage step-down transformers to allow maximum power and current to be delivered to the load.

The frequency response curve for a transformer-coupled audio amplifier appears in Figure 16–19. The low gain at the lower signal frequencies is caused by the low reactance of the transformer windings. The inductive reactance is low for the lower frequencies and increases for higher signal frequencies causing the gain to increase. The decrease in gain at the higher frequencies is caused by the input junction capacitance of the next transistor.

Example 16–2 Determining the turns ratio required to impedance match two amplifier stages

---

Problem

Calculate the turns ratio required to match the output impedance of stage 1 to input impedance of stage 2 for the amplifiers shown in Figure 16–17 if the output impedance of stage 1 is 4500 Ω and the input impedance of stage 2 is 1500 Ω.

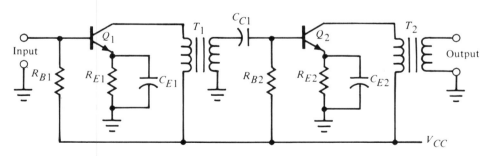

Figure 16–17

Solution

$$\text{Turns ratio } (a) = \sqrt{\frac{Z_0}{Z_i}} = \sqrt{\frac{4500}{1500}} = 1.73 : 1 = 1.73$$

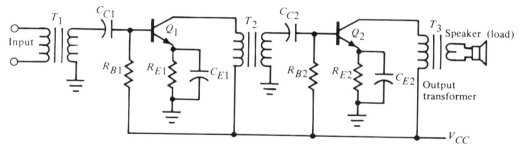

Figure 16–18 Output transformer provides impedance matching between the last amplifier stage and load.

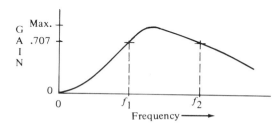

Figure 16–19 Frequency response curve of a transformer-coupled amplifier.

16-4.4 Transformer Coupling in RF Circuits. Transformer coupling is often used in RF amplifiers. Depending upon the bandwidth required, these can either be tuned or untuned. Transformer coupling is almost always used in tuned RF amplifiers. These amplifiers are designed to amplify a narrow band of signal frequencies. A tuned amplifier stage is one whose input, output, or both are tuned to receive a particular narrow band of signals.

The diagram of a tuned RF amplifier appears in Figure 16–20. The amplifier consists of a transistor connected in the common-emitter configuration. Voltage divider bias formed by resistors R_1 and R_2 forward biases the emitter-base junction. The interstage coupling transformer, T_1, has capacitors connected across both the primary and secondary windings. The inductance of the transformer windings, along with the capacitance of the capacitors, form LC resonant circuits. The primary circuit is a parallel resonant circuit, whereas the secondary circuit is a series resonant circuit. At first glance this appears to be a parallel resonant circuit also. However, the voltage induced across the secondary is such that there is but one path for current flow. The induced voltage can be represented by a gen-

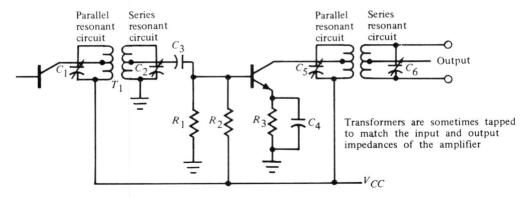

Figure 16–20   Tuned RF amplifier.

erator connected in series with the secondary circuit, as shown in Figure 16–21.

The amplifier appearing in Figure 16–20 utilizes both a tuned input and output circuit. Some amplifiers employ only a single tuned circuit in the input and/or output circuits. These are called single-tuned amplifiers. If both the primary and secondary windings are tuned, the amplifier is double-tuned.

Ideally, all the signal frequencies within that part of the frequency spectrum the amplifier is designed to amplify will be amplified the same amount. The frequency response curve would be rectangular, as shown in Figure 16–22(a), if it was possible. In actual practice, the frequency response curve resembles that of a resonant circuit. The response can be modified somewhat, as shown in Figure 16–22(b), by adjusting the amount of mutual coupling between the primary and secondary windings. Mutual coupling is affected by the coefficient of coupling (k). If the primary and secondary windings are far apart, little mutual coupling exists and the secondary voltage is low. If the windings are moved closer together, the secondary voltage increases until a peak is reached. As they are brought together even closer, the voltage decreases at the resonant frequency; however, two peaks occur at either side of resonance. The

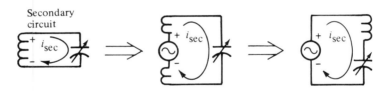

Figure 16–21   Series resonant input circuit to a tuned *RF* amplifier.

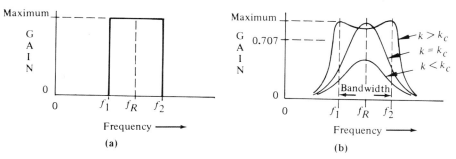

Figure 16–22 (a) Ideal and (b) actual frequency response curves associated with a tuned RF amplifier.

point at which the secondary voltage is maximum at the resonant frequency is called critical coupling (k_c). The primary and secondary circuits are undercoupled if the coefficient of coupling is less than the critical coupling value ($k < k_c$). The two circuits are critically coupled when the coefficient of coupling is equal to the critical coupling value ($k = k_c$), and overcoupled when the coefficient of coupling exceeds the critical coupling value ($k > k_c$). The actual shape of the frequency response curve for a particular amplifier depends upon the Q of the tuned circuits, coefficient of coupling, and whether single- or double-tuned circuits are used.

The primary and secondary transformer circuits can be tuned to the desired frequency band in one of two ways. One method is illustrated in Figure 16–23(a). Capacitors C_1 and C_2 are adjustable and can be tuned separately. The other method is shown in Figure 16–23(b). Fixed capacitors are connected across both the primary and secondary windings (for double tuning) and the inductance is varied by adjusting a movable ferrite slug located in the transformer core, as illustrated in Figure 16–24.

16-4.5 Direct Coupling. Some amplifiers are designed to amplify DC signals. These amplifiers cannot employ RC and transformer coupling. The coupling capacitor blocks the DC signal if RC coupling is used. Transformer coupling cannot be used because the magnetic field about

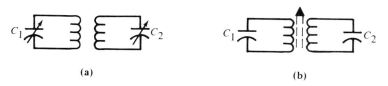

Figure 16–23 Methods of tuning an RF amplifier: (a) capacitive tuning; (b) inductive (slug) tuning.

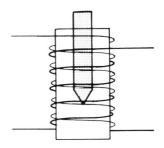

Figure 16–24   Diagram of a slug-tuned RF transformer.

the primary winding is stationary. Instead, direct coupling is utilized. Direct coupling is a type of coupling in which the output of one amplifier is directly connected to the input of the next.

   Direct-, or DC-, coupled amplifiers are more difficult to design than the *RC* and transformer coupled types. This is because of the transistor-biasing requirements. For a bipolar junction transistor the collector voltage is usually considerably higher than the base voltage. If the collector of one transistor is connected directly to the base of the next transistor, the transistor will go into saturation and no longer function as an amplifier due to the excessive emitter-base forward bias. This is illustrated in Figure 16–25. Eight volts appear at both the collector of Q_1 and base of Q_2. If the emitter of Q_2 has a potential of 2 V, the emitter-base voltage is 6 V, far in excess of what the transistor requires for normal amplifier operation. Instead, the transistor will be operating as a switch in the on position.

   Resistor values in adjacent stages are usually quite different and higher V_{CC} voltage values are often required in DC-coupled amplifiers when compared with those using *RC* and transformer coupling. For the two-stage amplifier appearing in Figure 16–26, resistor R_3 functions as

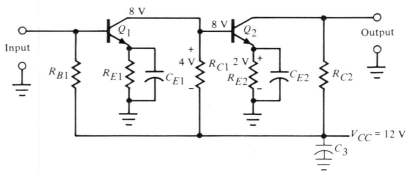

Figure 16–25   Direct coupling two amplifier stages together may provide excessive bias to the second stage.

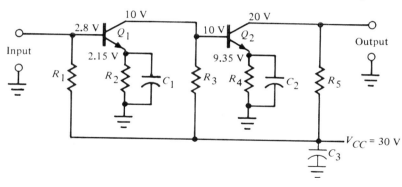

Figure 16–26 Two-stage DC-coupled BJT amplifier.

both the base-biasing resistor for Q_2 and the DC load for Q_1. The emitter resistors in the circuit of Figure 16–26 are dropping considerably different voltages. Resistor R_4 is dropping 9.35 V whereas a 2.15-V potential appears across R_2. This means that transistor Q_2 is a higher-power transistor and conducts more heavily than Q_1 or R_4 has a much higher resistance value than R_2. The resistance values of the base and emitter resistors are such that the emitter-base forward bias for both transistors is the same for both transistors (0.65 V).

Another method of direct coupling amplifier stages is to use complementary (*NPN* and *PNP*) transistors, as shown in Figure 16–27. This type of circuit arrangement does not require voltages as great as those needed when transistors having the same polarity are used. Again care must be taken by the circuit designer to ensure that the resistor values are such that the voltages developed will properly bias both transistors.

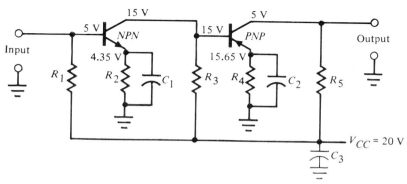

Figure 16–27 Two-stage complementary DC-coupled amplifier.

Since there are no coupling capacitors or transformers used between stages to limit the low-frequency response, it appears that the DC coupling method might be preferred in all amplifiers. DC-coupled amplifiers do have a couple of disadvantages, however. They have an inclination to drift. If the Q-point of the individual transistors shifts due to supply voltage variations, temperature changes, or changes in transistor characteristics, the shift is amplified by all succeeding stages. Secondly, unless complementary transistors are used, higher power supply voltages are required. The voltage requirements double for each additional amplifier stage.

The frequency response curve for a DC-coupled amplifier is shown in Figure 16–28. The gain is maximum and the response is flat from 0 Hz and doesn't begin to decrease until relatively high frequencies are reached. The reduction in gain at high frequencies is due to the input junction capacitance of the next stage. Because of its excellent low frequency response and wide bandpass characteristics, direct-coupled amplifiers are often used in stereophonic receivers.

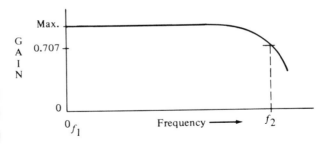

Figure 16–28 Frequency response curve of a direct-coupled amplifier.

16-5 FOLLOWER CIRCUITS

Follower circuits can be connected from either bipolar or field effect transistors. These are circuits connected in the common collector (for BJTs) or common drain (for FETs) circuit configurations. An emitter follower is shown in Figure 16–29. The circuit is easily recognized as the output signal is developed across the emitter resistor which serves as the load. The collector has no resistor and is at signal ground potential. This is accomplished by allowing the V_{CC} supply to bypass the signal to ground through the power supply. The emitter resistor is not bypassed with a capacitor. If it was, the signal voltage would not be developed. Instead,

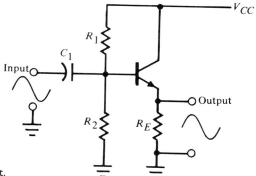

Figure 16–29   Emitter follower circuit.

a DC potential would appear across the output terminals. Because the emitter is unbypassed, degenerative feedback is present. This has the effect of reducing the voltage gain, increasing the input impedance, and decreasing the output impedance of the circuit. The emitter follower is characterized by a voltage gain which is less than one, a high input impedance, and a low output impedance.

The diagram of a source follower appears in Figure 16–30. The output voltage is developed across the unbypassed source resistor. The drain is at signal ground potential. Resistors R_1 and R_2 form a voltage divider network to provide the gate bias. Like the emitter follower, the source follower has a voltage gain which is less than one and has a low output resistance. It has a very high input resistance. The basic application for the follower circuits is impedance matching. Because of its high input and low output impedances, a follower circuit can be used in place of a transformer for matching the output impedance of an amplifier to a low-impedance load.

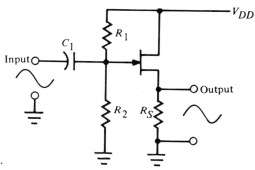

Figure 16–30   Source follower circuit.

16-6 THE PARAPHASE AMPLIFIER

The paraphase amplifier is often referred to as a phase-splitter circuit. It provides two outputs from one input, which are equal in amplitude but displaced 180°, as shown in Figure 16–31. The amplifier employs two load resistors, R_C in the collector circuit and R_E in the emitter circuit. These resistors have the same value. Since the collector and emitter currents are approximately equal, the amplitude of the signal voltage developed across each load resistor will be equal. The amplifier operates as both an emitter follower and as an amplifier connected in the common-emitter configuration. This results in the two output voltages being 180° out-of-phase with one another.

The paraphase amplifier can be used to provide two signals, 180° out-of-phase, to circuits which require this type of input. It is often used in place of a center-tapped transformer to provide the two input signals to push-pull amplifiers. It has the advantages of being less costly and smaller than a transformer.

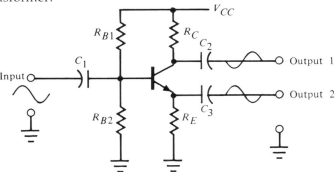

Figure 16–31
Paraphase amplifier circuit.

16-7 FEEDBACK

Feedback occurs when part of the output signal is fed back into the input of a circuit. Two general types of feedback are employed in electronic circuits—positive and negative. Positive feedback takes place when a portion of the output signal is fed back in-phase with the input signal. When a percentage of the output signal is fed back 180° out-of-phase with the input signal, negative feedback is being utilized.

Positive feedback is sometimes referred to as regenerative feedback and is used in oscillator circuits. Negative feedback, called inverse or degenerative feedback, is used in some amplifier circuits to increase bandwidth, change impedance, stabilize the gain, and reduce distortion. Negative feedback reduces the gain of an amplifier considerably.

SUMMARY

1. An amplifier circuit, or stage, is one which is designed to increase the amplitude of the input signal voltage, current, or power.
2. There are many different kinds of amplifiers which are used for various types of circuit applications. Different methods are used to classify amplifiers. The methods of classification can be used to describe the function of a particular amplifier.
3. Methods of classifying amplifiers include signal size, frequencies handled, bandwidth passed, type of coupling used, class of operation, and circuit configuration.
4. An amplifier operates on the principle of the input signal causing the DC input current and voltage to vary at the input signal rate.
5. A single amplifier stage is often not sufficient to raise the amplitude of the input signal to the level required. Amplifier stages are often connected in series, or cascade, to increase the signal to a higher level than that obtained from a single amplifier.
6. The total gain achieved by cascade-connected amplifiers is the product of the stage gain of the individual amplifiers.
7. There are three methods commonly used to couple the signal into and out of an amplifier: RC, transformer, and direct coupling.
8. The most popular method of coupling is the RC type. The coupling network consists of a coupling capacitor and the transistor biasing resistors.
9. Although transformers are larger and more expensive than coupling capacitors, they can provide additional gain or impedance matching if the proper turns ratios are used.
10. Transformer coupling can be used in both AF and RF amplifiers. The transformer has capacitors connected across one or both windings to form resonant LC (tuned) circuits for RF applications.
11. Neither RC or transformer coupling can be used when DC signals are to be amplified. Instead, DC coupling must be utilized.
12. Follower circuits (emitter or source) are special kinds of amplifier stages. They have a voltage gain which is less than one and the output signal is developed across the emitter or source resistor. The output signal is in-phase with the input. Follower circuits have a high input and low output impedance. They are often used to match the output impedance of an amplifier to a low impedance load.
13. Feedback occurs when a portion of the output signal is fed from the output to the input circuit of a stage. There are two types of feedback—positive and negative.
14. If the output signal is fed back in phase with the input signal, positive feedback is present. Negative feedback occurs when a portion of the output signal is fed back 180° out-of-phase with the input signal.
15. Positive feedback is not employed in amplifier stages. Negative feedback may be used in amplifier stages to stabilize the gain, change the input and output impedances, reduce distortion, reduce noise, and increase the bandwidth of an amplifier. Negative feedback significantly reduces the voltage gain of an amplifier stage.

PRACTICE EXERCISES

1. Identify the two types of amplifiers with respect to the relative size of their input signals.
2. Identify three methods of coupling the output signal from one stage to the input of the next.
3. Identify three types of amplifiers as classified by the frequency of the signals amplified.
4. If the output signal power is larger than the input signal power in an amplifier, where does the extra power come from?
5. Five amplifier stages are connected together in cascade. The voltage gains of the stages are 25, 19, 45, 31, and 60. What is the total voltage gain between the input of the first stage and the output of the last stage?
6. An RC-coupled amplifier used in the audio section of an AM receiver is shown in Figure 16–32. Calculate the input and output impedances and the voltage, current, and power gains of the first stage.

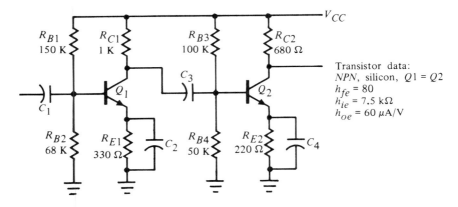

Figure 16–32

7. What causes the reduction of low frequency gain in RC-coupled amplifiers?
8. What creates the loss in high frequency gain in RC-coupled amplifiers?
9. Determine the transformer turns ratio required to impedance match an amplifier which has an output impedance of 8700 Ω to a load which has an impedance of 350 Ω.
10. What is the transformer often called which is used between amplifier stages?
11. What is the transformer called which couples the signal from the last amplifier to the load?
12. What is the general application of tuned RF amplifiers?
13. Identify two methods by which RF amplifiers can be tuned.
14. What determines the bandwidth of a tuned RF amplifier?
15. Under what conditions is direct coupling required in an amplifier?
16. Identify three disadvantages associated with direct coupling.

17. Identify two types of follower circuits.
18. Why is the emitter or source resistor unbypassed in a follower circuit?
19. Where is the DC load resistor located in a follower circuit?
20. What is the relative voltage gain of a follower circuit?
21. Identify the phase relationship between the input and output signals in a follower circuit.
22. What is a major application of a follower circuit?

ANSWERS TO PRACTICE EXERCISES

1. Amplifiers identified by the size of signals they amplify include small-signal (voltage) and large-signal (power) amplifiers.
2. Three methods of coupling the output signal from one stage of the input of the next are RC, transformer, and direct.
3. Three types of amplifier circuits as identified by the frequency of the signals handled are DC, AF, and RF.
4. The signal power in the output circuit comes from the DC power supply (V_{CC} or V_{DD}).
5. $A_v = (A_{v1})(A_{v2})(A_{v3})(A_{v4})(A_{v5}) = (25)(19)(45)(31)(60) = 39{,}757{,}500$
6. $\dfrac{1}{Z_i} = \dfrac{1}{R_{B1}} + \dfrac{1}{R_{B2}} + \dfrac{1}{h_{ie}} = \dfrac{1}{150k} + \dfrac{1}{68k} + \dfrac{1}{7.5k} = 0.000155$

   $Z_i = \dfrac{1}{0.000155} = 6493.51\ \Omega$

   $\dfrac{1}{Z_0} = \dfrac{1}{R_{C1}} + h_{oe} + \dfrac{1}{R_{B3}} + \dfrac{1}{R_{B4}} + \dfrac{1}{h_{ie}} = \dfrac{1}{1k} + 0.00006 + \dfrac{1}{100k} + \dfrac{1}{50k} + \dfrac{1}{7.5k} = 0.001223$

   $Z_0 = \dfrac{1}{0.001223} = 817.66\ \Omega$

   $A_v = \dfrac{-h_{fe}Z_0}{h_{ie}} = \dfrac{(-80)(817.66)}{7500} = -8.72$

   $A_i = \dfrac{h_{fe}}{1 + h_{oe}Z_0} = \dfrac{80}{1 + (0.00006)(817.66)} = 76.26$

   $A_p = \dfrac{(A_i)^2 Z_0}{Z_i} = \dfrac{(76.26)^2(817.66)}{6493.51} = 732.296$
7. The reduction of gain at low frequencies is caused by the reactance of the coupling and emitter (or source) bypass capacitors.
8. Amplifier gain at high frequencies is reduced because of the input junction capacitance of the transistor.
9. $a = \sqrt{\dfrac{Z_0}{Z_i}} = \sqrt{\dfrac{8700}{350}}\ \Omega = 4.99 : 1 \cong 5 : 1.$
10. A transformer which couples two amplifier stages together is often called an interstage transformer.
11. A transformer which couples the signal from an amplifier to a load is called an output transformer.

12. Tuned RF amplifiers are usually used to amplify a narrow band of RF signal frequencies.
13. Either the capacitance or the inductance of the tuned *LC* circuit can be varied.
14. The bandwidth of a tuned RF amplifier is determined by the *Q* of the tuned *LC* circuit(s) and the coefficient of coupling between the transformer windings.
15. Direct coupling is required when DC and very low frequency AC signals are to be amplified.
16. DC-coupled amplifiers are more difficult to design, have a tendency to drift, and usually require higher bias voltage supply potentials.
17. The two types of follower circuits are the emitter and source followers.
18. The emitter or source resistor in a follower circuit serves as the load to develop the output signal voltage. A bypassed resistor will result in a DC output voltage.
19. The DC load resistor is located in the emitter or source circuits.
20. The voltage gain of a follower circuit is always less than one.
21. The output signal is in-phase with the input signal.
22. Follower circuits are usually used for impedance-matching purposes.

CHAPTER EXAMINATION

1. List the two types of amplifiers as identified by the relative size of the signals they amplify.
2. Identify three methods of coupling amplifier stages together.
3. List three types of amplifiers as identified by the frequencies they amplify.
4. List two types of amplifiers as identified by the bandwidth of the frequencies they amplify.
5. What is the general application of a follower circuit?
6. What is the general application of a tuned RF amplifier circuit?
7. Identify the two general types of feedback.
8. What is the general application of a paraphase amplifier?
9. An amplifier has an input signal of 8.5 mV and an output of 1.25 V. Calculate its voltage gain.
10. An *RC*-coupled amplifier has an output impedance of 4500 Ω and uses a transistor which has an h_{fe} value of 100 and an h_{ie} which is 1000 Ω. Calculate the voltage gain of the stage.

Questions 11–15 pertain to the circuit in Figure 16–33.
11. Determine the input impedance of stage 1.
12. Calculate the output impedance of stage 1.
13. Compute the voltage gain of the first amplifier stage.
14. Calculate the current gain of the first stage.
15. What is the power gain of the first amplifier?
16. Three amplifier stages are connected together in cascade. If each amplifier has a voltage gain of 19, what is the gain from the input of the first amplifier to the output of the last amplifier?

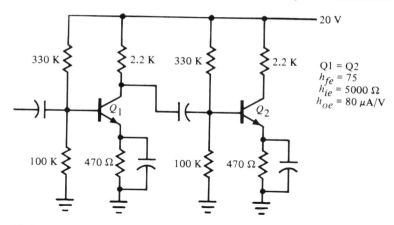

Figure 16–33

17. A transformer is used to impedance match an amplifier to a load. What should be the turns ratio if the output impedance of the amplifier is 4800 Ω and the load impedance is 4 Ω?

17

Linear Integrated Circuits

OBJECTIVES

Upon completion of this chapter you should be able to do the following:

1. Identify the types of integrated circuits by method of fabrication, type of transistor technology, component density, and function.
2. Identify three common methods of packaging integrated circuits.
3. Draw the schematic symbol used to represent the differential amplifier and identify both input and output terminals.
4. Identify or draw the schematic diagram of a differential amplifier.
5. Identify seven methods in which the differential amplifier can be operated with respect to the input and output conditions.
6. Describe the significance of the common-mode rejection ratio (CMRR).
7. Draw the schematic symbol used to represent the operational amplifier.
8. Identify seven applications for the operational amplifier.

17-1 INTRODUCTION

There are two general methods of forming circuits: those formed by connecting individual devices together (called discrete device circuits) and integrated circuits. Although not all discrete device circuits are available in integrated circuit format, many are, and the list increases each year.

In the dynamic history of electronics no development in the industry has moved as rapidly from concept to utilization as the integrated circuit. Integrated circuits (ICs) have replaced discrete device circuits in almost all computer applications and are rapidly being utilized in

410

communications, industrial, and consumer electronics. The development of the integrated circuit represents one more step towards more flexible, more efficient, and higher-performance electronic equipment.

Integrated circuits are manufactured in much the same way as transistors except that an entire circuit (or circuits) is produced rather than a single transistor. The manufacture of integrated circuits is a multibillion-dollar industry. Hundreds of different types of ICs are available for both linear and digital applications. Since the mid-1970s, the yearly production of integrated circuits has exceeded the number of individual transistors produced, and the differential increases every year. There are several methods used to classify integrated circuits. These are identified and discussed in the following paragraphs.

1. Method of fabrication
    a. monolithic
    b. hybrid

A monolithic integrated circuit is one whose entire circuitry is fabricated from a single substrate of silicon semiconductor material. The circuit can contain diodes, transistors, resistors, and capacitors. A hybrid IC is one which may contain two or more monolithic integrated circuits or one or more monolithic ICs and discrete devices. Monolithic integrated circuits are, by far, the more commonly used and the type that will be discussed in this chapter. Soldered connections attach the integrated circuit (often called a chip) to the pins of its case, as shown in Figure 17–1. As illustrated, the case is much larger than the chip to allow room for the external pin connections.

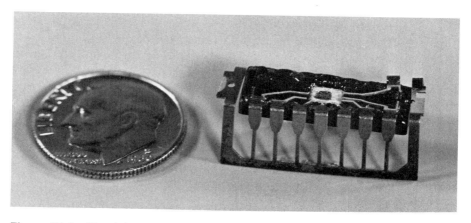

Figure 17–1 Monolithic integrated circuit.

2. Type of transistor technology
   a. BJT
   b. MOSFET

Like transistors, integrated circuits may be fabricated using either bipolar or field effect transistor technology. Bipolar devices are the more common, but there are a considerable number of MOSFET devices in use, especially in digital applications.

3. Component densities
   a. small-scale integration (SSI) 1 to 11 equivalent logic gates
   b. medium-scale integration (MSI) 12 to 99 equivalent logic gates
   c. large-scale integration (LSI) 100 to 10,000 equivalent logic gates
   d. very large-scale integration (VLSI) above 10,000 equivalent logic gates

The first integrated circuits were logic gating circuits used in digital computers. A logic gate is made up of a diode or a transistor to which one or more resistors are connected. The logic gate is used as a special kind of switch and is employed extensively in digital equipment. A system was developed to classify ICs as to the number of logic gates a particular IC contained. This system has continued today, even though many ICs contain circuits other than gates. The number of transistors a particular integrated circuit contains is roughly equivalent to the number of equivalent logic gates. Component density has increased tremendously since the integrated circuit was first developed. The first ICs had a density of 27 transistors. By 1972, the first calculator chips had a density of several thousand transistors. This has been increased to approximately 100,000 with the advent of the more advanced microprocessor chips. At the present time component density doubles each year. Some scientists think that the limit will be 45 million transistors using present silicon technology. Beyond that, it is thought that a new type of technology will have to be developed. Fortunately, this is several years in the future.

4. Function
   a. linear
   b. digital

The integrated circuit was first developed for digital applications in computers. Linear devices were developed as the state of the art advanced in

Figure 17–2   Dual-in-line packaged integrated circuits.

IC fabrication. Although there are still, by far, more digital than linear ICs, there are scores of different types of linear devices.

Integrated circuits may be packaged in one of several different kinds of cases. These include the dual-in-line package (DIP), the flat pack, and the metal can case. Of the three, the dual-in-line package is the most common. They are available in different sizes, depending upon the number of connecting pins. Some examples appear in Figure 17–2. Typical sizes include the 8-pin (four per side) 14-pin, and 16-pin packages. The connecting pins are oriented as illustrated in Figure 17–3. The top of the case has an indentation or dot at one end. The pins are numbered consecutively beginning with pin 1.

The flat pack is depicted in Figure 17–4. An indentation or dot appears in one corner on the top of the case. The pin closest to the inden-

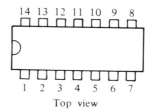

Figure 17–3   DIP pin identification.   Top view

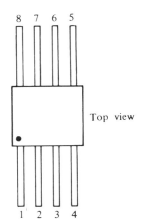

Top view

Figure 17–4   Flat-pack pin identification.

tation is pin 1. The remaining pins are numbered in sequence in the counterclockwise direction.

An IC packaged in a metal can case appears in Figure 17–5. It looks much like a transistor similarly packaged, only larger. The tab serves as a key for identifying the pin numbers, as illustrated in Figure 17–6. The pin located immediately to the left of the tab when viewing the case from the bottom is usually pin 1, when the tab is facing downward. The remaining pins are numbered in consecutive order in a clockwise direction. One should always check the manufacturer's specification sheet or an IC manual, or data book, for the pin locations for a particular integrated circuit, no matter what type of case is used.

As previously mentioned, the integrated circuit was first developed for digital applications in computers and involved relatively simple logic

Figure 17–5   IC packaged in a metal can case.

Figure 17–6   Metal can pin identification.   Bottom view

gating circuits. As the techniques of IC fabrication advanced, the manufacture of more complex digital integrated circuits was made possible. This led to the manufacture of single linear circuit ICs such as the differential amplifier. The operational amplifier was next developed and, more recently, other multistage and complete section ICs have been developed.

Although any circuit fabricated in IC format can be constructed using individual components, the integrated circuit equivalent provides many advantages. These include better matched circuits (important in balanced circuits), smaller size, lower cost, higher reliability, and higher efficiency. Integrated circuits have changed the way in which engineers design circuits and technicians troubleshoot and repair them. Design and troubleshooting emphasis is placed on a systems rather than an individual circuit approach. Instead of designing individual circuits, the design engineer must be aware of the different types of integrated circuits that will perform the required circuit function and be able to interface the IC with other integrated circuits or discrete device circuits. The technician who troubleshoots and repairs equipment must be aware of the circuit function of the IC and how it relates to other circuits within the equipment. Troubleshooting often involves making measurements at the input and output pins of the IC. If a circuit has failed within the IC package, it cannot be repaired. Instead, the complete IC must be replaced. The remaining portion of this chapter will deal with some of the more frequently used linear integrated circuits. Digital ICs will be discussed in Part Three.

17-2 THE DIFFERENTIAL AMPLIFIER

A differential amplifier is a balanced two-input two-output direct-coupled amplifier. Although it can be wired from discrete components, it is frequently used in IC format. The diagram of a basic differential amplifier is shown in Figure 17–7. The circuit consists of two identical amplifiers which are direct coupled to each other. Both transistors have identical characteristics; base resistors R_1 and R_4 have equal values, and resistors R_2 and R_3 in the collector circuit have the same resistance. Resistor R_5 in

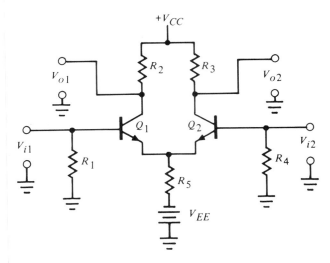

Figure 17–7 Differential amplifier.

the emitter circuit, and the emitter bias supply (V_{EE}) cause the differential amplifier to have a high input impedance.

The DC operating conditions for the circuit are illustrated in Figure 17–8. The collector currents, as well as the base currents in both transistors are equal. This causes both emitter currents to be identical. The two emitter currents combine, forming an emitter current (I_{ET}) which flows

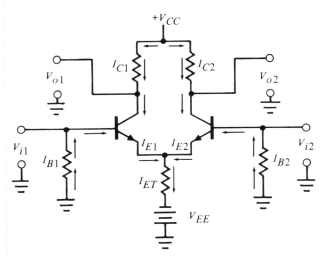

Figure 17–8 DC operating conditions of a differential amplifier.

through the emitter resistor ($I_{ET} = I_{E1} + I_{E2}$). Since the two stages are identical and the collector currents are equal, the output voltages (v_{o1} and v_{o2}) are equal. Often the output voltage is taken from both collectors, instead of each collector, with respect to ground. This is called the differential output and is equal to zero ($v_{o2} - v_{o1} = 0$). This is how the amplifier obtains its name.

The signal, or AC operating conditions are illustrated in Figure 17–9 where a signal is applied to the base of Q_1. During the positive alternation, the base, collector and emitter currents flowing through Q_1 increase, and the output voltage of Q_1 (v_{o1}) decreases. Transistor Q_1 operates as a normal common-emitter connected amplifier. The increase in emitter current causes the voltage developed across R_E (v_{re}) to increase. This voltage is directly coupled to the emitter of Q_2. Transistor Q_2 functions as a common-base connected amplifier. The increase in voltage dropped across R_E decreases the emitter-base bias applied to Q_2. The collector current decreases, causing the output voltage (v_{o2}) to increase.

During the negative alternation, the base, collector, and emitter currents associated with Q_1 decrease. The resulting decrease in voltage drop across R_E is coupled to the emitter of Q_2, causing Q_2 to conduct harder, resulting in a decrease in the output voltage. This completes the circuit action for one input cycle. The output of Q_1 is usually referred to as the inverting output, and the noninverting output is associated with Q_2. This assumes that whenever a signal is applied to the amplifier, it is applied to Q_1. If a signal is applied to Q_2 instead of Q_1, the outputs are reversed.

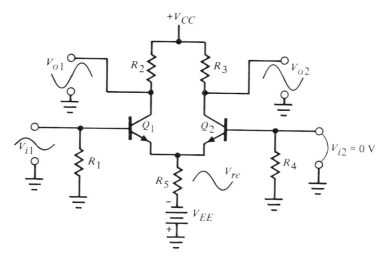

Figure 17–9 AC operating conditions of a differential amplifier.

Transistor Q_2 functions as a common-emitter connected amplifier directly coupled to Q_1, which operates as a common-base amplifier. For this reason the input to Q_1 is normally referred to as the noninverting ($+$) input, and the input to Q_2 is called the inverting ($-$) input. The schematic, or block diagram, symbol used to represent the differential amplifier (DA) appears in Figure 17–10.

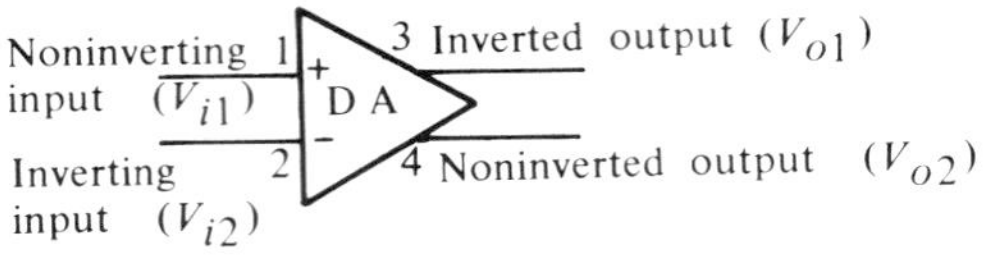

Figure 17–10 Schematic symbol used to represent the differential amplifier.

The differential amplifier may be connected for any one of a number of circuit operations, depending upon how the signals are applied to and taken from the amplifier. There are seven basic methods of operation as identified by the separate input and output conditions. Combinations of the input and output signal conditions increase the number of possible methods of operation. For example, the circuit appearing in Figure 17–9 is connected for single-ended input double-ended output operation. The basic methods of differential amplifier operations are illustrated in Figure 17–11.

Although both stages are supposed to be matched, in actual practice there is usually a slight difference in the characteristics between the two amplifier stages. A figure of merit used to describe the extent in which the circuits are matched is the common-mode rejection ration (CMRR).

$$CMRR = \frac{A_d}{A_c} \qquad\qquad (17\text{–}1)$$

As indicated in Equation 17–1, this is the ratio of the differential amplifier gain (A_d) to the gain of the amplifier connected in the common-mode configuration (A_c). The same signal is applied to both inputs when the differential amplifier is connected for common-mode operation, as illustrated in Figure 17–11(d). The two outputs should be equal in amplitude and 180° out-of-phase if both stages are perfectly matched. The differential output voltage is 0 V and the amplifier gain (A_c) is zero. If the two stages are mismatched, a differential output voltage will be present and the common-mode gain will be greater than zero. The common-mode rejection ratio is inversely proportional to the common-mode gain of the

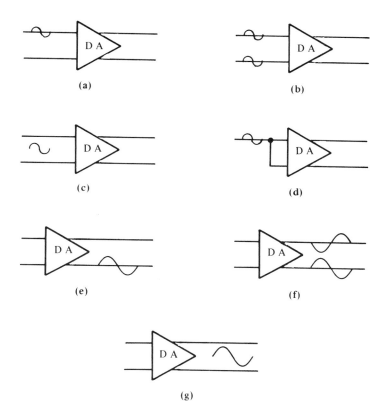

Figure 17–11   Methods of operating a differential amplifier: (a) single-ended input;(b) double-ended input; (c) differential input; (d) common-mode input; (e) single-ended output; (f) double-ended output; (g) differential output.

amplifier. The smaller the value of common-mode gain, the greater the value of the common-mode rejection ratio.

17-3 THE OPERATIONAL AMPLIFIER

The operational amplifier, often called the op amp, is the single most versatile linear integrated circuit device in existence today. A relatively simple device, it can replace entire circuit sections in many applications. The operational amplifier is a double-input single-output amplifier that usually employs negative feedback to control its operation. The op amp was originally constructed from individual components and was used in analog computers to perform arithmetic operations. The versatility of the op amp has allowed its use to be extended into numerous other areas of linear applications some of which are identified in Table 17–1.

TABLE 17–1   Some Selected Applications for the Operational Amplifier

Inverting amplifiers	Adder circuits
Noninverting amplifiers	Subtracter circuits
Voltage comparators	Integrator circuits
Follower circuits	Phase-shifter circuits
Differentiator circuits	Low-pass filters
Sinusoidal oscillators	

Although many different types of operational amplifier integrated circuits are manufactured, most contain at least the three stages shown in Figure 17–12. The input stage is a differential amplifier to provide a high input impedance. The midsection is usually made up of one or more differential amplifiers to provide the op amp with both a high voltage gain and wide bandpass characteristics. The output stage is often a follower circuit to provide a low output impedance and a relatively high current gain. The schematic diagram of a typical operational amplifier appears in Figure 17–13.

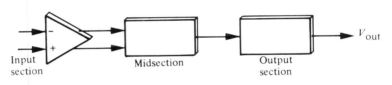

Figure 17–12   Block diagram of an operational amplifier.

Usually, instead of drawing the complete diagram of the op amp, the amplifier symbol, appearing in Figure 17–14, is used to represent the device. Although the op amp has a single output, it has the same inputs as the differential amplifier.

The application of negative feedback is the underlying principle which allows the operational amplifier to have such diverse applications. The feedback loop is introduced between the output and inverting input terminals. One of the advantages of using the IC operational amplifier is that one need not be concerned with its internal circuitry. External resistors, capacitors, and inductors can be connected to the input, output, and

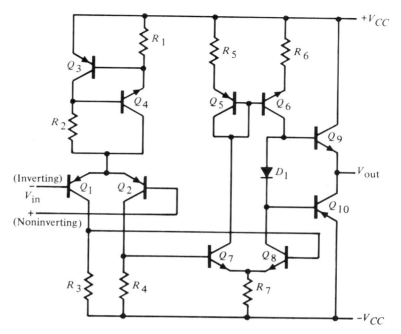

Figure 17–13   Schematic diagram of an operational amplifier.

Figure 17–14   Symbol used to represent the operational amplifier.

biasing case pins to cause the op amp to operate in the desired circuit application. There is almost no limit to the linear functions this device will perform. Several applications were identified in Table 17–1. The diagrams for these circuits appear in Figure 17–15.

17-4 LINEAR ICs IN CONSUMER ELECTRONICS

There has been a considerable amount of development in the application of linear integrated circuits in consumer electronics. It is possible to design and build entire radio and stereophonic receivers from integrated circuits. Many circuits and entire sections of a television receiver are presently available in IC format.

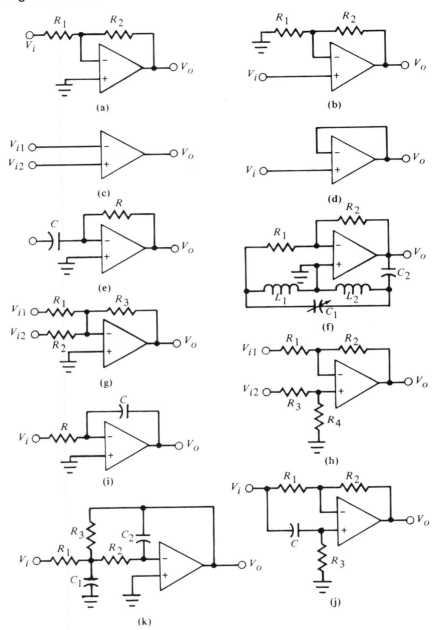

Figure 17–15 Circuit connections for selected op amp applications: (a) inverting amplifier; (b) noninverting amplifier; (c) voltage comparator; (d) follower circuit; (e) differentiator circuit; (f) sinusoidal oscillator; (g) adder circuit (summing amplifier); (h) subtractor (difference amplifier); (i) integrator circuit; (j) phase-shifter circuit; (k) low-pass filter.

The use of integrated circuits greatly reduces the size and parts requirements of the systems, or equipment, in which they are used. However, external devices such as coupling transformers, coupling and decoupling capacitors, and resistors used for feedback and biasing networks are still required.

SUMMARY

1. There are two types of integrated circuits: monolithic and hybrid. In a monolithic integrated circuit all the components are fabricated from a single silicon substrate. A hybrid integrated circuit may be made up of two or more monolithic ICs or one or more monolithic ICs and discrete devices connected together and enclosed in a single package. The monolithic integrated circuit is, by far, the more common of the two.
2. Monolithic integrated circuits can be manufactured using either BJT or MOSFET technology and can be classified as to their function—either linear or digital. Integrated circuits may be packaged in dual-in-line, flat pack, or metal can cases.
3. The differential amplifier is a two-input two-output balanced direct-coupled amplifier, which is often built in integrated circuit format. It can be used for many DC and AC signal applications and does not have the disadvantages of the cascade-connected direct-coupled amplifiers discussed in Chapter 16.
4. Ideally, both stages in a differential amplifier are perfectly matched. In an actual differential amplifier, there will usually be slight differences in the characteristics of the two stages due to irregularities which occur during the manufacturing process. The common-mode rejection ratio (CMRR) is used as a figure of merit to describe the symmetry of the circuit.
5. The operational amplifier (op amp) is the most popular and versatile of all the linear integrated circuits. The key to its versatility is the use of negative feedback employed in most of its applications. Originally used to perform arithmetic operations in analog computers, its use has been extended to many other amplifier applications. In addition, it can be used as a filter, a phase shifter, and a voltage comparator.
6. In addition to the differential amplifier and operational amplifier, there are scores of other linear IC devices designed for specific circuit applications. In the area of consumer electronics, linear IC devices are available which replace complete sections in radio and television receivers.

PRACTICE EXERCISES

1. Differentiate between hybrid and monolithic integrated circuits.
2. Identify the two types of integrated circuits with respect to type of transistor technology.

3. List the four categories of integrated circuits with respect to component density.
4. Identify three cases commonly used to package integrated circuits.
5. Draw a diagram of the top view of a 16-pin dual-in-line IC package and number all pins.
6. Draw a diagram of the top view of a 14-pin flat pack. Label all pins.
7. Sketch the bottom view of a 10-pin metal can case and number all the pins.
8. What is a differential amplifier?
9. Draw the schematic diagram of a differential amplifier.
10. Draw the schematic symbol used to represent the differential amplifier.
11. Identify four ways in which the input signal can be applied to a differential amplifier.
12. List three methods that can be used to take the signal from a differential amplifier.
13. What is the significance of the common-mode rejection ratio in a differential amplifier?
14. What is an operational amplifier?
15. What are seven applications for the operational amplifier?
16. Draw the block diagram of an operational amplifier.
17. Draw the symbol used to represent the op amp.
18. Describe the input and output impedance characteristics of an operational amplifier.

ANSWERS TO PRACTICE EXERCISES

1. Hybrid integrated circuits contain two or more monolithic ICs or one or more monolithic ICs connected to one or more discrete devices. A monolithic integrated circuit is one in which all the devices, both active and passive, are fabricated from the same silicon substrate.
2. Integrated circuits may employ either bipolar or metal oxide semiconductor field effect transistor technology.
3. Component density includes SSI, MSI, LSI, and VLSI.
4. Three common packaging methods include the dual-in-line (DIP), the flat pack, and the metal can.
5. See Figure 17–16.
6. See Figure 17–17.
7. See Figure 17–18.

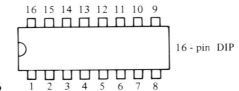

Figure 17–16

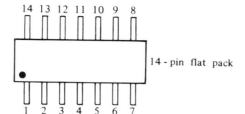

Figure 17–17

14 - pin flat pack

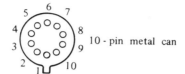

Figure 17–18

10 - pin metal can

8. A differential amplifier is made up of two matched amplifier stages which are direct coupled to one another.

9. See Figure 17–7.

10. See Figure 17–10.

11. The input signals to a differential amplifier can be applied in single-ended, double-ended, differential input, and common-mode fashions.

12. Methods in which the output signal can be taken are single ended, double ended, and differential.

13. The common-mode rejection ratio is a figure of merit used to describe how well balanced the amplifier stages are that form the differential amplifier.

14. An operational amplifier is a special type of direct-coupled amplifier which utilizes negative feedback in most of its applications. It is the most popular and versatile of all the linear integrated circuits.

15. See Table 17–1.

16. See Figure 17–12.

17. See Figure 17–14.

18. The operational amplifier has a high input and low output impedance.

CHAPTER EXAMINATION

Choose true or false for questions 1 to 6.

1. T F   An operational amplifier can be used as a low-frequency voltage amplifier.

2. T F   The differential amplifier can be operated for single-ended input operation.

3. T F   A differential amplifier can be used as a rectifier circuit.

4. T F   Negative feedback is usually employed in operational amplifier circuits.

5. T F   The monolithic IC is one whose components are all fabricated from a single silicon substrate.
6. T F   The CMRR is often used as a figure of merit for a differential amplifier circuit.
7. Draw the schematic diagram of a differential amplifier circuit.
8. Draw the schematic symbol for an operational amplifier.
9. List seven ways in which a differential amplifier can be operated with respect to the input and output signal conditions.
10. Identify three ways in which an integrated circuit can be packaged.

Power Amplifier Circuits

OBJECTIVES

Upon completion of this chapter you should be able to do the following:

1. Identify four ways in which power amplifiers differ from voltage amplifier stages.
2. List the four classes of amplifier operation and identify the approximate conduction period for each.
3. Describe what is meant by amplifier efficiency and calculate the efficiency of a power amplifier.
4. Calculate the power dissipated by a transistor.
5. Describe what is meant by a harmonic frequency and describe the relationship between the amplitude and frequency of a harmonic with respect to the amplitude and frequency of a fundamental signal.
6. Discuss the effect of harmonics on the shape of the fundamental signal.
7. Recognize or draw the schematic diagram of a single-ended class A audio frequency amplifier.
8. Recognize or draw the diagram of a push-pull amplifier stage.
9. Identify three advantages of using push-pull amplifiers compared to single-ended class A audio frequency amplifiers.
10. Identify or draw the diagram of a single-ended class C biased RF power amplifier and describe why a single-ended RF amplifier can be biased for class C operation.

18-1 INTRODUCTION

As identified in Chapter 16, there are two categories of amplifiers with respect to signal size: voltage (small signal) and power (large signal). Both types are usually found in most amplifier systems. Voltage amplifiers are used to increase the voltage amplitude of a signal. The amplified signal voltage is often used as an input to "drive" a power amplifier. A power amplifier is used to amplify the power of the signal delivered to a load such as a loudspeaker, cathode-ray tube deflection coils, relay coils, antenna, or motor.

Power amplifier stages differ from voltage amplifiers in a number of different ways. The active device (usually a transistor, although an IC or electron tube is sometimes used) is usually larger and heavier, to handle the larger amounts of power. Often the transistor is mounted on a heat sink to help dissipate the heat. The input signal to a power amplifier is usually quite high, ranging from a low of a few volts to a high of 30 or 40 V (or even higher in some cases). Circuit efficiency is a major concern in power amplifier stages. A power amplifier converts the DC power produced by the DC power supply into signal power. Class AB, class B, or even class C bias operation is sometimes used to increase the conversion efficiency. Impedance matching is important to transfer the power from the power amplifier to the load.

18-2 PRINCIPLES OF POWER AMPLIFIERS

18-2.1 Conduction Period.   Conduction period, often called class of operation, refers to the extent the active device is biased. There are four classes of operation: class A, class AB, class B, and class C. Class A bias is defined as that Q-point bias which allows output current to flow for 360° or for the duration of the input signal, as illustrated in Figure 18–1.

Class AB bias is depicted in Figure 18–2. The operating point is located between the Q-point location for class A operation and cutoff. For the class of AB operation shown in Figure 18–2, the output current flows from zero to approximately 240°, at which time the transistor cuts off and the output current becomes zero. The device remains at cutoff until the input signal reaches 300° and begins conducting again. Class AB bias re-

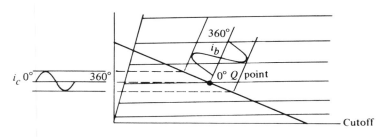

Figure 18–1   Class A bias operation for a transistor.

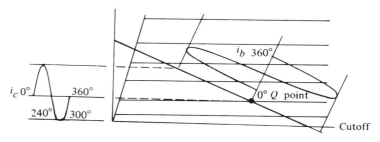

Figure 18–2   Class *AB* bias operation for a transistor.

sults in some distortion. The location of the *Q*-point in Figure 18–2 causes the output signal current to be clipped from 240° to 300°.

Class *B* bias is illustrated in Figure 18–3. The *Q*-point is located at cutoff. Without a signal applied to the input, the transistor is cut off and the output current is zero. When a signal is applied to the base, the transistor is forward biased during the positive alternation, and collector current flows from 0° to 180°. During the negative alternation, the transistor is biased below cutoff, and the collector current remains at zero. A class *B* biased amplifier has considerable distortion, as one-half of the input signal is missing from the output.

The last class of bias, class *C*, is shown in Figure 18–4. The operating point is located beyond cutoff. This means that the emitter-base junction is reverse-biased for class *C* operation. For the *Q*-point location shown in Figure 18–4, the output current flows from about 60° to 120° and is zero during the remaining portion of the input signal. An amplifier operating with class *C* bias has severe distortion.

Comparing the input signal requirements for each of the classes of amplifiers, as illustrated in Figures 18–1 through 18–4, it is evident that input signal amplitude requirements vary with the class of operation. It is smallest for class *A* operation and becomes progressively larger for

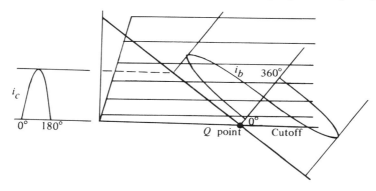

Figure 18–3   Class *B* operation for a transistor.

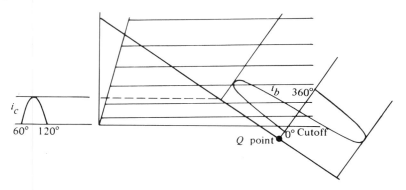

Figure 18–4   Class *C* operation for a transistor.

class *AB*, *B*, and *C* operation. Small signal amplifiers are usually biased class *A*. Large signal amplifiers may be biased class *A*, class *AB*, class *B*, or even class *C* for RF amplifiers.

18-2.2 Efficiency.   A power amplifier converts DC power from the V_{CC} power supply into signal power, which is delivered to the load. It is important that the conversion efficiency be as high as possible. The efficiency of an amplifier is the ratio of the output signal power (P_o) to the DC input power (P_i), as shown in the Equation (18–1).

$$\text{Percent efficiency} = \eta = \frac{P_o}{P_i} \times 100$$

(18–1)

Efficiency is usually expressed as a percentage; therefore, the ratio is multiplied by 100.

The DC input power is the power supplied to the amplifier by the V_{CC} power supply and is equal to the product of the V_{CC} supply voltage and the Q-point collector current, as indicated by Equation (18–2).

$$P_i = (V_{CC})(I_{CQ})$$

(18–2)

If the load is resistive, the output power is the product of the rms values of the output signal voltage and current. The rms value of a sinusoidal voltage or current can be determined by dividing the peak-to-peak value by $2\sqrt{2}$:

$$V_{rms} = \left(\frac{V_{pk-pk}}{2}\right)(0.707)$$

$$V_{rms} = \left(\frac{V_{pk-pk}}{2}\right)\left(\frac{1}{1.414}\right)$$

Since $1.414 = \sqrt{2}$

then $V_{rms} = \dfrac{V_{pk-pk}}{2\sqrt{2}}$

(18–3)

Therefore, the output signal power may be calculated by Equation (18–4).

$$P_o = \left(\frac{V_{pk-pk}}{2\sqrt{2}}\right)\left(\frac{I_{pk-pk}}{2\sqrt{2}}\right) = \frac{(V_{pk-pk})(I_{pk-pk})}{8}$$

(18–4)

The voltage and current values are those appearing across and flowing through the load, respectively. Assuming no losses in the transformer, the amplifier appearing in Example 18–1 has an efficiency of 18.75 percent.

Example 18–1   Calculating the efficiency of a power amplifier

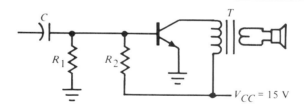

Figure 18–5

Problem

The amplifier shown above is connected to a 4-Ω speaker. If the DC current collector (I_{CQ}) is 400 mA and the signal voltage across the terminals is 3 V peak, calculate the efficiency of the stage. Assume that the speaker impedance is resistive.

Solution

1. $\eta = \dfrac{P_0}{P_i} \times 100 = \dfrac{1.125}{6}$ W $\times 100 = 18.75$ percent

2. $P_i = (V_{CC})(I_{CQ}) = (15 \text{ V})(0.4 \text{ A}) = 6$ W

3. $P_0 = \dfrac{(V_{pk-pk})(I_{pk-pk})}{8} = \dfrac{(6 \text{ V})(1.5 \text{ A})}{8} = \dfrac{9}{8} = 1.125$ W

4. $I_{pk-pk} = \dfrac{V_{pk-pk}}{R_L} = \dfrac{6 \text{ V}}{4} = 1.5$ A

The efficiency of an amplifier is related to its class of operation. The maximum efficiency of a class *A* amplifier is 25 percent except when transformer coupling is used. Transformer-coupled class *A* amplifiers have a maximum efficiency of 50 percent. A class *B* amplifier may have an efficiency as high as 78.5 percent. The maximum efficiency of a class *AB* amplifier lies between 25 and 78.5 percent, depending upon the type of coupling and Q-point location. Class *C* amplifiers have the highest efficiency, but these amplifiers can be used only at high frequencies. Actual amplifier effficiency is usually considerably less than the maximum possible value, however.

18-2.3 Transistor Power Dissipation.
The difference between the power delivered to the load and the power supplied by the V_{CC} power supply represents the power dissipated by the transistor. This is illustrated by Equation (18–5).

$$P_{transistor} = P_D = P_i - P_o \qquad\qquad (18\text{–}5)$$

Unlike a transistor used in a voltage amplifier stage, which may dissipate power ranging from a low of a few tenths of a milliwatt to a high of a few hundred milliwatts, power transistors must be capable of dissipating much higher amounts of power in the form of heat. The power amplifier stage appearing in Example 18–1 is typical of the amplifier used to drive the speaker in a moderately sized table radio. As shown in Example 18–2, even with the relatively low power required to drive the speaker, the transistor must dissipate 4.875 W of power. The power appearing at the speaker and the power dissipated by the transistor are both dependent upon the volume control setting.

Power transistors are usually easy to recognize. They are larger and are often packaged differently from low power transistors. Some typical

Example 18–2   Determining the power dissipated by a transistor

Problem
Calculate the power dissipated by the transistor used in the amplifier stage shown in Example 18–1.

Solution
1. $P_D = P_i - P_o$
2. $P_D = 6 - 1.125 = 4.875$ W

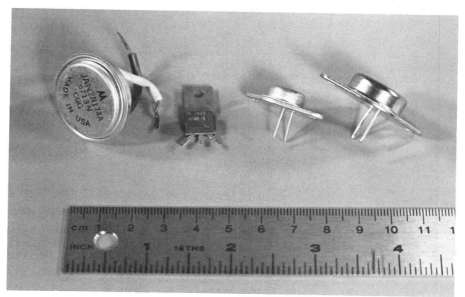

Figure 18–6 Representative types of power transistors.

power bipolar devices are shown in Figure 18–6. Most power transistors are of the bipolar type, either *PNP* or *NPN*. The junction and metal oxide semiconductor field effect transistors, at the present time, have limited applications as power devices.

Power transistors are often mounted on heat sinks. This is a metallic device which often has cooling fins and is used to conduct heat away from the transistor. Some representative types of heat sinks are shown in Figure 18–7.

Several different ratings and characteristics for small-signal transistors were identified in Chapter 12. These apply for power transistors as well. In addition, the maximum power (P_D) that can be dissipated by a transistor is another rating which must be taken into consideration when using power transistors. Although all transistors have a maximum power dissipation rating, this rating is not as important for low power small-signal transistors as it is for power transistors. The maximum power which can be dissipated by a transistor is dependent upon the ambient temperature in which the transistor is operated. Usually, P_D is specified at room temperature (25°C). At higher temperatures, the heat conduction is reduced and the transistor power dissipation capacity must be derated. If the transistor case becomes hot enough, P_D decreases to zero. Germanium transistors will operate at higher temperatures than silicon types

Figure 18–7 Representative types of heat sinks.

before their power dissipation capacity begins to decrease. Typical power derating curves are shown in Figure 18–8 for both a germanium and silicon power transistor. The actual derating curve or data required to derate a transistor is usually included in the manufacturer's specification sheet. If, for example, the transistor whose curve appears in Figure 18–8 (b) is operated at 50 °C, its power dissipation capacity is approximately 25 W.

18-2.4 Harmonics. A harmonic of a sinusoidal signal is another sinusoidal signal whose frequency is a multiple of the original frequency. The original signal is called the fundamental, or first harmonic. The relationship between the fundamental signal and associated harmonics is

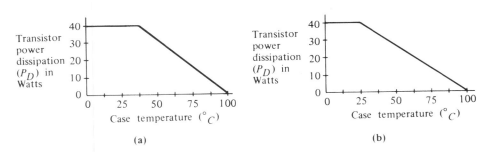

Figure 18–8 Typical power derating curves: (a) germanium transistor; (b) silicon transistor.

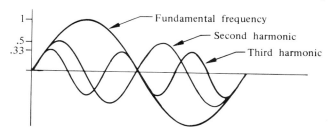

Figure 18–9 Sine wave and associated second and third harmonics.

shown in Figure 18–9. The second harmonic has twice the frequency of the fundamental, and its amplitude is approximately one-half the amplitude of the fundamental. The third harmonic has three times the frequency of the fundamental and about one-third the amplitude. Higher-order harmonics, although not shown, may also exist. Even-numbered harmonics are called even harmonics and odd-numbered harmonics are called odd harmonics.

Harmonics distort and change the shape of the fundamental signal. If a signal contains a significant number of odd harmonics, a square wave is formed. The sum of the individual odd harmonics and fundamental causes the slopes of the leading and trailing edges of the fundamental signal to become steeper and the top to become flat. Theoretically, an infinite number of odd harmonics is required to produce a square wave. For all practical purposes, however, a usable square wave can be produced with just a few odd harmonics. As illustrated in Figure 18–10, the presence of the third and fifth harmonics causes the fundamental signal to take on the characteristics of a square wave.

When both odd- and even-numbered harmonics are present, the fundamental signal becomes ramp, or sawtooth, shaped as shown in Figure 18–11.

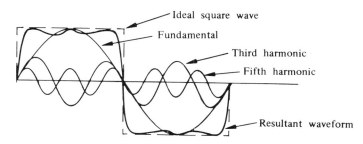

Figure 18–10 Square wave formed from the third and fifth harmonics.

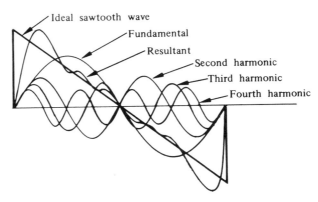

Figure 18–11   Sawtooth waveform formed from the second, third, and fifth harmonics.

The voice signals coming from a microphone is another example of a signal that has harmonics present. The voice tonal qualities of individuals differ because of the overtones produced. Overtones in speech are analogous to harmonics in electronic circuits. The microphone converts the speech sounds into equivalent electrical signals. Although the output signals of a microphone look rather distorted when viewed from an oscilloscope, they are sinusoidal in nature but contain a significant number of harmonics.

It is fair to say that harmonics are desirable in some applications and in others they are not. Signals that are square or sawtooth shaped are very important to the operation of some types of circuits such as those used in television receivers. In these cases the generation of harmonics is important; this is how these signals are produced. In other applications, such as radio communications, harmonics are usually extremely undesirable. Circuit designers utilize circuits that will eliminate or reduce the cause of harmonic signal generation. Harmonics are usually created by operating an active device in the nonlinear region of its *V-I* characteristics.

18-3 TYPES OF POWER AMPLIFIER STAGES

18-3.1 Single-ended Audio Frequency Amplifier.   The term *single-ended* is sometimes used to describe any amplifier which employs one transistor (or two or more connected in parallel) operated in the conventional common-emitter, common-base, or common-collector circuit configurations. A typical single-ended audio frequency power amplifier appears in Figure 18–12. The signal is *RC* coupled to the base, and the

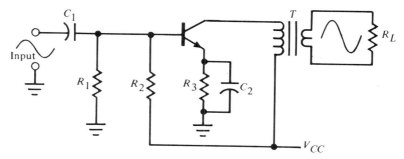

Figure 18–12   Single-ended audio frequency amplifier.

amplified output signal is transformer coupled to a load. Resistors R_1 and R_2 form a voltage divider network that provides the potential to forward bias the base-emitter junction. The output transformer has a turns ratio such that the output impedance of the transistor and load impedance are matched. The amplifier is biased class A to prevent distortion of the output signal.

18-3.2 Class A Push-Pull Audio Frequency Amplifier.   A push-pull power amplifier is one whose load current is dependent upon the conduction of two transistors connected back to back and which can be biased class A, class AB, or class B. The diagram of a class A push-pull amplifier is shown in Figure 18–13.

A push-pull amplifier is a type of balanced circuit. Transistors Q_1 and Q_2 should have identical, or very similar, characteristics. The amplifier requires two input signals which are equal in amplitude and 180° out of phase with each other. This requirement may be met by using a trans-

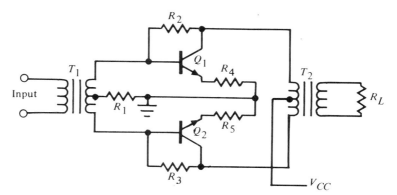

Figure 18–13   Class A push-pull audio frequency amplifier.

former that has a center-tapped secondary; or a paraphase amplifier may be used. V_{CC} is applied to each transistor via the center-tapped primary of the output transformer.

When a signal is applied to an amplifier, as illustrated in Figure 18–14, the positive alternation causes the base current of Q_1 to increase and that of Q_2 to decrease, since transformer T_1 produces two out-of-phase signals. This causes the collector current of Q_1 (i_{c1}) to increase and the collector current of Q_2 (i_{c2}) to decrease. As the collector current from Q_1 increases and moves upward through the top half of the output transformer, an expanding magnetic flux field is created which causes a voltage to be induced across the secondary winding. At the same time the decreasing collector current flowing downward through the bottom half of the primary of the output transformer causes the magnetic field about the windings associated with that current to collapse. This produces a voltage across the secondary winding which has the same polarity as that produced by Q_1. The two induced voltages have the same polarity even though one was created by an expanding field and the other by a collapsing field. This is caused by the direction of the collector currents flowing in the primary circuit. One current was moving upward while the other was moving downward.

During the negative alternation, the base current for Q_1 decreases and that for Q_2 increases. The collector current flowing from Q_1 decreases, causing the magnetic field about the top half of T_2 to collapse. This creates a voltage across the secondary which is opposite in polarity to that formerly induced, as shown in Figure 18–15. Simultaneously, the collector current flowing through Q_2 increases, causing the magnetic field about the bottom half of T_2 to expand. A voltage is induced across the secondary winding which has the same polarity as that induced by the

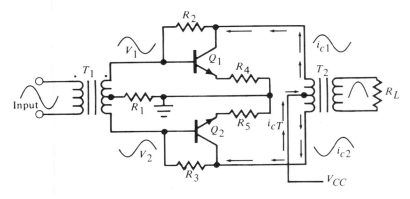

Figure 18–14   Analysis of class A push-pull amplifier during positive alternation.

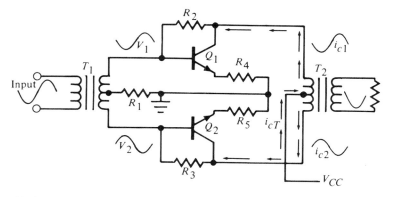

Figure 18–15 Analysis of class A push-pull amplifier during negative alternation.

field created by i_{c1}. This completes the output cycle. For one input signal cycle, one cycle of output signal appears across the secondary winding. Since the collector currents from both transistors cause like voltages to be induced across the secondary winding of T_2, the two signals are additive and the power delivered to the load is greater than that for a single-ended amplifier using the same transistor. The efficiency is approximately the same as that of a single-ended amplifier stage.

18-3.3 Class B Push-Pull Audio Frequency Amplifier. Push-pull amplifiers can be biased class B for higher operating efficiency. Although the efficiency is greater than that obtainable from a class A amplifier, the power delivered to the load is about the same as that for a single-ended amplifier using the same type of transistor.

The diagram of a push-pull class B amplifier appears in Figure 18–16. No emitter-base bias supply is required. Both transistors are cut off

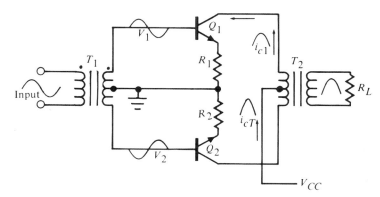

Figure 18–16 Analysis of a class B push-pull amplifier during positive alternation.

without any signal applied. When a signal is applied to the amplifier, the positive alternation causes Q_1 to become forward biased. Because of the phase split produced by the center-tapped secondary, Q_2 remains cut off. Since this transistor was already biased at cutoff, the negative signal drives the base beyond cutoff. The increasing collector current flowing upward through the top half of the primary winding of T_2 causes a voltage to be induced across the secondary, having the polarity indicated.

During the negative alternation, Q_1 is biased beyond cutoff, and Q_2 conducts. The increasing collector current flowing downward through the bottom half of the primary of T_2 causes a voltage to be induced across the secondary winding which is opposite in polarity of that produced when Q_1 was conducting as indicated in Figure 18–17. Taken collectively, no distortion has occurred. Transistor Q_1 produced the positive alternation while Q_2 produced the negative. The output signal across the load is an amplified reproduction of the input signal, even though each transistor conducted just one-half the time.

There is some distortion present caused by the slight delay between the time that one transistor cuts off and the other begins conducting, as illustrated in Figure 18–18. This is called crossover distortion and is caused by the barrier potential of the conducting diode. To overcome this problem, class B push-pull amplifiers are often operated with a slight amount of forward bias.

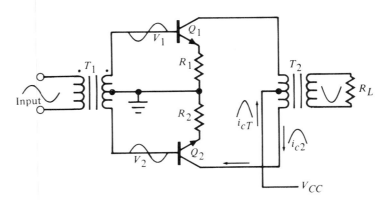

Figure 18–17 Analysis of class B push-pull amplifier during negative alternation.

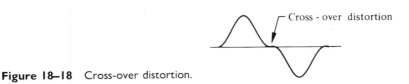

Figure 18–18 Cross-over distortion.

18-3.4 **Class *AB* Push-Pull Audio Frequency Amplifier.**   Class *B* push-pull amplifiers are more efficient than class *A* operated stages, but the output power is considerably less. Class *AB* operation is a compromise between class *A* and class *B* bias. The diagram of a class *AB* amplifier stage appears in Figure 18–19. The circuit looks exactly like the class

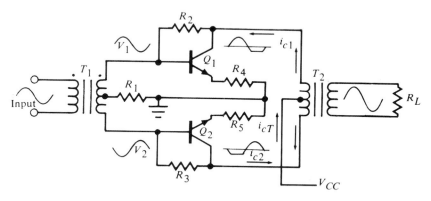

Figure 18–19   Class *AB* push-pull amplifier.

A amplifier. The only difference between the two circuits is the size of the biasing resistors. Like the class *B* amplifier, severe distortion occurs in each of the individual amplifiers. The voltage induced across the load is a composite signal made up of the output of the two transistors and is an amplified reproduction of the input signal.

18-3.5 **Complementary Symmetry Push-Pull Amplifier.**   A complementary symmetry amplifier is a push-pull amplifier that does not require either an input or an output transformer. This circuit is less expensive, less bulky, and considerably lighter than the other types of push-pull amplifier stages. The circuit can be biased class *A,* class *AB,* or class *B.* The diagram of a class *AB* biased circuit is shown in Figure 18–20. As indicated, the amplifier requires complementary transistors. Because transformers are not used, complementary symmetry amplifiers are often used as the power amplifier stage in direct-coupled amplifier systems. They are also frequently used as the output stage in monolithic operational amplifiers.

Push-pull amplifiers have many advantages when compared with single-ended amplifier stages. As previously noted, they can supply more power to a load and can be operated more efficiently. Another significant advantage is that they cancel even harmonics. Any even order harmonics

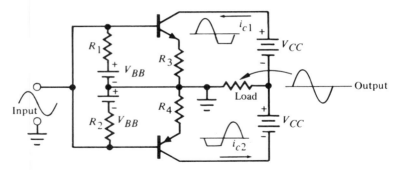

Figure 18–20 Class *AB* complementary symmetry push-pull amplifier.

present in the amplifier appear in phase at the collectors of the two transistors. Since the collector currents flow in opposite directions through the primary winding of the output transformer, the magnetic fields created by each are equal in magnitude and opposite in polarity and cancel each other.

18-3.6 RF Power Amplifiers. Radio frequency (RF) amplifiers may employ a number of different types of active devices depending upon the frequency and power requirements. For frequencies lying between 20,000 and a few hundred megahertz and an output power of a few to several tens of watts, silicon power transistors are usually used. For higher frequencies where moderate output power is required, special kinds of power transistors are used. Where high output power is required, special kinds of electron tubes are used.

Although RF power amplifiers may be operated with any class of bias, most are biased class *C* because of the higher resulting efficiency. Class *C* bias results in severe distortion since the output current flows for less than 180°. The *Q*-point for class *C* bias is located beyond the cutoff point of the active device. This means that for a bipolar transistor the emitter-base junction must be reverse biased. The output current of the transistor consists of a series of pulses, as illustrated in Figure 18–21. The collector current is severely distorted and bears little resemblance to the input signal. A tank circuit is often connected to the collector of the transistor to restore the missing portions of the signal.

A tank circuit is a parallel resonant *LC* circuit. A battery and a switch are connected to the tank circuit shown in Figure 18–22(a). If the capacitor is initially discharged, the moment the switch is closed, current flows into the tank circuit and the capacitor begins to charge as shown in

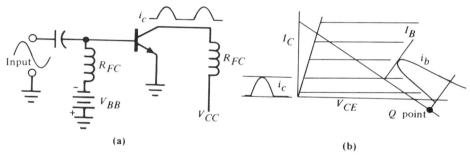

Figure 18–21   (a) Class *C* RF power amplifier and (b) associated *V-I* characteristics.

Figure 18–22(b). Current will not initially flow through the inductor because an inductor opposes a change in current intensity. If the switch is
opened after the capacitor has charged, as shown in Figure 18–22(c), the
capacitor discharges through the inductor, producing an expanding magnetic field about the coil. After the capacitor has fully discharged, Figure
18–22(d), there is no longer any current flowing through the coil to support the magnetic field, and the field collapses into the coil, producing a
self-induced voltage which causes the capacitor to charge, as shown in
Figure 18–22(e). The polarity of the voltage causes the capacitor to charge
in the opposite direction of the initial charge shown in Figure 18–22(b).
After the capacitor has charged, it again begins to discharge, and the
cycle repeats itself. If the voltage appearing across the tank circuit is plot-

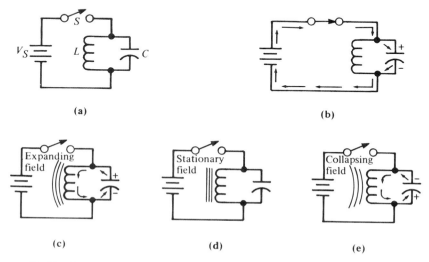

Figure 18–22   Flywheel action of a tank circuit.

ted with respect to time, the resulting graph represents a sinusoidal waveform. If there were no losses in the tank circuit (infinite Q), once energy was imparted to the circuit from the battery, the switch could be opened and a train of sinusoidal voltage waveforms would be produced indefinitely. However, resistance is present in the inductor, capacitor, and connecting wires and losses do occur. Each successive voltage cycle becomes lower in amplitude until they are completely gone, or are dampened out, as illustrated in Figure 18–23. To sustain the output, the switch would have to be closed at regularly timed intervals to allow the battery to resupply energy to the tank circuit. The sinusoidal voltage is produced by the action of the energy transfer between the reactive devices. This is called the flywheel effect. A tank circuit is able to produce a sinusoidal voltage because of the flywheel effect.

If a tank circuit is connected to the output of a class C biased active device, such as the transistor shown in Figure 18–24, the collector current and voltage represent pulses of energy which periodically replace the energy losses in the tank circuit. The values of the inductor and capacitor are chosen so that the resonant frequency of the tank circuit is the same as the amplifier input signal frequency. The tank circuit serves the purpose of reconstructing the output signal so that it is an amplified reproduction of the input signal.

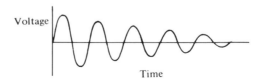

Figure 18–23   Dampening effect of a tank circuit.

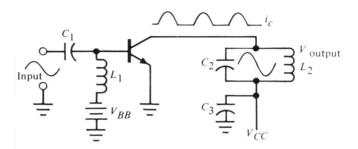

Figure 18–24   Class C RF power amplifier.

SUMMARY

1. A power amplifier is usually the last amplifier stage in an amplifier system or section. Its function is to provide power to a load.

2. A power amplifier usually employs a heavy transistor which is often mounted on a heat sink; requires a high input signal; may be biased class *A*, *AB*, *B*, or *C* (depending upon the type of circuit and frequency of operation); and usually has a coupling network to match its output impedance to the impedance of the load.

3. The output current for class *A* operation flows for the duration of the input signal. The *Q*-point is located in the midregion of the volt-ampere characteristics. The maximum efficiency of a transistor amplifier biased for class *A* operation is 50 percent. In most amplifiers the efficiency is considerably lower, however.

4. The output current for class *B* operation is 180°. The *Q*-point is located at cutoff. Output current flows for the duration of the positive alternation of the input signal. The maximum efficiency of a transistor amplifier biased class *B* is 78.5 percent.

5. Depending upon the location of the *Q*-point, the output current in a class *AB* amplifier flows for a period which is greater than 180° but less than 360°.

6. The output current of a class *C* amplifier flows for less than 180°.

7. A power amplifier is controlled by its input signal and *Q*-point location and converts DC power produced by the power supply into output signal power. The efficiency of the conversion process is important and is directly related to the class of operation.

8. Amplifier efficiency is the ratio of the output signal power to the DC input power coming from the DC power supply.

9. The difference between the DC input power and the output signal power is the power dissipated by the transistor in the form of heat. Power transistors are often mounted on heat sinks to help conduct heat away from the case.

10. Maximum power dissipation (P_D) is an important power transistor rating and is usually specified at room temperature. At higher temperatures heat cannot be conducted away from the transistor as efficiently, and the dissipation capacity decreases. Derating curves or data have to be used to determine the power dissipation capacity at elevated temperatures.

11. Harmonics are electrical signals sometimes produced by amplifiers and other active device circuits. They are often produced when the active device is operated in the nonlinear portions of the volt-ampere characteristics. A harmonic is a signal having a frequency which is either an even or odd multiple of the main (fundamental) signal frequency. The amplitude of the harmonic is inversely related to the harmonic number. This means that the second harmonic has an amplitude which is about one-half the amplitude of the fundamental signal frequency.

12. Harmonics distort the output signal of an amplifier stage. A square wave is produced if a significant number of odd harmonics are present, whereas a sawtooth-shaped wave is formed if a considerable number of both odd and even harmonics are present.

13. Push-pull amplifiers are used where it is necessary to provide more power to a load than can be supplied by a single transistor (when operated class *A*), provide a higher efficiency (when operated class *B*), or provide both higher power and efficiency (when biased class *AB*).
14. A complementary symmetry push-pull amplifier is one which does not require either an input or output transformer.
15. A single-ended audio frequency amplifier must be biased class *A* to prevent distorting the output signal. Audio frequency amplifiers may be biased class *AB* or *B* if push-pull amplifiers are used. An audio amplifier can never be biased class *C*.
16. Single-ended RF amplifiers are often biased class *C* to take advantage of the higher efficiency. A tank circuit connected to the output of the active device produces the output signal.

PRACTICE EXERCISES

1. List four ways in which power amplifiers differ from voltage amplifier stages.
2. List the four classes of amplifiers as classified by conduction period and identify the conduction period for each.
3. Why must single-ended audio frequency amplifiers by biased class *A*?
4. Why can audio frequency push-pull amplifiers be biased class *AB* or class *B*?
5. A single-ended class *A* power amplifier is connected to a 16 Ω speaker. The DC collector current (I_{CQ}) is 90 mA when connected to a 15 V V_{CC} supply. If the voltage across the speaker terminals is 2 V peak, determine the efficiency of the amplifier stage.
6. Calculate the power dissipated by the transistor in the amplifier described in exercise 5.
7. The power derating curve for a silicon power transistor is shown in Figure 18–25. What is the maximum power that can be dissipated by the transistor when the ambient temperature is 50 °C?

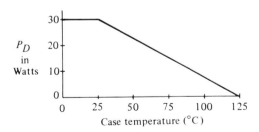

Figure 18–25

8. The output power of an amplifier connected to a motor is 50 W. If the efficiency of the amplifier is 20 percent, determine the DC input power to the amplifier.
9. If the V_{CC} supply is 20 V for the amplifier identified in exercise 8, what is the value of the Q-point collector current?

10. What is a harmonic?
11. Are harmonics desirable?
12. What is the frequency of the third harmonic of a 1.5 MHz signal?
13. What type of circuit eliminates even harmonics?
14. Describe what is meant by crossover distortion; identify its cause; and discuss what can be done to eliminate it.
15. Identify two advantages of using a class A push-pull amplifier compared with a single-ended amplifier employing the same transistor.
16. List two advantages of employing a class B push-pull amplifier compared with a single-ended amplifier utilizing the same transistor?
17. List three advantages of utilizing a class AB push-pull amplifier compared with a single-ended amplifier which uses the same transistor.
18. Draw the schematic diagram of a class A single-ended audio frequency amplifier.
19. Draw the schematic diagram of a class A push-pull AF amplifier.
20. Draw the schematic diagram of a class B push-pull AF amplifier.
21. Draw the schematic diagram of a class AB push-pull AF amplifier.
22. Draw the schematic diagram of a class C single-ended RF amplifier.
23. List two ways in which a complementary symmetry push-pull amplifier differs from a conventional push-pull amplifier.
24. Describe how a single-ended amplifier can be biased class C and yet maintain an output signal which is an undistorted replica of the input signal.

ANSWERS TO PRACTICE EXERCISES

1. Differences between power and voltage amplifiers include
   a. the active device is larger and heavier
   b. if a transistor is used as the active device, it is often mounted on a heat sink
   c. the input signal is larger in amplitude
   d. circuit efficiency is more important
   e. impedance matching is more important
2. Classification of amplifiers by conduction period include
   a. class A—360°
   b. class B—180°
   c. class AB—more than 180° but less than 360°
   d. class C—less than 180°
3. Single-ended audio frequency amplifiers must be biased class A to prevent distortion of the output signal.
4. Audio frequency push-pull amplifiers can be biased class AB or B because the output signal is reproduced by two transistors. When one transistor is cut off the other is conducting.
5. $\eta = \dfrac{P_o}{P_i} \times 100 = \dfrac{0.125}{1.35} \text{ W} \times 100 = 9.26 \text{ percent}$

   $P_i = (V_{CC})(I_{CQ}) = (15 \text{ V})(0.09 \text{ A}) = 1.35 \text{ W}$

$$P_o = \frac{(V_{pk-pk})(I_{pk-pk})}{8} = \frac{(4\text{ V})(0.25\text{ A})}{8} = 0.125\text{ W}$$

$$I_{pk-pk} = \frac{V_{pk-pk}}{load} = \frac{4\text{ V}}{16\ \Omega} = 0.25\text{ A}$$

6. $P_D = P_i - P_o = 1.35 - 0.125 = 1.225\text{ W}$

7.

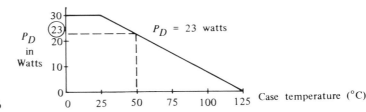

Figure 18–26

8. $\eta = \dfrac{P_0}{P_i} \times 100;\ P_i = \dfrac{P_0}{\eta} = \dfrac{50\text{ W}}{0.2} = 250\text{ W}$

9. $P_i = (V_{CC})(I_{CQ});\ I_{CQ} = \dfrac{P_i}{V_{CC}} = \dfrac{250\text{ W}}{20\text{ V}} = 12.5\text{ A}$

10. A harmonic is a sinusoidal signal which is either an odd or even multiple of the fundamental signal frequency and has an amplitude which is inversely related to the harmonic number.

11. Harmonics are usually undesirable. There are exceptions, however. If a square wave or sawtooth-shaped wave is desired, the circuits which produce these waves should be capable of generating harmonics.

12. The third harmonic of 1.5 MHz is 4.5 MHz (1.5 MHz × 3 = 4.5 MHz).

13. Push-pull amplifiers cancel even harmonics.

14. Crossover distortion is associated with class B push-pull amplifiers. It is caused by the slight delay occurring between the time the conducting transistor turns off and the nonconducting transistor turns on. Crossover distortion can be eliminated by maintaining a small forward bias on both transistors.

15. Advantages of class A push-pull operation include
   a. higher output power
   b. cancellation of even harmonics

16. Advantages of class B push-pull operation include
   a. higher efficiency
   b. cancellation of even harmonics

17. Advantages of class AB push-pull operation include
   a. higher output power
   b. higher efficiency
   c. cancellation of even harmonics

18. See Figure 18–12.
19. See Figure 18–13.
20. See Figure 18–16.
21. See Figure 18–19.

22. See Figure 18–24.
23. A complementary symmetry push-pull amplifier does not require either input or output transformers and utilizes complementary transistors.
24. An RF amplifier can be biased class C if connected to a tank circuit because of the flywheel effect. The collector current pulses provide energy to the tank circuit to overcome the losses in the circuit.

CHAPTER EXAMINATION

Choose true or false for questions 1 to 8.
1. T   F   The ninth harmonic of a signal which has a frequency of 925 Hz is 8316 Hz.
2. T   F   Single-ended RF amplifiers can be biased class C.
3. T   F   Crossover distortion is a problem associated with push-pull amplifiers which are biased class AB.
4. T   F   A square wave is formed by odd harmonics which distort the shape of the fundamental signal frequency.
5. T   F   A sawtooth wave is formed by even harmonics distorting the shape of the fundamental signal frequency.
6. T   F   The collector current in a class C operated amplifier flows for 180°.
7. T   F   Amplifier efficiency is more important in power amplifiers than it is in voltage amplifier stages.
8. T   F   An audio frequency amplifier may be biased class C if it has a tank circuit connected to its collector.
9. Draw the schematic diagram of a class B push-pull AF power amplifier.
10. A class C power amplifier has an efficiency of 85 percent. If the V_{CC} value is 30 V and the collector current (I_{CQ}) is 210 mA, calculate the output power.
11. How much power is dissipated by the transistor identified in question 10?
12. An AF power amplifier in an automobile stereo receiver is biased class A and draws 0.2 A of current. The voltage across the 4Ω speaker terminals measures 2.4 V peak-to-peak. What is the efficiency of the stage? (V_{CC} = 12.6 V)
13. List three advantages of using push-pull amplifiers compared to single-ended class A audio frequency amplifiers.
14. What class of operation is used by the push-pull amplifier shown in Figure 18–27?

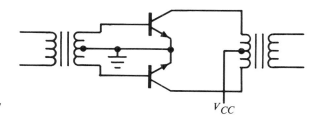

Figure 18–27 V_{CC}

15. What class of bias operation is utilized in the circuit shown in Figure 18–28?
16. What is the purpose of a heat sink?

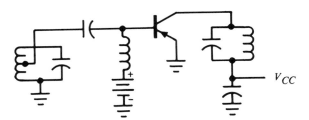

Figure 18–28

19

Oscillator Circuits

OBJECTIVES

Upon completion of this chapter you should be able to do the following:

1. Identify the two categories of oscillators.
2. List the major parts of a sinusoidal oscillator.
3. List three types of *LC* oscillators, describe the operation of each, identify the method by which feedback is accomplished in each, draw or recognize the diagrams of each, and describe the factors which determine their output frequency.
4. Draw or recognize the schematic diagram of an *RC* phase-shift oscillator and discuss how positive feedback is accomplished in the circuit.
5. Describe the piezoelectric effect.
6. Draw or recognize the schematic diagram of a crystal oscillator.
7. Draw or recognize the schematic diagrams of an astable, bistable, and mono-stable multivibrator, identify the stable states associated with each, identify the input signal requirements for each, and draw the output waveforms associated with each.
8. Describe how a sawtooth waveform can be obtained from a multivibrator.
9. Describe what a 555 IC timer is and identify two multivibrator circuits which can be constructed from the timer.

19-1 INTRODUCTION

Oscillators are circuits that produce AC and pulsating DC voltages. These types of voltages can be produced by electrical-mechanical means by using alternators and generators. This is how electrical power is generated

451

by utility companies. Electrical-mechanical methods of producing AC and pulsating DC voltages have some disadvantages. For one, they are very large and heavy. Secondly, they are physically incapable of generating the high frequency voltages required in many electronic applications. Low power AC or pulsating DC voltages ranging in frequency from almost zero to several hundred megahertz can be produced by oscillator circuits.

There are two major categories of oscillators: sinusoidal and relaxation. Sinusoidal oscillators are used to produce sinusoidal AC voltages. Nonsinusoidal AC and pulsating DC voltages are produced by relaxation oscillators. A majority of all electronics equipment employs one or both types of oscillators. Sinusoidal oscillators are used in both radio transmitters and receivers. Both types of oscillators are utilized in television transmitters and receivers. Computers, including the mini and micro types, employ a large number of relaxation oscillators. Oscillators are also used in radar systems and electronic test equipment.

19-2 PRINCIPLES OF SINUSOIDAL OSCILLATORS

A sinusoidal oscillator converts the DC power supplied to the circuit by the power supply into an AC sinusoidal signal. Oscillators look much like amplifier circuits, except that they do not require an input signal from a source or an amplifier stage to obtain an output signal. Instead, the oscillator generates its own output signal. An oscillator is made up of an amplifier, an output circuit, a feedback circuit, and an input circuit, as illustrated in Figure 19–1. A portion of the output signal is fed back in phase (positive feedback) to the input circuit to sustain oscillations. The oscillator has resistive losses, and the AC signal would soon be dampened if energy was not supplied to overcome the losses. An oscillator must not

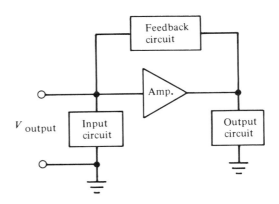

Figure 19–1 Basic parts of a sinusoidal oscillator.

only be capable of generating and sustaining a signal, but it must generate it at a rather precise frequency and maintain that frequency within defined limits.

There are scores of different types of sinusoidal oscillators. The more popular types include the *LC*, *RC* phase-shift, and crystal. These are discussed in the following sections.

19-3 *LC* OSCILLATORS

19-3.1 Introduction.   The sinusoidal voltage for these types of oscillators is developed by a parallel *LC* resonant (tank) circuit. As discussed in Chapter 18, a tank circuit is capable of producing a sinusoidal signal when it is energized, or shock excited. Energy imparted to the tank is transferred back and forth between the capacitor and inductor by a circulating current. This phenomenon is called the flywheel effect. The frequency of oscillation is determined by the values of the inductor and capacitor. The frequency of an *LC* oscillator can be determined from Equation (19–1).

$$f_r = \frac{1}{2\pi\sqrt{LC}} = \frac{0.159}{\sqrt{LC}} \qquad (19\text{–}1)$$

This is the same equation used in Chapter 10 to calculate the resonant frequency of an *LC* circuit. Energy must be applied to the tank circuit to replace that dissipated in the form of heat by the resistance of the tank circuit. This is accomplished by feeding part of the output signal back into the tank circuit. The feedback voltage must have sufficient amplitude to overcome the losses in the tank. Its polarity must be such that it aids the sinusoidal voltage developed by the tank circuit.

19-3.2 The Armstrong Oscillator.   The diagram of an Armstrong oscillator is shown in Figure 19–2. The primary winding of the transformer is called a tickler coil. The secondary winding and capacitor C_1 form the tank circuit. Capacitor C_2 prevents the base bias potential from being bypassed to ground. The RF choke prohibits the generated signal from entering the power supply. When the circuit is initially energized, the rise in collector current flowing through the tickler coil causes an expanding magnetic field to be built up about the tickler coil. The moving field cuts the secondary winding, causing a voltage to be developed across the tank circuit which shock excites it into operation. The resulting

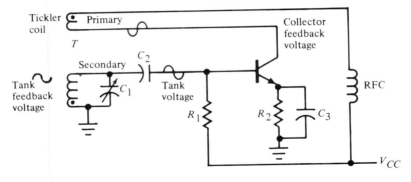

Figure 19–2 Armstrong oscillator.

sinusoidal voltage is coupled to the base of the transistor through capacitor C_2. The amplified voltage is fed back in phase to the tank circuit through the tickler coil. The feedback voltage is in phase with the tank circuit voltage by the 180° phase reversal which occurs between the base and collector of the transistor and the additional 180° phase shift occurring between the tickler coil and secondary windings of the transformer.

The output signal of an oscillator can be either directly, inductively, or capacitively coupled from either the input or output circuits of the active device. Direct coupling is seldom used, however, because it lowers the Q of the tank circuit considerably, due to the loading effect. Inductive coupling is illustrated in Figure 19–3. The signal is inductively coupled from the tank circuit to L_1.

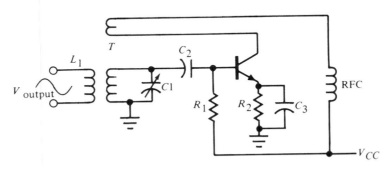

Figure 19–3 Signal inductively coupled from an Armstrong oscillator.

19-3.3 The Hartley Oscillator. This oscillator is a modification of the Armstrong type. Instead of using two separate transformer windings for the base and collector circuits, a tapped inductor is used, as shown in the circuit diagram appearing in Figure 19–4. The upper half of the in-

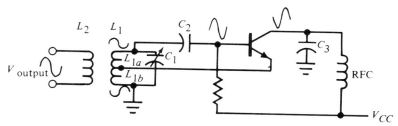

Figure 19–4 Hartley oscillator.

ductor (L_{1a}) is in the base circuit, and the lower half (L_{1b}) is in the AC collector circuit. The two halves of the inductor correspond to the secondary and primary windings, respectively, in the Armstrong oscillator. When the circuit is first turned on, the rise in collector current causes the output voltage of the transistor to decrease. This decrease in voltage (a negative pulse) is coupled through C_3 to the tank circuit, shock exciting it and causing it to oscillate. The resulting signal is coupled to the base of the transistor through C_2. It is amplified by the transistor and fed back to the tank circuit by the mutual inductance existing between L_{1a} and L_{1b}. The collector current variations created by the base signal causes the magnetic field about L_{1b} to cut L_{1a}. The feedback voltage is in-phase with the tank circuit voltage by the 180° phase shift occurring between the base and collector of the transistor and the additional 180° phase shift which exists across the opposite ends of the center-tapped inductor. The tank circuit is composed of the total inductance of L_1 ($L_{1a} + L_{1b}$) connected in parallel with C_1.

An operational amplifier can be employed as the active device in an oscillator. The diagram of an operational amplifier Hartley oscillator is shown in Figure 19–5. The frequency of the oscillator is determined by the values of L_1, L_2, and C_1.

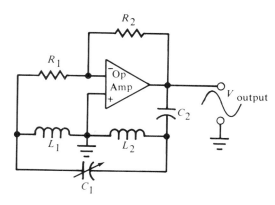

Figure 19–5 Op amp Hartley oscillator.

19-3.4 The Colpitts Oscillator. Both the Armstrong and the Hartley oscillators utilize inductive feedback to sustain oscillation. Some oscillators employ capacitive feedback. One rather common type of oscillator which uses capacitive feedback is the Colpitts. A diagram of this type of circuit appears in Figure 19–6. The frequency of oscillation is determined by the capacitance of C_1 and C_2, which is connected in parallel with the inductor. Capacitor C_2 is the feedback capacitor and is in the collector circuit while C_1 is in the base circuit. Feedback is accomplished by the coupling effect between C_2 and C_1. When the circuit is initially energized, the collector current increases, which causes the transistor output voltage to decrease. The decrease in voltage is coupled through C_4 to the tank circuit, causing that circuit to begin oscillating. The resulting sinusoidal voltage is coupled to the base through C_3. The signal is amplified and inverted 180°. An additional 180° phase shift occurs between C_1 and C_2 because of the grounded connection.

An operational amplifier can be used as the active device in a Colpitts oscillator just as it can in a Hartley. A Colpitts op amp oscillator is shown in Figure 19–7.

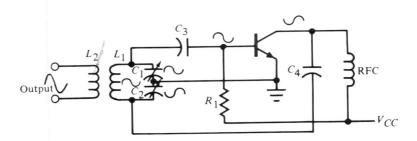

Figure 19–6   Colpitts oscillator.

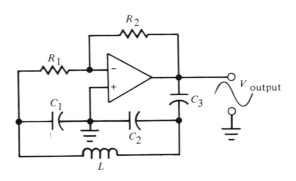

Figure 19–7   Op amp Colpitts oscillator.

19-4 THE *RC* PHASE-SHIFT OSCILLATOR

The Armstrong, Hartley, and Colpitts oscillators all use a tank circuit to generate a sinusoidal signal. Positive feedback is accomplished by the 180° phase shift between the input and output terminals of the active device and the 180° phase shift occurring between the feedback element (either an inductor or a capacitor) and the tank circuit. These circuits are often used as variable-frequency oscillators (VFOs) because their frequency can be changed by adjusting the tank capacitance. They are often used in radio receivers as local oscillators and beat frequency oscillators (BFOs).

Another type of oscillator is the *RC* phase-shift oscillator. Unlike the oscillators just discussed, this oscillator utilizes a series of *RC* networks to shift the active device output signal 180°. A resistor and capacitor connected in series form a phase-shift network due to the difference between the phase of the voltage applied across the network and the current flowing through it. The phase difference is dependent upon the reactance of the capacitor and the resistance of the resistor. A single *RC* phase-shift network is capable of shifting the phase of a signal a maximum of approximately 60°. Therefore, three phase-shift networks, connected in cascade, are required to accomplish a 180° phase shift.

The diagram of an *RC* phase-shift oscillator is shown in Figure 19–8. The feedback path is composed of three phase-shift networks: R_3C_3, R_2C_2, and R_1C_1. The feedback voltage is shifted 60° as it passes through each successive *RC* network so that the total phase shift from the collector to the base is 180°.

Unlike the other oscillators discussed so far, which utilize a tank circuit to form the signal, the feedback voltage in an *RC* phase-shift oscillator causes the conduction of the transistor to vary between saturation and cutoff. When the circuit is first energized, the rise in collector current causes the collector voltage to decrease. The decrease in voltage is shifted

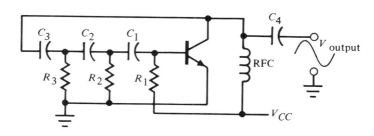

Figure 19–8   *RC* phase-shift oscillator.

180° by the *RC* phase-shift network and appears at the base as a positive voltage, causing the transistor to conduct more heavily. The resulting increase in collector current causes the collector voltage to decrease even further and the base voltage to become more positive. This process continues until the transistor goes into saturation. At this point the collector current is no longer increasing, and the voltage fed back to the base is less positive. This causes the collector current to decrease and the collector voltage to increase. The increase in collector voltage is shifted 180° as it passes through the *RC* phase-shift network and appears as a negative potential at the base, causing the transistor to conduct even less heavily. This process continues until the transistor reaches cutoff. At this time the collector current and the feedback voltage are both zero. One cycle of a sinusoidal signal has been produced. The transistor begins conducting because of the forward bias applied to the base by R_1, and the process repeats itself. The transistor must be biased class *A* or class *AB* for it to begin conducting again after it has reached cutoff. The frequency of operation is determined by the size of the resistors and capacitors used in the phase-shift network.

19-5 CRYSTAL OSCILLATORS

It is important that oscillators maintain their correct frequency. Gradual changes in oscillator frequency is called drift. All of the oscillators discussed so far drift somewhat. This is caused by such things as the coils forming the inductor in the tank circuit expanding and changing value because of the heat produced as current flows through them. Changes in the circuit variables of the circuit to which the oscillator is connected may also cause the oscillator to change frequency. In some applications frequency drift is not too critical, while in others it is essential that the oscillator maintain its correct frequency. For example, in AM broadcast transmitters, the oscillator frequency is not allowed to drift more than 20 Hz on either side of the carrier frequency. Where it is important that a signal frequency not drift, a crystal oscillator is used.

Some crystalline materials, such as quartz, exhibit the piezoelectric effect. If the crystal is caused to mechanically vibrate an AC voltage is developed. The converse of this principle is also true. When an AC voltage is applied across the crystal, it will vibrate. The vibrations will slowly become dampened and disappear after the voltage has been removed. If an AC potential, such as a feedback voltage, is applied to the crystal and is high enough in amplitude to overcome the inertial losses, the crystal will vibrate constantly, producing a continuous train of sinusoidal voltage waveforms.

Most crystals are temperature dependent. If the ambient temperature changes, the resonant frequency of the crystal will change. Where highly stable frequencies are required, such as in radio and television broadcast transmitters, microwave transmitters, and radar transmitters, the crystal oscillator is often mounted in an oven where a constant temperature can be maintained.

There are a number of different kinds of crystal oscillator circuits. The crystal is operated at its resonant frequency and takes the place of the tank circuit. A typical crystal oscillator circuit is shown in Figure 19–9. This particular circuit is called a Pierce oscillator. Capacitors C_1 and C_2 form a voltage divider network, with the voltage appearing across C_2 being the positive feedback potential applied to the crystal to maintain oscillation.

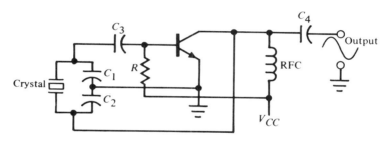

Figure 19–9 Pierce oscillator.

19-6 RELAXATION OSCILLATORS

19-6.1 Introduction. Relaxation oscillators are the other category of oscillators. These circuits provide an output voltage which is nonsinusoidal in shape and have numerous applications in areas such as computers, television, radar, and telemetry. There are several types of relaxation oscillators. Some of the more common types are discussed in the following sections.

19-6.2 The Astable Multivibrator. Multivibrators are a common type of relaxation oscillator. These circuits are widely used in computers and other digital equipment. They are also often found in other equipment such as oscilloscopes, television receivers, and radar. There are three types of multivibrators: astable, bistable, and monostable.

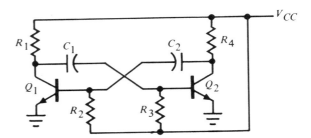

Figure 19–10 Astable multivibrator.

The astable, often called a free-running multivibrator, is made up of two *RC*-coupled amplifier stages which are cross-coupled to one another as shown in Figure 19–10. The output of each transistor provides the input to the other. The collector and base voltages associated with the circuit are shown in Figure 19–11. The voltages for both transistors are identical but are inverted from one another. The *RC* time constant of R_3C_1 and R_2C_2 determine the length of time each transistor is cut off and the frequency of operation. If equal values of resistors and capacitors are used in both *RC* networks, both transistors conduct and are cut off for equal periods of time and the output waveform is symmetrical. Occasionally, the circuit is designed to allow one transistor to remain cut off longer than the other and the output is nonsymmetrical, as illustrated in Figure 19–12.

The output voltage can be taken from the collector of either transistor and will be square or rectangular in shape, as depicted in Figures 19–11 and 19–12, respectively. If a sawtooth waveform is desired, a capacitor (C_3) can be connected from the collector of one transistor to ground, as shown in Figure 19–13. The capacitor charges through R_4 to the V_{CC} value

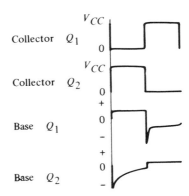

Figure 19–11 Voltages associated with an astable multivibrator.

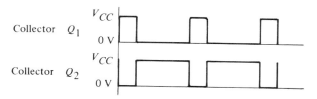

Figure 19–12 Collector voltages for a nonsymmetrical astable multivibrator.

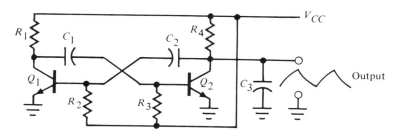

Figure 19–13 Obtaining a sawtooth waveform from an astable multivibrator.

during the time Q_2 is cut off. When Q_2 conducts, the capacitor discharges through the transistor. The R_4C_3 time constant is long compared to the time that Q_2 conducts. The capacitor has time to charge only to a partial value of V_{CC}, resulting in a linear charging slope.

19-6.3 The Bistable Multivibrator. The astable multivibrator has no stable state. Instead, the circuit oscillates between the on-off states (Q_1 on and Q_2 off, and Q_2 on and Q_1 off). The circuit is often used as a square or rectangular wave generator. Another popular relaxation oscillator is the bistable multivibrator. This circuit has two stable states (Q_1 on and Q_2 off, or Q_2 on and Q_1 off). It will remain in either one of the two states until an input sync, or trigger, pulse is applied and the state changes. The circuit remains in the new state until another trigger pulse is received and the circuit returns to its original state. Thus, the circuit switches from one state to another each time a trigger pulse is applied to an alternate transistor. The circuit is often called a flip-flop—a name which aptly describes its action. The diagram of a bistable multivibrator appears in Figure 19–14. Although bistable multivibrators are classified as a relaxation oscillator, they do not free-run, or oscillate, on their own accord. They change states only when a trigger pulse is applied. These circuits are frequently used as high-speed switches, especially in digital applications.

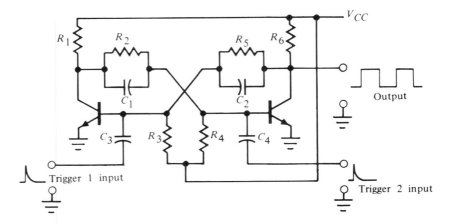

Figure 19–14   Bistable multivibrator.

19-6.4 The Monostable Multivibrator.   Unlike the astable multivibrator, which has no stable state, and the bistable multivibrator, which has two stable states, the monostable multivibrator has but one stable state. In this circuit one transistor is normally on and the other off. With the application of a trigger pulse, the states change. The normally on transistor goes into cutoff, and the normally off transistor begins conducting. This condition exists for only a short period of time, and the circuit reverts back to its original condition and remains there until another trigger pulse is received. The circuit is sometimes called a one-shot multivibrator.

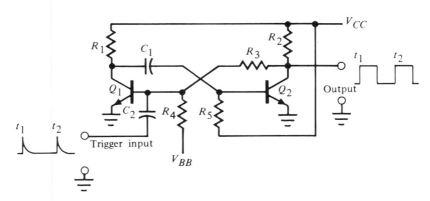

Figure 19–15   Monostable multivibrator.

The schematic diagram of a monostable multivibrator appears in Figure 19–15. This circuit is often used for wave-forming applications.

19-7 THE 555 IC TIMER

The multivibrators just discussed are connected from discrete devices. Multivibrators are also available in integrated circuit format. Several of these, along with their applications, will be discussed in Part Three. Timing is important in many different types of electronic systems. In equipment such as radar and computers, where many different events occur at controlled times, timing pulses are used to ensure proper sequencing of the required operations. Timing pulses—sometimes called synchronizing, trigger, or clock pulses—can be generated by astable multivibrators. In addition, there are several different types of integrated circuits designed and manufactured for clock, or timing, purposes. One of the most popular of these is the 555 IC timer.

The 555 IC timer is a monolithic integrated circuit which can be used as either an astable or a monostable multivibrator. It produces a square wave which has both an accurate and stable frequency. Available in either dual-in-line or metal can packages, the device requires only a V_{CC} supply and external resistors and capacitors to become operational. The diagram of the timer connected as an astable multivibrator appears in Figure 19–16. The RC time constant of the external resistors and capacitors determines the output frequency. The timer is shown connected as a monostable multivibrator in Figure 19–17.

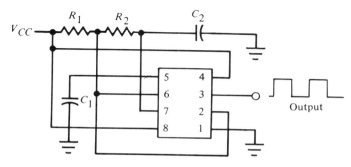

Figure 19–16 555 IC timer connected as an astable multivibrator.

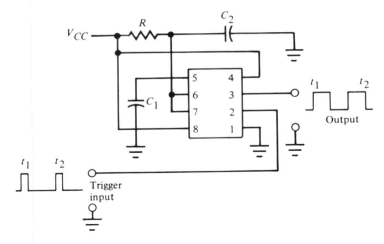

Figure 19–17 555 IC timer connected as a monostable multivibrator.

SUMMARY

1. There are two categories of oscillators: sinusoidal and relaxation.
2. Sinusoidal oscillators produce voltages that have sinusoidal waveforms. Relaxation oscillators produce pulsating DC voltages that are square or rectangular in shape. If the output is taken across a capacitor, a relaxation oscillator will produce a sawtooth, or ramp, waveform.
3. Sinusoidal oscillators are made up of an active device which serves as an amplifier (and often times as a switch), a feedback circuit, an input circuit, and an output circuit.
4. A sinusoidal oscillator generates its own signal. Positive feedback from the amplifier is required to overcome energy losses in the circuit to sustain oscillation.
5. There are several different types of sinusoidal oscillators. These can be classified as those which utilize an LC tank circuit to produce the sine wave, those which employ an RC network to achieve feedback, and those which use crystals.
6. Three commonly used LC oscillators include the Armstrong, Hartley, and Colpitts. Positive feedback is achieved in the Armstrong and Hartley oscillators from the phase inversion occurring between the input and output circuits of the active device and the additional 180° phase shift between two inductors or the primary and secondary windings of a transformer connected between the input and output circuits. Feedback in the Colpitts oscillator is accomplished by the normal phase inversion that occurs between the input and output of the active device and through capacitive coupling between the input and output circuits.
7. The frequency of oscillation of an LC oscillator depends upon the amount of inductance and capacitance in the tank circuit. The tank circuit generates the sinusoidal voltage.

8. *LC* oscillators are often used as variable-frequency oscillators (VFOs). If the capacitor in the tank circuit is variable, the frequency can be changed by varying the value of the capacitance.

9. The *RC* phase-shift oscillator is another popular type of sinusoidal oscillator. In this circuit the conduction rate of the active device forms the sine wave. Positive feedback is accomplished by the phase inversion occurring between the input and output of the active device and the 180° phase shift produced by the *RC* network. The *RC* feedback network is often made up of three separate *RC* branches. Each branch shifts the feedback signal 60°.

10. Certain crystals, such as quartz, exhibit the piezoelectric effect. If mechanical pressure is applied to two opposite surface areas of the crystal, an electrical potential is developed across the other two surfaces. If the crystal is caused to alternately become compressed and stretched, an AC voltage is developed. Conversely, if an AC voltage is applied across two opposite sides, the other two sides will alternately compress and stretch.

11. A crystal can be substituted for the tank circuit in a crystal oscillator circuit.

12. Multivibrators are a popular type of relaxation oscillator. There are three types of these circuits, each having its own unique operating characteristics. They are the astable, bistable, and monostable. Multivibrators are made up of two amplifier stages; the output of each is coupled to the input of the other.

13. The astable multivibrator has no stable state. It continually changes from one state to the other. One transistor conducts and then the other. The *RC* time constant of the coupling network determines the frequency of operation.

14. The output waveform can be taken from the collector of either transistor in an astable multivibrator and is square or rectangular in shape. The waveform has a sawtooth shape if the output voltage is taken across a capacitor connected from the collector of one transistor to ground.

15. A bistable multivibrator has two stable states. In either state, one transistor conducts and the other is cut off. It remains in this condition until a trigger pulse is applied and the circuit changes states. The conducting transistor goes into cutoff, and the cutoff transistor begins conducting. The circuit remains in this condition until the next trigger pulse is received. Trigger pulses are applied to alternate transistors.

16. A monostable multivibrator has a single stable state. One transistor is normally on and the other off. With the application of a trigger pulse, the circuit changes states for a short period of time and then reverts back to its original state. It remains in this condition until the next trigger pulse is received.

17. The 555 IC timer is a monolithic IC which can be connected and operated as either an astable or monostable multivibrator. When connected as an astable multivibrator, the output voltage has a frequency which is very stable. The circuit is often used as a timing generator.

PRACTICE EXERCISES

1. Identify the two categories of oscillators.
2. What kinds of waveforms are associated with the oscillators identified in exercise 1?

3. Identify the major parts of a sinusoidal oscillator.
4. What type of feedback is utilized in a sinusoidal oscillator?
5. Why is feedback employed in a sinusoidal oscillator?
6. Identify three kinds of LC oscillators.
7. How is the sine wave formed in an LC oscillator?
8. What determines the frequency of an LC oscillator?
9. How is positive feedback accomplished in an Armstrong oscillator?
10. What is the major difference between the Hartley oscillator and the Armstrong oscillator?
11. What are the main differences between a Hartley and a Colpitts oscillator?
12. Draw the schematic diagram of an Armstrong oscillator.
13. Draw the circuit diagram of an op amp Colpitts oscillator.
14. Draw the schematic diagram of an RC phase-shift oscillator which employs a bipolar junction transistor.
15. How is positive feedback accomplished in an RC phase-shift oscillator?
16. How is the sine wave formed in an RC phase-shift oscillator?
17. What is the piezoelectric effect?
18. Draw the schematic diagram of a Pierce oscillator.
19. What is a relaxation oscillator?
20. Identify three kinds of relaxation oscillators.
21. Draw the schematic diagram of an astable multivibrator.
22. Identify the number of stable states associated with an astable multivibrator.
23. What determines the frequency of operation of an astable multivibrator?
24. Draw the schematic diagram of a bistable multivibrator.
25. Identify the number of stable states associated with a bistable multivibrator.
26. How does the bistable multivibrator change states?
27. Draw the schematic diagram of a monostable multivibrator.
28. Identify the number of stable states associated with a monostable multivibrator.
29. How does the monostable multivibrator change states?
30. How can a sawtooth waveform be obtained from an astable multivibrator?
31. What is a 555 IC timer?

ANSWERS TO PRACTICE EXERCISES

1. The two categories of oscillators are the sinusoidal and relaxation types.
2. Sinusoidal waveforms are associated with sinusoidal oscillators. Relaxation oscillators produce square, rectangular, or sawtooth (ramp) waveforms.
3. A sinusoidal oscillator is made up of an active device, a feedback circuit, an input circuit, and an output circuit.
4. Positive feedback is utilized in sine wave oscillators.
5. Feedback is used to overcome resistance losses in an oscillator circuit.
6. Three kinds of LC oscillators include the Armstrong, the Hartley, and the Colpitts.
7. The sine wave is generated by the LC tank circuit in an LC oscillator.
8. The values of the capacitor and inductor forming the tank circuit determine the frequency of oscillation.

9. Positive feedback is accomplished by the phase inversion which occurs between the input and output of the active device and the 180° phase shift occurring between the tickler coil (transformer primary) and tank circuit inductor (transformer secondary). The energy is coupled from the output to the input by inductive feedback.

10. The Hartley oscillator employs a tapped inductor or two series-connected inductors with a tap at the common connection. The Armstrong oscillator utilizes a transformer.

11. A Hartley oscillator utilizes a tapped inductor and inductive feedback, whereas a Colpitts uses two series-connected capacitors with a tap at the common connection and capacitive feedback.

12. See Figure 19–3.

13. See Figure 19–7.

14. See Figure 19–8.

15. Positive feedback in an RC phase-shift oscillator is accomplished by the 180° phase shift occurring between the input and output terminals of the active device and the 180° phase shift produced by the RC network in the input circuit. The RC network is usually made up of three RC branches, each of which shifts the feedback signal 60°.

16. The sine wave is formed by the intensity at which the active device conducts. The Q-point travels between cutoff and saturation at a sinusoidal rate.

17. The piezoelectric effect is a phenomenon associated with some crystals. If an external mechanical force is applied to two sides of the crystal so that it is alternately stretched and compressed, an AC potential is developed across the other two sides. On the other hand, if an AC voltage is applied across two sides of the crystal, the other two sides will alternately stretch and compress.

18. See Figure 19–9.

19. A relaxation oscillator is a circuit that produces square, rectangular, or sawtooth (ramp) voltage waveforms.

20. Three kinds of relaxation oscillators include the astable multivibrator, bistable multivibrator, and monostable multivibrator.

21. See Figure 19–10.

22. An astable multivibrator has no stable states. Both transistors alternately switch on and off continuously.

23. The RC time constant of the coupling networks determines the length of time the nonconducting stage is turned off, which, in turn, determines the frequency.

24. See Figure 19–14.

25. The bistable multivibrator has two stable states.

26. The bistable multivibrator remains in one state—one transistor conducting and the other turned off, until a trigger pulse is received. The circuit changes states and remains in that state until the next trigger pulse is applied. Trigger pulses must be applied to alternate transistors unless a steering circuit is used.

27. See Figure 19–15.

28. A monostable multivibrator has one stable state.

29. The monostable multivibrator has a normally on and normally off transistor.

The circuit operates in this condition until a trigger pulse is received. The circuit changes states for a short period of time and then goes back to its original state and remains there until the next trigger pulse arrives.

30. A sawtooth waveform can be obtained from an astable multivibrator by connecting a capacitor between the collector and ground and taking the output voltage from across the capacitor. The capacitor charges during the time the transistor is cut off and discharges during the transistor conducting time. The charging time constant is long compared to the discharging time and a waveform is produced which is sawtooth in shape.

31. A 555 IC timer is a monolithic IC which is fabricated to be used as a trigger generator. The circuit can be operated as either an astable or multistable multivibrator to produce square, rectangular, or sawtooth voltages.

CHAPTER EXAMINATION

Choose true or false for questions 1 to 13.

1. T F   The Hartley oscillator utilizes inductive feedback.
2. T F   An oscillator crystal is equivalent to a resonant circuit.
3. T F   The Pierce oscillator is a type of crystal oscillator.
4. T F   The astable multivibrator has one stable state.
5. T F   The piezoelectric effect, as exhibited by oscillator crystals, is present in doped silicon crystals.
6. T F   The 555 timer is a monolithic IC primarily used to generate very stable sinusoidal voltage waveforms.
7. T F   The RC phase-shift oscillator produces a sawtooth (ramp) voltage waveform.
8. T F   The Colpitts oscillator utilizes capacitive feedback.
9. T F   The bistable multivibrator has two stable states.
10. T F   The frequency of an LC oscillator is determined by the RC time constant of the base biasing resistor and coupling capacitor.
11. T F   The Colpitts, Pierce, and Hartley oscillators all employ an LC tank circuit to generate the sine wave.
12. T F   The sine wave in an RC phase-shift oscillator is generated by the charging and discharging action of the capacitors in the feedback circuit.
13. T F   The monostable multivibrator has a single stable state.
14. Draw the schematic diagram of a BJT Hartley oscillator.
15. Draw the schematic diagram of a BJT Colpitts oscillator.
16. Draw the diagram of a bistable multivibrator circuit.
17. Describe how positive feedback is accomplished in an RC phase-shift oscillator.
18. List the major parts of a sinusoidal oscillator.
19. Identify the two categories of oscillators.
20. Describe how a sawtooth waveform can be generated by a relaxation oscillator.

20

Number Systems and Binary Codes

OBJECTIVES

Upon completion of this chapter you should be able to do the following:

1. Differentiate between analog and binary voltages.
2. Identify the number base for the binary, decimal, octal, and hexadecimal numbering systems.
3. Add and subtract binary numbers.
4. Convert from decimal numbers to binary numbers and vice versa.
5. Convert from octal numbers to decimal numbers and vice versa.
6. Convert from hexadecimal numbers to decimal numbers and vice versa.
7. Convert from octal numbers to binary numbers and vice versa.
8. Convert from hexadecimal numbers to binary numbers and vice versa.
9. Define the term *byte*.
10. Determine the maximum decimal number which can be expressed by a given binary number.
11. Compute the number of different binary numbers (words) which can be expressed by a given binary word length.
12. Convert from binary coded decimal (BCD) numbers to decimal numbers and vice versa.
13. Identify five codes which are used in various digital systems.
14. Describe the purpose of an alphanumeric code.
15. Subtract one binary number from another using the one's complement.
16. Subtract one binary number from another using the two's complement.

20-1 INTRODUCTION

Binary, or digital circuits, form the third general classification of circuits, the other two being passive and linear. Passive and linear circuits have been discussed in Parts One and Two of the book, respectively. Material in Part Three deals with some of the more commonly used techniques, devices, and circuits unique to digital electronic systems.

Digital circuits are newer than the passive and linear types and were first used in digital computers whose development began in the late 1940s. Only those engineers and technicians that designed and repaired computers had any real need for extensive knowledge in digital circuits for many years afterward. This has been changed with the advent of the integrated circuit and the microprocessor. Digital techniques have replaced many functions previously performed by linear circuits and even mechanical methods.

The microprocessor is a special kind of integrated circuit. It contains the entire central processing unit (CPU) of a computer. The microprocessor is revolutionizing not only the electronics industry, but other entire businesses and industries as well. Microprocessor chips are being used in the development of a whole new generation of "smart" machines. They are used in automated assembly processes, automobiles, farm machinery, and office machines, among other applications. In addition, they form the heart of the microprocessor and robot, two new technologies which are having a pronounced effect on society and the work world.

These changes have made it necessary for many engineers, technicians, and service persons who work in areas other than traditional electronics to become familiar with electronic techniques in the digital area. There are fewer different types of digital circuits and, for the most part, they are easier to understand than many of the linear types.

One reason that digital circuits are simpler is the nature of the signal voltages employed. Analog voltages are utilized in linear circuits. An analog voltage is one whose amplitude can have an infinite number of values with respect to time. Some examples of analog voltages appear in Figure 20–1. Digital voltages, on the other hand, have only two amplitude levels—a low level and a high level. These are sometimes referred to as the zero and one levels, respectively. The zero level can represent any voltage magnitude. The one level is represented by a voltage higher in amplitude than that of the zero level. Some examples of digital voltages

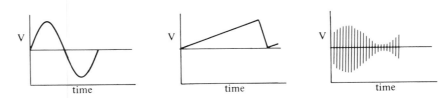

Figure 20–1 Examples of analog voltages.

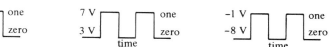

Figure 20–2   Examples of digital voltages.

appear in Figure 20–2. Digital voltages are sometimes called binary voltages since there are only two levels.

20-2 THE DECIMAL NUMBERING SYSTEM

Numbers are used by all of us in our day-to-day living. There are several different numbering systems used throughout the world. The decimal, or base 10, system is the one used by most industrialized countries. This numbering system consists of 10 separate numbers (0 to 9). An individual number is called a digit. Two or more digits are used to denote numbers which are larger than nine. Individual digits represent a particular weight by nature of their position. As indicated below, succeeding digits to the left of the unit's position ($\times 10^0$) increase by a power of 10. Succeeding digits to the right of the unit's position decrease by a power of 10.

$$10^n + \cdots + 10^3 + 10^2 + 10^1 + 10^0 + 10^{-1} + 10^{-2} + \cdots + 10^{-n}$$

A multidigit decimal number has a magnitude which is equal to the sum of the individual digit magnitudes and their positional weights, as indicated in Example 20–1. Subscripts are sometimes used to identify the base of the numbering system being used.

Example 20–1   Decimal notational system

Problem
Place the number 3521.25_{10} in power-of-10 format and add the individual magnitudes.

Solution
$3 \times 10^3 + 5 \times 10^2 + 2 \times 10^1 + 1 \times 10^0 + 2 \times 10^{-1} + 5 \times 10^{-2}$
$= 3000.00$
$\ \ 500.00$
$\ \ \ \ 20.00$
$\ \ \ \ \ \ 1.00$
$\ \ \ \ \ \ \ \ .20$
$\underline{\ \ \ \ \ \ \ \ .05}$
$\ 3521.25$

20-3 THE BINARY NUMBERING SYSTEM

Although we use the decimal system constantly, as mentioned previously, there are other numbering systems. Digital circuits use the binary system. This system has only two numbers—zero and one—and is sometimes called the base-two numbering system. This is an easy system to adapt to electronic circuits. The presence (or absence) of a particular voltage level can represent a zero while the presence of a higher-amplitude voltage can represent a one level. Like the decimal numbering system, additional digits (often called bits) are used to represent binary numbers which are greater than one. Each binary digit represents a particular power of two by nature of its position:

$$2^n + \cdots + 2^3 + 2^2 + 2^1 + 2^0 + 2^{-1} + 2^{-2} + \cdots + 2^{-n}$$

Digit magnitudes increase by a power of two for successive digits to the left of the unit's position. Magnitudes decrease by a power of two for successive digits to the right of the units position. Each digit for the binary number 1101.11 represents a specific binary weight, as shown in Example 20–2.

Binary numbers can be added and subtracted in much the same fashion as decimal numbers. The rules for adding binary numbers appear in Table 20–1.

The rules for subtracting binary numbers are shown in Table 20–2. Notice that the rules for adding and subtracting binary numbers are similar to those for subtracting decimal numbers.

Example 20–2   Binary notational system

Problem
Place the number 1101.11_2 in power-of-two format and add the individual magnitudes.

Solution
$1 \times 2^3 + 1 \times 2^2 + 0 \times 2^1 + 1 \times 2^0 + 1 \times 2^{-1} + 1 \times 2^{-2}$
$= 1000.00$
$\ 100.00$
$\ \ 00.00$
$\ \ \ 1.00$
$\ \ \ \ .10$
$\ \ \ \ .01$
$\overline{ 1101.11}$

TABLE 20–1   Rules for Adding Binary Digits

Digits	Sum	Carry
$0 + 0 =$	0	0
$1 + 0 =$	1	0
$0 + 1 =$	1	0
$1 + 1 =$	0	1

TABLE 20–2   Rules for Subtracting Binary Digits

Digits	Difference	Borrow
$0 - 0 =$	0	0
$1 - 0 =$	1	0
$0 - 1 =$	1	1
$1 - 1 =$	0	0

20-4 CONVERTING BINARY NUMBERS INTO DECIMAL NUMBERS

Since digital circuits utilize binary numbers and we use decimal numbers, it is necessary to know how to convert from the binary to the decimal numbering system if one is going to understand how digital systems operate. This procedure is rather simple and merely involves adding together the positional weights of the individual binary digits. Consider the binary number shown in Example 20–3. When the weights of the digits are added together, a decimal sum of 23.75 is obtained. A second binary number and its decimal equivalent is shown in Example 20–4.

Example 20–3   Converting from a binary to a decimal number

Problem
Convert 10111.11_2 to an equivalent decimal number.

Solution
10111.11_2
$= 1 \times 2^4 + 0 \times 2^3 + 1 \times 2^2 + 1 \times 2^1 + 1 \times 2^0 + 1 \times 2^{-1} + 1 \times 2^{-2}$
$= 16 + 0 + 4 + 2 + 1 + \frac{1}{2} + \frac{1}{4}$
$= 23.75_{10}$

Example 20–4 Converting from a binary to a decimal number

Problem
Convert 1101101.101_2 to an equivalent decimal number.

Solution
1101101.101_2
$= 1 \times 2^6 + 1 \times 2^5 + 0 \times 2^4 + 1 \times 2^3 + 1 \times 2^2 + 0 \times 2^1 + 1 \times 2^0 + 1 \times 2^{-1} + 0 \times 2^{-2} + 1 \times 2^{-3}$
$= 64 + 32 + 0 + 8 + 4 + 0 + 1 + \frac{1}{2} + \frac{0}{4} + \frac{1}{8}$
$= 109.625_{10}$

20-5 CONVERTING DECIMAL NUMBERS INTO BINARY NUMBERS

Decimal integers are converted into binary integers by successive division by two. Decimal fractions are converted into binary fractions by successive multiplication by two. As illustrated in Example 20–5, the decimal number 53 is equal to binary 110101. Notice that the remainders of each division operation form the individual binary digits. The first division operation forms the least significant bit (LSB). The quotient of the last division operation represents the most significant bit (MSB). Note that the division process continues until the last quotient is equal to one.

The process of converting from a decimal to a binary fraction is illustrated in Example 20–6. Successive multiplication by two is used to convert the decimal fraction into its binary equivalent. The integer to the left of the radix point of the first multiplication operation becomes the most significant bit. The multiplication process continues for the desired number of radix places. A decimal number containing both integers and fractions is converted into a binary equivalent in Example 20–7.

Example 20–5 Converting from a decimal to a binary number

Problem
Convert 53_{10} to an equivalent binary number.

Solution

$$
\begin{array}{ccccc}
\dfrac{26}{2\overline{)53}} & \dfrac{13}{2\overline{)26}} & \dfrac{6}{2\overline{)13}} & \dfrac{3}{2\overline{)6}} & \dfrac{\boxed{1}}{2\overline{)3}}\ \text{MSB} \\[4pt]
\underline{52} & \underline{26} & \underline{12} & \underline{6} & \underline{2} \\
\text{LSB}\ \ ① & ⓪ & ① & ⓪ & ①
\end{array}
$$

Thus, $53_{10} = 110101_2$

Example 20–6   Converting from a decimal to a binary fraction

Problem
Convert 0.63_{10} to an equivalent binary number.

Solution

	0.63	0.26	0.52
	2	2	2
MSB	⎡1⎤.26	⓪.52	①.04

Therefore, $0.63_{10} = 0.101_2$

Example 20–7   Converting from a decimal to a binary number

Problem
Convert 50.125_{10} into an equivalent binary number.

Solution

$$\begin{array}{ccccc}
25 & 12 & 6 & 3 & \boxed{1} \\
2\overline{)50} & 2\overline{)25} & 2\overline{)12} & 2\overline{)6} & 2\overline{)3} \\
50 & 24 & 12 & 6 & 2 \\
⓪ & ① & ⓪ & ⓪ & ①
\end{array}$$

0.125	0.250	0.5
2	2	2
⎡0⎤.250	⓪.500	①.0

Therefore, $50.125_{10} = 110010.001_2$

20–6 THE OCTAL NUMBERING SYSTEM

20-6.1 Introduction.   Another numbering system which is used in some digital equipment is the octal, or base-eight, system. This system utilizes eight numbers (0 to 7). Like the decimal and binary systems, additional digits, or bits, are used to represent numbers which are greater than seven as illustrated below.

0,1,2,3,4,5,6,7,10,11,12,13,14,15,16,17,20,21,22,23,24,25,26,27,30,31,$\cdots$

20-6.2 Converting Octal Numbers into Equivalent Decimal Numbers.   Octal numbers can be converted into decimal numbers in the same fashion as binary numbers. As shown below, each octal bit represents a particular power of eight by virtue of its position.

$$8^n + \cdots + 8^3 + 8^2 + 8^1 + 8^0 \ + \ 8^{-1} + 8^{-2}$$

An octal number is converted into an equivalent decimal number by summing the weights of the individual digits, as illustrated in Example 20–8.

Example 20–8 Converting from an octal to a decimal number

Problem
Convert 472.21_8 into an equivalent decimal number.

Solution

$$472.21_8$$
$$= 4 \times 8^2 + 7 \times 8^1 + 2 \times 8^0 + 2 \times 8^{-1} + 1 \times 8^{-2}$$
$$= (4)(64) + (7)(8) + (2)(1) + \frac{2}{8} + \frac{1}{64}$$
$$= 256 + 56 + 2 + 0.25 + 0.0156 = 314.2656$$

Therefore, $472.21_8 = 314.2656_{10}$

20-6.3 Converting Decimal Numbers into Equivalent Octal Numbers. Successive division by eight is used to convert decimal integers into octal integers. To convert decimal fractions into octal fractions, successive multiplication by eight is used. This process is illustrated in Example 20–9. Notice that this procedure is identical to that of converting decimals into equivalent binary numbers except that division and multiplication by eight is used instead of by two.

20-6.4 Converting Octal Numbers into Equivalent Binary Numbers. Both octal and binary numbers are used in some digital systems.

Example 20–9 Converting from a decimal to an octal number

Problem
Convert 368.23_{10} into an equivalent octal number.

Solution

$$
\begin{array}{ccccc}
\dfrac{46}{8\sqrt{368}} & \boxed{5}\; \\
8\sqrt{368} & 8\sqrt{46} & 0.23 & 0.84 & 0.72 \\
\underline{368} & \underline{40} & \underline{8} & \underline{8} & \underline{8} \\
\textcircled{0} & \textcircled{6} & \textcircled{1}.84 & \textcircled{6}.72 & \textcircled{5}.76
\end{array}
$$

Therefore, $368.23_{10} = 560.165_8$

It is easy to convert from octal to binary numbers. As shown in Example 20–10, this process merely involves converting each digit of the octal number into an equivalent three-bit binary number. A three-bit binary number is used since the highest binary number which can be counted using a three-bit binary number is 111 or octal 7. This is the highest single digit octal number, of course.

Example 20–10   Converting from an octal to a binary number

Problem
Convert 215.73_8 into an equivalent binary number.

Solution
   2   1   5 .   7   3
010 001 101. 111 011
Thus, $215.73_8 = 10001101.111011_2$

20-6.5 Converting Binary Numbers into Equivalent Octal Numbers.   This conversion process is the opposite of that just described. The binary number is divided into groups of three bits and the equivalent octal number is used to replace each three bit grouping, as indicated in Example 20–11.

Example 20–11   Converting from a binary to an octal number

Problem
Convert 110101111001.101011_2 into an equivalent octal number.

Solution
110 101 111 001. 101 011
 6   5   7   1 .   5   3
Therefore, $110101111001.101011_2 = 6571.53_8$

20-7 THE HEXADECIMAL NUMBERING SYSTEM

20-7.1 Introduction.   A popular numbering system used in many computers and microprocessor-based systems is the hexadecimal, which utilizes a base of 16. As illustrated below, both numbers and letters are used. Numbers 0 through 9 are used to represent the first 10 digits. Letters *A* through *F* are employed to represent the next six digits.

$$0,1,2,3,4,5,6,7,8,9,A,B,C,D,E,F,10,11,12,13,14,15,16,17,18,19,1A,1B,$$
$$1C,1D,1E,1F,20,21,22,23,24,25,26,27,28,29,2A,2B, \ldots$$

20-7.2 Converting a Hexadecimal Number into an Equivalent Decimal Number.

Hexadecimal numbers are converted into equivalent decimal numbers in the same fashion as binary and octal numbers except that the individual digits represent a base of 16. This process is illustrated in Example 20–12.

Example 20–12   Converting from a hexadecimal to a decimal number

Problem
Convert $B4C3.B4_{16}$ into an equivalent decimal number.

Solution
$B4C3.B4_{16}$
$= 11 \times 16^3 + 4 \times 16^2 + 12 \times 16^1 + 3 \times 16^0 + 11 \times 16^{-1} + 4 \times 16^{-2}$
$= 45056 + 1024 + 192 + 3 + 0.6875 + 0.0156$
$= 46275.7031$
Therefore, $B4C3.B4_{16} = 46275.7031_{10}$

20-7.3 Converting a Decimal Number into an Equivalent Hexadecimal Number.

Decimal integers are converted to hexadecimal numbers by successive division by 16. Fractions are converted by successive multiplication by 16, as shown in Example 20–13.

Example 20–13   Converting from a decimal to a hexadecimal number

Problem
Convert 209.85_{10} into an equivalent hexadecimal number.

Solution

```
      13
16√209      0.85     0.60     0.60
    16        16       16       16
    49       510      360      360
    48        85       60       60
     1      1360      960      960
           13.60     9.60     9.60
```

Since $13 = D$
Then, $209.85_{10} = D1.D99_{16}$

20-7.4 Converting a Hexadecimal Number into an Equivalent Binary Number. An equivalent four-bit binary number is used to replace each digit in the hexadecimal number, as indicated in Example 20–14. A four-bit number is used since the maximum binary count of a four-bit number is 1111 or decimal 15. Because the maximum single digit number in the hexadecimal is F (15_{10}), any hexadecimal number can be replaced with a four-bit binary number.

Example 20–14 Converting from a hexadecimal to a binary number

Problem
Convert $51D6.B3_{16}$ into an equivalent binary number.

Solution
```
   5    1    D    6  .  B    3
 0101 0001 1101 0110. 1011 0011
```
$= 101000111010110.10110011$
or, $51D6.B3_{16} = 101000111010110.10110011_2$

20-7.5 Converting a Binary Number into an Equivalent Hexadecimal Number. The binary bits are placed in groups of four, as shown in Example 20–15. Notice that the groups are formed at the radix point. Groups formed to the left of the radix point are the integers and those formed to the right are the fractions. Additional zeros can be added to complete the four-bit numbers forming the most significant and least significant bits.

Example 20–15 Converting from a binary to a hexadecimal number

Problem
Convert 1011100111.01101_2 into an equivalent hexadecimal number.

Solution
1011100111.01101_2
$= 0010\ 1110\ 0111.\ 0110\ 1000$
$\quad\ 2\quad E\quad 7\ .\ 6\quad 8$
Thus, $1011100111.01101_2 = 2E7.68_{16}$

20-8 BINARY WORD LENGTH

Most digital systems utilize binary numbers which contain a specific number of bits. Commonly used sizes include 8, 16, and 32. Groups of bits are frequently called words. A binary word can represent a number, letter, or symbol. The greater the word bit size, the larger the number of different word combinations which can be achieved. This is an important consideration in digital systems such as computers. The number of different binary numbers which can be expressed by a particular word length can be determined from Equation (20–1).

$$\text{Number of binary numbers} = 2^n$$
$$\text{where } n = \text{number of bits}$$

(20–1)

As illustrated in Example 20–16, four binary bits can represent 16 different binary words.

Example 20–16   Determining the number of different words a four-bit word length can represent

Problem
Determine the number of binary words which can be expressed by a four-bit word. List the words.

Solution
$2^n = 2^4 = 16$

0000	0100	1000	1100
0001	0101	1001	1101
0010	0110	1010	1110
0011	0111	1011	1111

The maximum decimal number which can be expressed by a binary word can be obtained from Equation (20–2).

$$\text{Maximum decimal number} = 2^n - 1$$

(20–2)

For the four-bit word appearing in Example 20–16, the number is 15 (1111).

The term *byte* is often used to provide some type of standard for binary word lengths. One byte typically represents 8 bits. An 8-bit word is 1 byte in length. A 16-bit word contains 2 bytes.

20-9 BINARY CODES

Most digital equipment utilizes one or more binary codes to facilitate the transfer of decimal numbers, letters, and symbols used by the operator to binary numbers which are utilized by the circuits within the system. Some of the more commonly used codes include the pure binary code, binary-coded-decimal (BCD) code, Gray code, excess-3 code, and alphanumeric.

The pure binary code is sometimes called the 8421 code. This is simply the binary numbering base previously discussed. Each binary bit represents a particular power of two, depending upon its position. For a four-bit number, the decimal equivalent for each bit is 8421.

The binary-coded-decimal (BCD) code is very popular because it has the characteristics of both the decimal and binary numbering systems. To convert a decimal number into an equivalent BCD number, each decimal digit is replaced by a four-bit binary number, as indicated in Example 20–17. Each four-bit word is replaced with its decimal equivalent to convert from a BCD to a decimal number, as shown in Example 20–18. Since the highest single decimal digit is nine, the maximum four-bit binary number which can be used with the BCD code is 1001. Numbers 1010, 1011, 1100, 1101, 1110, and 1111 are not utilized. These are called forbidden numbers in the BCD numbering system.

Example 20–17   Converting from decimal to binary coded decimal (BCD)

Problem
Convert 765_{10} into an equivalent BCD number.

Solution
765_{10}
= 7   6   5
= 0111 0110 0101
Therefore, 765_{10} = 0111 0110 0101 BCD

Example 20–18   Converting from BCD to decimal

Problem
Convert 0100 1001. 0010 0101 BCD into an equivalent decimal number.

Solution
0100 1001. 0010 0101 BCD
 4   9 . 2   5
Thus, 0100 1001.0010 0101 BCD = 49.25_{10}

The Gray code has the advantage of having no more than one bit change levels as successive numbers are counted. This reduces the chance of errors occurring since fewer circuits have to change states. Decimal numbers 1 through 15 and the corresponding Gray code values appear in Table 20–3. Observe that only one bit changes for successive changes in the binary count. The major disadvantage of the Gray code is that it cannot be used in arithmetic operations.

TABLE 20–3   Decimal and Equivalent Gray Code Numbers

Decimal	Gray	Decimal	Gray
0	0000	8	1100
1	0001	9	1101
2	0011	10	1111
3	0010	11	1110
4	0110	12	1010
5	0111	13	1011
6	0101	14	1001
7	0100	15	1000

The excess-3 (XS3) code is a type of BCD and can be used where arithmetic operations are required. To convert a decimal number into its excess-3 equivalent, the number 3 is added to each digit before it is converted into its equivalent excess-3 number, as shown in Example 20–19.

Alphanumeric codes are used to represent letters and symbols in addition to representing numbers. Although there are several of these codes, the most common is the American Standard Code for Information

Example 20–19   Converting from decimal to XS3

Problem
Convert 14_{10} into an equivalent XS3 number.

Solution
14_{10}
$= 1\ \ 4$
$+\underline{3} + \underline{3}$
$\ \ 4\ \ 7$
$= 0100\ \ 0111$
Therefore, $14_{10} = 0100\ \ 0111$ XS3

Interchange (ASCII). This is the type of code used by most teletypewriters. The teletypewriter is often used as an input-output device to a computer. There are two ASCII codes. One is a six-bit code in which 64 different characters can be represented. These represent the uppercase letters of the alphabet, decimal numbers 0 to 9, and sentence punctuation symbols. A seven-bit ASCII, called extended ASCII, is used in many digital systems. This code represents 128 different characters. In addition to decimal numbers 0 to 9, both lowercase and uppercase letters, along with additional sentence punctuation symbols, can be represented by this code.

20-10 SUBTRACTION USING THE ONE'S COMPLEMENT

Some computers subtract one binary number from another by using the one's complement. This involves taking the one's complement of the subtrahend and adding it to the minuend. The one's complement of a binary number is the inverted value of that number. Conversion merely involves changing the binary one bits to binary zero bits and the zero bits to binary one bits. Subtraction by the one's complement is illustrated in Example 20–20. Notice that this is a rather simple method of subtraction.

Example 20–20   Subtraction using the one's complement

Problem
Using the one's complement, subtract 0110 (the subtrahend) from 1011 (the minuend).

Solution
1. Write the minuend.   1011
2. Complement the subtrahend.   1001
3. Add the minuend and complemented subtrahend.   10100
4. Add the carry to the subtrahend.   └──→ 1
                                                          0101

All that is required is an adder circuit and an inverter to complement the subtrahend. If the subtrahend is larger than the minuend there will not be a carry bit. The absence of a carry bit indicates that the subtrahend has a larger value than the minuend and the resultant is negative, as indicated in Example 20–21. As shown, the resultant is the complement of the difference between the two numbers. When the resultant is negative, it must be inverted to obtain the correct value.

Example 20–21 Subtraction using the one's complement

Problem
Using the one's complement, subtract 111 from 101.

Solution

1. Write the minuend.	101
2. Complement the subtrahend.	000
3. Add the minuend and complemented subtrahend.	101
4. Invert the resultant.	010

20-11 SUBTRACTION USING THE TWO'S COMPLEMENT

Many computers and microprocessors subtract by using the two's complement. This process involves converting the subtrahend into the two's complement and adding it to the minuend. The two's complement of a number is the one's complement with a binary one added to the least significant bit. Subtraction by this process is shown in Example 20–22. Notice that the carry from the most significant bit is discarded. If the subtrahend is larger than the minuend, the resultant will be negative. As indicated in Example 20–23, the resultant must be inverted, or complemented, and a binary one added to the least significant bit (LSB).

Example 20–22 Subtraction using the two's complement

Problem
Using the two's complement, subtract 011011 from 101101.

Solution

1. Obtain the two's complement of the subtrahend.	011011
	= 100100
	1
	100101
2. Write the minuend.	101101
3. Add the minuend to the two's complemented subtrahend.	100101
	1010010
4. Discard the carry bit. The resultant is	010010

20-12 SIGNED NUMBERS

Both positive and negative numbers exist in any numbering system and circuits which perform arithmetic operations on binary data must be able to differentiate between the two. In most computers and microprocessors

Example 20–23   Subtraction using the two's complement

Problem
Subtract 1101 from 1001 using the two's complement.

Solution
1. Obtain the two's complement of the subtrahend.   0011
2. Add the minuend and the two's complemented subtrahend. 1001
                                                            0011
                                                            1100
3. Complement the remainder.   0011
4. Add one to the LSB.   1
   The resultant is   0100

the most significant bit of a binary word represents the sign of the number represented by that word. If the MSB is zero, a positive number is represented. A negative number is indicated if the MSB is one. Most computers and microprocessors utilize and store negative numbers in either the one's or two's complement format. The difference between representing a positive and a negative number is illustrated below.

$$+58_{10} = 00111010_2$$
$$-58_{10} = 11000110_2 \quad \text{(in two's complement format)}$$

Notice that the negative number is displayed in two's complement form. If negative numbers are to be added together, they are usually summed in complement format, as illustrated in Example 20–24.

Example 20–24   Adding two negative numbers

Problem
Convert the negative numbers -12 and -7 into an eight-bit binary format and obtain their sum.

Solution

1. $-12 = 10001100$
   $- 7 = 10000111$
2. Obtain the two's complement for both numbers and add.
   $-12 = 11110100$ (two's complement)
   $+(- 7) = 11111001$ (two's complement)
   $-19 = 111101101$ (two's complement)
   or $-19 = 00010011$ (pure binary)

SUMMARY

1. Binary, or digital, circuits form the third general classification of circuits, the other two being passive and linear.
2. Digital circuits operate at one of the two voltage levels—low or high.
3. Several different numbering bases are used in various digital systems. These include the decimal, binary, octal, and hexadecimal.
4. The octal or hexadecimal numbering bases are used to facilitate the transfer of information from the decimal system used by humans and the binary system used by digital circuits.
5. Decimal numbers can be converted to binary numbers and vice versa.
6. Decimal numbers can be converted to octal numbers and vice versa.
7. Binary numbers can be converted to octal numbers and vice versa.
8. Decimal numbers can be converted to hexadecimal numbers and vice versa.
9. Binary numbers can be converted to hexadecimal numbers and vice versa.
10. Digital equipment utilizes binary numbers which are grouped into a specific number of bits called words. The term *byte* is used to identify a specified word length. Usually, one byte represents an eight-bit word.
11. Since the data coming into a digital system from the outside world is in the form of decimal numbers, letters, or sentence punctuation symbols, various binary codes are used to accommodate the transition from the source to the binary system. These include the pure binary (8421), binary-coded-decimal (BCD), Gray, excess 3-(XS3), and alphanumeric.
12. Most digital systems use either the one's or two's complement to subtract one number from another.

PRACTICE EXERCISES

1. Add the following binary numbers.

   a. 1011   **b.**   1101001
        $+\underline{1101}$ $+\underline{0110000}$

2. Subtract the following numbers.

   a. 1101   **b.**   1001101
        $-\underline{0101}$ $-\underline{0110110}$

3. Convert the following numbers to equivalent numbers having the bases indicated.

   a. $11011.101_2 = $ ———————$_{10}$

   b. $497.51_{10} = $ ———————$_2$

   c. $723.25_8 = $ ———————$_{10}$

   d. $205.15_8 = $ ———————$_2$

   e. $10011.011_2 = $ ———————$_8$

   f. $128.72_{10} = $ ———————$_8$

   g. $CB2.A7_{16} = $ ———————$_{10}$

   h. $98B.62_{16} = $ ———————$_2$

   i. $29.57_{10} = $ ———————$_{16}$

   j. $100111011001.101101_2 = $ ———————$_{16}$

k. $309.21_{10} =$ _____BCD

l. 1001 0010 1000.0110 0100 BCD = _____$_{10}$

4. How many different numbers (words) can a six-bit binary word express?

5. What is the maximum decimal count of a six-bit binary word?

6. Subtract the numbers shown in exercise 2(a) using the one's complement.

7. Using the two's complement, subtract the numbers shown in exercise 2(b).

8. Define the term *byte.*

9. List five codes which may be used in digital equipment.

ANSWERS TO PRACTICE EXERCISES

1. a.
$$\begin{array}{r} 1011 \\ +\ \underline{1101} \\ 11000 \end{array}$$
b.
$$\begin{array}{r} 1101001 \\ +\ \underline{0110000} \\ 10011001 \end{array}$$

2. a.
$$\begin{array}{r} 1101 \\ -\ \underline{0101} \\ 1000 \end{array}$$
b.
$$\begin{array}{r} 1001101 \\ -\ \underline{0110110} \\ 0010111 \end{array}$$

3. a. $11011.101_2 = 1 \times 2^4 + 1 \times 2^3 + 0 \times 2^2 + 1 \times 2^1 + 1 \times 2^0 + 1 \times 2^{-1} + 0 \times 2^{-2}$

$+\ 1 \times 2^{-3} = 16 + 8 + 0 + 2 + 1 + 0.5 + 0.0 + 0.125 = 27.625_{10}$

b. $497.51_{10} = $
$$2\overline{\smash{)}497}\ \ 2\overline{\smash{)}248}\ \ 2\overline{\smash{)}124}\ \ 2\overline{\smash{)}62}\ \ 2\overline{\smash{)}31}\ \ 2\overline{\smash{)}15}\ \ 2\overline{\smash{)}7}\ \ 2\overline{\smash{)}3}$$

with quotients 248, 124, 62, 31, 15, 7, 3, 1

$$\begin{array}{cccccccc} \underline{496} & \underline{248} & \underline{124} & \underline{62} & \underline{30} & \underline{14} & \underline{6} & \underline{2} \\ 1 & 0 & 0 & 0 & 1 & 1 & 1 & 1 \end{array}$$

$$\begin{array}{ccc} 0.51 & 0.02 & 0.04 \\ \times\ \underline{\quad 2} & \underline{\quad 2} & \underline{\quad 2} \\ 1.02 & 0.04 & 0.08 \end{array} = 111110001.100_2$$

c. $723.25_8 = 7 \times 8^2 + 2 \times 8^1 + 3 \times 8^0 + 2 \times 8^{-1} + 5 \times 8^{-2}$

$= 448 + 16 + 3 + 0.250 + 0.078 = 467.328_{10}$

d. $205.15_8 = 010\ 000\ 101.001\ 101 = 10000101.001101_2$

e. $10011.011_2 = 010\ 011.011 = 23.3_8$

f. $128.72_{10} = $
$$8\overline{\smash{)}128}\ \ 8\overline{\smash{)}16}$$
with quotients 16, 2

$$\begin{array}{cc} \underline{128} & \underline{16} \\ 0 & 0 \end{array} \qquad \begin{array}{ccc} 0.72 & 0.76 & 0.08 \\ \times\ \underline{\quad 8} & \times\ \underline{\quad 8} & \times\ \underline{\quad 8} \\ 5.76 & 6.08 & 0.64 \end{array} = 200.560_8$$

g. $CB2.A7_{16} = 12 \times 16^2 + 11 \times 16^1 + 2 \times 16^0 + 10 \times 16^{-1} + 7 \times 16^{-2}$

$= 3072 + 176 + 2 + 0.625 + 0.0273 = 3250.652_{10}$

h. $98B.62_{16} = 1001\ 1000\ 1011.0110\ 0010 = 100110001011.0110001_2$

i. $29.57_{10} = $
$$16\overline{\smash{)}29}$$
quotient 1
$$\begin{array}{ccc} \underline{16} & \times\ \underline{\quad 16} & \times\ \underline{\quad 16} \\ 13 & 9.12 & 1.92 \end{array}$$
$0.57 \quad 0.12 = 1D.91_{16}$

j. $100111011001.101101_2 = 1001\ 1101\ 1001.1011\ 0100 = 9D9.B4_{16}$

k. $309.21_{10} = 0011\ 0000\ 1001.0010\ 0001$ BCD

l. $1001\ 0010\ 1000.0110\ 0100$ BCD $= 928.64_{10}$

4. $2^n = 2^6 = 64$

5. $2^n - 1 = 2^6 - 1 = 64 - 1 = 63$

6.   1101   (one's complement)
   + 1010
   10111
   └→ 1
   1000

7.   1001101   (two's complement)
   + 1001010
   10010111

8. A byte is a group of binary bits which form a word. Usually, one byte represents an eight-bit word.

9. Five codes used in various digital systems include the Gray, XS3, pure, BCD, and ASCII.

CHAPTER EXAMINATION

1. Define the term *byte*.
2. Describe what is meant by an alphanumeric code.
3. $637.24_8 = $ _____ $_{10}$
4. $D3B.A5_{16} = $ _____ $_2$
5. $82.05_{10} = $ _____ $_2$
6. $36.21_{10} = $ _____ $_8$
7. $913.79_{10} = $ _____ $_{16}$
8. $100101001.11001_2 = $ _____ $_8$
9. $1101101110001.00101_2 = $ _____ $_{16}$
10. $A5B.E7_{16} = $ _____ $_{10}$
11. Add the following two numbers.
    11101011
    + 11001100
12. Subtract the following two numbers.
    1010011
    − 0111001
13. Subtract the following two numbers using the one's complement.
    11011001
    − 10010110
14. Subtract the following two numbers using the two's complement.
    1101101
    − 0011011
15. How many different numbers can a five-bit binary word express?
16. What is the maximum decimal count which can be expressed by a five-bit binary word?

21

Digital Gating Circuits

OBJECTIVES

Upon completion of this chapter you should be able to do the following:

1. Identify the three basic gating circuits and draw the logic symbol for each.
2. Write the truth table for the AND, OR, and NOT circuits.
3. Identify the two inverting gate circuits and draw the logic symbol for each.
4. Write the truth table for the NAND and NOR gates.
5. Describe how an AND, OR, or NOT circuit can be made from a NOR gate.
6. Describe how an AND, OR, or NOT circuit can be made from a NAND gate.
7. Write the Boolean expressions for the output of the AND and OR circuits.
8. Write the Boolean expression for the output of a sum-of-products circuit.
9. Write the Boolean expression for a product-of-sums circuit.

21-1 INTRODUCTION

Circuits used in computers and microprocessors add, subtract, multiply, divide, count, sort, and store binary data. Although there are several different kinds of circuits to perform these functions, they are almost always formed from three different circuits. These are called gating circuits, or gates, and are the AND, OR, and NOT types. The NOT circuit is often called an inverter. An inverter connected to the output of the AND and OR gates forms two additional circuits called NAND and NOR gates. A gate is a circuit that has high output voltage level (binary one) whenever the input voltage levels meet predetermined conditions.

491

21-2 THE THREE BASIC GATING CIRCUITS

21-2.1 The AND Gate. The AND gate is a circuit whose output voltage is high, or binary one, when all the input voltages are high (binary one). This gate has two or more inputs and one output. The symbol for the AND gate appears in Figure 21–1. A two-input AND gate is shown in Figure 21–1(a) while a four-input AND gate is illustrated in Figure 21–1(b).

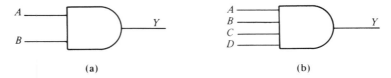

(a)   (b)

Figure 21–1 AND gate symbol: (a) two-input AND gate; (b) four-input AND gate.

An important aid in understanding the operation of a gating circuit is the truth table. A truth table describes the output state of a gate for all possible input conditions. The truth table for a three-input AND gate appears in Table 21–1. Notice that the output voltage remains low, or binary zero, until input *A and* input *B and* input *C* are all high. This is how the AND gate obtains its name.

Often, the input voltages to a gating circuit are in the form of pulses. For an AND gate the output voltage will be high only when all input voltages are high simultaneously, as shown in Figure 21–2.

AND gates have many applications. A simple application is used in some automobiles. These cars are equipped so that the ignition switch

TABLE 21–1 Truth Table for Three-Input AND Gate

Inputs	Output
A B C	*Y*
0 0 0	0
1 0 0	0
0 1 0	0
0 1 1	0
0 0 1	0
1 0 1	0
1 1 0	0
1 1 1	1

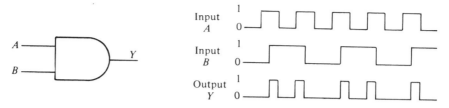

Figure 21–2   Output voltage is at a binary one level in an AND gate only when all the input voltage levels are binary one simultaneously.

will not start the engine until the clutch pedal is depressed and the seat belt fastened. Depressing the clutch pedal causes the voltage level of one input of a two-input AND gate to become high. Fastening the seatbelt allows the voltage level of the other AND gate input to become high. This causes the output voltage to become high, allowing the engine to start.

21-2.2 The OR Gate.   This is another type of gating circuit. The symbol for the circuit is shown in Figure 21–3. Like the AND gate, this gate has two or more inputs and one output. The output voltage will be high when any, or all, of the input voltages are high. For the circuit appearing in Figure 21–3(a) the output voltage is high when either input voltage *A or B* is high or when both input voltage levels are high. The output voltage is high for the gate shown in Figure 21–3(b) whenever a binary one appears at any input, as illustrated by the truth table shown in Table 21–2.

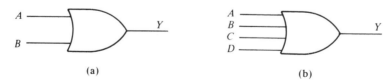

(a)   (b)

Figure 21–3   OR gate symbol: (a) two-input OR gate; (b) four-input OR gate.

21-2.3 The NOT Gate.   The third basic gate is the NOT circuit, commonly called an inverter circuit. The symbol for this circuit appears in Figure 21–4. As shown, the circuit has one input and one output. The output signal is always 180° out-of-phase with the input signal, hence the name inverter. This is the same symbol used for an amplifier except that a bubble appears at either the output or input terminals. The symbol appearing in Figure 21–4(a) with the bubble appearing at the output is the one most commonly used. Occasionally, the location of the bubble indi-

TABLE 21–2   Truth Table for Four-Input OR Gate

Inputs	Output
A B C D	Y
0 0 0 0	0
0 0 0 1	1
0 0 1 0	1
0 0 1 1	1
0 1 0 0	1
0 1 0 1	1
0 1 1 0	1
0 1 1 1	1
1 0 0 0	1
1 0 0 1	1
1 0 1 0	1
1 0 1 1	1
1 1 0 0	1
1 1 0 1	1
1 1 1 0	1
1 1 1 1	1

(a)   (b)

Figure 21–4   NOT gate symbol: (a) general symbol, also used to indicate an active high input; (b) symbol used to indicate an active low input.

cates the normal binary input level to the NOT gate. In this situation the symbol shown in Figure 21–4(a) indicates that the input to the inverter is normally at a binary one level. The symbol appearing in Figure 21–4(b) is used when the voltage level appearing at the input is usually a binary zero. These are often referred to as active high and active low inputs, respectively. The truth table for the inverter circuit is shown in Table 21–3. The bar appearing above the input and output letters indicates a NOT, or complemented, binary level. If input A in Figure 21–4(a) is a binary one, the output is "NOT A", or a binary zero. The input to the inverter shown in Figure 21–4(b) is NOT A (binary zero) and the output is A, or a binary one level.

TABLE 21–3 Truth Table for NOT Gate	
Input	*Output*
$\dfrac{A}{A}$	$\overline{A}$
	A

21-3 THE INVERTED GATES

21-3.1 The NAND Gate. The NAND gate is one of two gates formed by combining two of the basic gates just described. As illustrated in Figure 21–5(a), this circuit consists of an AND gate connected to an inverter (NOT AND). The symbol appears in Figure 21–5(b). Like the AND and OR gates, the NAND circuit has two or more inputs and one output. The inverter is usually part of the internal circuitry of the NAND gate. The truth table for a two-input NAND is shown in Table 21–4. Notice that the truth table is the reciprocal of that for an AND gate. The output is at a binary one level whenever any, or all, of its input voltage levels are at a binary zero level.

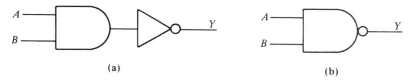

(a)   (b)

Figure 21–5   NAND gate: (a) equivalent circuit; (b) symbol.

TABLE 21–4 Truth Table for NAND Gate	
Inputs	*Output*
A B	*Y*
0 0	1
1 0	1
0 1	1
1 1	0

21-3.2 The NOR Gate. The NOR gate is formed by connecting an inverter to the output of an OR gate (NOT OR), as indicated in Figure 21–6(a). The symbol used to represent this circuit appears in Figure

21–6(b). The truth table for a two-input NOR gate appears in Table 21–5. The NOR gate output voltage levels are the inverse of the output voltages of an OR gate. The output voltage is at a binary one level only when all inputs are at a binary zero level.

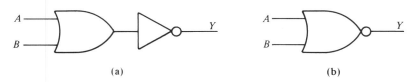

(a)   (b)

Figure 21–6 NOR gate: (a) equivalent circuit; (b) symbol.

TABLE 21–5 Truth Table for NOR Gate

Inputs	Output
A B	Y
0 0	1
1 0	0
0 1	0
1 1	0

21-3.3 General Applications. Most digital circuits are built from NAND and NOR gating circuits. This pair of circuits is sometimes referred to as the universal building blocks of digital circuits. There are certain advantages of using these gates rather than the more simple AND and OR circuits. The principal advantage being that the inverter in the circuit acts as a buffer and reduces the loading effects between the input and output circuits.

Both the NAND and NOR gates can be made to perform any one of the three basic gating functions. An inverter connected to the output of a NAND gate causes the circuit to function as an AND gate, as shown in Figure 21–7. The OR gate function can be obtained from a NOR gate by connecting an inverter to the output of the NOR gate, as illustrated in Figure 21–8.

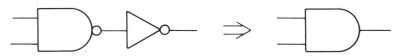

Figure 21–7 Inverter connected to the output of a NAND gate results in an AND gate.

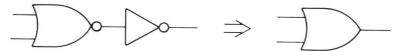

Figure 21–8 Inverter connected to the output of a NOR gate results in an OR gate.

Connecting an inverter to each input lead of a NAND gate causes that gate to operate as an OR gate, as shown in Figure 21–9. A NOR gate will function as an AND gate when inverters are connected to the input leads, as illustrated in Figure 21–10. Either a NOR gate or a NAND gate can be operated as an inverter when the input leads are connected together, as depicted in Figure 21–11. One could write a truth table for each equivalent circuit to verify its operation.

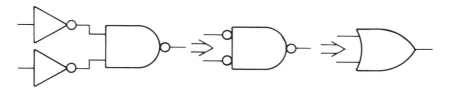

Figure 21–9 Inverters connected to the input leads of a NAND gate results in an OR gate.

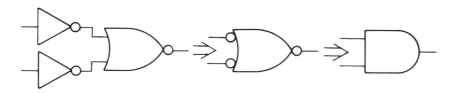

Figure 21–10 Inverters connected to the input leads of a NOR gate results in an AND gate.

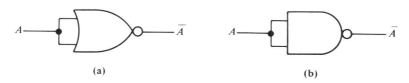

(a)   (b)

Figure 21–11 Connecting the input leads together causes the NOR and NAND gates to function as inverters: (a) NOR to NOT; (b) NAND to NOT.

21-4 BOOLEAN ALGEBRA

Boolean algebra is a special kind of mathematics used by those who design digital circuits. Actually, two binary numbering systems are involved in digital circuits. One is the binary numbering system discussed in Chapter 20. The second is a binary logic algebra system, which is called Boolean algebra. Boolean algebra allows one to express the output voltage of a gate in terms of its input voltages.

The Boolean expressions for the AND and OR gates appear in Figure 21–12. These circuits provide the Boolean product and sum functions, respectively. The output voltage of an AND gate is the Boolean product of the input voltages. The output voltage of an OR gate is the Boolean sum of the input voltages.

Boolean algebra can be used to express the output voltage when gates are connected together. For example, when an inverter is connected to the output of an AND gate, as shown in Figure 21–13, the output voltage is $\overline{AB}$ (NOT AB). The output of the AND gate is the Boolean product of the input voltages (AB). This value is then inverted by the inverter circuit. When two inverters are connected to the inputs of an AND gate, as shown in Figure 21–14, the output voltage is $\overline{A}\,\overline{B}$ (NOT A AND NOT B). This output voltage should not be confused with the output voltage of

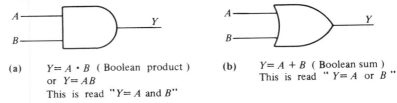

(a) $Y = A \cdot B$ (Boolean product)
       or $Y = AB$
       This is read "$Y = A$ and B"

(b) $Y = A + B$ (Boolean sum)
       This is read " $Y = A$ or B "

Figure 21–12 The AND and OR gates provide the Boolean product and sum functions, respectively: (a) AND gate; (b) OR gate.

Figure 21–13 Inverter connected to the output of an AND gate.

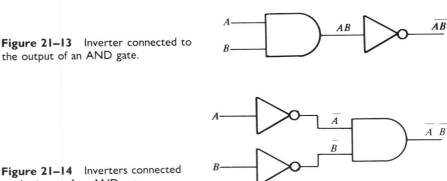

Figure 21–14 Inverters connected to the input of an AND gate.

Figure 21–15 Inverter connected to the output of an OR gate.

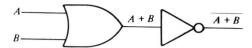

the circuit appearing in Figure 21–13. The results are not equal. $\overline{A}\,\overline{B}$ does not equal $\overline{AB}$.

An inverter is connected to the output of an OR gating circuit in Figure 21–15. The output voltage is $\overline{A+B}$ (NOT A OR B). When inverters are connected to the inputs of an OR gate, as illustrated in Figure 21–16, the output voltage is $\overline{A}+\overline{B}$ (NOT A OR NOT B). This output is not equal to the output of the gate appearing in Figure 21–15. This can be verified by the truth tables appearing in Tables 21–6 and 21–7.

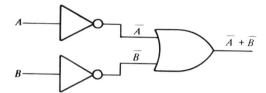

Figure 21–16 Inverters connected to the input of an OR gate.

TABLE 21–6	Truth Table for $Y=\overline{A+B}$		
A	B	$A+B$	$\overline{A+B}$
0	0	0	1
1	0	1	0
0	1	1	0
1	1	1	0

TABLE 21–7	Truth Table for $Y=\overline{A}+\overline{B}$			
A	B	$\overline{A}$	$\overline{B}$	$\overline{A}+\overline{B}$
0	0	1	1	1
1	0	0	1	1
0	1	1	0	1
1	1	0	0	0

21-5 COMBINATIONAL LOGIC CIRCUITS

The circuits illustrated in Figures 21–7 through 21–16 are called combinational logic circuits. These types of circuits are formed when two or more basic gates are connected together to achieve a desired function. The NAND and NOR gates can also be considered to be combinational logic circuits.

Consider the circuit shown in Figure 21–17. This circuit consists of two AND gates whose outputs are coupled to an OR gate. This type of combinational logic circuit is called a sum-of-products circuit. The OR gate sums the two products obtained from the AND gates. Another sum-of-products circuit is shown in Figure 21–18. These inputs are labeled as they might be in an actual computer.

When OR gates are connected to an AND gate, as illustrated in Figure 21–19, a product-of-sums circuit is formed. The output voltage of each OR gate is the Boolean sum of the input voltages. These form the input voltages to the AND gate. The output voltage of this gate is the Boolean product of its input voltages.

Almost all combinational logic circuits take the form of either the sum-of-products or product-of-sums format. More complex combinational logic circuits will be considered in Chapter 24.

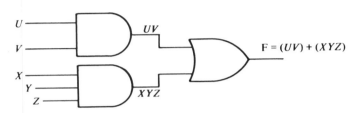

Figure 21–17 Sum-of-products circuit.

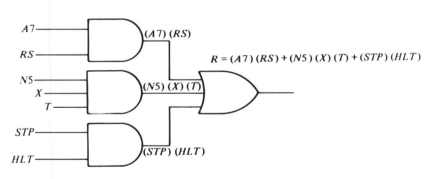

Figure 21–18 Sum-of-products circuit.

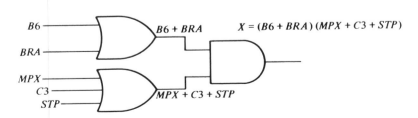

Figure 21–19 Product-of-sums circuit.

SUMMARY

1. Almost all digital circuits are made up of gating circuits (gates).
2. A gate is a circuit that has a high output voltage level (binary one) whenever the input voltage levels meet predetermined conditions.
3. There are three types of basic gates: the AND, OR, and NOT. The NOT gate is often referred to as an inverter.
4. The AND gate has two or more inputs and one output. A binary one voltage level is present at the output only when a binary one voltage level is present at all the input terminals.
5. An OR gate has two or more input terminals and one output. A binary one voltage level is present at the output whenever a binary one voltage level is present at any one or more of the input terminals.
6. The NOT gate is an inverter. If a binary one voltage level is applied to the input terminal, a binary zero is present at the output terminal or vice versa.
7. Two additional gates are formed by connecting NOT gates to the outputs of the AND and OR gates. These are called NAND and NOR gates, respectively.
8. A NAND gate is a NOT AND gate. This gate has a binary one output whenever any of its input voltage levels are binary zero.
9. A NOR gate is a NOT OR gate. Its output voltage is a binary one whenever all the input voltages are at a binary zero level.
10. Digital circuits are usually built from NAND or NOR gates. Any gating function can be produced by combining inverters with either of these two circuits.
11. Boolean algebra is a special type of binary mathematics used by computer scientists and engineers who design digital circuits and systems. Boolean algebra allows one to express the output voltage of a digital circuit in terms of its input voltages.
12. The output voltage of an AND gate is the Boolean product of its input voltages.
13. The output voltage of an OR gate is the Boolean sum of its input voltages.
14. Whenever two or more basic gates are connected together, a combinational gate is formed. Combinational gating circuits usually appear in one of two general formats and include the sum-of-products and product-of-sums.

PRACTICE EXERCISES

1. Draw the logic symbol for a three-input AND gate. Label the inputs and output.
2. Draw the logic symbol for a four-input OR gate. Label the inputs and output.
3. Draw the logic symbol for an inverter. Label the input and output.
4. Write the truth table for the AND gate drawn in exercise 1.
5. Develop the truth table for the OR gate drawn in exercise 2.
6. Draw the logic symbol for a two-input NAND gate.
7. Write the truth table for the NAND gate drawn in exercise 6.

8. Draw the logic symbol for a three-input NOR gate.
9. Develop the truth table for the NOR gate drawn in exercise 8.
10. Write the Boolean expression for the AND gate drawn in exercise 1.
11. Write the Boolean expression for the OR gate drawn in exercise 2.
12. Using a NAND gate and inverter(s), draw a diagram showing how the circuits should be connected to form an OR gate.
13. Draw a diagram showing how an AND gate can be formed from a NOR gate and inverter(s).
14. Draw a diagram of a NAND gate connected as an inverter.
15. Given the circuit shown in Figure 21–20, write the Boolean expression for the output.
16. Is the circuit shown in Figure 21–20 a product-of-sums or sum-of-products type?

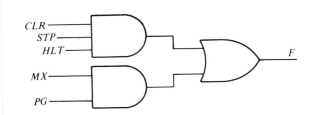

Figure 21–20

ANSWERS TO PRACTICE EXERCISES

1.

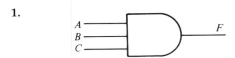

Figure 21–21   Three-input AND gate.

2.

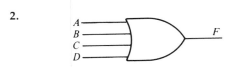

Figure 21–22   Four-input NOR gate.

3.

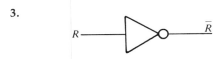

Figure 21–23   Inverter.

4.

TABLE 21–8	Truth Table for Three-Input AND Gate			
	A	B	C	F
	0	0	0	0
	0	0	1	0
	0	1	0	0
	0	1	1	0
	1	0	0	0
	1	0	1	0
	1	1	0	0
	1	1	1	1

5.

TABLE 21–9	Truth Table for Four-Input OR Gate				
	A	B	C	D	F
	0	0	0	0	0
	0	0	0	1	1
	0	0	1	0	1
	0	0	1	1	1
	0	1	0	0	1
	0	1	0	1	1
	0	1	1	0	1
	0	1	1	1	1
	1	0	0	0	1
	1	0	0	1	1
	1	0	1	0	1
	1	0	1	1	1
	1	1	0	0	1
	1	1	0	1	1
	1	1	1	0	1
	1	1	1	1	1

6.

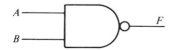

Figure 21–24   Two-input NAND gate.

7.

TABLE 21–10   Truth Table for Two-Input NAND Gate

A	B	F
0	0	1
1	0	1
0	1	1
1	1	0

8.

Figure 21–25   Three-input NOR gate.

9.

TABLE 21–11   Truth Table for Three-Input NOR Gate

E	F	G	H
0	0	0	1
0	0	1	0
0	1	0	0
0	1	1	0
1	0	0	0
1	0	1	0
1	1	0	0
1	1	1	0

10. $F = ABC$
11. $F = A + B + C + D$
12.

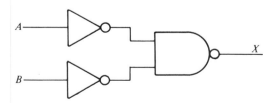

Figure 21–26   NAND gate connected to form an OR gate.

13.

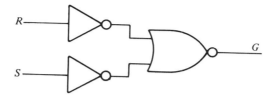

Figure 21–27   NOR gate connected to form an AND gate.

14.

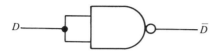

Figure 21–28   NAND gate connected to form an inverter.

15. $F = (CLR \cdot STP \cdot HLT) + (MX \cdot PG)$
16. Sum-of-products

CHAPTER EXAMINATION

1. The circuit shown in Figure 21–29 is that of a (an) _____ gate.
   - **a.** OR
   - **b.** AND
   - **c.** NOR
   - **d.** NAND

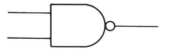

Figure 21–29

2. The Table 21–12 is the truth table for a two-input _____ gate.

TABLE 21–12   Truth Table

A	B	C
0	0	1
1	0	1
0	1	1
1	1	0

   - **a.** OR
   - **b.** AND
   - **c.** NOR
   - **d.** NAND

3. The _____ gate has a binary one output when any, or all, of the inputs
   are at a binary one level.
   - **a.** OR
   - **b.** AND
   - **c.** NOR
   - **d.** NAND

4. The _____ gate has a binary one output when all inputs are at a binary zero.
   a. OR
   b. AND
   c. NOR
   d. NAND

5. The circuit in Figure 21–30 performs the _____ function.
   a. OR
   b. AND
   c. NOT
   d. NAND

Figure 21–30

6. The circuit in Figure 21–31 performs the _____ function.
   a. OR
   b. AND
   c. NOT
   d. NOR

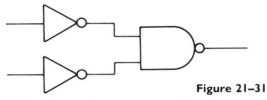

Figure 21–31

7. The circuit in Figure 21–32 performs the _____ function.
   a. OR
   b. AND
   c. NOT
   d. NOR

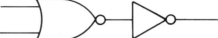

Figure 21–32

8. Which of the Boolean algebra equations appearing below expresses the output of a product-of-sums circuit?
   a. $F = ABCD$
   b. $F = A + B + C + D$
   c. $F = (AB) + (CD)$
   d. $F = (A + B)(C + D)$

9. Which of the following Boolean algebra equations expresses the output voltage of a four-input AND gate?
   a. $R = MX \cdot STP \cdot CLR \cdot HLT$
   b. $R = MX + STP + CLR + HLT$
   c. $R = (MX + STP) \cdot (CLR + HLT)$
   d. $R = (MX \cdot STP) + (CLR \cdot HLT)$

Choose true or false for questions 10 to 15.

10. T F   The OR gate is commonly called an inverter.
11. T F   The NOR gate is a type of inverting gate.
12. T F   The voltage output of an AND gate is high when all input voltage levels are high.
13. T F   The voltage level is low for the output of a NOR gate when all input voltage levels are low.
14. T F   A NAND gate can be made by connecting inverters to the input leads of a NOR gate.
15. T F   The OR gate output voltage represents the Boolean product of the input voltages.

22

Digital Integrated Circuits

OBJECTIVES

Upon completion of this chapter you should be able to do the following:

1. Describe what is meant by the functional capacity of an integrated circuit.
2. Identify the approximate maximum number of gates associated with SSI, MSI, LSI, and VLSI integrated circuit devices.
3. Define the terms *propagation delay, operating speed, power dissipation, noise immunity,* and *rise* and *decay times.*
4. Discuss the relationship between gate operating speed and gate power consumption.
5. Identify five digital integrated circuit logic families.
6. Identify three TTL subfamilies, list the nomenclature used to identify each, and compare the operating speed and power consumption for each with respect to standard TTL.
7. Discuss the purpose of three-state TTL devices.
8. Identify the basic gate formed by the internal circuitry of the TTL, ECL, and CMOS integrated circuits.
9. Identify the binary logic levels for TTL, ECL, and CMOS logic.
10. Identify the power supply voltage requirements and operating speed for standard TTL, ECL, and CMOS digital integrated circuits.
11. Identify the four ranges associated with operating speed and the types of integrated circuit logic families associated with each.

22-1 INTRODUCTION

The AND, OR, NAND, NOR, and inverter circuits can be connected by wiring together discrete components. Most modern digital equipment

507

utilizes these circuits in integrated circuit form, however. Integrated circuits are more reliable, operate faster, consume less power, are more compact, and are less expensive than equivalent discrete component circuits.

As discussed in Chapter 17, there are two general kinds of integrated circuits—the hybrid and monolithic. Digital integrated circuits are almost entirely made from the monolithic type. Monolithic integrated circuits are manufactured using either bipolar junction transistor (BJT) technology or metal-oxide-semiconductor field effect transistor (MOSFET) technology.

Monolithic integrated circuits are classified in several ways. One of the more common classification methods deals with the functional capacity of the circuit. This refers to the approximate number of gates a particular integrated circuit contains. Integrated circuits are classified as to their functional capacity as follows:

1. Small-scale integration (SSI), 1 to 11 gates
2. Medium-scale integration (MSI), 12 to 99 gates
3. Large-scale integration (LSI), 100 to 10,000 gates
4. Very-large-scale integration (VLSI), above 10,000 gates

22-2 DIGITAL INTEGRATED CIRCUIT (IC) SPECIFICATIONS

22-2.1 Introduction. Digital ICs have specifications just as discrete device transistors. Some of the more common include propagation delay, propagation speed, fan-in, fan-out, power dissipation, noise immunity, rise time, and decay time.

22-2.2 Propagation Delay. Propagation delay is the time required for a change in voltage level applied to the input of a gate to cause a change in the output voltage level (change states). Two different propagation delay values are usually identified. One represents the time required for the gate to switch from a high to a low voltage level (t_{pHL}) and the other indicates the time needed for the voltage to change from a low to a high level (t_{pLH}). Propagation delay is measured between the 50 percent levels on the corresponding leading and trailing edges of the input and output voltages, as illustrated in Figure 22–1. Propagation delay is measured in nanoseconds for most integrated circuits.

22-2.3 Propagation Speed. Often called operating speed, propagation speed identifies the maximum frequency at which binary data, in

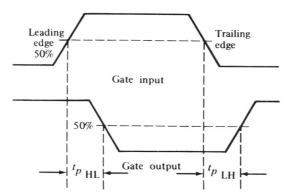

Figure 22–1   Measurement parameters for propagation delay.

the form of pulses, can be applied to a gate. Operating speed is usually measured in megahertz.

22-2.4 Fan-in.   Fan-in refers to the number of inputs that a particular gate can handle. Inputs to a gate usually come from the output of other gates. Each of these gate outputs is referred to as a unit load. A four-input gate, for example, requires one unit load for each input. The fan-in for the gate is four. The concept of unit loads is important in the design of digital circuits.

22-2.5 Fan-out.   The fan-out of a gate identifies the number of unit inputs that can be driven by a particular logic gate. The fan-out capacity of gate 1 appearing in Figure 22–2 must be at least three. Fan-in and fan-out are both affected by the amount of current required by a gate. For the circuit shown in Figure 22–2, the output current of gate 1 must be great enough to drive the input circuits of gates 2, 3, and 4. If the drive capacity is insufficient, the logic levels associated with gate 1 may not be correct.

Figure 22–2   Gate I must have a fan-out capacity of at least three.

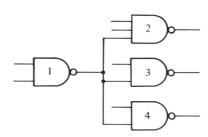

22-2.6 Power Dissipation. This specification refers to the power consumed by an individual gate within an integrated circuit. The unit of measurement associated with this variable is milliwatts per gate.

22-2.7 Noise Immunity. Noise immunity identifies the amount of noise which can appear on a gate input signal without causing the gate to change states.

22-2.8 Rise and Decay Times. Rise time (t_r) is the time required for a pulse to increase from 10 to 90 percent of its maximum value. Decay, or fall time (t_f) refers to the time that it takes a pulse to decrease from 90 to 10 percent of its maximum value, as illustrated in Figure 22–3.

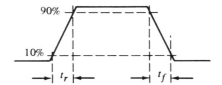

Figure 22–3 Measurement parameters for rise and decay times.

22-3 DIGITAL INTEGRATED CIRCUIT FAMILIES

22-3.1 Introduction. Digital integrated circuits are manufactured using different types of transistor technology and internal circuit arrangements. Each of these is called a logic family. Some of the characteristics for the more commonly used logic families are discussed in the following sections.

22-3.2 The TTL Family. Transistor-transistor logic (TTL) is the most common of all the logic families. Manufactured using bipolar junction technology, the circuit is composed of three sections, as shown in Figure 22–4. The input stage (Q_1) is a multiemitter transistor; the middle stage, Q_2, is a phase splitter; and the output stage consists of transistors Q_3 and Q_4 connected in series. This type of output is called a totem pole output. The entire circuit functions as a NAND gate.

The emitters of Q_1 serve as the input to the NAND gate. The number of emitters defines the number of inputs to the gate. The TTL circuit appearing in Figure 22–4 functions as a two-input NAND gate. A four-input NAND gate would have four emitters. There must be a separate emitter for each input.

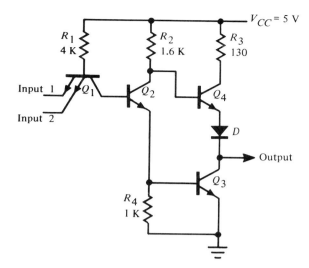

Figure 22–4 TTL circuit.

The phase splitter, Q_2, provides two signals 180° out-of-phase, which drive the output transistors (Q_3 and Q_4). The NAND gate output is taken across Q_3. Transistor Q_4 serves as an active "pull-up" load resistor for Q_3.

The input and output voltage levels for the TTL NAND gate appear in Table 22–1. A zero input voltage is equivalent to having either, or both, inputs at ground potential. The output is at a binary one level (3.6 V) whenever any of the inputs are at ground potential. This causes Q_3 to go into the cutoff condition and its collector rises to approximately 3.6 V. When both inputs are at a binary one level, Q_3 is fully turned on and the collector-emitter voltage is approximately 0.6 V. This level represents a binary zero. The input voltage level for a binary one may range from a low of 2.4 V to a high of 5 V. The specifications for the TTL family appear in Table 22–2.

TABLE 22–1 Truth Table for Two-Input TTL NAND Gate

Input 1 (V)	Input 2 (V)	Output (V)
0	0	3.6
2.4–5	0	3.6
0	2.4–5	3.6
2.4–5	2.4–5	0.6

TABLE 22–2   Operating Specifications for the TTL Family

TTL Specifications

Basic Gate: NAND
Transistor type: BJT
Nomenclature: 74XX/54XX
Required supply voltage: +5 V

Fan-out: 10
Power dissipation: 10mW/gate
Propagation delay: 10 ns
Maximum operating speed: 35 MHz
Noise immunity: 1 V
Logic levels
  binary one: 2.4–3.6 V
  binary zero: 0.4–0.6 V

Like transistors, the nomenclature used to identify integrated circuits has been standardized. This insures that a particular IC will have identical characteristics, no matter who manufactures it. Two general identification systems are used for TTL devices: a 7400 and a 5400 series. The 7400 series are devices manufactured for the consumer and industrial markets whereas the 5400 series are manufactured for military applications. Although the gating functions are identical for both, the 5400 series have closer tolerances and a wider operating temperature range. Individual manufacturers may also utilize their own numbering system. Fairchild, for example, has a 9300 series and Signetics manufactures an 8000 series of TTL logic gates. All TTL devices are compatible with each other regardless of the manufacturer.

22-3.3 TTL Subfamilies.   In addition to the TTL family just discussed, there are other special-purpose TTL integrated circuits called TTL subfamilies: low-power TTL, high-speed TTL, Schottky TTL, low-speed Schottky TTL, open-collector TTL, and three-state TTL. The TTL family discussed in Section 22-3.2 is called standard TTL to differentiate it from the subfamilies. Each of the different subfamilies are discussed in the following paragraphs.

The low-power TTL IC is similar in construction to standard TTL except that the resistor values used in the gating circuit are approximately 10 times larger in value than those used in the standard gate. This results in about one-tenth the power being consumed and a corresponding in-

crease in propagation delay to approximately 33 ns. An indirect relationship exists between propagation delay and power consumption in IC
gates. The less the propagation delay, the greater the power consumed
by the gate. The nomenclature used to identify the low-power TTL integrated circuit is similar to that used for standard TTL except the letter *L*
follows the 74 prefix (74LXX).

High-speed TTL ICs are essentially the same as standard TTL except
that the resistor values are reduced to decrease the propagation delay to
about 6 ns. This raises the power consumption to approximately 22 mW
per gate. The letter *H* is used in the nomenclature to identify this TTL
subfamily (744XX). Although high-speed TTL devices are still available
for purchase, they are considered obsolete and are being replaced by the
Schottky TTL subfamily.

The Schottky TTL subfamily is the fastest of all the TTL ICs and has
the shortest propagation delay (approximately 3 ns). This gate uses non-
saturated transistors to increase speed. The basic circuit is the same as
those for the other TTL gates except that Schottky clamped transistors are
used, as illustrated in Figure 22–5. The Schottky transistor is one which
does not go into saturation when fully turned on. The letter *S* is used in
the nomenclature to denote this subfamily (74SXX). The major disadvantage of this gate is its 19-mW power dissipation.

The low-speed Schottky TTL device has been a popular replacement
for the high-speed TTL integrated circuit. The letters *LS* are used in the
nomenclature to identify this type of IC (74LSXX).

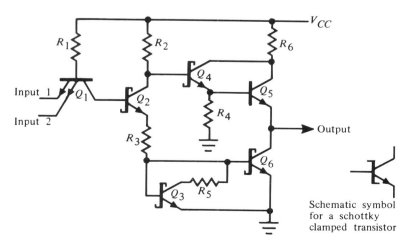

Figure 22–5   Schottky TTL circuit.

Open-collector TTL ICs are special kinds of gates which do not utilize a totem pole output. As shown in Figure 22–6, the output transistor is not connected to an internal load. Instead, the output is usually connected to an external resistor. This is the only method by which the outputs of several gates can be connected together. The open-collector TTL gate has the disadvantages of having larger propagating delays and generating more noise than the other types.

The three-state TTL gate is a special kind of gate in which the output can assume one of three states instead of the usual two. In addition to the usual binary zero and one states, this gate has an open state. The open-state condition represents a very high impedance which is equivalent to disconnecting the totem pole output circuit from the output connection of the gate. This integrated circuit is frequently used as a buffer to isolate other digital circuits from a transmission line (bus).

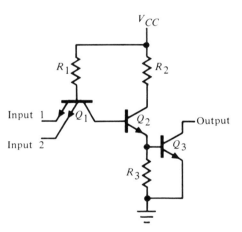

Figure 22–6 Open collector TTL circuit.

22-3.4 The ECL Family. Emitter-coupled logic (ECL) integrated circuits, like the TTL devices, utilize bipolar junction transistor technology. They operate at much higher speeds and have much shorter propagation delays than TTL gates but have the disadvantage of consuming more power. A diagram of an ECL gate appears in Figure 22–7. The heart of the circuit is a differential amplifier made up of transistors Q_3 and Q_4. These transistors, along with Q_1 and Q_6, cause the circuit to operate as a NOR gate. Some ECL circuits utilize an additional transistor (Q_5) to provide a second output which performs the OR gate function. The specifications for the ECL family appear in Table 22–3.

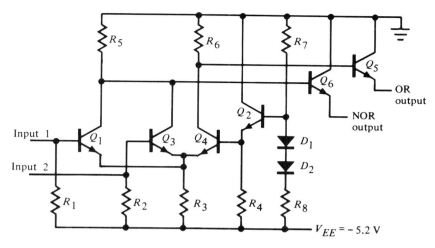

Figure 22–7   ECL circuit.

TABLE 22–3   **Operating Specifications for the ECL Family**

ECL Specifications

Basic gate: OR/NOR
Transistor type: BJT
Required supply voltage: -5.2 V
Fan-out: >50
Noise immunity: 0.2 V
Propagation delay: 2 ns
Maximum operating speed: 200 MHz
Logic levels
   binary one: -0.9 V
   binary zero: -1.75 V
Power dissipation per gate: 50 mW

Like TTL, the ECL device is easy to use; it is more expensive and consumes considerably more power, however. For these reasons, they are mainly used in larger more expensive systems where speed is important. A 10,000 numbering scheme is used for device identification.

22-3.5 The CMOS Family.   Complementary metal-oxide-semiconductor field effect transistor (CMOS) logic gates are often used to implement slower speed gating circuits. These gates can be manufactured with high component densities. The major disadvantage of CMOS logic is its

TABLE 22–4   Operating Specifications for the CMOS Family

CMOS Specifications

Basic gate: NOR
Transistor type: CMOS
Power supply voltage: 3 to 15 V (5 V typical)
Fan-out: >50
Propagation delay: 25 ns
Maximum operating speed: 10 MHz
Logic levels
   binary one: 70% of supply voltage
   binary zero: 30% of supply voltage
Power dissipation per gate: 0.01 mW

slow operating speed. The specifications for the gate are shown in Table 22–4. Notice that the operating speed is considerably lower than that for the TTL gates. This is compensated for somewhat by lower power consumption. A 4000 numbering sequence is usually used as the nomenclature for these devices. The functional capacity for CMOS logic is usually SSI and MSI. This device is manufactured using MOSFET technology. Complementary (N and P) MOS devices are used to form the gate.

22-3.6 The MOS Family.   There are two types of metal-oxide-semiconductor field effect transistor (MOSFET) integrated circuits—P-MOS and N-MOS. These devices are much slower than the TTL devices but consume much less power and can be fabricated having higher component densities. The P-MOS device is the easier to manufacture of the two. However, N-MOS logic is more commonly used because of its faster switching speeds. MOS logic gates are usually manufactured for MSI and LSI functional capacities. They are often used as the circuit structure for memories, arithmetic logic units, and microprocessors.

22-3.7 The I²L Family.   Integrated injection logic (I²L) gates are one of the newest types of digital logic gates. Unlike the other logic family members, no internal resistors are used in the gate circuitry. Like TTL and ECL devices, I²L logic gates utilize BJT technology. This circuit performs the NOR gate function and has a propagation delay of approximately 5 ns. It is characterized by high component density which makes it possible to produce it in LSI form.

22-4 SYSTEM OPERATING SPEED

With so many different kinds of digital integrated circuits available, the circuit designer seemingly has a wide choice of logic gates to choose from. Although such things as power supply voltage, word size, and binary level requirements influence the selection of a particular logic family type, the major factor affecting the decision is the speed at which the system has to operate.

System operating speed is divided into four frequency ranges: very high speed, high speed, medium speed, and low speed. Gating circuits are often synchronized with a train of digital pulses called clock pulses. The operating speeds, clock frequency ranges, and logic family type associated with each frequency range appears in Table 22–5.

TABLE 22–5   Clock Frequencies and Logic Family Types Associated with System Operating Speeds

System Operating Speed	Clock Frequency Range	Logic Family Type
Very high speed	Above 100 MHz	ECL
High speed	30–100 MHz	ECL and Schottky TTL
Medium speed	5–50 MHz	Standard TTL, Low speed Schottky TTL
Slow speed	Below 5 MHz	Low-power TTL, CMOS, MOS

22-5 COMMERCIALLY PACKAGED IC GATES

Scores of different kinds of digital ICs representing all the logic families are produced by the manufacturers of integrated circuits. Usually, several gates are contained in one integrated circuit package. These are all fabricated on a single silicon substrate, or chip. Examples of some TTL devices are shown in Figures 22–8, 22–9, and 22–10. Four two-input NAND gates incorporated into one chip appear in Figure 22–8. This is called a quad two-input NAND gate. The circuit is mounted in a dual-in-line package.

A dual four-input NAND gate is shown in Figure 22–9 while a quad two-input NOR gate is depicted in Figure 22–10.

Although the TTL circuit performs the NAND gate function, any gating function can be accomplished, as evidenced by the NOR gate cir-

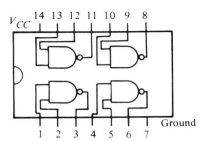

Figure 22–8 Quad two-input NAND gate.

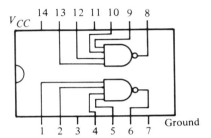

Figure 22–9 Dual four-input NAND gate.

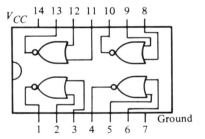

Figure 22–10 Quad two-input NOR gate.

cuit appearing in Figure 22–10. The OR, AND, and NOR functions can be reproduced by connecting inverters at the appropriate inputs and/or output of the NAND gate. An inverter can be made by connecting the inputs of a NAND gate together. Some typical TTL integrated circuits are listed in Table 22–6. Notice that each of the different types are available in at least two subfamilies.

Almost any gating function can be performed by the other logic families as well as TTL. Although the NOR gating function is performed by the basic CMOS circuit, it can be interconnected during manufacture to produce other gating functions. Some typical CMOS integrated circuits appear in Table 22–7.

TABLE 22–6   Selected TTL Integrated Circuits

Circuit Function	Number
Dual four-input AND gates	7421
Dual four-input AND gates	74LS21
Triple three-input AND gates	7411
Triple three-input AND gates	74H11
Triple three-input AND gates	74S11
Triple three-input AND gates	74LS11
Triple three-input AND gates (open collector)	74S15
Triple three-input AND gates (open collector)	74H15
Triple three-input AND gates (open collector)	74LS15
Eight-input NAND gate	7430
Eight-input NAND gate	74H30
Eight-input NAND gate	74S30
Eight-input NAND gate	74LS30
Dual four-input NAND gates (open collector)	7422
Dual four-input NAND gates (open collector)	74H22
Dual four-input NAND gates (open collector)	74S22
Dual four-input NAND gates (open collector)	74LS22
Quad two-input NAND gates	7401
Quad two-input NAND gates	7403
Quad two-input NAND gates	74H03
Quad two-input NAND gates	74LS03

TABLE 22–7   Selected CMOS Integrated Circuits

Circuit Function	Number
Eight-input NOR gate	4002
Triple three-input NOR gates	4025
Quad two-input NOR gates	4001
Quad two-input NAND gates	4011
Triple three-input NAND gates	4023
Dual four-input NAND gates	4068
Quad two-input AND gates	4081
Triple three-input AND gates	4073
Dual four-input OR gates	4072
Triple three-input OR gates	4075

The basic ECL gate performs the NOR function. However, some have two outputs and produce both the NOR and OR functions. Like the TTL and CMOS devices, these circuits can be interconnected during the manufacturing process to perform other gating functions. Some commonly used ECL gates appear in Table 22–8.

TABLE 22–8   Selected ECL Integrated Circuits

Circuit Function	Number
Dual four-input AND/NAND gates	10108
Hex AND gate	10197
Dual three-input OR gates	10110
Quad three-input NOR gates	10100
Quad two-input OR/NOR gates	10101
Dual three-input NOR gates	10111

There are numerous semiconductor companies which manufacture digital integrated circuits. Usually, two or three letters precede the IC number to identify the manufacturer. A list of some of the major manufacturers appears in Table 22–9 along with their identifying letters. For example, a dual four-input AND gate such as the 7421 may be manufactured by several of the manufacturers identified. If manufactured by Texas Instruments, its nomenclature will be SN7421. An IC having an

TABLE 22–9   Partial Listing of Integrated Circuit Manufacturers

Manufacturer	Identifying Letters
RCA	CD
Harris	Hm
Mitel	Sil
Hughes	HCMP
National	DM
Fairchild	F
Hitachi	HD
Motorola	MC
Intersil	IM
Synertek	SY
Signetics	NE
Mitsubishi	M
Texas Instruments	SN

MC7421 nomenclature indicates that the device was manufactured by Motorola. In either case, the circuits are identical.

All unused TTL inputs should be permanently held at a binary one level for minimum switching times and minimum noise sensitivity. This can be accomplished by connecting a resistor of approximately 1000 Ω between the unused input and 2.4- to 5-V source. A resistor connected in this fashion is sometimes called a pull-up resistor. Unused ECL inputs should be permanently held at a binary zero level by connecting a pull-down resistor between the input and ground.

SUMMARY

1. Gating circuits used in most digital systems, such as computers, and micro-processors, are of the integrated circuit type. IC gates consume less power, operate faster, have less propagation delay, are more compact, and are much more reliable than equivalent gates wired from discrete components.
2. Digital ICs have a variety of operating variables, or specifications, with which one must become familiar. These include propagation delay, operating speed, fan-out, power dissipation, noise immunity, and rise and decay time.
3. Gate operating speed and propagation delay are inversely proportional to one another. The shorter the propagation delay, the greater the maximum operating speed.
4. Propagation delay and power consumption are also inversely proportional. Gate operating speed and power consumption are directly proportional to each other, however.
5. Digital ICs are manufactured using different types of transistor technology and internal circuit connections. Each of these is called a logic family. Many different kinds of integrated circuits belong to each family. Common logic families include TTL, ECL, CMOS, MOS, and I²L. The TTL family is by far the most common. TTL ICs are further divided into subfamilies. These include low power (L), high speed (H), Schottky (S), low-speed Schottky (LS), open collector, and three-state.
6. The single factor which most determines the family from which a particular IC is selected is the system operating speed in which the integrated circuit must operate.
7. System operating speed refers to the maximum frequency at which the gates within the IC can switch, or change states. System operating speed is divided into four frequency ranges: very high speed, high speed, medium speed, and slow speed.
8. Although each IC family has its own basic gating scheme (NAND gate—TTL, OR/NOR—ECL, NOR—CMOS), any gating scheme can be reproduced during the manufacturing process by connecting inverters to the gate.
9. In addition to having different possible gating functions, members within a particular family group also differ by the number of gates contained within a particular IC package and the number of inputs to each gate.

10. TTL devices utilize a 54/7400 numbering series; CMOS employs a 4000 number sequence; and ECL ICs use a 10000 numbering sequence.

PRACTICE EXERCISES

1. Briefly define the following terms:
   a. Propagation delay
   b. Operating speed
   c. Fan-out
   d. Power dissipation
   e. Noise immunity
   f. Rise time
   g. Decay time
2. Identify the binary zero and one voltage levels for
   a. TTL logic
   b. CMOS logic
   c. ECL logic
3. Describe the relationship which exists between gate operating speed and power dissipation.
4. Identify the functional capacity for
   a. SSI devices
   b. MSI devices
   c. LSI devices
   d. VLSI devices
5. List five digital integrated circuit families.
6. What are the propagation delay, gate power consumption, and power supply requirements for the following integrated circuit families?
   a. Standard TTL
   b. CMOS
   c. ECL
7. Compare the operating speed and power consumption of the low-power, Schottky, high-speed, and low-speed Schottky TTL with the operating speed and power consumption of standard TTL.
8. What are the four frequency ranges associated with system operating speed?
9. What are the logic families associated with each of the ranges identified in exercise 8?
10. List the nomenclature used to identify TTL, CMOS, and ECL integrated circuit devices.
11. Identify the logic gate associated with the basic circuitry making up the following IC families:
    a. ECL
    b. TTL
    c. CMOS
12. Although each logic family has its own unique gate, almost any gating function is available in any logic family. Discuss how these other gates are formed.

13. Draw the schematic diagram of the standard TTL gating circuit.
14. Identify the transistor technology used in the manufacture of the following IC families:
    a. I²L
    b. TTL
    c. ECL
    d. CMOS
15. Identify the output voltage levels for the TTL NAND gate.
16. What most determines the selection of a particular IC family for a given circuit application?
17. List three triple three-input TTL AND gates.
18. Identify one eight-input TTL NAND gate.
19. To what digital IC family does the 4001 device belong?
20. What kind of IC is identified by the number 10111?
21. The letters SN represent which integrated circuit manufacturer?
22. What should be done with unused TTL inputs?
23. Draw the schematic diagram of an ECL circuit.
24. What is a common application for three-state TTL logic ICs?
25. What kind of digital IC is identified by the number 74LS30?

ANSWERS TO PRACTICE EXERCISES

1. a. Propagation delay is the time required for a gate or inverter to change states.
    b. Operating speed is the maximum frequency at which digital data can be applied to a gate.
    c. Fan-out refers to the number of other gate inputs a particular gate can drive.
    d. Power dissipation is the power consumed by a single gate in a digital integrated circuit.
    e. Noise immunity is the amount of noise which can be superimposed on a gate input signal without the gate changing states.
    f. Rise time is the time required for a pulse to increase from 10 to 90 percent of its maximum value.
    g. Decay time is the time required for a pulse to decrease from 90 to 10 percent of its maximum value.

2.

IC Family	Zero level	One level
a. TTL	0.4 to 0.6 V	2.4 to 3.6 V
b. CMOS	30 percent of V_{CC}	70 percent of V_{CC}
c. ECL	-1.75 V	-0.9 V

3. Gate operating speed and gate power dissipation are directly proportional. The faster the operating speed, the greater the power dissipation.
4. a. SSI: 1 to 11 gates
    b. MSI: 12 to 99 gates
    c. LSI: 100 to 10,000 gates
    d. VLSI: more than 10,000 gates

5. Digital integrated circuit families include TTL, CMOS, MOS, ECL, and I²L.
6. **a.** TTL: 10 ns, 10 mW, 5 V
   b. CMOS: 25 ns, 0.01 mW, 3 to 15 V
   c. ECL: 2 ns, 50 mW, −5.2 V
7. **a.** Low power (L)—lower operating speed and less power consumption
   b. Schottky (S)—faster operating speed and greater power consumption
   c. High speed (H)—faster operating speed and greater power consumption
   d. Low-speed Schottky (LS)—faster operating speed and greater power consumption
8. The frequency ranges associated with system operating speed include
   (a) slow speed—clock rate less than 5 MHz;
   (b) medium speed—clock rate 5 to 50 MHz;
   (c) high speed—clock rate 30 to 100 MHz; and
   (d) very high speed—clock rate in excess of 100 MHZ.
9. Digital logic families associated with system operating speed ranges include
   (a) slow speed—low-speed TTL, MOS, and CMOS;
   (b) medium speed—standard TTL and low-power Schottky TTL;
   (c) high speed—ECL and Schottky TTL; and
   (d) very high speed—ECL.
10. Digital IC identification nomenclature includes 54/7400 series for TTL, 4000 series for CMOS, and 10,000 series for ECL.
11. The basic gate for ECL ICs is the NOR gate. Some ECL devices have two outputs, in which case both the OR and NOR gating functions are available. The basic TTL circuit functions as a NAND gate and the CMOS circuit serves as a NOR gate.
12. Other gates are formed by connecting inverters internally to the basic gating circuit. An inverter can be made by connecting together the inputs of one of the basic gates. Inverters may be connected to the inputs, the output, or to both the inputs and the output of a basic gate to perform some other gating function.
13. See Figure 22–4.
14. The transistor technology used in the fabrication of I²L, TTL, and ECL digital ICs is bipolar junction. Complementary (P and N) MOSFET technology is used in the manufacture of CMOS IC devices.
15. The output voltage levels for the TTL NAND gate is 0.4 to 0.6 V for a binary zero (output transistor fully turned on) and 2.4 to 3.6 V for a binary one (output transistor cut off).
16. The system operating speed dictates to a large degree the selection of a particular IC family.
17. Three triple three-input TTL AND gates include the 7411, 74LS11, and 74H11.
18. The 7430 is an eight-input TTL NAND gate.
19. The 4001 IC is a CMOS device.
20. The 10111 is a dual three-input ECL NOR gate.
21. SN is a prefix used to identify Texas Instruments as the manufacturer.
22. Unused TTL inputs should be connected to a binary one voltage level through a pull-up resistor.
23. See Figure 22–7.

24. Three-state TTL logic devices are often used as buffers for isolation purposes.
25. The 74LS30 is an eight-input low-speed Schottky TTL NAND gate.

CHAPTER EXAMINATION

1. The DC voltage requirement for the ECL digital family is
   a. 5 V
   b. 5.2 V
   c. 12.25 V
   d. none of the above
2. The time required for a pulse to change from 10 to 90 percent of its maximum value defines
   a. rise time
   b. operating speed
   c. propagation delay
   d. binary level transition period
3. The NAND gate function is produced by the internal circuitry of the _____ logic family.
   a. I^2L **c.** ECL
   b. TTL   **d.** CMOS
4. The binary zero and one levels for ECL digital ICs are
   a. 0 and 5 V   **c.** -1.75 and -0.9 V
   b. 0.01 and 3.5 V   **d.** none of the above
5. The propagation delay for standard TTL devices is _____.
   a. 1 ns   **c.** 25 ns
   b. 10 ns   **d.** none of the above
6. _____ is the fastest of the several types of TTL devices.
   a. Standard TTL   **c.** High-speed TTL
   b. Schottky TTL   **d.** Low-speed Schottky TTL
7. The _____ IC family is the slowest and consumes the least amount of power.
   a. I^2L **c.** ECL
   b. TTL   **d.** CMOS
8. _____ digital ICs can be driven faster than any of the other IC family devices.
   a. TTL   **c.** MOS
   b. ECL   **d.** CMOS
9. The output binary zero and one levels for TTL gates are approximately
   a. 0.1 and 5 V   **c.** 0.6 and 3.50 V
   b. 0.9 and 1.75 V   **d.** none of the above
Choose true or false for questions 10 to 22.
10. T F   The functional capacity of an integrated circuit refers to the logic function performed by the internal circuitry forming the gate.

11. T F   The TTL logic family utilizes bipolar junction technology.
12. T F   The faster a gate is driven, the greater the amount of power consumed by the gate.
13. T F   An integrated circuit has the number 74S26 printed on its case. This circuit is a slow-speed TTL device.
14. T F   The gating function performed by the internal circuitry of CMOS ICs is the AND function.
15. T F   MOS integrated circuits would probably be used in integrated circuits driven by digital, or clock, pulses having a frequency of 150 MHz.
16. T F   The DC voltage requirements for CMOS devices is often 5 V.
17. T F   CMOS IC devices are often used in high operating speed system applications.
18. T F   Integrated circuits capable of being driven by pulses having frequencies lying between 5 and 50 MHz operate in the high-speed operating range.
19. T F   LSI devices usually contain 1 to 11 gates.
20. T F   The AND gating function is performed by the internal circuitry of the ECL integrated circuit family.
21. T F   Noise immunity refers to the amplitude of the noise generated by the gates when they change states.
22. T F   Gate power dissipation and operating speed are inversely proportional to one another.

23

Flip-Flop Circuits

OBJECTIVES

Upon completion of this chapter you should be able to do the following:

1. List the three types of multivibrator circuits and identify the type associated with the flip-flop.
2. Draw the logic diagram of an S-R flip-flop.
3. Identify four types of flip-flops.
4. Discuss what is meant by the set and reset states of a flip-flop and explain how the state of a flip-flop can be determined.
5. Describe the operation of the S-R, T, D, and J-K flip-flops by discussing the normal input conditions and the input conditions which must exist for the flip-flops to change states.
6. Draw the schematic symbols for the S-R, T, D, and J-K flip-flops and identify all inputs and outputs.
7. Draw or recognize the output waveforms of the S-R, T, D, and J-K flip-flops for specified input conditions.
8. Discuss an application for the S-R, T, D, and J-K flip-flops.

23-1 INTRODUCTION

The flip-flop is one of the basic building blocks of digital circuits. The flip-flop is a type of multivibrator circuit. As discussed in Chapter 19, there are three different types of multivibrator circuits: the astable, bistable, and monostable. Astable and monostable multivibrators can be used to generate clock pulses to synchronize digital circuits. Bistable multivibra-

527

tors are used as flip-flops in such applications as shift registers, frequency counters, frequency dividers, and memory circuits.

The bistable multivibrator is formed by connecting together two inverted gates. Either the NOR or the NAND may be used. The output of each gate is coupled to one of the inputs of the other. The circuit has two stable states. In one state one gate is on and the other off. The multivibrator remains in this condition until a change in the voltage level applied to one of the other inputs causes it to change states. With the application of a change in voltage levels, the circuit "flips" into the other state. The multivibrator remains in this state until another change in voltage levels occurs, and the circuit "flops" back into its original state, hence the name flip-flop. There are several different types of flip-flops: the *S-R*, *T*, *D*, and *J-K*.

23-2 THE *S-R* FLIP-FLOP

The logic diagram and schematic symbol for an *S-R* (set-reset) flip-flop is shown in Figure 23–1. The circuit consists of two NAND gates connected together so that the output of each stage is connected to one of the inputs of the other stage. The circuit has two inputs—set and reset (*S* and *R*) and two outputs (*Q* and $\overline{Q}$). When the circuit is initially energized, either gate can be conducting and the other cut off due to small mismatches in the characteristics of the two gates. If gate 1 is turned off and gate 2 is in the on state, the output of gate 1 is high (binary one) and that of gate 2 is low (binary zero). In this condition a binary one is coupled from the output of gate 1 to one input of gate 2, as indicated in Figure 23–2. At the same time a binary zero voltage level is coupled from the output of gate 2 to one of the inputs to gate 1. The other two inputs to the circuit are normally maintained at a binary one level. The circuit will remain in this

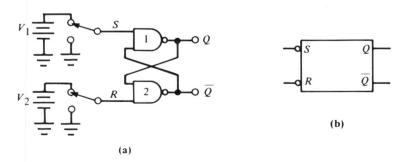

Figure 23–1   NAND gate *S-R* flip-flop: (a) logic diagram; (b) schematic symbol.

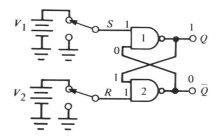

Figure 23–2 NAND gate *S-R* flip-flop circuit conditions when gate I is cut off and gate 2 conducting.

state, output Q at a binary one level and output $\overline{Q}$ at a binary zero level, until the reset input to gate 2 is momentarily brought to a binary zero level by depressing the reset switch, as shown in Figure 23–3. At this time the output of gate 2 goes from a binary zero to a binary one level. This voltage is coupled to the input of gate 1, causing that gate's output to fall from a binary one to a binary zero level. This agrees with the NAND gate logic discussed in Chapter 21. The circuit remains latched in this condition until the set switch is momentarily depressed, as illustrated in Figure 23–4. This causes the flip-flop to return to its original state.

A flip-flop is in the set state when the output of gate 1 is high (binary one) and gate 2 low (binary zero). The circuit is in the reset state when the output of gate 2 is high and gate 1 low. The outputs of a flip-flop are often identified as Q and $\overline{Q}$. The Q output is associated with gate 1 and is usually referred to as the normal output. When Q is high, the

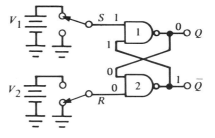

Figure 23–3 Depressing the reset switch causes the flip-flop to change states.

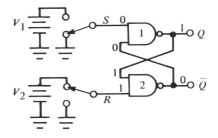

Figure 23–4 Depressing the set switch causes the flip-flop to change states.

flip-flop is in the set state. The $\overline{Q}$ output is associated with gate 2 and is called the complemented, or inverted, output. A voltmeter or LED can be connected to the Q output to determine the state of the flip-flop.

The S-R flip-flop is often called a latch. When the circuit is in the set state, it remains latched in this condition. It can be unlatched, or reset, by applying a binary zero to the reset input. Applying a binary zero to the set input will not cause the flip-flop to change states. If the flip-flop is in the reset state, it can be set by applying a binary zero level to the set input. It cannot be set by applying a binary zero to the reset input. Bubbles appear on the input terminals of the NAND gate latch symbol shown in Figure 23–1(b) to indicate that a binary zero (active low) causes the flip-flop to change states.

Although switches can be used to apply binary zero levels to the inputs of the flip-flop, usually electrical signals are applied, as shown in Figure 23–5. Normally both inputs are maintained at a binary one voltage level. When a change in state is required, the voltage level of the desired input is changed from a binary one to a binary zero. If the flip-flop appearing in Figure 23–5 is in the set state, it will reset at time t. As soon as the circuit resets, both inputs are again maintained at a binary one voltage level. The only way to set the flip-flop is to cause the input voltage to the S input to momentarily fall to a binary zero level.

The truth table for the NAND gate latch is shown in Table 23–1. Notice that if both the set and reset inputs are maintained at a binary one level, the flip-flop can be either in the set or reset state. The actual state depends upon what has occurred during the previous input conditions. Also, when the circuit is first energized, it can go into either state. The truth table verifies the operation of the circuit as it was previously discussed. Notice that if the latch is in the reset state, a binary zero applied to the S input causes the circuit to change states and become set. No change occurs whenever a binary zero is applied to the S input if the circuit is already in the set state. A binary zero voltage level applied to the R input causes the latch to change states and become reset if the circuit was already in the set state. If the latch is in the reset state and a binary zero voltage level is applied to the R input, no change occurs. The flip-

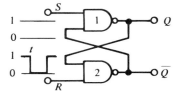

Figure 23–5   Resetting a NAND gate flip-flop with a binary voltage.

TABLE 23–1   Truth Table for NAND Gate Flip-Flop

Inputs		Outputs	
S	R	Q	$\overline{Q}$
1	1	Indeterminate state. Can either be set or reset.	
0	1	1	0
1	0	0	1
0	0	Disallowed state.	

flop remains reset. The last condition appearing in the truth table occurs if both inputs are at a binary zero voltage level simultaneously. This condition is called the disallowed state and is undesirable as it can produce unwanted operations in other circuits connected to the latch.

Latches can also be connected from NOR gates. The operation of the NOR gate latch is exactly like that of the NAND gate latch except that the *S* and *R* inputs are normally maintained at a binary zero voltage level. A binary one voltage level causes the flip-flop to either set or reset. A NOR gate latch is shown in Figure 23–6. Notice that the positions of the *S* and *R* inputs are reversed from those on the NAND gate latch. The truth table for the NOR gate latch is shown in Table 23–2.

Latches have limited applications and are primarily used to build more advanced flip-flops. Another use is that of a switch buffer. Most mechanical switches have some contact bounce. This means that when a switch is initially opened or closed, its contacts bounce open or closed for a brief interval of time. This creates short-term, or transient, voltages which can travel down conductors to digital circuits causing them to trigger, or change state. To prevent unwanted triggering from occurring, a

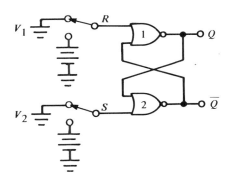

Figure 23–6   NOR gate latch.

TABLE 23–2   Truth Table for NOR Gate Flip-Flop

Inputs		Outputs	
S	R	Q	$\overline{Q}$
0	0	Indeterminate state. Can be either set or reset.	
1	0	1	0
0	1	0	1
1	1	Disallowed state.	

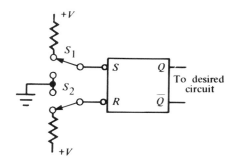

Figure 23–7   Latch used as a switch buffer.

latch is often placed between the switch and another digital circuit, as illustrated in Figure 23–7. The latch is normally kept in the reset state. The required circuit is energized by depressing S_1. This causes the flip-flop to set and Q becomes high, energizing the required circuit. Contact bounce created by S_1 does not affect the output of the flip-flop. The circuit can be deenergized by depressing S_2 and resetting the flip-flop.

23-3 THE T FLIP-FLOP

The T flip-flop is a simple type of circuit consisting of two gates connected to a latch, as illustrated in Figure 23–8. Gate 1 serves as the set input to the latch and gate 2 acts as the reset input. Gates 1 and 2 obtain their inputs from the outputs of the latch and from an external source of rectangular pulses. These are often called clock, or timing, pulses. Clock pulses are used to synchronize the operations in a digital system so that they occur at the proper time. Clock pulses cause the T flip-flop to change states. When the circuit changes states, it is said to toggle.

The logic diagram and schematic symbol of a T flip-flop is shown in Figure 23–9. Although the circuit can be either in the set or reset state,

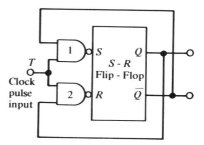

Figure 23–8 Diagram of a *T* flip-flop.

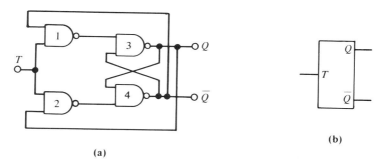

(a)

(b)

Figure 23–9 (a) Logic diagram and (b) schematic symbol for a *T* flip-flop.

for discussion purposes it is assumed to be in the reset condition. This causes a binary zero to be applied from the Q output of gate 3 to one input of gate 2. A binary one is applied to one input of gate 1 from the output of gate 4. As illustrated by the synchrogram (timing diagram) appearing in Figure 23–10, at time t_0, the clock pulse goes from a binary zero to a binary one voltage level. This places a binary one on one input of both gates 1 and 2. This causes the inputs to gate 2 to be binary one and binary zero, respectively, and the output to be binary one. Both inputs to gate 1 are at a binary one level. The output of this gate is binary

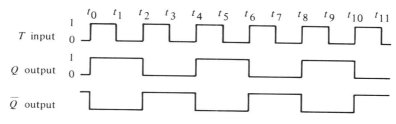

Figure 23–10 Relationship between input clock pulses and output pulses for a *T* flip-flop.

zero, which sets the *S-R* flip-flop formed from gates 3 and 4. These input conditions cause the *T* flip-flop to change states (toggle). The circuit toggles when the clock pulse level changes from a binary zero to a binary one level.

At time t_1 the clock pulse level falls from a binary one to a binary zero. The clock pulse inputs to gates 1 and 2 are now at a binary zero level. The other input to gate 2 comes from gate 3 and is a binary one. These input conditions cause the output of gate 2 to remain at a binary one level. The input to gate 1, which comes from gate 4, is a binary zero. The input conditions to gate 1 are such that its output remains at a binary one level. Since the outputs of both gates 1 and 2 are binary one, the latch remains in its set state and the *T* flip-flop does not toggle.

With the application of the second clock pulse at time t_2, the clock input to gates 1 and 2 rises from a binary zero to a binary one voltage level. Since the input to gate 2, which comes from gate 3, is a binary one, the output of gate 2 changes from a binary one to a binary zero. The output of gate one remains at a binary one level. These conditions cause the latch to go from the set to the reset state, and the flip-flop toggles. This process continues. At time t_4 the *T* flip-flop toggles and goes into the set state. It resets at time t_6. Notice that the outputs of the *T* flip-flop have the same frequency but they are complements of one another. Also observe that the output frequency is one-half the input frequency. It takes two clock pulses to complete an entire output pulse cycle.

The *T* flip-flop is level triggered. The circuit toggles whenever the clock pulse level changes from a binary zero to a binary one. *T* flip-flops can be used as frequency dividers since the output frequency is one-half the input pulse frequency. These circuits can be connected together in cascade for division by successive powers of two, as illustrated in Figure 23–11. The output frequency is $\frac{1}{16}$ the input pulse frequency.

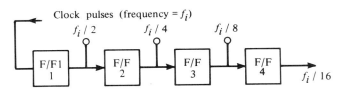

Figure 23–11 Four *T* flip-flops connected in cascade to produce a frequency division of 16.

23-4 THE *D* FLIP-FLOP

The *D* flip-flop, like the *T* flip-flop, is a type of clocked flip-flop. As indicated in Figure 23–12, the circuit consists of an inverter and four NAND

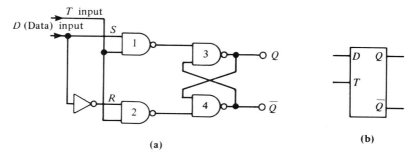

Figure 23–12 (a) Logic diagram and (b) schematic symbol for a *D* flip-flop.

gates. Gates 3 and 4 are connected to form a latch. Gates 1 and 2 provide the set and reset inputs to the latch and are called enabling gates. The enabling gates determine whether or not the binary data coming into the flip-flop from the *D* (data) input are passed on to the latch. The inverter is used to ensure that the *S* and *R* latch inputs are complementary to prevent it from going into the disallowed state.

Clock pulses applied to the *T* input control the flip-flop. This input is used to determine whether the input data will be recognized or ignored by the latch. When the clock pulse is high (binary one) the data on the *D* line passes through the enabling gates to the latch and is "stored." If the clock pulse is low (binary zero), the data on the *D* line is ignored and the latch does not change states. A flip-flop is often used to "store" binary data. A binary one is stored when the flip-flop is in the set condition (*Q* is at a binary one level) and a binary zero is stored in the reset condition.

The pulses for the *T* and *D* inputs are shown in Figure 23–13 along with the *Q* output conditions for the *D* flip-flop appearing in Figure 23–12. As indicated, the *D* flip-flop is initially in the reset state (*Q* is zero). At time t_0 the input to enabling gate 1 from the *D* input is high and the input to gate 2 from the inverter is low. The *T* input to gates 1 and 2 is low causing the the latch to remain in the reset state. At time t_1 the clock pulse level changes from a low to a high level. This causes the binary levels at both the *D* and *T* inputs to be high simultaneously. This causes the

Figure 23–13 Input and output data for the *D* flip-flop appearing in Figure 23–12.

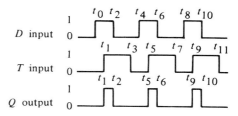

output of gate 1 to become a binary zero while the output of gate 1 remains at a binary one level. Since the output of gate 1 controls the set function of the latch, the conditions are such that the latch sets. The data on the D input drops to binary zero at time t_2. Because the clock pulse is still high, the output of gate 1 changes from a binary zero to a binary one. At the same time, the output of gate 2 changes to a binary zero. Gate 2 controls the reset function of the latch and the conditions are such that the latch switches into the reset state and the Q output becomes a binary zero.

This process continues. As successive data and clock pulses are applied to the D and T inputs, respectively, the Q output of the flip-flop is a reproduction of the data coming into the D input as long as the clock pulses are at a binary one level. While the clock pulses are low, the data coming into the D input are ignored and the flip-flop retains the data present during the last time the clock pulse was high.

The primary application of the D flip-flop is its use as a memory element to store a binary bit of data. The circuit just discussed is a level-triggered flip-flop. It changed states whenever the clock input was high and the D input level changed. Another popular type of D flip-flop is the edge triggered. This flip-flop changes states during the leading edge of the clock pulse.

23-5 THE J-K FLIP-FLOP

The J-K flip-flop is the most versatile of all the flip-flops. It can perform the S-R, T, and D flip-flop functions in addition to performing operations these other circuits cannot perform. As depicted in the diagram appearing in Figure 23–14, the J-K flip-flop is made up of two latches—a master and a slave. Enabling gates are connected to the inputs of each latch. Clock pulses applied to the inputs of the enabling gates control each

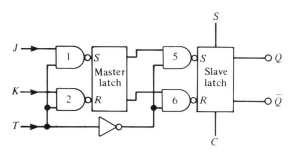

Figure 23–14 Diagram of a J-K flip-flop.

latch. An inverter is used to complement the clock pulses applied to enabling gates 5 and 6 from those applied to gates 1 and 2. The master latch is used to control the slave latch. The state, or output condition, of the *J-K* flip-flop is determined by the slave latch. If the *Q* output of the *J-K* flip-flop is at a binary zero level, the slave latch (and the *J-K* flip-flop) is in the reset state. Although the clock pulses applied to the *T* input control the *J-K* flip-flop, the *J* and and *K* inputs to the master latch determine how the flip-flop will be controlled.

The slave latch can also be controlled by the set and reset (sometimes called the set and clear) inputs. They are used to preset or reset the *J-K* flip-flop. These inputs override all other input conditions. A binary one voltage level is maintained at both inputs. The flip-flop is set by momentarily applying a binary zero level (such as ground) to the set input. The circuit is reset by momentarily applying a binary zero to the reset input. Although the circuit shown in Figure 23–14 has both set and clear inputs, some *J-K* flip-flops have only a clear input. The set input is omitted.

The logic diagram and schematic symbol for a *J-K* flip-flop appears in Figure 23–15. NAND gates 1 and 2 are the enabling gates for the master latch. Gates 3 and 4 form the master latch. NAND gates 5 and 6 are the enabling gates for the slave latch which consists of gates 7 and 8. Depending upon the desired input conditions, the *J-K* flip-flop can be operated in three different ways. The different operating conditions are referred to as modes of operation and include the *T*, *J-K*, and *S-C*.

In the *T* mode the *J-K* flip-flop operates much like a *T* flip-flop, except that the circuit toggles when the clock pulses change from a high to a low level. Both the *J* and *K* inputs and the *S* and *C* inputs are maintained at a binary one voltage level. As illustrated by the synchrogram appearing in Figure 23–16, the flip-flop is initially in the reset state. At

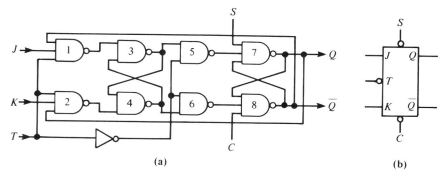

(a)   (b)

Figure 23–15   (a) Logic diagram and (b) schematic symbol for a *J-K* flip-flop.

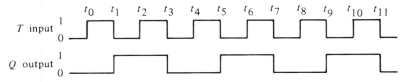

Figure 23–16 *T* mode of operation.

time t_0 the clock pulse is high and the conditions are such that the flip-flop cannot change states. When the clock pulse falls to binary zero at time t_1, the output of the master latch causes the slave latch to set. The output of the *J-K* flip-flop is now a binary one. When the clock pulse changes from a binary zero to a binary one level, at time t_2, the output of the master latch does not cause the slave latch to change states. The flip-flop remains in the set condition. This process continues with the slave latch resetting at time t_3. The output frequency is one-half the input pulse frequency, just as it is for the *T* flip-flop. Unlike the *T* flip-flop which toggles whenever the clock pulse level changes from a binary zero to a binary one, the *J-K* flip-flop toggles when the clock pulse level changes from a binary one to a binary zero. This is the purpose of the bubble appearing at the *T* input.

   The *J-K* mode is the type of operation most often used with the *J-K* flip-flop. When the *J*, *S*, and *C* inputs are at a binary one level and a binary zero is applied to the *K* input, the flip-flop will set whenever the clock pulse applied to the *T* input falls from a high to a low level. The flip-flop will go into the reset state whenever the clock pulse level changes from a high to a low while the *K*, *S*, and *C* inputs are at a binary one level and the *J* input is a binary zero. This is illustrated by the synchrogram shown in Figure 23–17. The flip-flop will remain in its previous

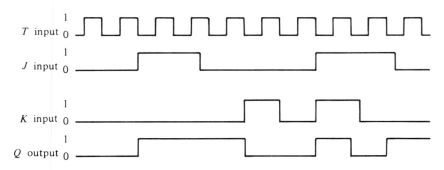

Figure 23–17 *J-K* mode of operation.

state if both the J and K inputs are at a binary zero level and the clock pulse changes from a high to a low level.

The S-C mode of operation is used to either preset or clear the flip-flop. It will go into the set state when a binary zero is applied to the S input and the J, K, T, and C inputs are all maintained at a binary one level. The flip-flop will reset when a binary one is present at all the other inputs and a binary zero is applied to the C input. When used in this fashion, the J-K flip-flop operates as an S-R flip-flop, or latch.

23-6 COMMERCIALLY PACKAGED IC FLIP-FLOPS

Flip-flops can be formed by connecting together discrete components, by interconnecting IC gates, and by fabricating them in IC format. Most are of the latter type with many variations of the latch, D, and J-K flip-flops being available. The T flip-flop is not commonly manufactured. Instead, its function is reproduced by modifying the D or J-K circuits, as illustrated in Figure 23–18. The circuit appearing in Figure 23–18(b) is merely a J-K flip-flop operating in the T mode. Integrated circuit flip-flops are available in most IC logic families. Some commonly used CMOS, ECL, and TTL devices are listed in Table 23–3.

D flip-flops can have set and clear inputs to preset or clear the circuit just as do some J-K flip-flops. Inputs to flip-flops are often categorized as being either synchronous or asynchronous. Synchronous inputs do not directly control the output state of the flip-flop. Instead, they establish the conditions, and a clock pulse determines when the output state will change. Asynchronous inputs are those which do cause the output state of the flip-flop to change, regardless of the absence or presence of clock pulses. The D input to a D flip-flop and the J and K inputs to a J-K flip-flop are examples of synchronous inputs. The S and C inputs to any flip-flop are examples of asynchronous inputs.

Most D and J-K flip-flops are level triggered. They change states, if the other input conditions allow, when the clock pulse level changes. There are some edge-triggered D and J-K flip-flops. These types of cir-

(a)   (b)

Figure 23–18   Obtaining the T flip-flop function from (a) the D and (b) the J-K flip-flops.

TABLE 23–3   Selected Types of IC Flip-Flops

Family	Type of Flip-Flop	Number
CMOS	Quad NOR R-S latch	4043
	Quad NAND R-S latch	4044
	Quad D flip-flop	4042
	Dual D flip-flop	4013
	Quad D flip-flop	4076
	Hex D flip-flop	4017
	Dual J-K flip-flop	4027
	Dual J-K flip-flop	4095
ECL	Dual D flip-flop	10130
	Quad D flip-flop	10133
	Quad D flip-flop	10533
TTL	Quad S-R latch	74279
	Quad S-R latch	74LS279
	Dual D flip-flop	7474
	Dual D flip-flop	74LS74
	Dual D flip-flop	74H74
	Dual D flip-flop	74S74
	J-K flip-flop	74105
	J-K flip-flop with S and C	7472
	J-K flip-flop with S and C	74H72
	J-K flip-flop with C	74107
	J-K flip-flop with C	74LS107
	J-K flip-flop with C	74H107
	Dual J-K flip-flop with S and C	7476
	Dual J-K flip-flop with S and C	74LS76
	Dual J-K flip-flop with S and C	74H76

cuits change state during the time that it takes the clock pulses to change levels.

The D and J-K flip-flops are, by far, more commonly used than the other two types. The J-K is the more versatile of the two and can perform the functions of the other three if the input voltage levels are proper or if modified to operate as a D flip-flop, as illustrated in Figure 23–19.

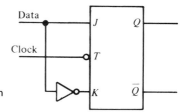

Figure 23–19 Obtaining the D flip-flop function from a J-K flip-flop.

Flip-flops are often used as memory elements, counters, and frequency dividers. When used as a memory element it will store one bit of binary data. If the flip-flop is in the set state, a binary one is being stored. A binary zero is being stored if the circuit is in the reset state. Flip-flops can be connected together in cascade to store additional bits or words.

In a sense, there is a hierarchy of digital circuits. For example, the three basic gates (AND, OR, and NOT) are used to build the more advanced inverted gates (NAND and NOR). The inverted gates are used to build the latch. The latch is used in building the other types of flip-flops. These types of flip-flops are used in building registers (short-term memory), frequency counters, and frequency dividers all of which form important sections in computers and microprocessors.

SUMMARY

1. Flip-flop circuits are types of bistable multivibrators. There are four general types of flip-flops. These include the S-R, T, D, and J-K.
2. The S-R (set-reset) flip-flop can be connected from either NAND or NOR gates. The flip-flop is in the set state if the normal (Q) output is at a binary one level and the complemented ($\overline{Q}$) output is a binary zero. The circuit is in the reset state if the complemented output is high and the normal output is low.
3. Both the S and R inputs are normally maintained at a binary one level for a NAND gate latch. If the flip-flop is in the reset state, it can be set by momentarily applying a binary zero level to the S input. If the flip-flop is in the set state, it can be reset by applying a binary low to the R input.
4. The S-R flip-flop is frequently called a latch because it remains latched in the set or reset output state until the S or R input voltage levels are changed.
5. The latch has limited applications by itself. It is sometimes used as a switch buffer to prevent switch contact bounce from triggering other digital circuits. Its major application is in its use in more sophisticated flip-flop circuits.
6. The T flip-flop is formed by connecting inverted gates to the inputs of a latch. The outputs of the gates serve as the set and reset inputs to the latch. The inputs to the gates come from the latch outputs and from timing, or clock, pulses. This flip-flop can be used as a frequency counter or frequency divider. Its output pulse frequency is one-half the input frequency.

7. The *D* flip-flop is formed by connecting inverted (enabling) gates to the *S* and *R* inputs of a latch. An inverter is connected between the data (*D*) inputs of both latches so that the data inputs to the enabling gates are complements of one another. This flip-flop has two inputs—one for binary data and the other for clock pulses. The enabling gates will accept data coming in on the *D* line when the binary data and clock pulse levels are both high. The data is stored by the latch. When the clock pulse level is low, the data does not pass through the enabling gates and is not stored by the latch; hence it is ignored.

8. The *J-K* flip-flop is the most versatile of the four types of flip-flops. The functions performed by the other three flip-flops can be accomplished with this circuit.

9. The *J-K* flip-flop is made up of four enabling gates and two latches—a master and slave. The master latch controls the slave latch. The output of the slave latch represents the output of the flip-flop.

10. There are many different versions of the *S-R, D,* and *J-K* flip-flops manufactured from most of the IC families. Many of the *D* and *J-K* devices have one or more asynchronous (*S-C*) inputs in addition to the usual *D* or *J-K* inputs. These allow the flip-flop to be cleared, or preset, to a desired state prior to applying binary data.

11. The *D* and *J-K* flip-flops are often used in memory applications. A binary one is being stored when the output latch circuit is in the set state. The reset state represents the storage of a binary zero.

PRACTICE EXERCISES

1. Identify the three types of multivibrators.
2. Which one of the multivibrators identified above is associated with the flip-flop?
3. Draw the logic diagram of an *S-R* flip-flop.
4. What is meant by the set and reset states of a flip-flop? How can these states be determined?
5. What is meant by the indeterminate state of a latch?
6. How can the output state of a NAND gate latch be changed?
7. What are the normal input conditions to a NAND gate latch?
8. What are the normal input conditions to a NOR gate latch?
9. How can the output state of a NOR gate latch be changed?
10. Identify two applications for the *S-R* flip-flop.
11. Draw the logic diagram of a *T* flip-flop.
12. What causes the output state of a *T* flip-flop to change?
13. Describe what is meant by level triggering.
14. What is the relationship between the input and output pulse frequency for a *T* flip-flop?
15. What are two applications for the *T* flip-flop?
16. Draw the logic diagram of a *D* flip-flop.
17. What input conditions are required for the latch to store data in the *D* flip-flop?
18. Draw the output waveform for a *D* flip-flop for the *D* and *T* inputs shown in Figure 23–20 if the flip-flop is initially in the reset state.

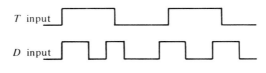

Figure 23–20 Q output _____

19. Discuss an application for the D flip-flop.
20. Draw the logic diagram of a J-K flip-flop.
21. Identify the three modes of operation for the J-K flip-flop.
22. What should the input conditions be if the J-K flip-flop is to be operated in the T mode?
23. For the inputs shown in Figure 23–21, draw the output of a J-K flip-flop if the flip-flop is initially in the reset state.

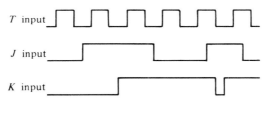

Figure 23–21 Q output _____

24. What is the difference between asynchronous and synchronous inputs to a flip-flop? Identify examples of each.
25. Draw a diagram showing how a D flip-flop can be connected to operate as a T flip-flop.

ANSWERS TO PRACTICE EXERCISES

1. The three types of multivibrators include the astable, bistable, and monostable.
2. Flip-flop circuits are a type of bistable multivibrator.
3. See Figure 23–1.
4. A flip-flop is in the set state if the Q output is at a binary one level and the $\overline{Q}$ output is binary zero. The state of a flip-flop can be determined with a voltmeter or LED.
5. When a flip-flop is first energized it can be either in the set or reset state providing the inputs are as they should be (both high for NAND gate flip-flops).
6. A NAND gate latch can be changed by applying a binary zero to the R input if it is in the set state or by applying a binary zero to the S input if the flip-flop is in the reset state.
7. The inputs are both maintained at a binary one level.
8. On a NOR gate latch, the inputs are normally maintained at a binary zero level.

9. If the NOR latch is in the set state, it can be reset by applying a binary one to the R input. In the reset state, it can be set by applying a binary one to the S input.

10. The S-R flip-flop is sometimes used as a buffer to isolate a switch from digital circuits. It is also the basic building block for the T, D, and J-K flip-flops.

11. See Figure 23–9.

12. The T flip-flop changes states whenever the clock pulse applied to the input changes from a binary zero to a binary one level.

13. Level triggering is that type of triggering which causes a flip-flop to change state whenever the binary, or voltage, level of the input control pulse changes.

14. The output pulse frequency is one-half the input frequency.

15. T flip-flops are used in pulse frequency division and pulse counting applications.

16. See Figure 23–12.

17. The clock pulse applied to the T input must be at a binary one level.

18.

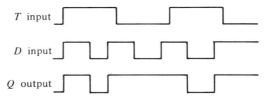

Figure 23–22

19. The D flip-flop can be used to store a binary bit.

20. See Figure 23–15.

21. The J-K flip-flop can operate in the S-R, T, and J-K modes.

22. The J, K, S, and R (C) inputs should all be maintained at a binary one level if the J-K flip-flop is to be operated in the T mode.

23.

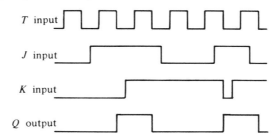

Figure 23–23

24. Asynchronous inputs are those such as the S and R (or C) which cause the flip-flop to change states regardless of the other input conditions. Synchronous inputs are those which establish the conditions for a flip-flop to change states. The flip-flop does not change states until the timing, or clock, pulse changes states, however.

25. See Figure 23–18(a).

CHAPTER EXAMINATION

1. The disallowed state of a NAND gate latch occurs in which of the following input conditions?
   a. both inputs low
   b. both inputs high
   c. S input low, R input high
   d. S input high, R input low

2. If both inputs to a NAND gate are high, the state of the latch is
   a. set
   b. reset
   c. disallowed
   d. either set or reset

3. A J-K flip-flop is in the reset state. The S, C, and J inputs are all at a binary one voltage level and the K input is binary zero. What is the state of the flip-flop at the end of one clock pulse?
   a. set
   b. reset
   c. disallowed
   d. either set or reset

4. Both inputs to a NAND gate latch should be held _____ unless the state of the latch is being changed.
   a. low
   b. high

5. What state is a flip-flop in when the normal output is high?
   a. set
   b. reset

6. A binary _____ is being stored by a flip-flop when the complemented output is low.
   a. one
   b. zero

7. If all other inputs are high, most J-K flip-flops will change states whenever a clock pulse applied to the T input changes from
   a. low to high
   b. high to low

8. Draw the logic diagram of an S-R flip-flop.

9. Draw the schematic symbol for the D flip-flop. Label all inputs and outputs.

10. Draw the schematic symbol for a J-K flip-flop and label all inputs and outputs.

Choose true or false for questions 11 to 20.

11. T F   The Q output of a D flip-flop is correct for the input conditions shown in Figure 23–24.

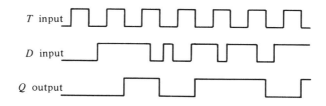

Figure 23–24

12. T F   The D flip-flop is the most versatile of all the flip-flops.
13. T F   The S-R flip-flop is often used as a frequency divider.
14. T F   The J and K inputs to a J-K flip-flop override all other inputs.

15. T F   A major application of a latch is that of switch buffering.
16. T F   Both inputs are normally maintained at a binary zero level for a NOR gate latch.
17. T F   Flip-flops are a type of astable multivibrator.
18. T F   If a *J-K* flip-flop is in the reset state, it will set when the clock pulse goes from a high to a low level when *K* is low and all other inputs are high.
19. T F   Data coming into the *D* input of a *D* flip-flop is stored when the clock pulse is high.
20. T F   The *Q* output of a *J-K* flip-flop is correct for the inputs shown in Figure 23–25 (*S* and *C* = 1).

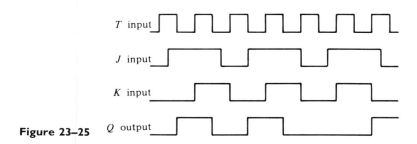

Figure 23–25

T input

J input

K input

Q output

24

Combinational Logic Circuits

OBJECTIVES

Upon completion of this chapter you should be able to do the following:

1. Draw the logic diagram and schematic symbol for the EXCLUSIVE-OR gate and identify its output for various input level conditions.
2. Draw the logic diagrams and schematic symbols for the half-adder (HA) and full-adder (FA) circuits and identify their output levels for various input binary level conditions.
3. Draw the diagram of a parallel adder and describe how this circuit is able to add two binary numbers together.
4. Draw the diagram of a one's complement subtracter and describe how this circuit is able to subtract one binary number from another.
5. Discuss the purpose of a decoder, identify the gate associated with the circuit, and design a decoder circuit capable of decoding a binary word.
6. Discuss the function of an encoder circuit.
7. Describe the purpose of a multiplexer circuit.
8. Explain the purpose of a demultiplexer circuit.
9. Discuss the purpose of a code converter circuit.

24-1 INTRODUCTION

Digital circuits can be divided into two broad categories: combinational logic and sequential logic circuits. Combinational logic circuits include EXCLUSIVE-OR gates, half adders, full adders, subtracters, decoders, encoders, multiplexers, demultiplexers, and code converter circuits. Se-

547

quential logic circuits include frequency counters, frequency dividers, shift registers, and memory circuits.

Both categories of circuits are important and both appear in most digital systems. Combinational logic circuits are formed from the gates discussed in Chapter 21. Although some sequential circuits include gates, these types of circuits are primarily formed from the flip-flops included in the last chapter. Some of the more commonly used combinational logic circuits are discussed in this chapter. Sequential logic circuits will be included in the next chapter.

24-2 THE EXCLUSIVE-OR GATE

This gate is an extension of the other gating circuits. The circuit consists of two inverters, two AND gates, and an OR gate all connected together, as shown in Figure 24–1(a). Often referred to as the XOR gate, the schematic symbol appears in Figure 24–1(b).

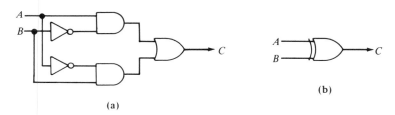

(b)

(a)

Figure 24–1   EXCLUSIVE-OR gate: (a) logic diagram; (b) schematic symbol.

The truth table for the circuit is shown in Table 24–1. As indicated, the truth table is similar to that of the OR gate, except when both inputs are at a binary one level. The OR gate's output is high when both inputs are high, whereas the output of the EXCLUSIVE-OR gate is low when both inputs are high. This means that the output of the EXCLUSIVE-OR gate is at a binary zero level whenever both inputs are at the same binary level. Whenever the input levels are complements of one another, the output is at a binary one level. The Boolean output is expressed by the statement $Y = A \oplus B$ which means Y equals A exclusive of B.

The basic EXCLUSIVE-OR gate is a two-input circuit. In IC format they can be manufactured with any number of inputs. The output of an EXCLUSIVE-OR gate having more than two inputs is a binary one whenever an odd number of binary ones are present at the inputs to the gate.

EXCLUSIVE-OR gates are often used for testing the parity of a binary word. In many digital systems a parity bit is created by a parity gen-

TABLE 24–1   Truth Table for EXCLUSIVE-OR Gate

Inputs		Output
A	B	C
0	0	0
1	0	1
0	1	1
1	1	0

erator. This bit is sent along with the regular binary data to test the various circuits that handle the data to ensure that they are operating properly. The parity bit is employed to make the total number of one bits in a binary word either even or odd, depending upon the type of parity employed. There are two types of parity—even and odd. If odd parity is used, each binary word contains an odd number of bits. A problem exists in the circuitry if one of the one bits is missing. The data can be checked with an EXCLUSIVE-OR gate. The gate output will be a binary one whenever an odd number of binary ones are present at the input to the gate. EXCLUSIVE-OR gates are often used with other logic gates to form such combinational logic circuits as arithmetic adders and subtracters.

An inverter can be connected to the output of an EXCLUSIVE-OR gate to form an EXCLUSIVE-NOR gate. The output of a two-input EXCLUSIVE-NOR gate is a binary one whenever both inputs are at the same binary level.

24-3 HALF-ADDER CIRCUITS

The half-adder is a combinational logic circuit used to add together two single-bit binary numbers. The logic diagram of the circuit is shown in Figure 24–2(a), and the schematic symbol appears in Figure 24–2(b). The circuit is formed by connecting the inputs of an EXCLUSIVE-OR gate and

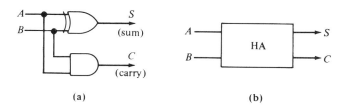

(a)   (b)

Figure 24–2   Half-adder circuit: (a) logic diagram; (b) schematic symbol.

an AND gate in parallel. The circuit has two inputs and outputs. The two binary bits which are to be added together are applied to the circuit at inputs A and B. The sum (S) and carry (C) serve as the outputs.

The truth table for the circuit appears in Table 24–2. As indicated, the circuit abides by the rules for binary addition. When both inputs are binary zero, the sum and carry outputs are both binary zero. When either input is binary one and the other a binary zero, the sum output is binary one and the carry output is binary zero. When both inputs are binary one, the sum output is binary zero and the carry output is binary one. Because the half-adder has no carry input, it has only limited application by itself. The main use of the circuit is in its application in the full-adder circuit.

TABLE 24–2   Truth Table for Half-Adder Circuit

Inputs		Outputs	
A	B	S	C
0	0	0	0
1	0	1	0
0	1	1	0
1	1	0	1

24-4 FULL-ADDER CIRCUITS

This circuit is used to add two binary bits together where the provision for a carry bit input is required. The logic diagram and schematic symbol for the circuit appear in Figure 24–3. The circuit consists of two half-adders and an OR gate connected together. It has three inputs and two outputs. The two binary numbers which are to be added together are applied at inputs A and B. If a carry bit is present, it is applied to the carry

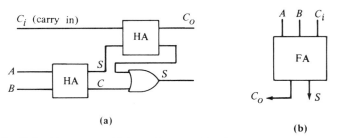

(a)

(b)

Figure 24–3   Full-adder circuit: (a) logic diagram; (b) schematic symbol.

input (C_i). The outputs represent the sum (S) of the two numbers and a carry (C_o).

As indicated by the truth table shown in Table 24–3, the circuit obeys the rules for binary addition. When all three inputs are binary zero, both outputs are binary zero. When the A and B inputs are binary zero and a carry bit is present at input C_i, the S output is binary one and the carry output is binary zero. If one follows the remaining input conditions through the truth table and observes the output conditions, it is observed that the only time that both the S and C_o outputs are at a binary one level is when all three inputs are at a binary one level.

TABLE 24–3   Truth Table for Full-Adder Circuit

	Inputs		Outputs	
A	B	C_i	S	C_o
0	0	0	0	0
0	0	1	1	0
0	1	0	1	0
0	1	1	0	1
1	0	0	1	0
1	0	1	0	1
1	1	0	0	1
1	1	1	1	1

24-5 PARALLEL BINARY ADDER CIRCUITS

When it is necessary to add together two binary numbers which are more than one bit in length, a parallel adder such as that illustrated in Figure 24–4 is used. This circuit consists of one half-adder and three full-adders and is capable of adding together two four-bit binary numbers. Additional full-adders can be connected in cascade to add longer bit numbers.

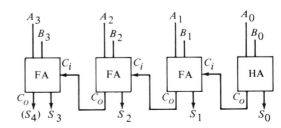

Figure 24–4   Four-bit parallel adder circuit.

When two numbers are to be added together, the bits are applied simultaneously in parallel fashion to each stage forming the adder. Since no carry input is required to add the least significant bits, a half-adder is employed to sum these two numbers.

Each adder has two outputs—a sum and a carry. The sum outputs can be connected to some type of indicator to display the binary level present, or they can be connected to a storage medium such as a shift register. The carry outputs are connected to the next full adder, except for the last stage. The carry output of this circuit represents the most significant bit of the sum of the two numbers.

The binary numbers 1101 and 1011 are shown being added together in the parallel-adder circuit appearing in Figure 24–5. The sum appearing at the output of the circuit is 11000.

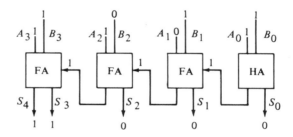

Figure 24–5   Addition of two binary numbers using a parallel adder.

24-6 ONE'S COMPLEMENT SUBTRACTER CIRCUITS

There are several methods of subtracting one binary number from another. An easy method is to use the one's complement with the circuit shown in Figure 24–6. The one's complement subtracter consists of a se-

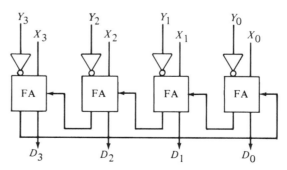

Figure 24–6   Four-bit one's complement subtracter.

ries of full-adders connected together in cascade. One input to each adder is connected to an inverter to complement that number. The carry output of each stage is connected to the carry input of the next stage, except for the last adder. The carry output of this stage is connected to the carry input of the first adder completing the subtracting process.

In Figure 24–7, 1001 is shown being subtracted from 1011. The subtrahend (1001) bits are applied to the Y inputs and the minuend (1011) applied to the X inputs. An inverter is connected between the Y input and the adder to complement the subtrahend bits. As indicated by the sum outputs, the difference between these two numbers is 0010.

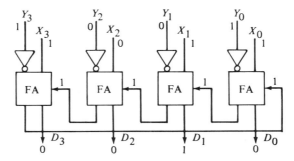

Figure 24–7 Subtraction of two binary numbers using a one's complement subtracter circuit.

24-7 DECODER CIRCUITS

Decoders are combinational logic circuits used to detect the presence of a particular binary word or number. The basic decoder circuit consists of an AND gate. The AND gate can be used to detect the presence of a binary number, or word, no matter how large. The number of inputs to the gate must be equal to the number of bits making up the binary word to be detected. The decoder shown in Figure 24–8 detects the presence of the binary word 11. The output of the AND gate will be binary one only when both inputs are at a binary one level. When either, or both, inputs are low, the output is binary zero. The only input conditions which will cause the output to become high is when both inputs are high.

An inverter can be connected to one input to the AND gate, as illustrated in Figure 24–9(a). The decoder now detects the presence of the

Figure 24–8 Two-bit decoder.

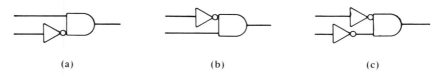

(a)   (b)   (c)

Figure 24–9 Examples of two-bit decoders: (a) 10 decoder; (b) 01 decoder; (c) 00 decoder.

binary word 10. The inverter causes both inputs to the AND gate to be at a binary one level when the binary word 10 is present at its inputs. An inverter connected to the other input lead decodes the binary 01, as shown in Figure 24–9(b), whereas inverters connected to both inputs decodes the binary word 00, as indicated in Figure 24–9(c).

A decoder capable of detecting the presence of a four-bit number is shown in Figure 24–10. Its inputs are connected to the outputs of four flip-flops. If each flip-flop is in the set state, the decoder detects the presence of the binary word 1101. The output of a decoder can be sent to an amplifier whose output is used to light a bulb, ring a bell, or energize a relay. A decoder, in a sense, is an electronic equivalent of a combinational lock. For a given binary word, there is only one unique bit combination that will "unlock" the gate.

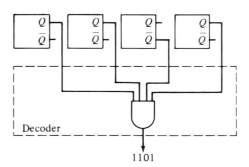

Figure 24–10 Four-bit decoder.   1101

24-8 BINARY-TO-DECIMAL DECODERS

These circuits are used to convert a binary number into an equivalent decimal number. Because digital circuits utilize binary numbers and humans use decimals, most digital systems employ binary-to-decimal decoders to convert the results of the binary numbers being operated upon to equivalent decimal numbers. The logic diagram of a two-bit binary-to-decimal decoder appears in Figure 24–11. The inputs to the AND gates

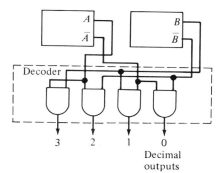

Figure 24–11 Two-bit binary-to-decimal decoder.

come from the outputs of two flip-flop circuits. As indicated by the truth table in Table 24–4, this relatively simple circuit detects the binary numbers equivalent to decimal numbers 0, 1, 2, and 3. The output of each AND gate represents a specific decimal digit.

TABLE 24–4   Truth Table for Two-Bit Binary-to-Decimal Decoder

Decoder Inputs		Decoder Outputs			
$\overline{A}$	$\overline{B}$	$\overline{0}$	$\overline{1}$	2	3
0	0	1	0	0	0
0	1	0	1	0	0
1	0	0	0	1	0
1	1	0	0	0	1

24-9 BCD-TO-DECIMAL DECODERS

BCD-to-decimal decoders are used to convert binary-coded decimal numbers into equivalent decimal numbers. They are often used to drive displays such as light-emitting diodes (LEDs). A popular BCD-to-decimal decoder is the seven-segment decoder appearing in Figure 24–12. This circuit provides seven different outputs to drive a light-emitting diode array similar to the one appearing in Figure 24–13. The LED array consists of a series of light-emitting diodes arranged in such a way that a specific alphanumeric character is displayed whenever a particular sequence of segments are lighted. The number 7 is displayed, for example, when segments a, b, and c are lighted. When segments f, e, b, c, and g are energized, the letter H is produced.

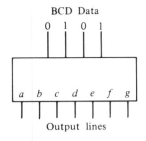

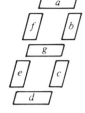

Figure 24–12   Seven-segment BCD-to-decimal decoder.

Figure 24–13   LED array.

In operation, the LED array is connected to the output pins of the seven-segment decoder. If the BCD number 0101 is applied to the input terminals of the decoder, the resulting binary levels on lines a, f, g, c, and d cause LED segments a, f, g, c, and d to light, displaying the decimal number 5.

24-10 ENCODER CIRCUITS

Encoders perform the opposite function of decoder circuits. These circuits generate a specific binary code. A common application for an encoder circuit is to change a teletypewriter keyboard number, letter, or symbol into an equivalent binary code.

There are a number of different types of encoder circuits. The logic diagram of a decimal-to-BCD encoder circuit is shown in Figure 24–14. The input lines to the NAND gates are normally maintained at a binary one level. Whenever a binary zero voltage level appears on any one of the input lines, such as would be the case if a teletypewriter key was de-

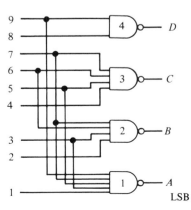

Figure 24–14   Decimal-to-BCD encoder.

pressed, a four-bit BCD output code is generated. If a binary zero is applied to input line 9, for example, the output of NAND gates 2 and 3 remain at a binary zero level while the output of gates 1 and 4 changes to a binary one level. This generates the BCD number 1001. The encoder circuit appearing in Figure 24–14 is capable of generating BCD numbers 0 through 1001. A separate encoder circuit is required for each additional digit for numbers greater than 9.

24-11 MULTIPLEXER CIRCUITS

Multiplexing is a method of sending multiple signals along a single conductor. There are two types of multiplexing: frequency division multiplexing (FDM) and time division multiplexing (TDM). When multiplexing is employed in a digital system, a type of time division multiplexing is utilized. Multiplexers, sometimes called data selector circuits, are used in digital equipment when binary data coming from several different sources are sent one at a time down a single conductor to a common destination. A block diagram of a multiplexer circuit appears in Figure 24–15. Binary data arrives at the circuit on the input lines from sources A, B, C, and D. The signals present at the data select lines determine which one of the inputs is selected and allowed to appear at the output.

Data on the input lines can come from a number of different sources. One common application of a multiplexer circuit is illustrated in Figure 24–16. Binary data contained in registers A, B, and C can be transferred in serial format to register D. This type of application is sometimes used in a computer that employs several different inputs. The computer is capable of handling the data from one source at a time. The data from the three sources are stored in the input registers. The computer selects the data it wants to operate on by generating a data select signal which causes the data from one of the registers to travel through the multiplexer

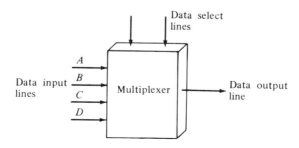

Figure 24–15 Block diagram of multiplexer circuit.

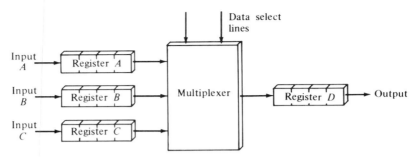

Figure 24–16 Multiplexer used to transfer data from one register to another.

and be loaded into register D where it is transferred to the circuits that perform the required operations. A register is a group of cascade-connected flip-flops used to store binary data.

Multiplexers are identified by the number of inputs, or channels, they are capable of handling. Common integrated circuit multiplexers include two inputs to one output (2 to 1), 4 to 1, 8 to 1, and 16 to 1. The diagram of a 2 to 1 multiplexer circuit is shown in Figure 24–17. Information on data line 1 will pass through AND gate 1 and the OR gate and appear at the output when the data select line is at a binary zero level. Whenever a binary one is applied to the data select line, AND gate 2 is enabled, allowing information present on data line 2 to appear at the output.

Multiplexers are also used to convert parallel binary data into equivalent serial data. This is a common application in computers. Data are usually moved from one circuit to another within the computer in parallel fashion to make better use of its rapid operating speed. Output devices located outside the computer, such as a teletypewriter or line printer are much slower and often require serial binary data. A multiplexer connected as shown in Figure 24–18 can be used to accomplish this transformation.

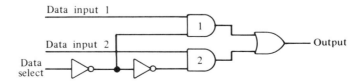

Figure 24–17 Two-to-one multiplexer circuit.

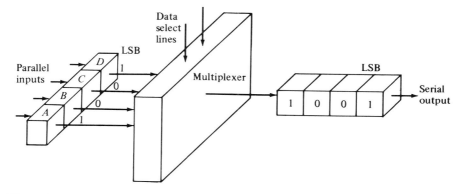

Figure 24–18 Multiplexer used to convert parallel binary data into equivalent serial data.

24-12 DEMULTIPLEXING CIRCUITS

The demultiplexer, sometimes referred to as a data routing circuit, performs the opposite function of the multiplexer. The demultiplexer circuit has a single input and multiple outputs. Available in integrated circuit format, commonly used devices include one input to two outputs (1 to 2), 1 to 4, 1 to 8, and 1 to 16. Demultiplexers may be employed whenever binary data must be transferred from a single source to several different destinations at different times. An application is shown in Figure 24–19.

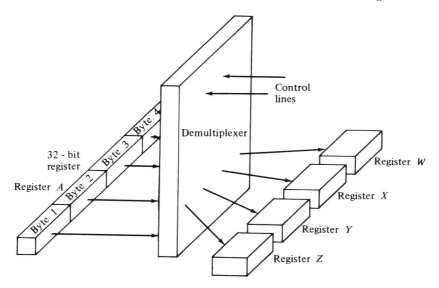

Figure 24–19 Application of a one-to-four demultiplexer.

In this diagram a four-byte word is stored in register A. The demultiplexer allows each one of the bytes to be stored in separate one-byte registers. Signals present at the control line determine which one of the output registers will receive data at a particular time.

Demultiplexer circuits may be employed to convert serial data into equivalent parallel data. Input devices connected to a computer commonly generate serial binary data. A demultiplexer, connected as shown in Figure 24–20, can be used to convert the serial data into equivalent parallel data that can be used by the computer. The binary levels present at the control lines determine which one of the output lines will be active at a particular time.

The diagram of a one-to-four demultiplexer appears in Figure 24–21. The circuit is made up of four three-input AND gates which are controlled by two inverters. The binary levels of the signals present on the control lines determine which one of the AND gates is enabled at any particular time. The truth table appearing in Table 24–5 identifies the control line levels required to convert the binary word 1101 from serial to parallel format.

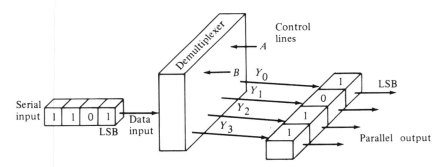

Figure 24–20   Demultiplexer used as a serial-to-parallel binary converter.

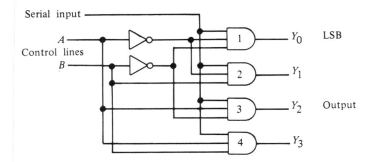

Figure 24–21   Logic diagram of a one-to-four demultiplexer.

TABLE 24–5   Truth Table Illustrating the Binary Levels Required at the Control Lines to Convert 1101 from Serial to Parallel Format

		Inputs			Outputs			
	Serial Input	Control Line A	Control Line B		Y_0	Y_1	Y_2	Y_3
(LSB)	1	0	0		☐1	0	0	0
	0	0	0		0	☐0	0	0
	1	1	0		0	0	☐1	0
	1	1	1		0	0	0	☐1

24-13 CODE CONVERTER CIRCUITS

As mentioned in Chapter 20, many computer, microprocessor, and other similar digital systems utilize two or more binary codes. A code converter is a combinational logic circuit which converts one code into another. Some of the more commonly used code converts include binary-to-BCD, BCD-to-binary, binary-to-Gray, Gray-to-binary, 8421-to-XS3, and XS3-to-8421.

24-14 COMMERCIALLY PACKAGED IC COMBINATIONAL LOGIC CIRCUITS

For each of the combinational logic circuits discussed in the previous sections, there are a variety of different types. Some typical circuits appear in Table 24–6.

TABLE 24–6   Some Selected Combinational Logic Integrated Circuits

Family	Circuit Function	Number
CMOS	4-bit full adder	4008
	4-bit arithmetic array	4057
	Quad EXCLUSIVE-OR gate	4030
	Quad EXCLUSIVE-OR gate	4070
	Quad EXCLUSIVE-NOR gate	4077
	BCD-to-decimal decoder	4028
	Dual 4-channel multiplexer	4539
	16-channel digital multiplexer	4320
		(continued)

TABLE 24–6 Some Selected Combinational Logic Integrated Circuits *(cont.)*

Family	Circuit Function	Number
ECL	4-bit adder	100181
	6-bit adder	10080
	Dual high-speed adder/subtracter	10180
	Quad EXCLUSIVE-OR gate	10113
	Triple 2-input EXCLUSIVE-OR/NOR gate	10107
	Dual 8-input multiplexer	100163
	16-input multiplexer	100164
	Triple 4-input multiplexer	100171
TTL	2-bit binary full adder	7482
	4-bit binary full adder	7483
	4-bit binary full adder	74LS83
	Dual full adder	74H183
	Quad 2-input EXCLUSIVE-OR gate	7486
	Quad 2-input EXCLUSIVE-OR gate	74LS86
	BCD-to-decimal decoder	7442
	BCD-to-decimal decoder	74LS42
	Excess 3 to decimal decoder	7443
	BCD-To-Binary Converter	74184
	8-input multiplexer, complemented output	74151
	16-input multiplexer, inverted output	74150

SUMMARY

1. There are two major categories of digital circuits. These include the combinational logic and sequential logic types.
2. Commonly used combinational logic circuits are the EXCLUSIVE-OR, half-adder, full-adder, parallel adder, one's and two's complement subtracters, decoder, encoder, multiplexer, demultiplexer, and code converter.
3. The EXCLUSIVE-OR gate is an extension of the other gating circuits and has a binary one output when either one of the two inputs are binary one and the other a binary zero. When both inputs are either at a binary one or binary zero level, the output is binary zero.
4. The half-adder circuit is used to add two single-bit numbers together. The circuit has provisions for a sum and a carry output.
5. A full-adder has three inputs and two outputs. This circuit is used to add two single-bit numbers and has provision for a carry input. The output represents the sum and carry values.
6. Adders can be connected together in cascade when binary numbers having

lengths greater than one bit are to be added together. The bits are loaded into the adder in parallel fashion. A half-adder can be used to add the least significant bits together since no carry input is required.

7. A simple method of subtracting one number from another is to use a one's subtracter circuit. This circuit is constructed by connecting an inverter to one of the input terminals. One's subtracter circuits can be connected together in cascade to subtract numbers of any size.

8. Decoders are used to detect the presence of a particular binary number (word). The basic decoder is an AND gate and, depending upon the number of inputs, detects the binary numbers 11, 111, 1111, and so forth. Inverters can be connected to one or more input leads to detect the presence of other numbers.

9. Binary-to-decimal decoders are used to convert a binary number into an equivalent decimal number. A seven segment BCD-to-decimal decoder is used to convert binary-coded decimal data into an equivalent decimal number. The output of this circuit is often used to drive an LED array.

10. An LED array is a group of seven light-emitting diodes arranged so that any alphanumeric character can be displayed when the proper sequence of LEDs are lighted.

11. Encoder circuits are used to generate binary codes. The basic encoder circuit is the NAND gate. A separate NAND gate is required for each binary bit that exists in the code to be created.

12. Multiplexers are combinational logic circuits used to allow several sources of data to time share a common output transmission line (bus). They are also useful for converting parallel data into serial data.

13. Demultiplexers are used in applications where it is required to separate data that has been time shared, or transmitted in serial fashion, and send them to two or more different destinations. These circuits can be employed to convert serial data into parallel data.

14. Code converters are used in those applications where it is necessary to convert from one type of binary code to another.

PRACTICE EXERCISES

1. Draw the logic diagram of the EXCLUSIVE-OR gate.
2. Draw the schematic symbol for the EXCLUSIVE-OR gate.
3. What is the binary output level of an EXCLUSIVE-OR gate if one input is binary one and the other binary zero?
4. Draw the logic diagram and schematic symbol of a half-adder circuit.
5. The inputs to a half-adder circuit are both binary one. What are the output levels?
6. Draw the diagram of a parallel adder circuit capable of adding together two six-bit binary numbers.
7. The numbers 110110 and 100011 are to be added together in the adder drawn in exercise 6. Show the binary levels at the output of each stage.
8. Draw the diagram of a one's subtracter capable of subtracting one eight-bit number from another.

9. Subtract the binary number 01001010 from 11001101 using the subtracter circuit drawn in exercise 8. Show the binary levels present at the output of each stage.
10. Design a six-bit decoder which will decode the binary number 101101.
11. What is the purpose of a seven-segment BCD-to-decimal decoder?
12. What alphanumeric character is being displayed when diodes a, f, g, c, and d are lighted in an LED array?
13. Draw the diagram of a decimal-to-BCD encoder circuit.
14. Explain how the encoder drawn in exercise 13 is able to generate the BCD number 0111.
15. What is the purpose of a multiplexer circuit?
16. What kind of combinational logic circuit is used to convert a Gray code binary number into a pure binary number?
17. What kind of circuit function is performed by the 74184?
18. What is the difference between the 7483 and 74LS83 integrated circuits?

ANSWERS TO PRACTICE EXERCISES

1. See Figure 24–1(a).
2. See Figure 24–1(b).
3. The output level is binary one.
4. See Figure 24–2.
5. When both inputs to a half adder are binary one, the sum output is binary zero and the carry output is binary one.
6.

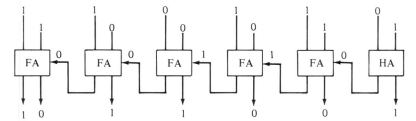

Figure 24–22

7. See Figure 24–22.
8.

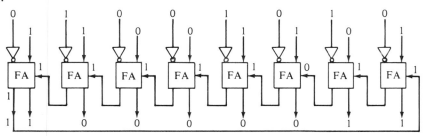

Figure 24–23

9. See Figure 24–23.

10.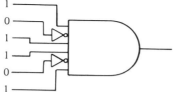

Figure 24–24

11. The seven-segment BCD-to-decimal decoder is used to convert a BCD number into an equivalent decimal number. The decimal number is displayed by an LED array whose input comes from the seven-segment decoder.

12. The number 5 is being displayed when diodes *a*, *f*, *g*, *c*, and *d* are lighted.

13. See Figure 24–14.

14. All input lines are normally maintained at a binary one level. Input line 7 to NAND gate 3 is brought low. This causes the output of NAND gates 1, 2, and 3 to rise to a binary one level while the output of NAND gate 4 remains low. Therefore the output is BCD 0111.

15. A multiplexer circuit is used when data from two or more sources are required to be sent on a common transmission line by a time-sharing process. The circuit can also be used to convert parallel data into serial data.

16. A Gray-to-binary code converter should be used.

17. The 74184 is a TTL BCD-to-binary converter.

18. The 7483 is a standard TTL device whereas the 74LS83 is a low-speed Schottky IC. Both are four-bit binary full adders.

CHAPTER EXAMINATION

1. The _____ is a combinational logic circuit which generates a particular binary word or number.
   a. decoder
   b. encoder
   c. multiplexer
   d. demultiplexer

2. The output of the EXCLUSIVE-OR gate is a binary zero when
   a. both inputs are low.
   b. both inputs are high.
   c. both inputs are at the same level.
   d. one input is high and the other input low.

3. A _____ circuit is used to change a BCD number into an equivalent decimal number.
   a. decoder
   b. encoder
   c. multiplexer
   d. code converter

4. A _____ is used when it is desired to send data from two or more sources through a single transmission line.
   a. decoder
   b. encoder
   c. multiplexer
   d. demultiplexer

5. A _____ circuit is used to send data coming from a single source to two or more separate destinations.
   a. decoder
   b. encoder
   c. multiplexer
   d. demultiplexer

6. Draw the logic diagram of an EXCLUSIVE-OR gate.

7. Design a decoder circuit that will detect the presence of the binary number 11010.

8. Draw the logic diagram of a full-adder circuit.

9. Draw the schematic symbol of a one's subtracter circuit.

Choose true or false for questions 10 to 20.

10. T F   A half-adder circuit is made up of two AND gates whose outputs are connected to the input of a NOR gate.

11. T F   A BCD-to-decimal encoder is used to provide the inputs to an LED array.

12. T F   The decoder in its simplest design consists of an AND gate.

13. T F   A half-adder has two inputs and three outputs.

14. T F   A code converter is used to convert a binary number into an equivalent decimal number.

15. T F   A full-adder circuit has input provisions for the two numbers to be added together and a carry input.

16. T F   An EXCLUSIVE-OR gate is a type of sum-of-products circuit.

17. T F   A one's subtracter is a full-adder circuit which has an inverter connected to one of its outputs.

18. T F   A full-adder circuit has three inputs and three outputs.

19. T F   The sum output of a full-adder is a binary one and the carry output is binary zero when one input is high, the other low, and the carry input is low.

20. T F   An encoder circuit is used to generate a particular code to represent an event which has occurred.

25

Register and Counter Circuits

OBJECTIVES

Upon completion of this chapter you should be able to do the following:

1. Describe three applications for shift registers.
2. Identify the four types of registers with respect to the method in which data is placed into and taken from the register.
3. Recognize the logic diagrams of the serial-in serial-out and parallel-in parallel-out shift registers.
4. Describe, with the aid of diagrams, how data is shifted into and out of a serial-in serial-out shift register.
5. Describe the difference between an MOS static and dynamic register.
6. Recognize the logic diagrams of the ripple up-counter, down-counter, and up-down counter, synchronous counter, and BCD counter.
7. Describe how a counter can be used as a frequency divider and calculate the output frequency of both a binary and BCD counter.

25-1 INTRODUCTION

This chapter deals with some of the more important sequential logic circuits found in digital equipment and include shift registers and counters. These circuits are composed of various types of flip-flops and in some cases gates, which are used to perform different kinds of circuit applications.

567

25-2 SHIFT REGISTERS

25-2.1 Introduction.   Shift registers, sometimes referred to as registers, are used in almost all digital systems. The primary application of this group of circuits is to provide temporary storage of binary information. Computers and microprocessors, for example, utilize shift registers for many different short-term storage applications. They are often identified by the application they perform in a system. A partial block diagram of a microprocessor is shown in Figure 25–1. Four registers appear in the diagram: the accumulator, program counter, address register, and instruction register.

Shift registers are classified as to how data is placed into and taken from the circuit. These include serial-in serial-out (SISO), serial-in parallel-out (SIPO), parallel-in serial-out (PISO), and parallel-in parallel-out (PIPO). These different methods are illustrated in Figure 25–2.

25-2.2 Serial Shift Registers.   Shift registers in which data are either shifted into or out of in a series, or serial, fashion are called serial shift registers. The process of shifting data into and out of a register in serial fashion is illustrated in Figure 25–3. In these diagrams the binary word 1001 is to be loaded into the register one bit at a time. As shown in Figure 25–3(a), the binary word 1011 is already in the register and must be shifted out as the new word is placed into the register. The circuit requires two inputs, one for the data and the other for the shift pulses. The shift pulses are clock pulses which determine when the bits will be loaded into the register. With the application of the first shift pulse, the

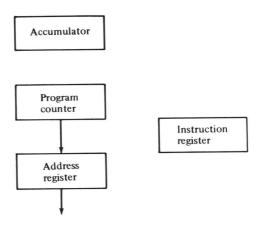

Figure 25–1   Some registers which appear in microprocessors.

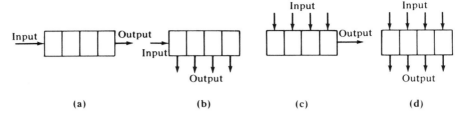

Figure 25–2   General types of shift registers: (a) SISO; (b) SIPO; (c) PISO; (d) PIPO.

least significant bit of the word to be stored enters the register first, as shown in Figure 25–3(b). At the same time, the least significant bit of the number initially stored in the register is shifted out. Each bit of the word initially stored in the register has been shifted to the right with the application of the first shift pulse. After the second shift pulse has been applied, two bits of the word initially stored in the register have been shifted out, and two bits of the new word appear in the shift register, as indicated in Figure 25–3(c). Three bits of the original word have been

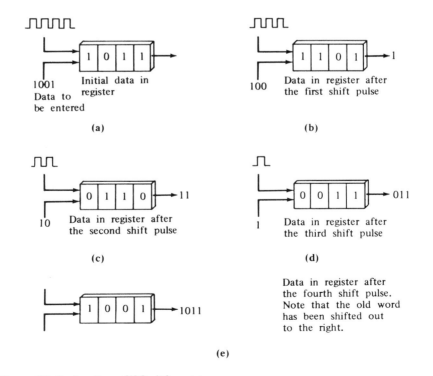

Figure 25–3   Loading a SISO shift register.

shifted out with the application of the third shift pulse, as shown in Figure 25–3(d). With the application of the fourth shift pulse, the new word is stored in the register and the old one has been shifted out, as shown in Figure 25–3(e). It took four shift pulses to completely load the register. The data was moved serially, one bit at a time, into the circuit.

A shift register consists of a group of flip-flops connected together in cascade. Each flip-flop is capable of storing one bit of data. There must be one flip-flop stage for each binary bit forming the word to be stored. A four-bit serial shift register is shown in Figure 25–4. The register is formed by four J-K flip-flops connected together in cascade. The data to be stored are applied to the J and K inputs of the first flip-flop. An inverter is connected to the K input to complement the data entering the two inputs. The toggle (shift) pulse inputs are connected together in parallel so that the shift pulses are applied to each flip-flop simultaneously. The clear input to each flip-flop is connected in parallel with the clear inputs of the other flip-flops to allow the register to be cleared and reset to zero.

The bits forming the binary word 0011 are to be loaded into the register shown in Figure 25–4. The circuit is cleared so that the data in the register is initially 0000. This makes the Q output of each flip-flop zero. The register is loaded as follows:

1. The shift pulses and data are both applied to the register. As the first shift pulse level changes from a high to a low at time t_1, as shown in Figure 25–5, the data input is high, which causes flip-flop 1 to set.
2. As the level of the second shift pulse falls from a high to a low, at time t_2, flip-flop 1 remains set and flip-flop 2 sets, as indicated in Figure 25–5.
3. When the shift pulse changes from binary one to binary zero, at time, t_3, flip-flop 1 resets, flip-flop 2 remains set, and flip-flop 3 sets.
4. At time t_4, flip-flop 1 remains reset, flip-flop 2 resets, flip-flop 3 remains set, and flip-flop 4 sets as the shift pulse goes from a high to a low. The data now have all been shifted into the register. Flip-flops 1 and 2 are both low and

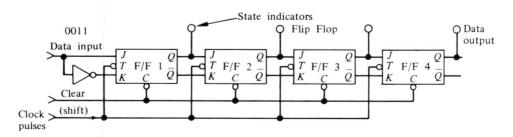

Figure 25–4 Four-bit SISO shift register.

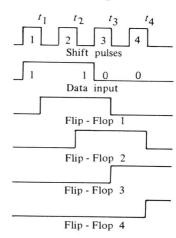

Figure 25–5 Loading a four-bit SISO shift register.

flip-flops 3 and 4 are high, indicating that the word 0011 is being stored in the register.

Notice that the most significant bit was shifted into the register first. This bit is shifted from flip-flop to flip-flop as the shift pulses change from a high to a low. The first stage is controlled by the data to be entered. All other flip-flops are controlled by the preceding flip-flops. This register is capable of storing a four-bit binary number, or word. One flip-flop is required for each word bit. Additional flip-flops can be connected in cascade to store longer words. Word lengths of either 8 bits (one byte) or 16 bits (two bytes) are common in computers and microprocessors. If a 16-bit word length is employed, the shift registers contain 16 flip-flops.

Most shift registers are designed to shift data in one direction only. In the register appearing in Figure 25–4, the data were shifted to the right as the register was loaded. This type of circuit is sometimes called a shift right register. Some shift registers are designed to shift data to the left and are referred to as shift left registers.

The serial shift register appearing in Figure 25–6 allows data to be shifted either right or left. This is a rather common type of register and has an additional input line called the mode input, which controls the direction of shift.

25-2.3 Parallel Shift Registers. A popular type of shift register is the parallel loading register such as that illustrated in Figure 25–7. This register can be loaded much more rapidly than the serial input type. The entire register can be loaded with the application of one shift pulse. If,

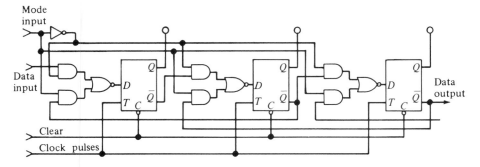

Figure 25–6   Left-right shift register.

for example, the binary word 11 is to be loaded in the register shown in Figure 25–7, a shift pulse is applied at the same time as the data. This condition allows each flip-flop to set, indicating that the data have been entered and each is storing a binary one bit.

   25-2.4 MOS Shift Registers.   The registers just discussed are built from bipolar integrated circuits and are available in various word lengths. Typical word length storage ranges from a low of 4 bits to a high of 32 (four bytes). MOS shift registers are usually used where very large amounts of storage is required. These registers are characterized by their high component densities and low power requirements. Most MOS registers are loaded and unloaded in serial fashion (SISO).

   There are two types of MOS shift registers: static and dynamic. A static shift register is one in which the clock pulses can be removed with-

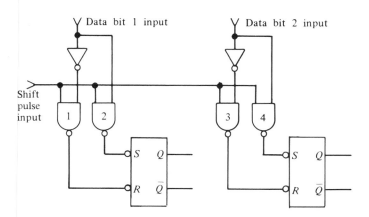

Figure 25–7   Parallel loading shift register.

out the stored data being lost. This characteristic is the same as that for the bipolar register. Data is lost in a dynamic register if the clock pulses are removed. The clock pulses must continually be present to recirculate, or refresh, the data in order for it to be retained.

Bipolar and MOS static shift registers both utilize flip-flops to store data. MOS dynamic shift registers, on the other hand, store data in the internal capacitance associated with a MOSFET inverter. A one-bit dynamic MOS shift register is shown in Figure 25–8. The leakage of the capacitance is the reason why the dynamic register has to be continually refreshed.

Both the static and dynamic shift registers are commonly used as large-scale temporary storage mediums. The dynamic register can be made smaller, operates at higher speeds, and consumes less power than the static type. The dynamic register has the disadvantage of having to have the data recirculated approximately every 2 ms. For the single-bit register shown in Figure 25–8, two out-of-phase clock pulses are required to store one bit of data.

25-2.5 Commercially Packaged IC Shift Registers.   In addition to being used to store data, shift registers are used for other applications. Serial input parallel output registers can be used to convert serial binary data into equivalent parallel data, for example. The binary data is fed into the register in serial format, the clock pulses are stopped, and the data is read out in parallel form. This is often the type of register used when a keyboard or teletypewriter is used as a computer input. The teletypewriter generates a series of pulses each time a key is depressed. These serial pulses are fed into a serial input shift register and then unloaded in parallel fashion into the computer. Data is usually fed from one circuit to an-

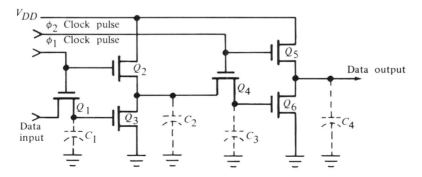

Figure 25–8   Two-bit MOS dynamic shift register.

other in parallel in a computer because of its faster loading and unloading times. Parallel-to-serial registers can be used to convert parallel data into series data. If a teletypewriter is being used as an output indicator for a computer, a PISO shift register can be used to convert the parallel data coming from the computer into the serial data required to drive the teletypewriter. Numerous IC shift registers are manufactured using both BJT and MOSFET technology. Some typical circuits are listed in Table 25–1.

TABLE 25–1   Some Selected IC Shift Registers

Family	Type of Register	Number
CMOS	4-bit PIPO shift register	4035
	8-bit synchronous PISO shift register	4014
	32-bit SIPO shift register	4332
ECL	4-bit shift register	10000
MOS	512-bit dynamic shift register	5016
	512-bit static shift register	5057
	1024-bit static shift register	5058
	Quad 100-bit static shift register	5061
TTL	4-bit PIPO shift register	74195
	4-bit PIPO left-right shift register	7495
	4-bit PISO shift register	7496
	16-bit SISO shift register	74LS673

25-3 COUNTERS

25-3.1 Introduction. A counter is a circuit made up of flip-flops and, in some cases, gates which count binary pulses. Almost anything, including events and items, that can be converted into an electrical pulse can be counted by a counter. Counters are also used for frequency division and for generating pulses for sequential binary operations. There are several types of counters. Some of the more common types are the up-counter, down-counter, up-down counter, synchronous counter, and BCD counter. The up and down counters are nonsynchronous and are often referred to as ripple counters.

25-3.2 Up-counters. The diagram of a four-stage up-counter appears in Figure 25–9. The S and C inputs allow the counter to be preset

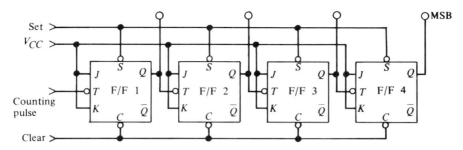

Figure 25–9   Four-bit up-counter.

or cleared prior to beginning the counting sequence. The output of each flip-flop serves as the input to the next stage.

The timing diagram for the circuit shown in Figure 25–9 appears in Figure 25–10. If the counter is initially cleared, the output of each flip-flop is zero. When pulses are applied to the T input of the first J-K flip-flop, that flip-flop sets when the level of the first pulse changes from a high to a low at time t_1. Since the state of the first flip-flop represents the least significant bit, the count is 0001. At time t_2 the second pulse level changes from a high to a low. Flip-flop 1 changes from the set to the reset states, causing flip-flop 2 to set resulting in a count of 0010. Flip-flops 1 and 2 are both set at the end of the third pulse, resulting in a count of 0011. At time t_4 flip-flops 1 and 2 reset and flip-flop 3 sets, causing a count of 0100 to be indicated. This process continues until a binary count of 1111 (decimal 15) is achieved. This is as high as this circuit will count. At the end of the sixteenth pulse all of the flip-flops have reset and the counter has

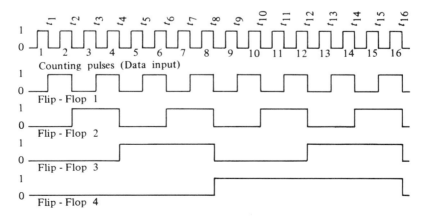

Figure 25–10   Timing diagram for the counter shown in Figure 25–9.

recycled back to 0000. Additional flip-flops can be added to the counter to extend its counting range. The maximum count of a ripple counter is $2^n - 1$, where n represents the number of flip-flops forming the counter.

25-3.3 Down-counters. The circuit just discussed is called an up-counter. Every time an input, or counting, pulse arrived at the input of the counter, the binary count increased by one. At times it is advantageous to have a counter that will count from some predetermined value toward zero. This type of counter is called a down-counter. The diagram of a four-bit down-counter appears in Figure 25–11. The only difference between this circuit and the up-counter shown in Figure 25–9 is that the complemented output of each stage is connected to the input of the next flip-flop. The content, or state of each flip-flop, is still determined from the normal output.

As indicated by the synchrogram appearing in Figure 25–12, the counter has been preset and all flip-flops are initially in the set state, indicating a binary count of 1111. When the counting pulses are applied, flip-flop 1 resets when the level of the first pulse falls from a high to a low at time t_1, resulting in a count of 1110. At the end of the second counting pulse, flip-flop 1 sets and flip-flop 2 resets, while stages 3 and 4 remain in the set state. This results in a count of 1101. This process continues until all of the flip-flops are reset and indicating a count of 0000 at the end of the fifteenth counting pulse. The counter recycles with application of the sixteenth counting pulse and the process is repeated. One should note that flip-flops 2, 3, and 4 toggle when their input voltage levels change from a low to a high. This is due to the triggering method employed. These stages are triggered by the complemented outputs of the previous flip-flops.

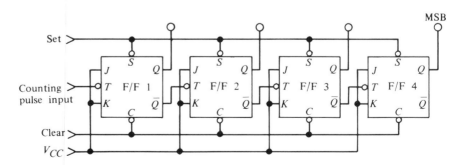

Figure 25–11 Four-bit down-counter.

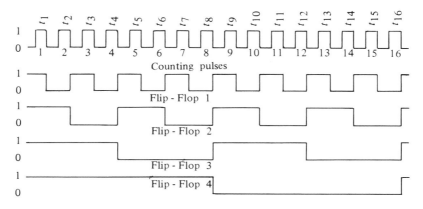

Figure 25–12   Timing diagram for the counter shown in Figure 25–11.

25-3.4 Up-Down Counters.   Sometimes it is desirable to have a counter that will count either up or down. Such a counter is called an up-down counter, the diagram of which is shown in Figure 25–13. Enabling gates are connected between each cascade-connected flip-flop. These determine whether the normal or complemented outputs toggle the following flip-flop. The count control input determines whether the counter counts up or down. Whenever a binary one level is applied to the count control, the counter functions as an up-counter. The circuit functions as a down-counter when a binary zero is applied to the count control input.

When the count control is at a binary one level, all the gate 1's are enabled. The normal output of each flip-flop is coupled through gates 1 and 3 into the T input of the following stage. The gate 2's are enabled when the count control is a binary zero. This condition allows the com-

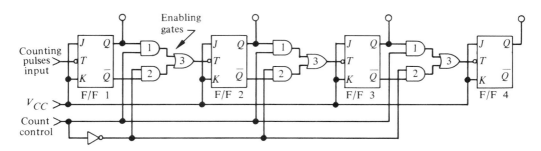

Figure 25–13   Four-bit up-down counter.

plemented output of each flip-flop to be coupled through gates 2 and 3, and the counter functions as a down-counter.

The pulses which enter the counters just discussed enter the first stage and pass (ripple) through the other flip-flops stage by stage. Since each flip-flop has some propagation delay, the total delay of the counter is the sum of the individual flip-flop delays and becomes excessive at high frequencies. The maximum counting frequency of ripple counters is approximately 7 MHz. Beyond this frequency, the flip-flop state changes cannot maintain the pace of the input pulses, and counting errors occur. Although flip-flops having a shorter propagation delay could be used, such as those utilizing ECL logic, these have a higher power consumption and are more expensive.

25-3.5 Synchronous Counters. Because of the excessively long propagation delay associated with ripple counters, synchronous counters are used to count higher frequency pulses. The diagram of a four-bit synchronous counter is shown in Figure 25–14. In this type of counter the counting pulses are applied simultaneously to each flip-flop in the counter to cause them all to be able to change states at the same time. The total propagation delay of a synchronous counter is only that of a single flip-flop. The operation of each flip-flop is controlled by voltage levels present at the J and K inputs. These inputs are maintained permanently at a binary one level for flip-flop 1. Every time a counting pulse is applied to this flip-flop it will toggle as the counting pulse level changes from a high to a binary low. The J and K inputs to flip-flop 2 are connected to the normal output of flip-flop 1. The only time this flip-flop

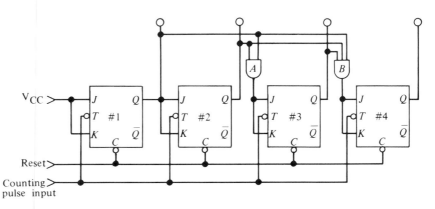

Figure 25–14 Four-bit synchronous counter.

changes states is when the output of flip-flop 1 is high. The *J* and *K* inputs to flip-flop 3 are controlled by the normal outputs of flip-flops 1 and 2. Flip-flop 3 can change states only when the outputs of stages 1 and 2 are high. This provides a high to the *J* and *K* inputs from AND gate *A*.

Flip-flops 1, 2, and 3 control flip-flop 4. The normal outputs must all be high in order for a high to appear at the output of AND gate *B*. This allows flip-flop 4 to toggle with the application of a counting pulse.

The timing diagram for the four-bit synchronous counter appears in Figure 25–15. The counter is initially cleared, and the count is 0000. With the application of the first counting pulse, flip-flop 1 sets, and the remaining stages remain in the reset state indicating a binary count of 0001. At the end of the second counting pulse, flip-flop 2 sets, flip-flop 1 resets, and flip-flops 3 and 4 remain in the reset state indicating a count of 0010. Both flip-flops 1 and 2 are in the set condition, and flip-flops 3 and 4 are in the reset state at the end of the third counting pulse, resulting in a count of 0011. Flip-flop 3 sets at the end of the fourth counting pulse, while the remaining flip-flops are in the reset state giving a count of 0100. This process continues until flip-flop 4 sets at the end of the eighth counting pulse. At this time the other flip-flops are in the reset state and the count is 1000. Additional counting pulses cause the counter to count to 1111 upon completion of the fifteenth counting pulse. At the end of the sixteenth counting pulse, the counter recycles and the count is again 0000. This counter is much faster than the ripple counter since each counting pulse does not have to pass through every flip-flop stage. Like the ripple counter, the count for the synchronous counter can be extended by connecting additional stages in cascade.

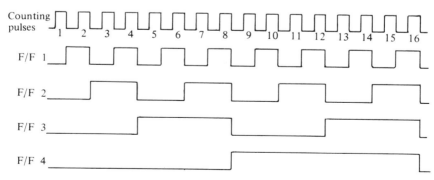

Figure 25–15 Timing diagram for the synchronous counter shown in Figure 25–14.

25-3.6 BCD Counters. The binary-coded decimal counter, some-times called a decade counter, is a synchronous counter that counts by tens. The circuit has 10 discrete states which represent the numbers 0 through 9. The diagram of a BCD counter appears in Figure 25–16. As illustrated, the output of flip-flop 1 toggles flip-flops 2 and 4, while flip-flop 3 is toggled by the output of flip-flop 2. Unlike the other four-bit counters which count to 1111 and then recycle, the BCD counter counts to 1001 (decimal 9) and then recycles.

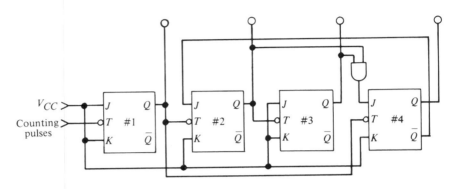

Figure 25–16 BCD counter.

When the counter is cleared, the output of each flip-flop is binary zero. The application of counting pulses cause the flip-flops to change states, as indicated by the timing diagram shown in Figure 25–17. At the end of the first counting pulse, flip-flop 1 toggles and goes into the set state. Flip-flops 2, 3, and 4 remain reset, indicating a count of 0001. When the second counting pulse is applied, flip-flop 1 resets, causing flip-flop

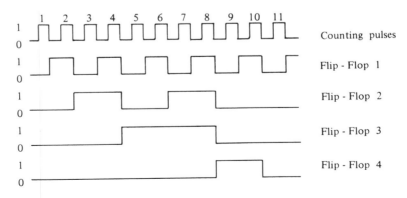

Figure 25–17 Timing diagram for a BCD counter.

2 to become set. The count is now 0010. Flip-flops 3 and 4 remain reset. Flip-flop 1 sets, flip-flop 2 remains set, and flip-flops 3 and 4 remain reset at the end of the third counting pulse, indicating a count of 0011. Stages 1 and 2 reset at the end of the fourth counting pulse, which causes flip-flop 3 to set. Stage 4 remains in the reset condition. The binary count is now 0100. This process continues until the end of the eighth counting pulse. At that time flip-flops 1, 2, and 3 reset and flip-flop 4 sets, indicating a count of 1000. Notice that flip-flop 4 cannot set until stages 1, 2, and 3 are set. When the output level of flip-flop 1 changes from a high to a low, flip-flop 4 sets. At the end of the ninth counting pulse, flip-flop 1 sets, flip-flop 4 remains set, and flip-flops 2 and 3 remain in the reset condition for a count of 1001, or decimal 9. With the application of the tenth counting pulse, conditions are such that flip-flops 1 and 4 go into the reset state and stages 2 and 3 remain reset. The count now is 0000, indicating that the counter has recycled. The process is repeated for additional counting pulses.

A single BCD counter can count from 0000 through 1001. Counters can be connected in cascade, as shown in Figure 25–18, when counting requirements above 1001 are required. Each BCD counter stage represents one decimal digit. The counter in Figure 25–18 has a maximum BCD count of 1001 1001 1001 1001 or decimal 9999. Every time 10 counting pulses are received by the input counter (the least significant bit counter), that counter recycles and toggles the next. The remaining counters are toggled the same way. The counter appearing in Figure 25–18 contains the binary number 1000 1001 0110 0010 (decimal 8962). This means that 8962 pulses have entered the counter since it was last cleared.

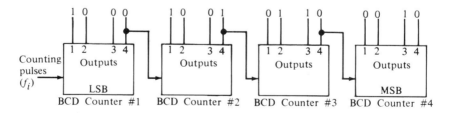

Figure 25–18 Four-stage BCD counter.

25-3.7 Frequency Dividers. Counters can also be used as frequency dividers. For example, the output pulse frequency of each flip-flop in the ripple counter appearing in Figure 25–19 is one-half the pulse input frequency. If the counting pulse frequency is 50 kHz, the output

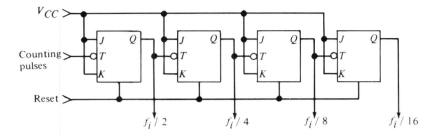

Figure 25–19   Four-bit frequency divider.

pulse frequency of flip-flop 1 is 25 kHz. The frequency of the output pulses from flip-flops 2, 3, and 4 are 12.5, 6.25, and 3.125 kHz, respectively. Each J-K flip-flop is operating in the T mode, which means that the output pulse frequency of each is one-half of its input pulse frequency. Overall, the four-bit counter has divided the input pulse frequency by 16. If the counter had five stages, the output pulse frequency would be 1.5625 kHz, which represents a frequency division of 32. Equation 25–1 can be used to determine the output frequency of a binary frequency divider.

$$f_o = \frac{f_i}{2^n}$$

(25–1)

f_o is the output pulse frequency, f_i represents the input pulse frequency, and n identifies the number of flip-flop stages contained within the counter.

BCD counters can also be used as frequency dividers. When used for this purpose, each BCD counter stage divides its input pulse frequency by 10. If the input pulse frequency is 100,000 Hz for the BCD counter shown in Figure 25–18, the pulse output frequency is 10 Hz. Each counter stage divides the frequency by 10. Equation (25–2) can be used to calculate the output frequency of a decade counter.

$$f_o = \frac{f_i}{10^n}$$

(25–2)

25-3.8 Commercially Packaged IC Counters. Several different kinds of counter circuits are available in IC format. Some representative types are listed in Table 25–2.

TABLE 25–2   Some Selected IC Counters

Family	Type of Counter	Number
CMOS	7-stage binary counter	4024
	8-stage binary counter	4404
	12-stage binary counter	4040
	14-stage binary counter	4020
	Dual synchronous binary counter	4520
	Dual synchronous decade counter	4518
	Presettable decade up-down counter	40192
ECL	4-bit binary counter	10016
	Decade counter	10537
TTL	4-bit ripple counter	7493
	Dual binary synchronous counter	74177
	Binary up-down synchronous counter	74191
	Decade synchronous counter	74160
	Decade up-down synchronous counter	74190

SUMMARY

1. Shift registers are used in almost all digital systems. The primary purpose of these circuits is to temporarily store binary data. They can also be used to convert serial binary data into parallel data and vice versa.
2. Shift registers are classified as to the method in which data enter and exit the circuit. These methods include serial-in serial-out (SISO), serial-in parallel-out (SIPO), parallel-in serial-out (PISO), and parallel-in parallel-out (PIPO).
3. The memory medium in most shift registers is the flip-flop. A separate flip-flop stage is required for each binary bit stored in the register.
4. Data are entered into a serial shift register one bit at a time. A separate shift pulse is required to shift each binary bit into the register.
5. Serial shift registers can be classified as to the direction in which data are loaded into them and include right-shift, left-shift, and left-right shift.
6. The entire shift register can either be loaded or unloaded with the application of a single shift pulse when a register is either parallel loaded or unloaded.
7. Shift registers may be formed from either BJT or MOS circuitry. MOS shift

registers can be manufactured with high component densities and are used where large amounts of storage is required.

8. There are two types of MOS shift registers: static and dynamic. The operation of the static register is much like that of the BJT register. The dynamic register, on the other hand, has to be continuously refreshed to retain data.

9. Counter circuits are used to count electrical pulses. These may be clock pulses or pulses which represent almost any item or event. Some of the more common types of counters include the up-counter, down-counter, up-down counter, synchronous counter, and BCD counter. The up and down counters are sometimes called ripple counters.

10. Ripple counters have excessive delay and are limited to counting pulses whose frequencies are less than 7 MHz. Synchronous counters are used for higher frequency counting applications.

11. BCD counters, sometimes called decade counters, are synchronous counters that count by tens.

12. Counters can also be used as frequency dividers. The output pulse frequency of each stage within a counter is one-half the frequency of that stage's pulse input frequency. A four-stage binary counter divides the pulse input frequency by 16, for example. Each stage in a decade counter divides its input frequency by 10. A four-stage decade counter divides the input pulse frequency by 10,000.

PRACTICE EXERCISES

1. List three applications for shift registers.
2. Identify four shift registers used in microprocessors.
3. What are the four classifications of shift registers with respect to the method in which data are shifted into and out of the circuit?
4. What is the purpose of the shift pulses used in shift registers?
5. How many shift pulses are required to load an eight-bit word into a serial input shift register?
6. How many shift pulses are required to load an eight-bit word into a parallel input shift register?
7. What controls the direction of shift in a left-right shift register?
8. What is the major difference between a dynamic and static MOS shift register?
9. Identify three types of ripple counters.
10. What is the major difference between a ripple up-counter and a down-counter circuit?
11. How many states does a BCD counter have?
12. When will the J input of the last flip-flop in a BCD counter be at a binary one level?
13. The input frequency of the counting pulses applied to an eight-stage binary frequency divider is 1.25 MHz. What is the output frequency?
14. The input pulse frequency to a five-stage BCD counter is 8.25 MHz. What is the output frequency?

15. What kind of circuit is shown in Figure 25–20?

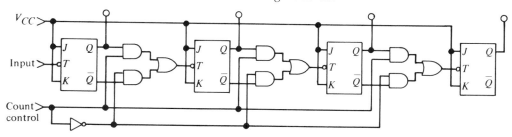

Figure 25–20

16. What kind of circuit appears in Figure 25–21?

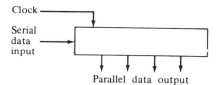

Figure 25–21

ANSWERS TO PRACTICE EXERCISES

1. Shift registers can be used to temporarily store binary data, convert serial binary data into parallel data, and convert parallel binary data into serial data.
2. Shift registers used in many microprocessors are the address register, instruction register, program counter, and accumulator.
3. Shift register classifications include serial-in serial-out (SISO), serial-in parallel-out (SIPO), parallel-in serial-out (PISO), and parallel-in parallel-out (PIPO).
4. Shift pulses are clock, or timing, pulses which determine when the binary bits will be loaded into the register.
5. Eight shift pulses are required to load an eight-bit word into a serial input shift register. One shift pulse is required for each bit entered into the register.
6. One shift pulse is required to load an eight-bit word into a parallel shift register. With the application of the shift pulse, each bit is loaded into its respective flip-flop.
7. The binary voltage level at the mode input controls the direction of shift in a left-right shift register.
8. The data is stored in the internal capacitance of a MOSFET inverter and has to be periodically refreshed to be retained in a dynamic MOS register.
9. Ripple counter types are the up, down, and up-down.
10. The major difference between the ripple up and down-counter circuits is the connection used between adjacent stages. The normal output is connected to

the T input for the up-counter, whereas the complemented output is connected to the T input for the down-counter.

11. A BCD counter has 10 separate stages, 0000 through 1001.
12. The J input of the last flip-flop in a BCD counter will be at a binary one level when flip-flops 2 and 3 are in the set state.
13. When the input pulse frequency is 1.25 MHz, the output frequency is 4882.8125 Hz $[(1.25 \times 10^6)/2^8 = (1.25 \times 10^6)/(2.65 \times 10^2)]$.
14. If the input pulse frequency to a five-stage BCD counter is 8.25 MHz, the output frequency is 82.5 Hz $[(8.25 \times 10^6)/10^5]$.
15. The circuit shown in Figure 25–20 is an up-down counter.
16. The circuit appearing in Figure 25–21 is a serial-in parallel-out shift register.

CHAPTER EXAMINATION

1. The circuit shown in Figure 25–22 is that of a (an)
   a. PISO register   c. up-down counter
   b. down-counter   d. synchronous counter

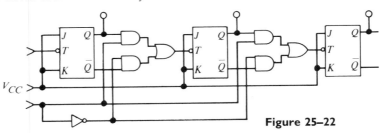

Figure 25–22

2. The circuit diagram in Figure 25–23 is that of a (an)
   a. PIPO register   c. up-down counter
   b. BCD counter   d. synchronous counter

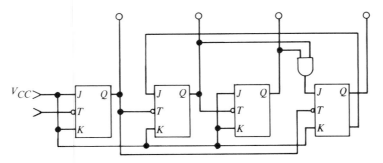

Figure 25–23

3. The circuit shown in Figure 25–24 is that of a
   a. SISO register   c. PISO register
   b. PIPO register   d. PIPO register

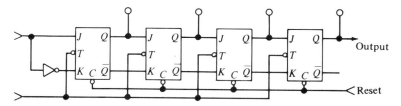

Figure 25–24

4. The diagram of the circuit in Figure 25–25 is that of a (an)
   a. up-counter   **c.** up-down counter
   b. down-counter   **d.** synchronous counter

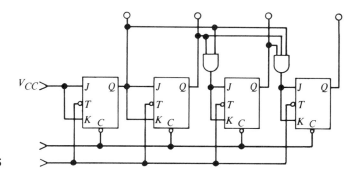

Figure 25–25

Choose true or false for questions 5 to 15.
   5. T F   MOS shift registers are characterized by their limited storage capacity.
   6. T F   A binary counter which contains eight flip-flops has an output pulse frequency which is one-eighth the input pulse frequency.
   7. T F   Up and down ripple counters require no clock pulses to synchronize their operation.
   8. T F   Counters can be used to convert serial data into equivalent parallel binary data.
   9. T F   BJT shift registers are commonly used where large amounts of binary data must be stored.
   10. T F   A synchronous counter requires clock pulses, in addition to counting pulses, to properly operate.
   11. T F   Registers can be used to convert parallel data into serial binary data.
   12. T F   Four shift pulses are required to serially load a four-bit shift register.
   13. T F   Clock pulses must continuously be present in MOS static shift registers.
   14. T F   A counter made up of three BCD counter circuits has an input pulse frequency of 33.33 kHz. The output pulse frequency is 11.11 kHz.
   15. T F   A three-stage binary counter will count to 111 and then recycle.

26

Memory Systems

OBJECTIVES

Upon completion of this chapter you should be able to do the following:

1. Define the terms *read, write,* and *access time* as they relate to digital memory.
2. Differentiate between volatile and nonvolatile memory.
3. Discuss the need for memory address.
4. Identify the three functional categories of memory systems.
5. Identify the kinds of mediums used in each of the memory categories listed in objective 4.
6. Describe how a ferrite core is able to store a bit of binary data.
7. Differentiate between RAM and ROM semiconductor memory and discuss the organizational schemes used for storing binary information.
8. Describe how a binary bit is written into a BJT RAM.
9. Differentiate between ROMs, PROMs, and EPROMs and describe how each is programmed.
10. Describe how RAMs and ROMs are typically used in a computer.

26-1 INTRODUCTION

The operation of digital systems such as computers and microprocessor-based equipment depends upon their ability to store binary information. This information, in the form of binary words, consists of a series of instructions and data to be operated upon and is referred to as the program. Some new terms are introduced in this chapter. These include *reading, writing, programming, access time, volatile memory,* and *nonvolatile memory.* Reading refers to the process of taking, or retrieving, a binary word from memory. Writing is the process of placing a binary word into memory. Programming is the process of writing instructions and data into memory. Access time is the time required to locate the correct memory address and either write a binary word into or read a word out of memory. Volatility refers to what happens to the information stored in memory when the power is turned off or is inadvertently removed from the memory system. Volatile memory systems are those in which the information is lost when the power is removed. Information is retained when power is removed from nonvolatile memory mediums.

All memory systems are divided into a number of segments, as illustrated in Figure 26–1. Each memory segment is identified by a particular address. The binary contents in each segment, in general, consist of one of two types of information. One type consists of the binary data. This might be a binary number which was written into that memory segment for the purpose of being added to another number, for example. The other type is instructional information. This is also in binary form and corresponds to instructions such as add, subtract, branch, halt, and so forth. Information is placed into memory during the programming phase. The relationship between data and instructions as they might appear in memory is shown in Figure 26–2.

Each memory segment is large enough to hold an entire word. Although a four-bit word length is used in the system appearing in Figure 26–2, most computers and microprocessor-based systems utilize 8-, 16-, or 32-bit words. The diagram appearing in Figure 26–3 serves to illustrate the function of memory in a computer. Data and instructions can be written into and read from the memory unit. Data from memory can be placed into the arithmetic and logic unit (ALU) and operated upon. The results of the operation may be sent to an output device or stored in memory.

Address	Memory Contents
0000	
0001	
0010	
0011	
0100	
0101	

Figure 26–I Memory organization.

Address	Memory Contents	Type of Contents
0000	1000	Instruction
0001	1001	Data
0010	0101	Instruction
0011	1110	Data
0100	0001	Instruction
0101	0100	Data

Figure 26–2 Relationship between data and information in memory.

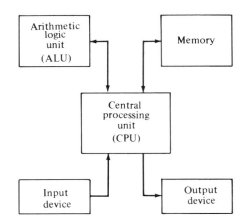

Figure 26–3 Block diagram of a simple computer.

Although there are several different types of memory systems and mediums, they can be divided into three broad functional categories: main memory, mass memory, and shift register memory. Main memory is that memory built into the digital system. Mass memory can be connected to the system to extend its memory capacity. Shift register memory is that used within the system to store information for short periods of time while operations are being performed on the data. An example where all three categories are utilized is the microcomputer. A particular microcomputer might have a main memory capacity of 64 kilobytes. A disk drive can be added which extends the capacity to perhaps 1 megabyte. Eight-bit shift registers within the microprocessor unit hold the various instructions and data while the computer is in operation.

26-2 MAIN MEMORY

26-2.1 Introduction. Two types of mediums are used in main memory systems: magnetic core and semiconductor. Magnetic core memory is the older of the two and is used in very large computer systems. Semiconductor memory is much smaller and consumes less power. Each of these mediums is discussed in the following sections.

26-2.2 Magnetic Core Memory. This memory medium consists of an array of small toroidal ferrite cores, as depicted in Figure 26–4. Each core serves as an individual memory cell that can store a binary zero or one. Cores are placed together to form a plane. Two conductors, called the X and Y lines, pass through each cell. These are used to both address and write into a particular cell. For example, if lines X_2 and Y_3 are both

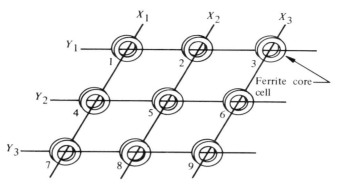

Figure 26–4 Magnetic core memory.

active, or enabled, current will flow through both conductors, causing cell 8 to become magnetized and switch into the binary one state. The other cells through which these conductors pass remain unchanged because only one-half the current flows through them. The magnetic properties of the cells are such that it takes current flowing through both conductors to fully magnetize and cause them to change from the zero to the binary one state. If the direction of current flow is reversed in both conductors, the cell becomes magnetized in the opposite direction and changes from the binary one to binary zero state. After the cell has been written into, the current through both conductors can be removed and the magnetic state of the cell will be retained because of its residual magnetism. Thus, a ferrite core can be used as a binary storage cell because of its magnetic properties. When the core is magnetized in one direction, a binary one is being stored. When the core is magnetized in the opposite direction, a binary zero is stored.

A third conductor, called a sense line, is passed through the center of each cell, as shown in Figure 26–5. This line is enabled whenever the binary bit stored by a cell is to be read. To read a particular cell, the cell is caused to go into the zero state by passing a current through the required X and Y conductors in the zero direction. If the cell is in the binary one state, a voltage will be induced across the sense line, as indicated in Figure 26–6, due to the rapid change in the magnetic flux field caused by the cell being magnetized in the binary zero direction. If the cell is storing a binary zero, there is little change in the magnetic flux field, and the voltage induced across the sense line is minimal. Reading a cell then is simply a matter of detecting whether or not a voltage is developed across the sense line. This is a destructive type of read out. Each cell will be storing a binary zero after it has been read. To overcome this rather serious

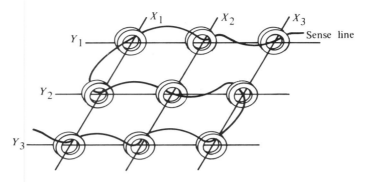

Figure 26–5 Magnetic core memory with sense line.

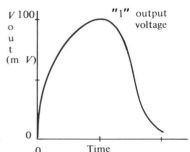

Figure 26–6 Voltage induced across the sense line when a binary one is read from a ferrite core.

shortcoming, the bit is usually stored in a flip-flop and then written back into the cell after the read operation. Magnetic core memory is nonvolatile. Because the ferrite cores have a high degree of retentivity, the information stored in the cells is not lost when the power is removed from the system. Magnetic core memory has constant-access time. This means that the access time is the same no matter where the binary word is stored. Constant-access time is often referred to as random-access time.

26-2.3 Semiconductor memory. There are two types of semiconductor memory: random-access memory (RAM) and read-only memory (ROM). Both BJT and MOS transistor technology are used in either type. RAM memory is often referred to as read-write memory. This means that information can be written into and read from the memory system. In ROM memory systems information is permanently written into the system during its manufacture. The information can be read from the memory whenever desired, but new information cannot be written into it. RAMs and ROMs are both fabricated in integrated circuit format. RAMs are volatile memory systems. The contents in these systems are lost when the power is turned off. ROMs, like magnetic core, are nonvolatile memory systems. Both RAM and ROM memory have constant-access time.

Bipolar and MOS RAMs are both used in various computer and microprocessor-based applications. Bipolar RAMs are used for relatively small storage systems, whereas MOS RAMs are employed where applications require storage of larger amounts of information. Bipolar RAMs are made up of individual flip-flops called cells, which are arranged in rows and columns to form an array. A cell consists of two multiemitter transistors connected together as a flip-flop, as illustrated in Figure 26–7. The state of the flip-flop can be read from the cell by applying a binary one to both the X and Y select inputs. Depending upon the state of the flip-flop, the presence of a zero or one will be indicated on the 0 or 1 sense line. The cell can be written into by maintaining both the X and Y select inputs at a binary one level and applying a binary one to one of the sense lines and a binary zero to the other. This either sets or resets the flip-flop. The flip-flop remains in that state when the X and Y select lines are returned to their normal binary zero level.

MOS RAM memory, like bipolar RAM, is made up of cells arranged in an array. There are two types of MOS RAMs—the static and dynamic. The diagram of a static cell is shown in Figure 26–8. The heart of the cell is the flip-flop, made up of transistors Q_2 and Q_3. Like the bipolar cell, a binary bit remains stored in the static cell until set or reset by a new write operation or until the power is turned off.

The diagram of a dynamic MOS RAM cell appears in Figure 26–9. Like the dynamic MOS shift registers discussed in the last chapter, the dynamic MOS RAM utilizes the internal gate-to-channel capacitance (C_{GC}) of a MOSFET inverter to store a binary bit. These cells have to be re-

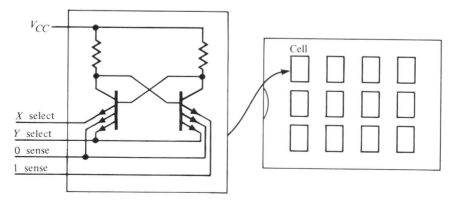

Figure 26–7 BJT RAM cell.

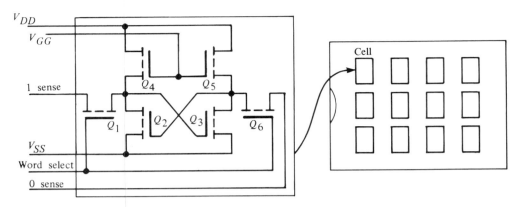

Figure 26–8   Static MOS RAM cell.

freshed approximately every 2 ms since the charge on this capacitance tends to leak off. This is accomplished by recirculating the binary information through an external circuit and allowing it to be continually written back into the cell. Although dynamic cells have the disadvantage of having to be continually refreshed, they have the advantage of having few components per cell. This allows for memory systems that have high storage capacity and low power consumption.

We are now ready to turn our attention to ROMs. Like RAMs, either bipolar or MOS transistor technology can be utilized in the manufacture of read-only memory systems. In BJT ROMs binary information is stored in one-bit cells similar to that appearing in Figure 26–10. The most common method of programming a ROM is to program it during its fabrication. The information to be stored is given to the manufacturer by the user and is permanently written into the individual cells. The cell shown

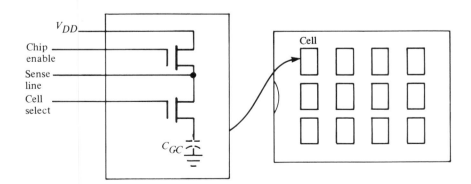

Figure 26–9   Dynamic MOS RAM cell.

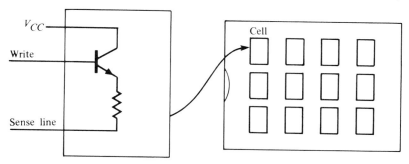

Figure 26–10   BJT ROM cell.

in Figure 26–10 is storing a binary zero. If a binary one is required, the resistor appearing in the emitter circuit is not connected.

Another type of ROM is the programmable read-only memory, or PROM. Information can be written into the PROM by the user. A PROM cell looks much like a ROM cell except that the emitter resistor is fabricated as a fuse. With the fuse connected to the emitter, a binary zero is being stored. A binary one is written into the cell by causing enough current to flow through the fuse to "burn" it open. Special instruments are available for programming PROMs. After the information has been written into the PROM it behaves like a ROM. It cannot be reprogrammed.

Yet another type of ROM is the erasable programmable read-only memory, or EPROM. This type of memory system behaves like a ROM, can be programmed by the user like a PROM, and can be reprogrammed by the user with a special ultraviolet light programming instrument. PROMs and EPROMs are often used where ROM memory is required and the equipment in which they are used will be produced only in limited quantities. They are also used for ROM applications by engineers and technicians when prototyping circuits and digital systems. After the prototype has been perfected and the equipment is ready to be mass produced, the information to be programmed into the ROM is sent to a semiconductor manufacturer who manufacturers the device.

Semiconductor RAMs and ROMs are fabricated to store a specified number of binary bits. Memory capacity is usually indicated in kilobits. Since the actual number of bits a series of flip-flops can store is a function of the binary base (2^n), the actual capacity will not be an even thousand. As indicated in Table 26–1, a 1k memory system will actually store 1024 bits, a 2k system will store 2048 bits, and so forth.

Individual cells within a memory IC are connected during the manufacturing process to store particular binary word lengths. A 1k RAM or

TABLE 26–1   Some Typical Semiconductor Memory Storage Capacities

Number of Storage Bits	Memory Size
1024	1k
2048	2k
4096	4k
8192	8k
16384	16k
32768	32k
65536	64k

ROM can be connected during fabrication to store 1024 one-bit words (1024×1), 512 two-bit words (512×2), 256 four-bit words (256×4), or 128 eight-bit words (128×8).

Storage capacity can be increased by connecting memory devices together. Eight 1024×1 RAMs or ROMs can be connected together to store 1024 eight-bit words, for example. An application of two RAMs used for storage appears in Figure 26–11. This is a simplified diagram of a microprocessor-based system. To use either one of the two memories, the desired RAM must be addressed by the microprocessor (MPU). The address

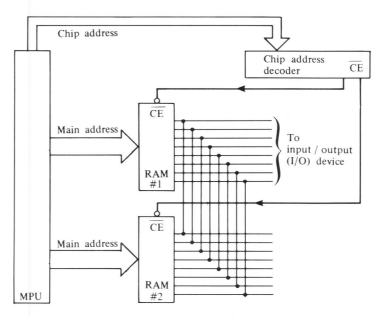

Figure 26–11   Simplified diagram of a microprocessor-based system employing multiple RAM memory.

is decoded by the chip address decoder. This causes the $\overline{\text{chip enable}}$ ($\overline{\text{CE}}$) input to the RAM being addressed to change from a binary one to a binary zero level enabling that RAM. The memory location within either RAM where data are to be written into or read out of is identified by the address coming from the microprocessor.

The binary word length used in a particular digital system limits the quantity of main memory available for that system. Sixteen different addresses can be obtained from a 4-bit word, 64 for a 6-bit word, 256 for an 8-bit word, 4096 for a 12-bit word, and 65,536 for a 16-bit word.

Scores of different types of RAMs and ROMs are produced by semiconductor manufacturers. Some common types appear in Table 26–2. As indicated, memory devices differ by transistor logic family type, bit capacity, and word organizational scheme.

TABLE 26–2   A Selected Listing of Semiconductor Memories

Family	Type	Number of Bits	Organization	Number
MOS	Static RAM	4,096	1024×4	2114
	Static RAM	4,096	4096×1	4017
	Static RAM	16,384	2048×8	4028
	Dynamic RAM	1,024	1024×1	1103
	EPROM	4,096	512×8	6834
	EPROM	16,384	2048×8	4716
	Static ROM	4,096	512×8	3514
	Static ROM	8,192	1024×8	6830
	Dynamic ROM	8,192	1024×8	8865
	Static ROM	16,384	2048×8	4216
	Static ROM	32,768	4096×8	6833
	Static ROM	65,536	8192×8	4264
CMOS	Static RAM	512	512×1	2222
	Static RAM	1,024	256×4	5101
	Static RAM	1,024	1024×1	6508
TTL	Tri-state PROM	1,024	256×4	74S287
	Open collector PROM	4,096	512×8	74S472
	Tri-state ROM	2,048	512×4	74S370
	Open collector ROM	1,024	256×4	74S187
	Tri-state RAM	64	16×4	74LS189
	Tri-state RAM	256	256×1	74S200

26-3 MASS MEMORY STORAGE

26-3.1 Introduction. Memory mediums in this category are capable of storing large amounts of binary information inexpensively. Access time is not constant and is relatively slow when compared with main memory, however. A variety of mediums are used in mass memory systems: magnetic tape (reel to reel and cassette), magnetic disk (solid and floppy), magnetic drum, punched tape, punched cards, magnetic bubble, and charge-coupled device. The characteristics of each of these mediums are discussed in the following sections.

26-3.2 Magnetic Tape. This is a popular type of mass memory. Both cassette and reel-to-reel types are used. The cassette tape type is very similar to that used in the ordinary audio tape recorder. This is an especially popular mass medium for microcomputers. Cassette magnetic tapes are available that will store up to 3600 bits/in.

Reel-to-reel tape is made up of a ½-in. wide plastic ribbon covered with a thin layer of magnetic material. Binary data bits are placed on either seven or nine tracks. Packing densities of 200, 556, 800, and 1600 bits/in. are available. A tape which has a packing density of 800 bits/in. and is 2400 ft long can hold approximately 20 million binary bits.

26-3.3 Magnetic Disks. Two types of magnetic disk memory systems are in use: the rigid and the floppy. The rigid disk memory system is made up of a solid metal disk which has an oxide coating. As indicated by Figure 26–12, this medium resembles a long-playing phonograph record.

Floppy disks are a popular mass memory medium system used with microcomputers. Inexpensive, some can store up to two million bits. A rather common type of floppy disk is the diskette shown in Figure 26–13.

26-3.4 Magnetic Drums. Magnetic drum memory is made up of a cylinder whose surface area has been coated with a thin magnetic material. The circumference of the cylinder is divided into a number of different tracks. The drum rotates at a very high speed, which allows for data transfer rates up to approximately 800,000 bytes/s.

26-3.5 Punched Tape. This memory medium is especially popular in numerical tape controlled (NC) and computer numerical tape controlled (CNC) machines found in many machine shops and manufactur-

Figure 26–12   Rigid disk memory.

ing industries. Data represented by holes are punched in tracks which run the length of the tape, as illustrated in Figure 26–14.

26-3.6 Punched Cards.   This has long been a common mass memory storage medium. This medium has the advantage of storing very large amounts of data at little cost. It is very slow, however. Holes punched in the card, as shown in Figure 26–15, may represent numbers, letters, or symbols.

26-3.7 Magnetic Bubble.   This is one of the newest and most complex type of mass memory system. Fabricated in integrated circuit format, the chip is formed by depositing a thin layer of a magnetic substance onto

Figure 26–13 Diskette memory.

a crystalline substrate. Binary bits are represented by magnetic bubbles which develop when the cell is placed between two magnetic fields. This medium is nonvolatile, and some chips have a storage capacity of one million bits. At the present time, magnetic bubble memories have slower access times and are much more expensive than other types of semiconductor memories.

Figure 26–14 Punched paper tape memory.

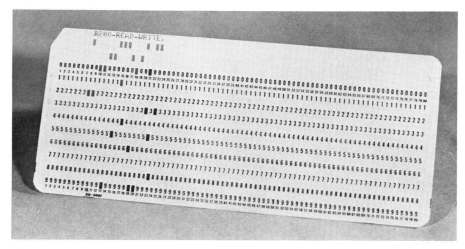

Figure 26–15 Punched paper card memory.

26-3.8 Charged-coupled Device. Charge-coupled device (CCD) memory is also one of the newer types of memory mediums. Like the MOS RAM devices, the storage medium in this type of memory is a capacitance which has to be periodically refreshed. Its storage capacity lies between that of MOS RAM and magnetic disk and is sequentially accessed.

26-3.9 A Summary of Mass Memory Mediums. All of the mass memory mediums just discussed are nonvolatile; the information is retained when power is removed or when the memory unit is removed from the memory system.

26-4 SHIFT REGISTER MEMORY

Shift registers are used for the temporary storage of information in binary form. These were discussed in Chapter 25. They have many applications in computers and microprocessors, especially in the arithmetic logic and central processing units where data are being operated upon. Their use in the microprocessor will be discussed in the next two chapters.

SUMMARY

1. Memory circuits and systems are essential to the operation of computers and microprocessor-based equipment. Memory is used to store binary information. A memory medium is divided into segments, each of which is large

enough to contain, or store, one binary word. Each segment is assigned its own unique address.

2. There are three main categories of memory: main, mass, and shift register. Main memory is usually housed within the computer itself and contains the information currently being used. Mass memory includes those mediums in which large quantities of data are stored outside the computer. Shift register memory is a short-term memory medium often used to hold data and instructions within the central processing unit as the data is being operated upon.

3. Two different mediums are used in main memory: magnetic core and semiconductor. Magnetic core memory is made up of ferrite core cells. A cell is able to store a binary bit because of its magnetic properties. If magnetized in one direction, a binary one is being stored. A binary zero is represented when the cell is magnetized in the opposite direction.

4. RAMs and ROMs form the two types of semiconductor main memory. Both are random access. RAMs can be both written into and read out of at will. ROMs, on the other hand, are usually written into once. Although data can be read from a ROM at any time, new data cannot be written back into this type of memory medium. Data are not destroyed when read out of either a RAM or ROM.

5. RAM is a type of volatile memory. Data are lost when the power to the memory is turned off. ROMs are nonvolatile and retain their information permanently. Both RAMs and ROMs can be fabricated using either bipolar or MOS transistor technology.

6. RAMs are used by the programmer to store both data and instructions that form the program. This information is variable and can be changed by the programmer. During the implementation of a program, information stored in the mass memory system is usually written into the main memory in information segments, or blocks, before entering the computer or microprocessor.

7. Most ROMs are programmed by the manufacturer by writing into the ROM the information supplied by the user. There are two types of ROMs which can be programmed by the user if the user has the special equipment required to program them. These include the PROM and EPROM.

8. Several different mediums are used in mass memory systems: magnetic tape, magnetic disk, magnetic drum, punched tape, punched cards, magnetic bubble, and CCD.

PRACTICE EXERCISES

1. Define the following terms:
   a. read   c. access time   e. nonvolatile memory
   b. write   d. volatile memory
2. What are the three general types of memory systems?
3. Identify two kinds of mediums used in main memory.
4. Describe how a magnetic core cell is able to store a binary bit.
5. How is a binary bit read out of a magnetic core cell?
6. What prevents the readout process from destroying the data in magnetic core data?

7. Is magnetic core memory volatile or nonvolatile? Explain.
8. What is meant by a memory that has random access?
9. Discuss the major differences between RAM and ROM memory.
10. How is a binary bit written into a bipolar RAM cell?
11. Identify the two types of MOS RAM cells.
12. What is the purpose of the chip enable ($\overline{CE}$) input on a RAM integrated circuit? What is the purpose of the bar over this input?
13. What is the major difference between a conventional ROM, a PROM, and an EPROM?
14. What factor primarily limits the amount of main memory a digital system can have?
15. Identify seven kinds of mediums used in mass memories.

ANSWERS TO PRACTICE EXERCISES

1. **a.** *Read* refers to the process of retrieving a binary bit or word from memory.
   b. *Write* is the process of placing a binary bit or word into memory.
   c. *Access time* is the time required to locate the correct memory segment, as identified by the address, and either write a binary word into or read a word out of that segment.
   d. *Volatile memory* refers to those memory mediums in which data is lost whenever the power is removed.
   e. *Nonvolatile memory* mediums are those which retain their stored information after the power is turned off or the medium has been removed from the digital system.
2. General types of memory systems are main, mass, and shift register.
3. Magnetic core and semiconductor mediums are used in main memory systems.
4. Current flowing through the X and Y lines, which pass through the cell, causes the cell to become magnetized. Depending upon the direction of magnetization, the magnetized cell represents either a binary zero or a binary one.
5. A binary zero is written into the cell and the resulting voltage induced across the sense line is monitored. If the cell was in the binary one state, the resulting change in the magnetic field causes a voltage to be induced across the sense line. Very little voltage is induced if the cell was already in the zero state.
6. The readout process causes a binary zero to be written into each cell. To save the original data, it is dumped into a parallel-in parallel-out shift register. This is easily accomplished. If a cell is storing a binary one, the voltage induced across the sense line sets a flip-flop in the register. After the readout process is completed, the data from the register is written back into the cells.
7. Magnetic core memory is nonvolatile. The ferrite core cells have a high degree of retentivity and retain their magnetism with the power removed.
8. Random access means that the access time is constant no matter where the binary information is located in memory. Main memory is random access.

9. RAMs can be written into at will by the user or programmer. ROMs are usually written into once, and the information is permanently retained. RAMs are volatile whereas ROMs are nonvolatile.

10. A binary bit is written into a bipolar RAM cell by holding the X and Y inputs at a binary one level and applying a binary one to one of the sense lines and a binary zero to the other. This either sets or resets the cell flip-flop.

11. The two types of MOS RAM cells include the static and dynamic.

12. The chip enable input is used to select and enable the memory integrated circuit so that binary information can be written into or read out of the cells. The bar indicates that this input is normally maintained at a binary one level. The circuit is enabled whenever the input level changes to a binary zero.

13. The user supplies the information, or program, to the manufacturer, who writes the information into the ROM during the fabrication process. A PROM can be programmed by the user if a PROM programming instrument is available. An EPROM can be programmed, erased, and reprogrammed by the user with an EPROM programming instrument.

14. Word length determines the maximum number of different addresses available for main memory.

15. Mass memory mediums are magnetic tape, magnetic disk, magnetic drum, punched tape, punched cards, magnetic bubble, and CCD.

CHAPTER EXAMINATION

1. Which of the following is not a type of memory system?
   a. mass
   b. main
   c. magnetic core
   d. shift register

2. The _____ is usually programmed at the time it is manufactured.
   a. RAM
   b. ROM
   c. PROM
   d. EPROM

3. What type of memory can be written into by the user at will?
   a. RAM
   b. ROM
   c. PROM
   d. EPROM

4. Which one of the following memory mediums is constant access?
   a. magnetic tape
   b. magnetic disk
   c. magnetic drum
   d. magnetic core

Choose true or false for questions 5 to 16.

5. T F   Access time refers to the time required to locate the proper memory segment and either write a binary word into or read a word out of that segment.

6. T   F   A volatile memory medium is one in which the binary information is lost, or destroyed, after a read operation.
7. T   F   MOS transistor technology can be used in RAMs, ROMs, and shift register memory.
8. T   F   Shift register memory is a type of nonvolatile memory medium.
9. T   F   ROMs are used to store binary information that is used over and over again by a digital system.
10. T   F   RAMs and ROMs are used for short-term information storage.
11. T   F   With the exception of punched tape, punched cards, and CCD mediums, information can be stored in mass memory because of the magnetic properties of the storage medium.
12. T   F   An input to a RAM or ROM, which has a bar over it such as $\overline{WE}$, indicates that that input is active whenever a binary zero is applied.
13. T   F   RAMs, ROMs, and magnetic core memory all have constant access times.
14. T   F   Magnetic tape (reel-to-reel and cassette) is a type of medium used in main memory.
15. T   F   Once a ROM has been written into, it cannot be written into again.
16. T   F   A 2048×8 RAM is one capable of storing 2048 eight-bit words.

27

Introduction to the Microprocessor

OBJECTIVES

Upon completion of this chapter you should be able to do the following:

1. Draw a functional block diagram of a computer.
2. Describe a microprocessor in terms of the block diagram of a computer.
3. Identify the three computer application categories, describe two examples for each category, and identify the category in which the microprocessor is best utilized.
4. Discuss the function of the arithmetic and logic unit and control unit in a microprocessor.
5. Draw a block diagram of a microprocessor.
6. Identify the major circuits associated with the arithmetic and logic unit and discuss the purpose of each.
7. List the major circuits associated with the control unit and describe the function of each.
8. Identify the three buses used in microprocessors.
9. Discuss the purpose of using an address word length which is twice as long as an information word.
10. Discuss the general characteristics of the Motorola 6800 MPU by describing its physical characteristics, DC voltage requirements, typical power dissipated, maximum clock frequency, and word length.

27-1 INTRODUCTION

A technological revolution is occurring in society which has been brought on by the microprocessor. Applications for this device have been tremendous. Millions of microprocessor-based systems are presently in operation, and many experts think that the applications for these devices are just now beginning to be fully recognized. This means that almost all technicians and engineers who work in the various industrial and consumer-related technical professions are soon going to be coming in contact with the microprocessor if they haven't already done so. This does not mean that all need to become skilled system analysts, programmers, or technicians. Established professions already exist for electrical engineers and computer science personnel who design and program microprocessors. Many post-secondary vocational-technical programs exist for the purpose of training electronic technicians to maintain and repair microprocessor-based systems. However, many engineers and technicians whose jobs traditionally have not required an extensive understanding of electronics are now finding that their jobs require knowledge and skills in adapting, maintaining, and repairing microprocessor equipment.

Technicians in the consumer industry, for example, are finding microprocessors used in everything from television sets to sewing machines. In the automotive industry several million microprocessors are used each year in ignition systems, emission controls, in monitoring engine variables, digital dashboard instruments, memory seat and steering wheel positions, electronic radio tuning, and keyless entry. It is estimated that in the future a fully equipped new automobile will contain approximately 15 microprocessors.

Millions of microprocessors are used in the nation's manufacturing industries. Of these, approximately 30 percent are used in production control equipment. This has allowed for the creation of a new generation of "smart" machines. Operations performed manually in the past are now performed by programmable controllers and robots. This has increased production, reduced manufacturing time, reduced production costs, and increased product quality. An additional 40 percent are used in production monitoring, test and inspection, and factory data collection.

Two new industries, robotics and microcomputers, have been created because of the development of the microprocessor. The microprocessor is also making a tremendous impact on society with its applications in video games and the home, or personal, microcomputers. The last three chapters in this book deal with the microprocessor. Material presented in these chapters will serve to familiarize you with some microprocessor applications, microprocessor architecture and organization, and interfacing and programming concepts.

Some new terms are introduced in this chapter. Two of these are *bus* and *programming*. Although both will be discussed later in further detail, it is appropriate that both be identified now. A bus is a group of parallel conductors used to move binary information from one circuit to another. A program consists of a list of instructions which tells a computer or microprocessor how to treat the data it is handling. Instructions are stored in memory and are listed in a step-by-step sequential manner. The microprocessor usually executes them in that order. Occasionally, it is necessary to deviate from that sequence, in which case an instruction will cause the microprocessor to jump ahead or behind in the program sequence to perform special kinds of functions such as branching, running a subroutine, or handling an interrupt. Upon completion, it resumes carrying out the instructions in the regular program sequence.

27-2 CONCEPTS OF MICROPROCESSORS

27-2.1 The Evolution of the Microprocessor. The microprocessor is a product of both active device and computer technology. The triode electron tube was developed in 1906 and was the device used to generate and amplify electrical signals until well after the advent of the transistor in 1948. It took a number of years for the state of the art in transistor manufacturing to reach a level where they became a common replacement for electron tubes. By 1962, transistor technology had advanced to the stage where multiple transistors could be fabricated on a single semiconductor substrate and the small-scale integrated (SSI) circuit was born. Within a few years circuit density had increased to the point where medium-scale integrated (MSI) circuits were common. Further developments soon led to the creation of the large-scale integrated (LSI) circuit.

Advances in computer technology paralleled the changes in active devices. As new active devices were developed and their manufacturing techniques perfected, engineers rapidly incorporated them into computers to build smaller, faster, and more efficient systems. The digital computer, first developed in the 1940s utilized electron tubes. With the advent of the transistor, a second generation of computers began appearing by the end of the 1950s. This generation was considerably smaller and more efficient than its predecessor. A third computer generation began appearing toward the end of the 1960s which employed small-scale integrated circuits.

The existence of large-scale integrated circuit technology and the knowledge of computer engineering available in the early 1970s led to the development of the microprocessor. The first microprocessor appeared on the market in 1971. Although crude when compared to the microproc-

essors available today, it was the forerunner of what has become a phenomenon in the relatively short history of technology.

27-2.2 A Simple Computer.

A functional block diagram of a com-
puter is shown in Figure 27–1. The heart of the system is the central processing unit (CPU). Computers perform operations on binary data. The
type of operations performed depends upon the kind of instructions
given it by the operator via the program. It is in the CPU that all the operations, or manipulations, on the data are performed. The data may be
stored in memory or come from an outside source by way of an input
device. The data, after they have been manipulated, are sent outside the
CPU. The memory section may be either main memory, mass memory,
or both. The input device is often a keyboard. Common output devices
include CRT monitors and printers.

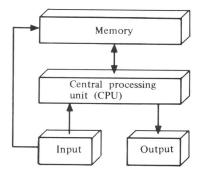

Figure 27–1 Functional block diagram of a
computer.

27-2.3 What is a Microprocessor?

A microprocessor is the CPU
portion of a computer which is fabricated on a single semiconductor substrate. It is manufactured using large-scale or very large-scale integration
techniques. Most microprocessors utilize N channel MOS transistor technology. The microprocessor chip is approximately ¼ in. square. It is often
packaged in a 40-pin dual-in-line case which measures 0.6 in. by 2 in. The
abbreviations MPU (microprocessor unit) and µP are often used in literature when referring to a microprocessor.

27-2.4 General Applications for Microprocessors.

Computers can
be divided into three general categories according to their major application: those used for data processing, those employed primarily for scientific computation, and those used for monitoring and control purposes.

Microprocessors can be used in computers for all three categories.
They are used most frequently in monitoring and control applications,

however. Prior to the development of the MPU, these functions were performed primarily by digital circuits. This method was often inflexible, complex, and expensive. Changes in the monitoring and control process usually required extensive circuit modifications. Microprocessors have changed this. MPUs can be programmed to perform functions that formerly required a substantial amount of circuitry. A process change with the microprocessor involves only writing a new program. Thus, the program (called software) has replaced circuits (hardware). This is what makes the microprocessor such an ideal control unit. Along with its low cost, this is what has allowed many machines, consumer products, and industrial processes, which previously had no applications for electronics, to become computer controlled. Equipment and machines in which a microprocessor is employed is called a microprocessor-based system. The MPU is the heart of such a system. However, just as the human body has to have some external parts, such as arms and legs, to be complete, external devices and circuits have to be connected to the microprocessor for it to function and be complete. These are called peripherals and often include circuits and devices such as a clock pulse generator, main memory, mass memory, and input-output equipment. In addition, a program must be written into and stored in the memory which tells the microprocessor what to do. One should understand that the microprocessor in itself is not a computer. It is an integrated circuit that contains the central processing unit of a computer. A computer requires memory and input-output equipment. A computer that has a microprocessor as its CPU is called a microcomputer.

27-3 MICROPROCESSOR ARCHITECTURE

27-3.1 The Block Diagram. The microprocessor is fabricated from a single semiconductor substrate. The circuits forming the integrated circuit are utilized in various arithmetic, shift register, and decoder circuits. These circuits and their relationships to one another are referred to as the MPU's architecture. The microprocessor can be divided into two general sections for the purpose of analysis. As indicated in Figure 27–2, these are the control and the arithmetic and logic units.

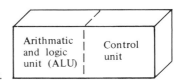

Figure 27–2 Conceptual diagram of a microprocessor.

The control unit obtains the program instructions from memory one at a time, decodes them, and provides control signals which are sent to other parts of the system. The arithmetic and logic unit implements the commands produced by the control unit.

A block diagram of a microprocessor and its associated peripherals appears in Figure 27–3. A major portion of the microprocessor is made up of shift registers. Buses are used to connect the various circuits together. MPUs are available which use 4-, 8-, 16-, and even 32-bit word lengths. The longer the word bit size, the more powerful the microprocessor. Most microprocessors utilize an 8-bit data and instruction word and a 16-bit address word. A 16-bit address word allows 65,536 main

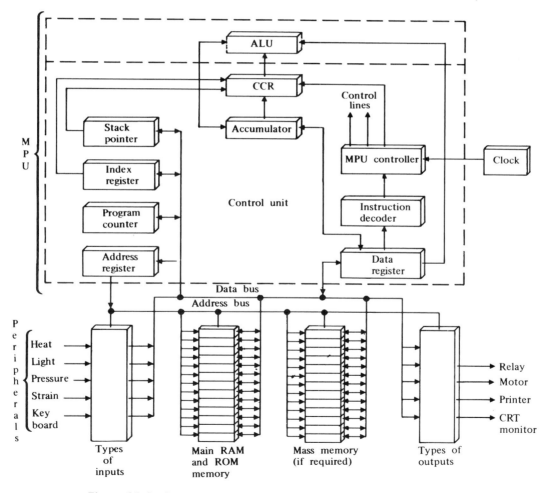

Figure 27–3   Block diagram of a microprocessor system.

memory segments to be addressed. In these MPUs shift registers that store data and instructions have a storage capacity of 8 bits while those that store addresses have a capacity of 16 bits. Each main memory segment holds 8 bits, or one byte of data. Thus, these systems are capable of storing 65,536 (64k) bytes of data.

Peripheral devices or circuits include a clock, input and output devices, main memory, and mass memory. Almost any kind of data can be applied to the input peripheral. Some of those shown in Figure 27–3 require transducers to convert mechanical properties into equivalent electrical signals.

27-3.2 The Arithmetic and Logic Unit. The arithmetic and logic unit is made up of logic gates and shift registers. This unit has three inputs: the data register, condition code register, and accumulator. It is in this section that mathematical and logic operations are performed on the data words supplied to the microprocessor. Parallel adders and subtracters, OR gates, AND gates, and EXCLUSIVE-OR gates are usually employed in this section.

27-3.3 The Control Unit. Although the exact number and names of the circuits vary from MPU to MPU, those appearing in the control unit section of the diagram of the microprocessor appearing in Figure 27–3 are the program counter, address register, data register, accumulator, index register, stack pointer, instruction decoder, MPU controller, and condition code register (CCR).

The program counter is a shift register used to keep track of the program as it is taken from memory, a step at a time, and implemented. When the microprocessor is first energized and prepared for operation, the address of the first instruction is placed in the program counter. As the program begins, the instruction stored in memory at that address is placed on the data bus and sent to the data register. Simultaneously, the program counter is incremented to the address of the second instruction. In this fashion the program counter keeps track of the instructions as the program is being run.

The address register, sometimes called the memory address register (MAR), or address buffer, holds the address of the RAM or ROM memory section where the desired instruction or data word is stored.

The data register temporarily stores any information appearing on the data bus. In addition, whenever an instruction is read from memory, it is stored in this register during the time that it is being decoded and executed.

The most important register in any microprocessor is the accumulator. Data to be operated upon, and the results of these operations, are stored in the accumulator. Some microprocessors have two accumulators. This extends the applications of the MPU and at the same time decreases the amount of main memory required.

The index register is employed when the program being run contains a loop. The binary word in the index counter decrements every time the program loop is completed and is checked for zero. The loop is continued if the number is not zero. The program exits the loop when the number contained in the index counter is finally zero.

To understand the use of the stack pointer shift register, the principles of stack memory have to be understood. Stack memory is a technique used to store binary words in reserved sections RAM when the program contains provisions for interrupts and subroutines. Whenever an interrupt or subroutine occurs and the normal program routine is disrupted, those shift registers which have instructions, data, or addresses essential to the program operation have their contents transferred to stack memory. They are held there while the microprocessor is detoured to perform the operations dictated by the source that interrupted the program. After the interrupt or subroutine is completed, the information stored in the stack is transferred back into their original registers. The status of the microprocessor is now what it was prior to the initiation of the interrupt or subroutine. The stack pointer is a register which is used as a counter to monitor the binary information in the stack memory while a branch or interrupt in the regular program is occurring.

Whenever an instruction is read from RAM or ROM it is stored in the data register while it is being decoded by the instruction decoder. The instruction decoder decodes the instruction and the resulting signal is sent to the MPU controller.

The MPU controller generates the control signals required for the MPU to carry out the instruction. A different control signal is produced for each decoded instruction received from the instruction decoder.

The condition code register (CCR) is sometimes referred to as the status register or flag register. Each flip-flop within this register is called a flag. The individual flags are set by the results of the arithmetic and logic operations performed within the ALU section of the microprocessor. Each flag monitors a particular function within the ALU. Some common flag functions appear in Table 27–1.

TABLE 27–1 Microprocessor Flag Functions

Flag Function	Flag Designation
Carry-borrow flag	C
Two's complement Overflow indicator	V
Zero indicator	Z
Negative indicator	N
Interrupt mask	I
Half carry	H

27-3.4 Buses.   Data and instruction words are transferred from register to register within the MPU and from the MPU to outside main memory and other peripherals. A means must be provided to transfer this information. This is accomplished by means of buses. A bus is a group of conductors forming a transmission line. Most information within the MPU is handled in parallel fashion for faster operation. Because of this, each binary bit must have its own conductor. An eight-bit binary word requires a bus that has eight conductors. Two general kinds of buses are used in microprocessors—unidirectional and bidirectional. A unidirectional bus allows information to be sent in one direction only. Binary information can flow in either direction (at different times) in a bidirectional bus.

Three different bus systems are employed to move data and instructions in most microprocessors: the address, data, and control buses. The relationship of each to the microprocessor system is illustrated in Figure 27–4.

As shown in Figure 27–4, the address bus connects the MPU with the main memory and the input-output (I/O) devices. Any other peripheral devices used will also be connected to the address bus. Since the addresses originate within the microprocessor, a unidirectional bus is used. Although most microprocessors employ an eight-bit (one-byte) binary word length, many utilize a two-byte address.

After the particular memory IC and segment location has been addressed by the MPU, the data bus is used to either send or receive information within the MPU. As indicated in Figure 27–4, this is a bidirectional bus. The bus is also connected to the input-output peripheral devices and, depending upon which one is being addressed, can carry information to the MPU from the peripheral or vice versa. In a microprocessor utilizing an eight-bit word length, this bus is made up of eight separate conductors.

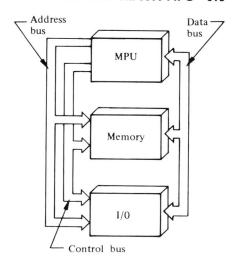

Figure 27–4 Relationship of the buses used in a microprocessor system.

The control bus carries signals that control and sequence the events, which allow the microprocessor and its associated peripherals to execute the operation identified by the program step.

27-3.5 The Clock. The clock pulse generator, or clock, is used to provide the timing pulses required to trigger the shift registers and to satisfy the other synchronization requirements in the microprocessor system. In some microprocessors, the clock is part of the MPU, while in others, a separate integrated circuit is required. The clock pulse is divided into two separate pulses ($\emptyset$1 and $\emptyset$2) in many microprocessors. When this is the case, $\emptyset$1 provides part of the timing requirements while $\emptyset$2 provides the other part.

27-4 THE MOTOROLA 6800 MPU

There are several dozen microprocessors manufactured by approximately 30 different semiconductor manufacturers produced for various applications. Although there are many distinct differences between most of them, there are also many similarities. It is not a burdensome task to learn how another microprocessor operates if one understands how one functions. One of the more popular microprocessors is the Motorola 6800 (MC6800). This device is introduced in the next paragraph and will be discussed in greater detail in the next chapter. Other microprocessors will be introduced in Chapter 29.

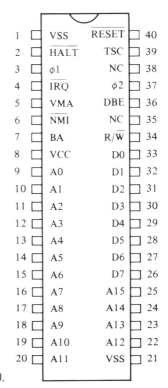

Pin	Left	Right	Pin
1	VSS	$\overline{\text{RESET}}$	40
2	$\overline{\text{HALT}}$	TSC	39
3	$\phi1$	NC	38
4	$\overline{\text{IRQ}}$	$\phi2$	37
5	VMA	DBE	36
6	$\overline{\text{NMI}}$	NC	35
7	BA	R/$\overline{\text{W}}$	34
8	VCC	D0	33
9	A0	D1	32
10	A1	D2	31
11	A2	D3	30
12	A3	D4	29
13	A4	D5	28
14	A5	D6	27
15	A6	D7	26
16	A7	A15	25
17	A8	A14	24
18	A9	A13	23
19	A10	A12	22
20	A11	VSS	21

Figure 27–5 Pin designation for the Motorola 6800 MPU.

The Motorola 6800 MPU is encapsulated in a dual-in-line 40-pin case, as illustrated in Figure 27–5. The DC voltage requirement is 5 V, the typical power dissipation is 600 mW, and the maximum clock frequency is 1 MHz. The MC6800 is an NMOS dynamic device which utilizes an 8-bit binary data and instruction word and a 16-bit address word. The block diagram of the device is shown in Figure 27–6. The 6800 MPU looks much like the microprocessor appearing in Figure 27–3; there are some obvious differences, however. The index register, program counter, and stack pointer are divided into two sections (*H* and *L*). These registers all store addresses. Since the address word size is 16 bits (two bytes), the *H* registers store the most significant byte, and the *L* registers store the least significant address byte. Two accumulators are utilized—*A* and *B*. Pins 9 through 20 and 22 through 25 connect the MPU to the external address bus. The eight-line external data bus is connected to pins 26 through 33. The two clock pulse signals are connected to the MPU control bus via pins 3 and 37. The remaining pins are used to connect the DC supply, reset, halt, and various hardware controls to the control bus within the MPU.

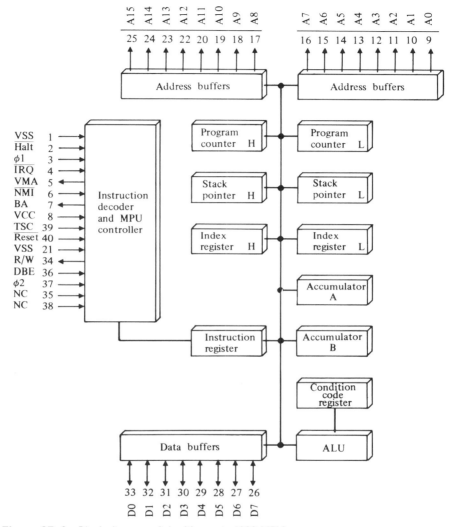

Figure 27–6   Block diagram of the Motorola 6800 MPU.

SUMMARY

1. A microprocessor is the central processing unit of a computer which is fabricated on a single semiconductor substrate.

2. Computers can be grouped into three general categories according to their main application: data processing, scientific computation, and monitoring and control. Although the microprocessor can be utilized in computers designed for any one of the three categories, it is best used for monitoring and control purposes.

3. Several dozen different microprocessors are manufactured by approximately 30 different semiconductor manufacturers. Although they differ in architecture and organization, most can be divided into two general sections—the control unit and the arithmetic and logic unit. The purpose of the control unit is to obtain the instructions from memory, one at a time, decode them, and cause the resulting control signals to be sent to the various parts of the MPU. The arithmetic logic unit executes the commands issued by the control unit.

4. Circuits in the arithmetic and logic unit include parallel adders, subtracters, and gates. Common circuits employed in the control section include the program counter, address register, accumulator, index register, stack-pointer, instruction decoder, MPU controller, and the condition code register.

5. Buses are used to transfer the binary information from one circuit to another within the MPU and between the microprocessor and its peripherals. Three bus systems are used in most MPUs: the address, data, and control.

6. The Motorola 6800 MPU is a dynamic NMOS device which is mounted in a 40-pin DIP case. It utilizes an 8-bit data and instruction word, a 16-bit address word, and employs two accumulators.

PRACTICE EXERCISES

1. What is a microprocessor?
2. List the three categories of computers as identified by their primary applications.
3. For which one of the categories is the microprocessor best suited?
4. What kinds of peripheral circuits and devices are required for the microprocessor to function as a complete system?
5. What is the purpose of the arithmetic and logic unit?
6. What kinds of circuits are commonly used in the ALU section of the microprocessor?
7. What is the function of the control unit in the microprocessor?
8. What kinds of circuits are usually used in the control unit?
9. What is the primary advantage of using longer binary bit words in a microprocessor?
10. What is the purpose of the program counter?
11. What function does the address register perform?
12. What is the function of the index register?
13. Describe the function of the data register.
14. What is the purpose of the accumulator?
15. Discuss the purpose of the condition code register.
16. List the three buses used in microprocessors.
17. What is the purpose of the clock in a microprocessor-based system?
18. Why are address words in some microprocessors twice the length of data and instruction words?
19. What are the word bit sizes used in the Motorola 6800 MPU?

ANSWERS TO PRACTICE EXERCISES

1. A microprocessor is the central processing unit of a computer which is fabricated on a single semiconductor substrate.

2. The three categories of computers are those used for data processing, scientific computation, and monitoring and control purposes.
3. Although the microprocessor can be used for all three applications, it is best utilized for monitoring and control applications.
4. Commonly used peripheral circuits and devices used with the microprocessor are the main memory, a clock pulse generator, and input and output devices or equipment. In some instances mass memory is also required.
5. The arithmetic and logic unit executes the instruction. It is here where the mathematical and logic operations are performed.
6. Parallel adders, subtracters, OR gates, AND gates, and EXCLUSIVE-OR gates are the types of circuits utilized in the ALU section.
7. The control unit fetches the program instructions from memory, one at a time, decodes them, and provides control signals which are sent to other parts of the microprocessor system.
8. The control unit is made up of various shift registers, a decoder, and a controller.
9. The longer the binary word, the more operations the MPU can perform, and the greater the memory-addressing capability of the microprocessor.
10. The program counter is used to keep track of the program instructions located in memory while the program is being run.
11. The address register holds the address of the peripheral or memory section being addressed.
12. The index register is used when the program contains a loop.
13. The data register is used to store an instruction when it is read from memory and decoded. It is also used to store data which is to be written into memory while the particular memory section is being addressed.
14. The accumulator is the most important register in the MPU. Data and instruction words are loaded into this circuit first before they are shifted into memory or other registers within the MPU.
15. The condition code register monitors the status of an operation that has taken place in the microprocessor. The outputs of this flip-flop are used to set flags to check for overflow, carry-borrow, zero, a negative number, half-carry, and interrupt.
16. The buses used in the microprocessor include the address, data, and control.
17. The clock, or clock pulse generator, is used to synchronize the events and operations occurring in the microprocessor system.
18. Longer address words are used in some microprocessors to increase main memory size capability.
19. The Motorola 6800 MPU utilizes data and instruction words which are eight bits in length and a 16-bit address word.

CHAPTER EXAMINATION

1. The _____ is used to keep track of the binary words in the stack memory.
   a. stack pointer   c. index register
   b. data register   d. address register

2. The _____ holds the data word which is to be written into memory.
   a. stack pointer   **c.** index register
   b. data register   **d.** address register

3. The heart of a computer is its
   a. CPU   **c.** accumulator
   b. memory   **d.** input-output devices

4. The _____ controls all the other sections in a computer system.
   a. CPU   **c.** accumulator
   b. memory   **d.** input-output

5. The program instructions for a computer are stored in its
   a. CPU   **c.** accumulator
   b. memory   **d.** arithmetic and logic unit

6. Which one of the following is not a classification of computer applications?
   a. data processing   **c.** monitoring and control
   b. inventory control   **d.** scientific computations

7. A register which contains the memory address of the instruction being read from memory best describes the function of the
   a. program counter   **c.** instruction register
   b. address register   **d.** condition code register

8. The data word length associated with the 6800 MPU is _____.
   a. 4   **c.** 16
   b. 8   **d.** 32

Choose true or false for questions 9 to 21.

 9. T   F   The major difference between a computer and a microcomputer is the size.

10. T   F   The microprocessor usually does not contain main memory on the chip itself.

11. T   F   Software has replaced a considerable amount of hardware for microprocessor applications in monitoring and control.

12. T   F   The index register is used to hold data when it is first placed into the microprocessor.

13. T   F   The stack pointer and program counter perform similar functions.

14. T   F   The condition code register is used to hold addresses when the program contains an interrupt or subroutine.

15. T   F   The data bus is a bidirectional bus.

16. T   F   The stack pointer is the most important register in the microprocessor.

17. T   F   Each data or instructional word that enters the microprocessor is first loaded into main memory.

18. T   F   The clock is used in the microprocessor system to allow operating personnel to keep track of the time that it takes the microprocessor to execute an instruction.

19. T   F   The major purpose of the ALU section is to execute instructions.

20. T   F   The control unit takes the program instructions from memory and decodes them.

21. T   F   The MC6800 uses a 16-bit address word.

28

Interfacing Circuits and Programming Techniques

OBJECTIVES

Upon completion of this chapter you should be able to do the following:

1. Identify three problems associated with connecting peripherals to a microprocessor.
2. Discuss the purpose of the general-purpose interface bus (GPIB), the peripheral interface adapter (PIA), the universal asynchronous receiver transmitter (UART), CMOS buffers, analog-to-digital (A/D) and digital-to-analog (D/A) converters, and three-state buffers.
3. Identify the four types of languages used to program computers and discuss the difference between machine and assembly language.
4. Describe what is meant by an instruction set.
5. Define the terms *mnemonic, opcode,* and *operand.*
6. Describe how instructions are classified and identify the seven classes of instructions used by the MC6800 MPU.
7. Discuss what is meant by address modes and identify the six addressing modes used by the MC6800.

28-1 INTRODUCTION

As discussed in the last chapter, externally connected devices (peripherals) have to be connected to the microprocessor to cause it to perform some function. A microprocessor connected to a keyboard, printer, CRT monitor, RAM, ROM, and mass memory forms a microprocessor-based system called a microcomputer. A microcomputer is a general-purpose microprocessor-based system. Depending upon the type of program being run, the system can be used for personal or small business accounting, maintaining control of inventory in a small business, or estimating the cost of a construction project for a contractor. Other kinds of micro-processor based systems are "dedicated" to performing a repetitive, albeit, highly sophisticated series of tasks. The types of peripherals connected to the MPU are often quite different for the two kinds of systems. The inputs to the dedicated microprocessor-based system might be temperature, strain, stress, DC pulses, AC voltage, or almost any mechanical or electrical property. The dedicated microprocessor usually won't require much RAM and probably won't utilize mass memory. Instead, most, if not all, of its program is stored in ROMs. In addition, appropriate transducers must be used to convert the physical phenomenon into equivalent electrical signals if any of the inputs are mechanical properties. The resulting electrical signals are usually analog in nature and have to be converted into equivalent binary words before the microprocessor can manipulate them. The output from the microprocessor might be used to turn a motor, light an LED, drive a printer, or energize a relay. The binary output signals have to be converted into an equivalent analog voltage for some of these applications.

Interfacing circuits are required for the MPU to communicate with its peripherals. Interfacing circuits make the MPU and peripherals compatible with one another since the DC supply voltages, binary voltage levels, and operating speed of the MPU and its peripherals are often different.

Engineers and technicians, when confronted with the problem of applying a microprocessor to a particular application, are concerned with two activities: interfacing the microprocessor and programming it. The first part of this chapter deals with the principles of interfacing, while the second part is concerned with the techniques of programming.

28-2 MICROPROCESSOR INTERFACING CIRCUITS

28-2.1 Introduction.   Peripherals are connected to the MPU via one or more buses, as illustrated by the RAM and ROM circuits connected to the address and data buses appearing in Figure 28–1. Three potential problems exist in this type of arrangement. One, the logic families used in the MPU and various memory devices may not be compatible with one another. Second, data can originate at any one of the devices and be transferred via the data bus to any other. The other devices should re-

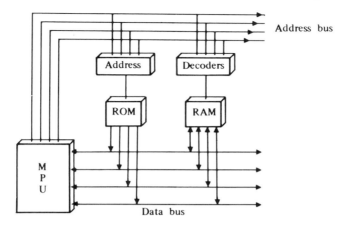

Figure 28–1   MPU bus arrangement.

main inhibited and not be affected by the data transfer. Third, to prevent any data contained in the other peripherals connected to the common bus from affecting the binary logic levels of data being transferred on the data bus, the outputs of these devices have to be isolated. The first problem is solved by employing a special bus or special integrated circuits which provide compatibility between devices and equipment fabricated from different logic families. The second problem is solved by providing each peripheral with an address (in addition to the addresses assigned to the memory sections). A solution to the third problem is to connect a special three-state buffer between the output of the peripheral and the data bus. Each of these is discussed in the following sections.

28-2.2 The General-Purpose Interface bus.   In general, there is little compatibility between most types of microprocessors and circuits and equipment built from different logic families. This presents a major problem when two or more microprocessor-based systems or circuits built from unlike transistor logic families are connected together on a common data bus. This problem has been alleviated to a considerable degree by the general-purpose interface bus (GPIB). This is a 16-line bus developed by Hewlett-Packard and eventually adapted by the Institute of Electrical and Electronic Engineers (IEEE) as an interfacing standard. It is often referred to as the IEEE 488 bus and can accommodate up to 15 different devices. Although all microprocessors are not compatible with the bus, many microprocessor manufacturers build an integrated circuit that allows their MPU to interface with it. The MC68488, manufactured by Motorola, allows the MC6800 MPU to be used with the bus.

28-2.3 The Peripheral Interface Adapter. Most manufacturers of microprocessors build a family of support circuits which simplify the problem of interfacing a particular MPU with its auxiliary circuits and devices. Motorola manufactures several for the MC6800 microprocessor. The most important of these is the MC6820 peripheral interface adapter (PIA). This is an IC enclosed in a 40-pin dual-in-line package. The PIA has two channels; one can be used to interface input peripherals and the other channel used to interface output peripherals. A typical application for the PIA is shown in Figure 28–2. The PIA is particularly useful for interfacing the MPU with analog-to-digital (A/D) converters, digital-to-analog (D/A) converters, and other circuits used for monitoring and control applications.

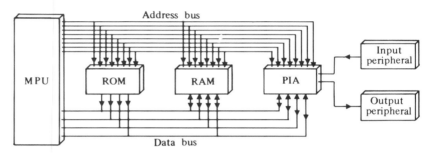

Figure 28–2   Interfacing input and output peripherals with a PIA.

28-2.4 The Universal Asynchronous Receiver Transmitter. Another popular interfacing circuit is the universal asynchronous communications receiver transmitter (UART). This circuit is used to convert serial data into equivalent parallel data and vice versa. Binary data is transferred between circuits within the MPU in parallel. Outside the MPU, the data may be transferred either in a parallel or serial format between the microprocessor and peripherals. The parallel method is faster. However, the bus must contain one conductor for each word bit. Data is transmitted much slower when it is transferred serially since each bit must be transferred one after another. This is not as detrimental as it might first appear for many applications and is the most common method of transferring data between the MPU and its peripherals. Most peripherals are slow compared to the microprocessor and cannot handle rapid transfers of data. This is especially true of keyboards and line printers. The rate at which data are transmitted serially is referred to as baud rate and is measured in the number of bits transferred per second. If 9600 bits per second are transferred serially, the baud rate is 9600. The UART controls the baud rate in a microprocessor-based system where serial data transmission is used. Most microprocessor manufacturers build a UART or an equivalent circuit for their MPU. Motorola builds the asynchronous communications interface adater (ACIA) for the MC6800 MPU. This circuit, MC6850, is used for the same general applications as the UART. It is often used as the parallel-to-serial converter, which allows the use of telephone lines to transfer data over long distances.

28-2.5 Interfacing CMOS to TTL Integrated Circuits. Whenever CMOS and TTL devices are used in the same microprocessor-based system, an interfacing circuit must be connected between the two devices. If the CMOS device is used to drive the TTL device, the output current of the CMOS gates is not sufficient to drive the TTL gates. A commonly used technique involves connecting a CMOS buffer between the two integrated circuits, as illustrated in Figure 28–3. The buffer supplies the current required to drive the gates in the TTL device.

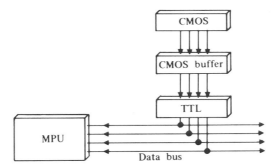

Figure 28–3   Interfacing CMOS and TTL logic devices with a CMOS buffer.

When a TTL device is used to drive a CMOS integrated circuit, another problem is present. The gates in the TTL circuit have more than enough current to drive the gates in the CMOS circuit. However, the binary one levels are different. The binary one output level of a TTL gate may be as low as 2.4 V, and a CMOS gate requires a binary one input level of at least 3 V to operate. One solution involves connecting a pull-up resistor between the gates, as shown in Figure 28–4. This causes the binary one level of the TTL gates to approach the V_{CC} potential during the high state.

28-2.6 Analog-to-Digital (A/D) Converters. Sometimes, the data fed into a microprocessor-based system are in analog format and must be converted into equivalent binary data. Several techniques may be used to

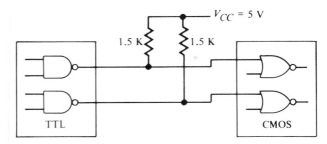

Figure 28–4   Interfacing CMOS and TTL logic devices with a pull-up resistor.

accomplish this task with the required circuitry fabricated in IC format. Semiconductor manufacturers produce dozens of different kinds of A/D converters. Most are compatible with either TTL or CMOS logic devices. The digital output word length varies, depending upon the type of converter. Although most produce the conventional 8421 binary code, A/D converters are available which convert analog data into equivalent binary-coded-decimal data.

28-2.7 Digital-to-Analog (D/A) Converters.   After the data have been operated upon within the microprocessor, the digital data may have to be converted into an equivalent analog signal. This is accomplished by a digital-to-analog (D/A) converter. Various methods are used to achieve this conversion. Like the A/D converters, most are available in integrated circuit form. The resulting analog voltage may be amplified and used to energize a relay, drive a motor, or perform a variety of other controlling functions.

28-2.8 Three-State Buffers.   The three-state logic buffer is a TTL device that has a third, high-impedance state in addition to the usual high and low states. There are several types of these buffers. In general, they have two inputs and one output. As illustrated in Figure 28–5, the inputs include the data and enable/disable and the data appears at the output. The output data is in phase with the input in the buffers shown in Figure 28–5(a) and (b). The enable/disable input allows data applied to the data input terminal to either pass through or to be prevented from passing the buffer and appearing at the output terminal. The buffers appearing in Figure 28–5(a) and (c) are enabled when a binary one is applied to the enable/disable input. These same circuits are inhibited when a binary zero is applied to this input, and the output assumes a very high-impedance state which is similar to disconnecting the output from

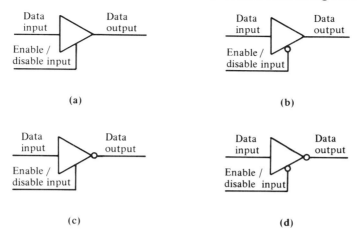

Figure 28–5   Types of three-state buffers: (a) noninverting binary one enabled; (b) non-inverting binary zero enabled; (c) inverting binary one enabled; (d) inverting binary zero enabled.

the remaining part of the circuit. The output data are inverted in the buffers shown in Figure 28–5 (c) and (d). Sometimes, it is desirable to enable a three-state buffer with a binary zero. In this situation either the buffers shown in Figure 28–5(b) or (d) may be used.

Several different types of three-state buffers are available for various applications. Usually, four or more buffers are incorporated into one IC package. Many integrated circuits, such as RAMs and ROMs, have three-state buffers incorporated in their output circuits and do not require separate buffers, as illustrated in Figure 28–6. The buffers remain in the

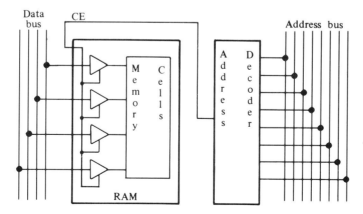

Figure 28–6   RAM with three-state buffers.

high-impedance inhibited state until a chip enable (CE) signal is applied to the input of the chip.

28-2.9 Memory-Mapped I/O.   Peripherals connected to the MPU via the data bus are isolated from the bus by internally or externally connected three-state buffers. When data is to be transmitted by or received from the peripheral, its associated buffers must be enabled. There are several methods by which this may be achieved. The method used in many microprocessors, including the MC6800, is the memory-mapped I/O technique. Each peripheral connected to the data bus is assigned an address. Activating a particular peripheral merely involves addressing it. An address decoder decodes the address, and the resulting signal is used to enable the three-state buffers, as shown in Figure 28–6. Data can then be placed onto or taken from the data bus.

28-2.10 Interrupts and Polling.   Since the microprocessor is much faster than most peripheral devices, several peripherals may be connected to the input of a microprocessor to take advantage of its high speed. This is commonly done in dedicated microprocessor-based systems. Two methods are used to allow for the use of multiple inputs. One of these is the use of interrupts. This provision is built into most MPUs. An interrupt is initiated by a signal generated by an input peripheral. When the microprocessor receives the signal, it completes the instruction it is working on and then turns its attention to the input peripheral requesting attention.

The second method is called polling. An address is assigned to each input peripheral. The MPU is programmed to select and interrogate the different inputs at predetermined intervals. Although some circuitry may be involved, this is primarily a software solution to interfacing multiple input peripherals.

28-3 PROGRAMMING TECHNIQUES USED IN THE MICROPROCESSOR

28-3.1 Types of Languages.   A program consists of a list of instructions, or statements, which cause the microprocessor to perform operations on data. An operation identifies an activity such as adding, subtracting, obtaining a square root, or sorting data. The program is placed into main memory through an input peripheral such as a keyboard. Since the microprocessor can handle only binary words and numbers, the instructions must appear in memory in binary form. The microprocessor has no intelligence of its own. It must be instructed, in detail, as to how to proceed through an operation. This causes the instruction list of even a seemingly simple operation to become rather lengthy. Writing the program and placing it into the microprocessor becomes a very tedious task since every word and number has to be converted into an equivalent binary word or number. This is called machine language programming. Each MPU instruction is assigned a binary number, as illustrated by those appearing in Table 28–1.

TABLE 28–1   Binary Number Machine Language

Instruction	Associated Binary Number
Reset	10110011
Store	01111001
Clear	11011101
Add	00101001

Programming by machine language can be simplified by using hexadecimal numbers, as shown in Table 28–2. The binary number associated with each instruction has been replaced with its equivalent hexadecimal number. A hexadecimal-to-binary code converter converts the hexadecimal number to a binary number before it is placed into memory.

TABLE 28–2   Hexadecimal Number Machine Language

Instruction	Associated Hexadecimal Number
Reset	B3
Store	79
Clear	DD
Add	29

Originally, all computers and, later on, microprocessors, were programmed using machine language. As time progressed, higher forms of languages were developed which greatly simplified the programming process. These include assembly language and the compiler and interpret languages. Assembly language overcomes much of the tediousness of programming in machine language. Short words or abbreviations, called mnemonics, are used to represent the different instructions. Each different MPU has a certain number of instructions which it can execute. This is called an instruction set. A hexadecimal number, called an opcode, is assigned to each mnemonic. When the opcode is entered into the MPU, a program stored in ROM, called the assembler, converts the opcode into the appropriate binary number. A partial listing of the instruction set for the MC6800 MPU appears in Table 28–3.

TABLE 28–3 Partial Listing of MC6800 Instruction Set

Mnemonic	Instruction
BCC	Branch if clear flag is zero.
CLR	Clear memory section
INS	Increment stack pointer register
JMP	Jump to address
LDA A	Load memory section into accumulator A
SBA	Subtract the contents in accumulator B from the contents stored in accumulator A. Store difference in accumulator A.
DEC	Decrement memory

Most microprocessors are programmed using assembly language, except those used in microcomputers. Computers and microcomputers are usually programmed using one of the several higher-level languages.

When compiler language is employed, a compiler program is stored in ROM which changes the compiler language instructions into equivalent machine language instructions. FORTRAN is a popular compiler language used in science and engineering applications. One FORTRAN statement contains all the instructions required to solve a mathematical equation. A common compiler language used for data processing applications is COBOL. This language allows a complete program to be sent from the compiler and stored in memory for future use.

Interpret languages are somewhat similar to the compiler languages except that each program instruction is translated individually and executed in sequence immediately. The most common form of this language is BASIC. This is the language used in most microcomputers.

28-3.2 The MPU Program.   Assembly language is used to program most microprocessors. A program is made up of a list of statements which tells the microprocessor what to do. Each statement contains three components: an address, opcode, and operand. The address identifies the particular memory section where the opcode or operand is located.

The operand is the data which is to be operated upon by the MPU as identified by the opcode.

28-3.3 Classes of Instructions.   Each microprocessor has its own instructional set from which programs can be written. It is sometimes convenient to group the instructions according to the types of operations they perform within the MPU. The MC6800 MPU has 72 instructions which can be grouped into seven categories: data movement, arithmetic, logic, jump and branch, data test, index register and stack pointer, and condition code.

The instructions appearing in the data movement category cause the data to be transferred between a register and a memory segment, between registers, or between a peripheral and a register. Arithmetic instructions give the MPU the capability of performing arithmetic operations such as addition and subtraction. The logic instructions allow the microprocessor to perform various logic, or Boolean algebra, manipulations on the data. Jump and branch instructions cause the program to bypass or branch ahead to other instructions instead of incrementing to the immediately following instruction. Data test instructions allow the data, or operands, to be compared. The resultants affect the condition code register and cause a flag to be set. The index and stack pointer registers are controlled by the index register and stack pointer instructions. These registers can be loaded, unloaded, incremented, and decremented with these instructions. In addition, data can be transferred between the two registers. The condition code instructions allow selected flags within the condition code register to be either set or reset.

28-3.4 Addressing Modes.   Addressing modes refer to the way an instruction addresses its operand. Some statements require more memory locations than others and require more time to implement. The MC6800 utilizes six different addressing modes: the implied, immediate, direct, indexed, relative, and extended modes.

The implied, sometimes called the inherent, addressing mode consists of one-byte instructions, or statements, whose operand is implied in the opcode. As illustrated in Figure 28–7, these instructions do not require an operand from program memory.

The immediate addressing mode requires two bytes of memory. The first byte is the opcode and the second byte is the operand, which is located in the memory section immediately following the opcode, as shown in Figure 28–8.

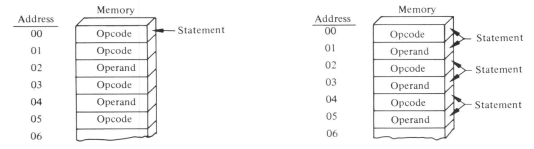

Figure 28–7 Implied addressing mode.   **Figure 28–8** Immediate addressing mode.

The address of the operand comes immediately after the opcode in the direct addressing mode, as indicated in Figure 28–9.

The index register is used to generate the address of the operand when the indexed addressing mode is employed. As illustrated in Figure 28–10, the data byte following the opcode, called the offset address, is added to the number stored in the index register. The address of the operand is the sum of these two numbers.

The relative addressing mode is similar to index addressing except that the offset byte following the opcode is added to the number in the

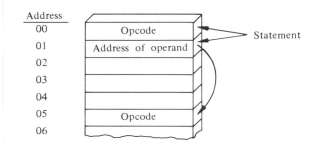

Figure 28–9 Direct addressing mode.

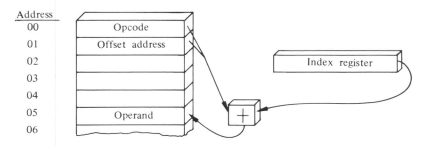

Figure 28–10 Index addressing mode.

program counter. These instructions allow the microprocessor to branch, or jump, from one memory address to another.

The extended address mode is used when the operand immediately following the opcode in memory is two bytes long.

SUMMARY

1. Interfacing circuits are required for the microprocessor to communicate with its peripherals. They provide compatibility between the microprocessor and its externally connected circuits and equipment.

2. A number of different kinds of circuits and devices may be used to satisfy a variety of interfacing requirements. In many applications the general-purpose interface bus (GPIB) can be used to provide compatibility between digital systems utilizing different microprocessors or peripherals fabricated from unlike transistor logic families. Many microprocessor manufacturers build an interfacing circuit that allows their microprocessor to be used with the bus.

3. Most microprocessor manufacturers produce a number of supporting integrated circuits that allow their microprocessor to become compatible with different types of peripherals.

4. CMOS buffers are connected between CMOS and TTL integrated circuits when it is required that the CMOS device drive the TTL device.

5. Three-state buffers are used to isolate a peripheral connected to the data bus until that peripheral is addressed and enabled.

6. A/D and D/A converters are required if the signals utilized by the input-output peripherals are in analog format.

7. The four types of languages associated with computers and microprocessors are machine, assembly, compiler, and interpret. Assembly language is used to program most microprocessors. Each instruction is assigned a mnemonic. The program consists of a list of statements. Each statement contains an address, opcode, and operand. The opcode and operand are placed in memory. The opcode occupies one byte of memory. Depending upon the addressing mode used, the operand may occupy one or two bytes of memory space.

8. Instructions associated with a particular microprocessor can be grouped according to their functions. The MC6800 has 72 instructions. These can be grouped into seven categories: data movement, arithmetic, logic, jump and branch, data test, index register and stack pointer, and condition code.

9. The method in which the microprocessor carries out an instruction depends upon the addressing mode used. Six different addressing modes can be used with the MC6800: the implied, immediate, direct, indexed, relative, and extended.

PRACTICE EXERCISES

1. Identify three potential problems associated with connecting peripheral devices together on a common data bus.

2. How can the problems identified in exercise 1 be overcome?

3. What is the purpose of the IEEE 488 bus?
4. What type of device is used to allow CMOS gates to drive TTL gates?
5. What is the purpose of the universal asynchronous receiver transmitter (UART) and asynchronous communications interface adapter (ACIA) circuits?
6. What is a peripheral interface adapter (PIA)?
7. When would an analog-to-digital (A/D) converter be used in a microprocessor-based system?
8. What is the purpose of a digital-to-analog (D/A) converter?
9. Describe the purpose of a three-state buffer.
10. List three levels of program language.
11. Identify the three parts of a program statement.
12. Describe the purpose of the address, opcode, and operand in an assembly language program.
13. Identify the seven classes of instructions used with the MC6800 MPU.
14. List the six methods used with the MC6800 MPU to address the operand.
15. List two types of compiler language and identify the general application of each.

ANSWERS TO PRACTICE EXERCISES

1. The problems associated with connecting devices onto a common bus are compatibility, addressing, and isolation.
2. Special interfacing buses and circuits can be employed to make the devices compatible. Each peripheral can be assigned an address. The peripheral remains inhibited until addressed. Three-state buffers can be used to isolate the devices from the bus.
3. The IEEE 488 bus, commonly known as the general-purpose interface bus, is used to assist in making different digital devices and equipment compatible with one another.
4. A CMOS buffer connected between the CMOS and TTL integrated circuits allows CMOS gates to drive TTL gates.
5. The UART and ACIA are used to interface serially operated peripherals with the MPU.
6. The PIA is used to interface input and output peripherals with the microprocessor.
7. An A/D converter changes analog data into digital data. It is used when the input data is analog in nature.
8. A D/A converter changes digital data into equivalent analog signals. It is used when the output peripheral is used to drive a motor, energize a relay, or perform some other similar function.
9. A three-state buffer is used to isolate the gates connected to its input and output circuits when in the inhibit state.
10. The three levels of program language are machine language, assembly language, and compiler and interpret language.
11. The three parts of a program statement are the address, opcode, and operand.

12. The address identifies the memory location where the program instruction is located. The opcode describes the operation, for example, HALT, ADD, BRANCH, and so forth. The operand is the data which is to be operated upon as identified by the opcode.

13. The seven categories of instructions associated with the MC6800 are data movement, arithmetic, logic, jump and branch, data test, index register and stack pointer, and condition code.

14. Addressing methods, or modes, are the implied, immediate, direct, indexed, relative, and extended.

15. FORTRAN and COBOL are both types of compiler language. FORTRAN is often used for scientific computation, and COBOL is used for data processing applications.

CHAPTER EXAMINATION

1. An interfacing circuit that converts parallel data into equivalent serial data best describes the
   a. PIA   **c.** IEEE 488 bus
   b. UART   **d.** three-state buffer

2. Which of the following types of languages is the most fundamental?
   a. BASIC   **c.** Machine
   b. FORTRAN **d.** Assembly

3. A (An) _____ identifies action such as adding, subtracting, and shifting data.
   a. opcode   **c.** program
   b. operand   **d.** operation

4. Most microprocessors are programmed using _____ language.
   a. machine   **c.** assembly
   b. compiler   **d.** interpret

5. The address represents the _____ of the instruction in memory.
   a. type   **c.** action
   b. class   **d.** location

6. The _____ is used to interface analog input data with the microprocessor.
   a. A/D converter   **c.** three-state buffer
   b. JEEE 488 bus   **d.** CMOS buffer

Choose true or false for questions 7 to 18.

7. T   F   A three-state buffer is required to interface CMOS and TTL devices.

8. T   F   The third state, in a three-state TTL device, represents an impedance level that is midway between the low and high states.

9. T   F   One advantage of using CMOS logic with TTL logic is that they are compatible with one another and no interface circuit is required.

10. T   F   The major purpose of the PIA is to convert serial data into equivalent parallel data.

11. T   F   The interrupt is a method of using multiple RAMs with the MPU.

12. T   F   Peripherals connected to the MPU are assigned an address just as memory segments are and remain inactive unless addressed.

13. T   F   Many semiconductor memory devices have three-state buffers built into them.
14. T   F   BASIC is a type of compiler language.
15. T   F   The instruction is identified in the form of a mnemonic when assembly language is used.
16. T   F   One of the categories of instructions used with the MC6800 is the index register and stack pointer.
17. T   F   Each individual instruction is assigned a binary number when machine language is used.
18. T   F   The immediate mode is a type of addressing mode used with the MC6800 MPU.

| 29

A Survey of Microprocessor Devices

OBJECTIVES

Upon completion of this chapter you should be able to do the following:

1. List six different eight-bit microprocessors and identify the major manufacturer of each.
2. List five different 16-bit MPUs and identify the primary manufacturer of each.
3. Discuss the major differences between the 8080 and 8085 MPUs.
4. Describe the main differences between the 8080 and the Z-80 MPUs.

29-1 INTRODUCTION

The tremendous research and development and subsequent production of the many types of microprocessors available for use today is one of the marvels of the American semiconductor industry. Paging through a catalog of semiconductor devices, one finds scores of different kinds of microprocessors listed, which are produced by approximately three dozen manufacturers. Some of these have very specialized applications, while others are employed in many diversified systems.

The first microprocessors were placed on the market in the early 1970s. Almost immediately, engineers began finding almost unlimited applications for the devices. Tremendous competition soon developed between the various semiconductor manufacturing companies to produce more powerful and less expensive MPUs. Initially costing several hundred dollars each, within a few years microprocessors were available

637

in bulk lots for just a few dollars apiece. This follows the route taken by other integrated circuits. As manufacturing techniques were perfected, costs plummeted. Someone once remarked if the parts used in an automobile decreased in price as much as the devices used in a computer, a Rolls Royce would cost $45. Some of the more popular microprocessors are identified and discussed in the following sections.

29-2 FOUR-BIT MICROPROCESSORS

These comprised the first generation of microprocessors. Intel Corporation led the way when their 4004 was introduced in 1971. This MPU utilized a 4-bit data word, had an 8-bit instruction register, and employed a 12-bit program counter. The device had 45 instructions and was housed in a 16-pin dual-in-line package.

Intel and other semiconductor manufacturing companies immediately began improving upon the design of the 4004 with the objective to build more powerful and easier to program devices. This resulted in MPUs such as Intel's 4040. This device was encapsuled in a 24-pin DIP case and had 60 instructions. Other four-bit microprocessors developed at about the same time included Motorola's 141000, Rockwell's PPS4, National Semiconductor's COPS, and Texas Instruments' TMS1000. The TMS1000 included some on board RAM, ROM, and input-output interfacing.

Millions of four-bit microprocessors have been incorporated into hundreds of very diverse applications. Today, few, if any, new microprocessor-based equipment is designed around four-bit devices. However, millions of these microprocessors continue to be produced each year as replacements for those devices already in use.

29-3 EIGHT-BIT MICROPROCESSORS

Eight-bit devices form the second generation of MPUs. Intel's 8008, an upgraded version of the 4004, was the first eight-bit device to reach the market. Housed in an 18-pin DIP case, the device had an instructional set of 48 instructions. Intel soon followed this product with an entirely new designed device—the 8080. This was the first really high-powered microprocessor to be placed on the market. It was the first microprocessor for which a complete software program was developed. It is encapsulated in a 40-pin case and requires three different DC operating potentials (± 5 V and 12 V). It requires an external 2 MHz clock and typically dissipates 780 mW of power.

The block diagram of the 8080 appears in Figure 29–1. It is an eight-data bit MPU which utilizes a 16-bit address. Like most other microprocessors, it can be divided into two sections—a control unit and an arithmetic and logic unit. The control unit is made up of many of the same kinds of registers found in the MC6800 MPU discussed in the last chapter. The 8080 contains a program counter, stack pointer, address register, instruction register, flag flip-flops, accumulator, and a temporary register which stores operands for the ALU. Registers W and Z are used to temporarily hold instructions and cannot be controlled by the programmer. Registers B, C, D, E, H, and L are general-purpose shift registers which can be operated either as six separate 8-bit registers to hold data or as three separate 16-bit registers to store addresses.

Five status flags are utilized in conjunction with the arithmetic and Boolean algebra operations performed in the ALU. These include the zero (Z) flag, the carry (CY) flag, the sign (S) flag, the parity (P) flag, and the auxiliary (AC) flag. Five addressing modes are employed: the direct, the register, the register indirect, the immediate, and the implied.

A number of different support ICs are manufactured for the 8080. These include the 8224 clock generator, the 8251 programmable communications interface, the 8216 bidirectional bus driver, and the 8228 system controller and bus driver. This was the microprocessor used in the MITS Altair 8800 microcomputer—the microcomputer that initiated the beginning of the personal computer industry.

Zilog Incorporated soon marketed the Z-80 as an improved version of the 8080. One of the major differences between the two microprocessors is the number of internal general-purpose registers each has. The 8080 has six—B, C, D, E, H, and L. The Z-80 has the same six but, in addition, has six more: the B', C', D', E', H', and L'. The Z-80 is enclosed in a 40-pin DIP case and requires only a single 5-V DC bias potential. The MPU dissipates approximately 1100 mW of power. One of the more popular features of the Z-80 is that it can use the software developed for the 8080. The Z-80 is the microprocessor used in Radio Shack's TRS-80 personal computer.

The 8085 MPU, manufactured by Intel Corporation, is also an upgraded version of the 8080. The chip is housed in a 40-pin DIP case. The MPU requires a single 5-V DC supply, consumes approximately 850 mW of power, and has its own clock. The block diagram of the device appears in Figure 29–2. The diagram looks very much like that of the 8080 shown in Figure 29–1. Major differences in the 8085 include the omission of the W and Z registers, the inclusion of a data/address buffer, and the utilization of a multiplexed address/data bus. Many of the support ICs designed for the 8080 can also be used with the 8085.

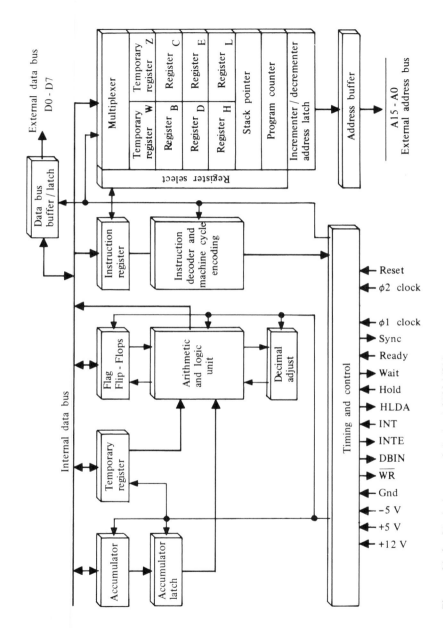

Figure 29–1 Block diagram of the Intel 8080 MPU.

640

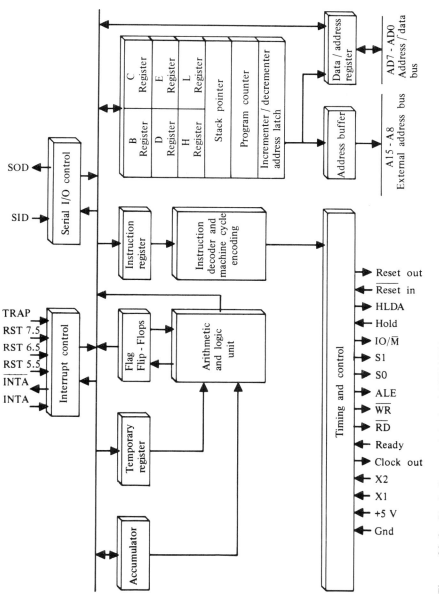

Figure 29-2 Block diagram of the Intel 8085 MPU.

641

The MC6800 has been a popular microprocessor. In addition to this MPU, Motorola manufactures other microprocessors, several of which have a 6800 nomenclature. These include the 6801, 6802, 6805, and 6809. All are eight-bit microprocessors encapsulated in a 40-pin case. The peripheral integrated circuits built for the 6800 can be used with these devices. The 6802 has the same internal architecture as the 6800 but in addition includes an internal clock. The 6809 is one of the most versatile 8-bit MPUs available. It has two 16-bit index registers, two 16-bit indexable stack pointers, and two 8-bit accumulators which can be operated as a single 16-bit accumulator.

The MSC6502 is another popular eight-bit microprocessor. Developed by MOS Technology as an improved version of the MC6800, it is the microprocessor used in the Apple and the Commodore PET microcomputers.

29-4 SIXTEEN-BIT MICROPROCESSORS

The trend most recently has been in the development of 16-bit (and in some cases 32-bit) microprocessors. These MPUs are capable of performing more operations and addressing greater amounts of memory than 8-bit microprocessors. Sixteen-bit devices are the third-generation microprocessors and are a result of higher component densities brought about by advancements in LSI technology.

Common types of 16-bit devices are Motorola's MC68000, Zilog's Z8000, National's INS8900, Texas Instruments' TMS9940, Western Digital's MP1600, and Intel's 8086. All are enclosed in a 40-pin DIP case except for the MC68000, which utilizes a 64-pin case. All are NMOS-type devices. A few 16-bit microprocessors employ other types of transistor logic, however. Texas Instruments produces the SBP9900A which uses I^2L logic.

The MC68000 chip contains approximately 68,000 equivalent transistors, which is about twice as many used in the other 16-bit MPUs. This was the first microprocessor to employ very large-scale integrated (VLSI) circuits.

What lies ahead in microprocessor development? VLSI technology exists for larger word devices, and component densities will continue to increase. However, bigger is not always better. Some computer scientists and engineers feel that the applications for the more complex larger word microprocessors are not keeping pace with advances in MPU design. These individuals think that the benefits of some of the more flexible eight-bit devices have yet to be fully exploited. One thing is almost for certain—applications for microprocessors will continue to increase. Persons planning on entering almost any field of technology would be wise to learn more about these devices.

SUMMARY

1. Some of the more commonly used eight-bit microprocessors include the 8080, 8085, Z-80, 6800, 6801, 6802, 6805, 6809, and 6502.
2. The 8080, 8085, and Z-80 processors all have some similarities. The 8085 and Z-80 devices were developed as improved versions of the 8080.
3. The 6800 series of MPUs are all manufactured by Motorola. Some of these are improved versions of the 6800, while others are quite different and are built for different applications.
4. Most 16-bit microprocessors utilize NMOS transistor technology and are encapsulated in a 40-pin DIP case.
5. Some popular 16-bit microprocessors are the TMS9940, MP1600, 8086, INS8900, MC68000, SBP9900, and Z8000.

PRACTICE EXERCISES

1. List six types of eight-bit microprocessors and identify the manufacturer of each.
2. What are the major differences between the 8080 and 8085?
3. Discuss the major differences between the 8080 and the Z-80.
4. Which one of the 16-bit microprocessors identified in this chapter utilizes I^2L transistor logic?
5. Which one of the 16-bit microprocessors is enclosed in a 64-pin case?
6. List five types of 16-pin microprocessors and identify the manufacturer of each.

ANSWERS TO PRACTICE EXERCISES

1. Six eight-bit microprocessors are the 8080, 8085 (Intel); Z-80 (Zilog); 6800, 6801, 6802, 6805, and the 6809 (Motorola).
2. The 8085 has an on-board clock, a data/address register, the W and Z registers have been eliminated, and employs a multiplexed address/data bus.
3. The W and Z registers have been eliminated and six additional general-purpose registers have been added to the Z-80 MPU.
4. The SBP9900A employs I^2L transistor logic.
5. The MC68000 is enclosed in a 64-pin case.
6. Five 16-bit microprocessors are the TMS9940 (Texas Instruments), the MP1600 (Western Digital), the 8086 (Intel), the INS8900 (National), the MC68000 (Motorola), and Z8000 (Zilog).

CHAPTER EXAMINATION

Choose true or false.
1. T   F   The 8080 is an up-graded version of the Z-80 MPU.
2. T   F   The 8085 utilizes an eight-bit data word and 16-bit address word.
3. T   F   The 8080 MPU has six general-purpose shift registers and the Z-80 has twelve of the same type.
4. T   F   The Z-80 MPU is manufactured by Intel Corporation.
5. T   F   The 8080 MPU has its own internal clock.
6. T   F   The 8086, MC12000, MP1600, and MC6802 are all examples of 16-bit microprocessors.
7. T   F   The 8086 MPU is manufactured by Intel Corporation.

Answers to Chapter Examinations

CHAPTER 1

1. a	**8.** T	**14.** T	**20.** T
2. c	**9.** F	**15.** T	**21.** F
3. b	**10.** T	**16.** T	**22.** T
4. a	**11.** F	**17.** F	**23.** F
5. d	**12.** T	**18.** F	**24.** T
6. F	**13.** F	**19.** F	**25.** F
7. T			

CHAPTER 2

1. b	**6.** d	**11.** 18,700 Ω	**16.** 3.3 V
2. a	**7.** c	**12.** 0.001 A	**17.** 0.0187 W
3. a	**8.** a	**13.** 5.6 V	**18.** $53.90
4. a	**9.** c	**14.** 4.7 V	**19.** 87 V
5. b	**10.** d	**15.** 5.1 V	**20.** 0.45 A

CHAPTER 3

1. $R_T = 24\ \Omega$	**4.** (a) 400 Ω	**5.** $R_{AB} = 7.33\ \Omega$	**10.** F
$I_T = 0.417$ A	(b) 0.05 A	**6.** $I_T = 1.624$ A	**11.** T
$I_1 = 0.167$ A	(c) 10 V	**7.** F	**12.** T
$I_2 = 0.250$ A	(d) 10 V	**8.** F	**13.** F
2. $R_T = 2\ \Omega$	(e) .033 A	**9.** T	**14.** F
$I_T = 3$ A	(f) .0167 A		**15.** T
3. $V_{R1} = 12$ V	(g) 5.01 V		

CHAPTER 4

1. F
2. F
3. F

4. F
5. F
6. $R_{th} = 30$ kΩ

7. $V_{th} = V_S = 15$ V
8. $V_0 = 90.9$ V
9. $V_{R3} = 39.06$ V

10. $R_{int} = 75.05$ Ω
11. 12.5 percent

CHAPTER 5

1. c
2. a
3. d
4. d
5. b

6. c
7. b
8. b
9. d
10. d

11. c
12. b
13. F
14. F
15. T

16. T
17. F
18. F
19. F
20. T

CHAPTER 6

1. d
2. a
3. b
4. a
5. d

6. c
7. d
8. d
9. c
10. c

11. a
12. b
13. b
14. c
15. d

16. c
17. c
18. d
19. c
20. b

CHAPTER 7

1. d
2. b
3. c
4. b
5. c
6. d

7. a
8. c
9. c
10. c
11. a
12. b

13. c
14. a
15. d
16. a
17. a

18. b
19. d
20. c
21. d
22. b

CHAPTER 8

1. b
2. d
3. b
4. c
5. b
6. b

7. c
8. b
9. a
10. a
11. d
12. F

13. F
14. T
15. T
16. T
17. T
18. F

19. F
20. T
21. F
22. T
23. F

CHAPTER 9

1. $91.21\ \Omega\angle 52.13°$
2. $123\ \text{mV}\angle -52.13°$
3. $1170.96\ \Omega\angle 38.35°$
4. $0.000854\ \text{A}\angle -38.35°$

5. T
6. T
7. F

8. F
9. T
10. T

11. T
12. T
13. F

CHAPTER 10

1. 40 W
2. 89.4 VA
3. 0.447
4. $39.05\ \Omega\angle 50.19°$
5. $0.0512\ \text{A}\angle -50.19°$
6. $V_R = 1.28\ \text{V}\angle -50.19°$
   $V_L = 3.58\ \text{V}\angle 39.81°$
   $V_C = 2.048\ \text{V}\angle -140.19°$

7. 4492 Hz
8. 231,778 Hz
9. 0.004 A
10. 5.82
11. 39824.39 Hz
12. 0.0004 W
13. 187.49 W
14. 124.96 W

15. T
16. T
17. F
18. T
19. F
20. F
21. F
22. T

CHAPTER 11

1. T
2. T
3. F
4. F
5. T
6. T
7. T

8. T
9. F
10. F
11. F
12. F
13. F

14. F
15. F
16. F
17. F
18. T
19. T

20. T
21. F
22. T
23. F
24. F
25. T

CHAPTER 12

1. a
2. d
3. a
4. b
5. b
6. c
7. b
8. a
9. 19.8 μA
10. 0.891 mA
11. 8.22 V
12. Fixed
13. To stabilize the Q-point for temperature variations

14. Collector feedback
15. 71.5 μA
16. 4.27 V
17. 15 mA
18. 1.5 V
19. F
20. F
21. F
22. T
23. T
24. T

25. F
26. T
27. T
28. F
29. F
30. T
31. F
32. F
33. T
34. T

CHAPTER 13

1. T	8. F	14. F
2. F	9. T	15. F
3. T	10. F	16. $V_{DS(Q)} = 7$ V; $I_{D(Q)} = 2.5$ mA
4. F	11. F	17. $V_{GS} = -.924$ V
5. F	12. T	18. $V_{GS} = 0.995$ V
6. F	13. T	19. $V_{DS} = -5.2$ V
7. T		

CHAPTER 14

1. a	6. c	11. F	16. F
2. d	7. d	12. F	17. F
3. c	8. a	13. F	18. T
4. d	9. d	14. F	19. T
5. a	10. F	15. F	20. F

CHAPTER 15

1. See Figure 15–20(a)	7. T
2. $V_{DC} = 26.98$ V; $I_{DC} = 1.255$ A	8. F
3. 84.84 V	9. F
4. 37.32 V	10. F
5. 298.56 Ω	11. F
6. T	

CHAPTER 16

1. Small signal (voltage) and large signal (power)
2. RC, transformer, and direct
3. DC, AF, and RF
4. tuned and untuned
5. impedance matching
6. to amplify a narrow band of RF signals
7. positive and negative
8. to provide the input signals to a circuit which requires two input signal voltages that are equal in amplitude and 180° out-of-phase with each other
9. 147.059
10. −450
11. 4694.84 Ω
12. 1337.79 Ω

13. -20.067
14. 67.75
15. 1307.93
16. 6859
17. 34.64 : 1

CHAPTER 17

1. T
2. T
3. F
4. T
5. T
6. T
7. See Figure 17–7
8. See Figure 17–14
9. Single-ended input, double-ended input, differential input, common mode input, single-ended output, double-ended output, and differential output.
10. Dual-in-line, flat pack, and metal can.

CHAPTER 18

1. F
2. T
3. F
4. T
5. F
6. F
7. T
8. F
9. See Figure 18–16
10. 5.355 W
11. .945 W
12. 7.14 percent
13. **a.** higher output power (when biased class A or AB)
    b. higher efficiency (when biased class AB or B)
    c. cancellation of even harmonics
14. Class B
15. Class C
16. To aid in conducting heat away from the transistor

CHAPTER 19

1. T	**3.** T	**5.** F	**7.** F
2. T	**4.** F	**6.** F	**8.** T

9. T
10. F
11. F
12. F
13. T
14. See Figure 19–4
15. See Figure 19–6
16. See Figure 19–14
17. A 180° phase shift is accomplished between the input and output terminals of the active device and an additional 180° shift occurs as the feedback signal travels through the RC network in the input circuit.
18. Input circuit, output circuit, feedback circuit, and amplifier
19. Sinusoidal and relaxation
20. By taking the output from across a capacitor connected between the collector and ground

CHAPTER 20

1. A byte is a group of binary bits typically considered to be eight binary bits.
2. An alphanumeric code is a binary code capable of representing decimals, letters, and sentence symbols in binary word format.
3. 415.3125_{10}
4. 110100111011.10100101_2
5. 1010010.00001_2
6. 44.15_8
7. $391.CA_{16}$
8. 451.62_8
9. $1B71.28_{16}$
10. 2651.9023_{10}
11. 110110111
12. 11010
13. 1000011
14. 1010010
15. 32
16. 31

CHAPTER 21

1. d	5. c	9. a	13. F
2. d	6. a	10. F	14. F
3. a	7. a	11. T	15. F
4. c	8. d	12. T	

CHAPTER 22

1. d	7. d	13. F	18. F
2. a	8. b	14. F	19. F
3. b	9. c	15. F	20. F
4. c	10. F	16. T	21. F
5. b	11. T	17. F	22. F
6. b	12. T		

CHAPTER 23

1. a	**6.** a	**11.** F	**16.** T
2. d	**7.** b	**12.** F	**17.** F
3. a	**8.** See Figure 23–1.	**13.** F	**18.** T
4. b	**9.** See Figure 23–12(b).	**14.** F	**19.** T
5. a	**10.** See Figure 23–15(b).	**15.** T	**20.** T

CHAPTER 24

1. b
2. c
3. a
4. c
5. d
6. See Figure 24–1(a).
7.

8. See Figure 24–3(a).
9.

10. F
11. F
12. T
13. F

14. F
15. T
16. T
17. F
18. F
19. T
20. T

CHAPTER 25

1. c	**5.** F	**9.** F	**13.** F
2. b	**6.** F	**10.** F	**14.** F
3. a	**7.** T	**11.** T	**15.** T
4. d	**8.** F	**12.** T	

CHAPTER 26

1. c	**5.** T	**9.** T	**13.** T
2. b	**6.** F	**10.** F	**14.** F
3. a	**7.** T	**11.** T	**15.** T
4. d	**8.** F	**12.** T	**16.** T

CHAPTER 27

1. a	**7.** b	**12.** F	**17.** F
2. b	**8.** b	**13.** T	**18.** F
3. a	**9.** F	**14.** F	**19.** T
4. a	**10.** T	**15.** T	**20.** T
5. b	**11.** T	**16.** F	**21.** T
6. b			

CHAPTER 28

1. b	**6.** a	**11.** F	**15.** T
2. c	**7.** F	**12.** T	**16.** T
3. a	**8.** F	**13.** T	**17.** T
4. c	**9.** F	**14.** F	**18.** T
5. d	**10.** F		

CHAPTER 29

1. F	**5.** F
2. T	**6.** F
3. T	**7.** T
4. F	

Index

AC voltage:
    average values, 360, 365
    effective value, 125–126
    peak value, 125–126
    peak-to-peak value, 125–126
Acceptor atoms, 252
Accumulator, 613, 616
ACIA, 625
Adders:
    full, 550
    half, 549–550
    parallel, 551–552
Address:
    bus, 614
    memory, 589
    register, 612
    word, 611
Addressing modes, 631–632
Alpha current gain, 288–289
Alphanumeric codes, 484–485
Alternating current (AC), 122–126
ALU, 589, 610, 612
Alternation, 123
American Standard Code for Information
    Interchange (ASCII), 485
Ammeter, 37
Ampere (A), 9–10
Amplifier:
    classifications, 382–384

configurations, 384
classes of operation, 384
differential, 415–419
direct-coupled, 399–402
large signal, 383, 427–431
operational, 419–421
push-pull, 437–442
RC-coupled, 383, 388–394
small-signal, 383
transformer-coupled, 383, 394–399
AND gate, 492–493
Analog signals, 250, 472
Analog-to-digital (A/D) converters, 625–626
Anode, 259, 348
Apparent power, 227
Arctangent, 206
Armstrong oscillator, 453–454
Arithmetic and logic unit (ALU), 589, 610, 612
Assembly language, 629–630
Astable multivibrator, 459–460, 463, 527
Asynchronous Communications Interface
    Adapter (ACIA), 625
Atom, 5, 250
Atomic number, 5, 250
Avalanche breakdown, 265, 339
Average power, 225
Average voltage:
    half-wave, 360–361
    full-wave, 365–366